TRANSFORMATIONS OF SURFACES

BY

LUTHER PFAHLER EISENHART

PROFESSOR OF MATHEMATICS
IN PRINCETON UNIVERSITY

CHELSEA PUBLISHING COMPANY
NEW YORK, N. Y.

SECOND EDITION, 1962

THE FIRST EDITION OF THIS BOOK WAS PUBLISHED IN 1923, BY PRINCETON UNIVERSITY PRESS, WITH THE COOPERATION OF THE NATIONAL RESEARCH COUNCIL. THE PRESENT, SECOND EDITION IS A REPRINT OF THE FIRST, WITH CORRECTION OF ERRATA.

LIBRARY OF CONGRESS CATALOGUE CARD NO. 62-11699

PRINTED IN THE UNITED STATES OF AMERICA

Preface

The present reprint of this book is made with my full authorization and approval. I have taken advantage of this opportunity to correct a number of the errata that appeared in the first edition.

Luther Pfahler Eisenhart.

Preface

During the past twenty-five years many of the advances in differential geometry of surfaces in euclidean space have had to do with transformations of surfaces of a given type into surfaces of the same type. Before this period Bianchi and Bäcklund had established their transformations of a pseudospherical surface into pseudospherical surfaces, the essential feature of which is that a given surface and any transform are the focal surfaces of a *W* congruence. Furthermore, Bianchi (Lezioni, § 383) established the so-called theorem of permutability of such transformations; that is, if S_1 and S_2 are two transforms of S there can be found a fourth surface S' which is a transform of both S_1 and S_2. Later (footnote 41) he showed that there is a similar theorem of permutability for transformations such that a given surface and a transform are the focal surfaces of a *W* congruence.

In 1899 Guichard (f. n. 100) announced two theorems concerning the deformations of a quadric of revolution which led to the transformations of Darboux of isothermic surfaces. In such a transformation a surface and its transform are the sheets of the envelope of a two-parameter family of spheres with the lines of curvature corresponding on the two sheets. Families of spheres of this type are associated with cyclic systems of circles, which Ribaucour was the first to investigate extensively, and consequently two surfaces which are the sheets of the envelope of a two-parameter family of spheres with lines of curvature in correspondence are said to be in the relation of a transformation of Ribaucour. Bianchi showed that for transformations of Ribaucour (f. n. 54) and in particular for transformations of Darboux of isothermic surfaces (f. n. 64) there is a theorem of permutability in the sense mentioned above.

When two surfaces are in the relation of a transformation of Ribaucour, the lines joining corresponding points on the surfaces form a congruence whose developables meet the surfaces in their lines of curvature. The transformations of Darboux are a particular case of transformations of conjugate systems, or nets, with equal point invariants, such that the lines joining corresponding points of such a net and a transform form a congruence whose developables meet the surfaces on which the nets lie in these nets and corresponding points of the two nets divide harmonically the focal segment of the corresponding lines of the congruence; these transformations were first studied by Koenigs (f. n. 17) and are called transformations *K*.

When two nets and the congruence of the joins of corresponding points are so related that the developables of the congruence meet the surfaces on which the nets lie in these nets, we say that either net is obtained from the other by a fundamental transformation, or more briefly a transformation *F*. We have remarked that transformations of Ribaucour and transformations *K* are of this type. The general transformations *F* for 3-space have been studied by Jonas and the author (f. n. 15) and a theorem of permutability of these transformations has been established.

Most, if not all, of the transformations which have been developed in recent years are reducible to transformations *F* or to transformations of the type such that a surface and a transform are focal surfaces of a *W* congruence. It is the purpose of this book to develop these two types of transformations and thereby to coordinate the results of many investigations.

October, 1922.

Luther Pfahler Eisenhart.

Contents

Chapter I.

Conjugate nets and congruences.

Chapter II.

Transformations F.

Chapter III.

Sequences of Laplace.

Chapter IV.

Surfaces and congruences in 3-space.

Chapter V.

Transformations Ω. W congruences.

Chapter VI.

Orthogonal nets.

Chapter VII.

Transformations of Ribaucour.

Chapter VIII.

Circles and spheres.

Chapter IX.

Rolling surfaces.

Chapter X.

Surfaces applicable to a quadric.

Chapter I.

Conjugate nets and congruences.

1. **Geometric entities of euclidean n-space.** A point in euclidean space of n dimensions is determined by a system of n numbers $x^1, \ldots x^n$, called the *coordinates* of the point, which are a generalization of cartesian coordinates in euclidean 3-space. We refer to the point as $P(x)$. Thus x typifies all of the coordinates. In like manner $P(y)$ is the point whose coordinates are $y^1, \ldots y^n$. The distance d between $P(x)$ and $P(y)$ is defined by the equation

$$d^2 = (y^1 - x^1)^2 + \ldots + (y^n - x^n)^2 = \sum (y - x)^2.$$

As thus used Σ indicates the sum of all terms of the type $(y^i - x^i)^2$, but we write it in the above form without subscripts or superscripts, and shall do so in what follows.

If $X^1, \ldots X^n$ are n numbers, the points whose coordinates are of the form

$$y = x + uX,$$

where u is a parameter, lie on a *line* through $P(x)$. The quantities X are called *direction-parameters* of the line. Evidently they are determined only to within a factor. This equation represents each of the n equations $y^i = x^i + uX^i$. It is important that the reader should become familiar with this notation. It is understood that u is the same for all n equations.

Two non-coincident lines whose corresponding direction-parameters X and Y are proportional are said to be *parallel*. The angle of inclination of two non-parallel lines of direction-parameters X^i and Y^i is defined to be

$$\cos\theta = \frac{\sum XY}{\sqrt{\sum X^2 \cdot \sum Y^2}}.$$

When $\cos\theta = 0$ the lines are said to be *perpendicular*.

The locus of the points whose coordinates are of the form

$$y = x + uX + vY,$$

where u and v are parameters, is a *plane*. The locus of the points whose coordinates satisfy a relation of the form

$$a^1 x^1 + a^2 x^2 + \dots + a^n x^n + a^{n+1} = 0,$$

where the a's are constants, is called a *hyperplane*. For the sake of brevity we write the above equation in the form $\sum ax + a^{n+1} = 0$. In particular, $x_i = 0$ is the equation of a *coordinate hyperplane*.

Two hyperplanes

$$\sum_{i=1}^{n} a^i x + a^{n+1} = 0, \quad \sum_{i=1}^{n} b^i x + b^{n+1} = 0$$

are said to be *parallel* when the corresponding quantities a^i and b^i $(i = 1, \dots n)$ are proportional. The angle of inclination θ of two non-parallel hyperplanes is defined by

$$\cos\theta = \frac{\sum_{i=1}^{n} a^i b^i}{\sqrt{\sum (a^i)^2 \cdot \sum (b^i)^2}}.$$

When $\cos\theta = 0$, the two hyperplanes are said to be *perpendicular*. In particular, any two coordinate hyperplanes are perpendicular.

A line is a special type of *curve*, which by definition is the locus of a point whose coordinates x are functions[1]) of a parameter u. The *tangent* to a curve at a point is the line through the point whose direction-parameters are $\frac{dx}{du}$.

A plane is a special case of a *surface*, the latter being defined to be the locus of a point whose coordinates x are functions of two parameters u and v. The points of the surface for which v has the same value is called a *parametric curve* $v =$ const. There is a one-parameter family of curves $v =$ const. on a surface.

---

[1]) In this treatment the parameters may be real or complex, and the only requirements made of the functions is that they and their derivatives (to such order as the latter appear in the development) are uniform and continuous.

When u and v are replaced by functions of two new parameters u' and v', we get new parametric curves, and conversely any two one-parameter families of curves can be made parametric.

As in the case of 3-space [§ 25][2]), it can be shown that the tangents to all the curves at an ordinary point P of a surface lie in a plane, called the *tangent plane* at the point.

2. Conjugate nets. Normal parameters. When the parameters of a surface are such that the coordinates x are solutions of the same equation of the Laplace form,

$$(1) \qquad \frac{\partial^2 \theta}{\partial u \partial v} = \frac{\partial \log a}{\partial v} \frac{\partial \theta}{\partial u} + \frac{\partial \log b}{\partial u} \frac{\partial \theta}{\partial v},$$

the parametric curves are said to form a *conjugate net*, or simply a *net*. As a consequence of this definition a net in 3-space consists of a conjugate system of curves [§ 80]. Equation (1) is called the *point equation of the net*. We speak of the net as $N(x)$.

As in the case of ordinary space, if we put

$$(2) \quad E = \sum \left(\frac{\partial x}{\partial u}\right)^2, \quad F = \sum \frac{\partial x}{\partial u} \frac{\partial x}{\partial v}, \quad G = \sum \left(\frac{\partial x}{\partial v}\right)^2, \quad H^2 = EG - F^2,$$

it is readily found that [cf. § 63]

$$(3) \qquad \frac{\partial \log a}{\partial v} = \frac{G \frac{\partial E}{\partial v} - F \frac{\partial G}{\partial u}}{2H^2}, \qquad \frac{\partial \log b}{\partial u} = \frac{E \frac{\partial G}{\partial u} - F \frac{\partial E}{\partial v}}{2H^2}.$$

The functions E, F, G are called the *fundamental coefficients* of the net.

The functions $\frac{\partial x}{\partial u}$ and $\frac{\partial x}{\partial v}$ are direction-parameters of the tangents to the curves $v =$ const. and $u =$ const. respectively, of a net whose point equation is (1). The same is true of the functions α' and β' defined by

$$\frac{\partial x}{\partial u} = p' \alpha', \quad \frac{\partial x}{\partial v} = q' \beta',$$

---

[2]) A reference in square brackets, thus [§ 25], is to the author's Differential Geometry, Ginn and Co., 1909; in parentheses, thus (§ 25), is to the present volume.

p' and q' being functions of u and v. If these equations be differentiated with respect to v and u respectively, we have in consequence of (1)

$$(4)\qquad \frac{\partial \alpha'}{\partial v} = m_1 \alpha' + n_1 \beta', \quad \frac{\partial \beta'}{\partial u} = m_2 \alpha' + n_2 \beta',$$

where

$$m_1 = \frac{\partial}{\partial v} \log \frac{a}{p'}, \qquad n_1 = \frac{q'}{p'} \frac{\partial \log b}{\partial u},$$

$$m_2 = \frac{p'}{q'} \frac{\partial \log a}{\partial v}, \qquad n_2 = \frac{\partial}{\partial u} \log \frac{b}{q'}.$$

The coordinates of points on the tangents to curves $v =$ const. and $u =$ const. have the respective forms

$$x + r\alpha', \quad x + t\beta'.$$

By means of (4) we find that the derivatives of these functions with respect to v and u respectively are linear in α' and β'.

Conversely, if a surface is referred to any system of parametric curves, a point on the tangent to $v =$ const. has coordinates of the form $x + t\frac{\partial x}{\partial u}$. When v varies the direction-parameters of the tangent are

$$\frac{\partial x}{\partial v} + \frac{\partial t}{\partial v} \frac{\partial x}{\partial u} + t \frac{\partial^2 x}{\partial u \, \partial v}.$$

Hence if this tangent is to be in the tangent plane to the surface, the preceding expression must be a linear combination of $\frac{\partial x}{\partial u}$ and $\frac{\partial x}{\partial v}$, and we have the theorem:

A necessary and sufficient condition that a system of curves on a surface form a net is that any point on the tangent to a curve $v =$ const. moves in the tangent plane as v varies.

This theorem gives a geometric characterization of a net in the sense that the tangents to $v =$ const. are characteristics of the tangent planes along a curve $u =$ const. It will be convenient at times to refer to the tangent plane to a surface on which a given net lies as the *tangent plane of the net.*

Evidently any functions proportional to α' and β' are also direction-parameters. We wish to consider now the particular parameters α and β, such that

$$\frac{\partial x}{\partial u} = a\alpha, \quad \frac{\partial x}{\partial v} = b\beta \tag{5}$$

in which case equations (4) become

$$\frac{\partial \alpha}{\partial v} = n\beta, \quad \frac{\partial \beta}{\partial u} = m\alpha, \tag{6}$$

where m and n are functions of u and v given by

$$\frac{\partial b}{\partial u} = an, \quad \frac{\partial a}{\partial v} = bm. \tag{7}$$

Following Guichard we say that the α's and β's are the *normal parameters* of the net.

Conversely, if we have n pairs of functions α and β satisfying equations of the form (6), where m and n are given functions of u and v, each pair of functions a and b satisfying (7) leads by quadratures of the form (5) to a net. Thus the complete integration of (7) determines a family of nets, such that at points with the same values of u and v on the nets the tangents to the curves $v =$ const. and $u =$ const. are parallel. A representation of all these nets is given by drawing through the origin lines whose direction-parameters are the α's and β's. We call this representation a *point net*.

3. Determination of nets on a surface. Consider the differential equation

$$A\frac{\partial^2 \theta}{\partial u^2} + 2B\frac{\partial^2 \theta}{\partial u \partial v} + C\frac{\partial^2 \theta}{\partial v^2} + D\frac{\partial \theta}{\partial u} + E\frac{\partial \theta}{\partial v} = 0, \tag{8}$$

where A, B, C, D and E are functions of u and v. If we change the independent variables, putting

$$u' = \varphi_1(u, v), \quad v' = \varphi_2(u, v),$$

the resulting equation is of the form

$$(9)\quad A'\frac{\partial^2\theta}{\partial u'^2}+2B'\frac{\partial^2\theta}{\partial u'\partial v'}+C'\frac{\partial^2\theta}{\partial v'^2}+D'\frac{\partial\theta}{\partial u'}+E'\frac{\partial\theta}{\partial v'}=0,$$

where

$$A'=A\left(\frac{\partial u'}{\partial u}\right)^2+2B\frac{\partial u'}{\partial u}\frac{\partial u'}{\partial v}+C\left(\frac{\partial u'}{\partial v}\right)^2,$$

$$B'=A\frac{\partial u'}{\partial u}\frac{\partial v'}{\partial u}+B\left(\frac{\partial u'}{\partial u}\frac{\partial v'}{\partial v}+\frac{\partial v'}{\partial u}\frac{\partial u'}{\partial v}\right)+C\frac{\partial u'}{\partial v}\frac{\partial v'}{\partial v},$$

$$C'=A\left(\frac{\partial v'}{\partial u}\right)^2+2B\frac{\partial v'}{\partial u}\frac{\partial v'}{\partial v}+C\left(\frac{\partial v'}{\partial v}\right)^2.$$

From these expressions it follows that if φ_1 and φ_2 are resolutions of

$$A\left(\frac{\partial\varphi}{\partial u}\right)^2+2B\frac{\partial\varphi}{\partial u}\frac{\partial\varphi}{\partial v}+C\left(\frac{\partial\varphi}{\partial v}\right)^2=0,$$

equation (9) is of the form (1). Since φ_1 and φ_2 must be functionally independent, they are obtained by solving the two differential equations of the first order which are factors of

$$(10)\qquad A\,dv^2-2B\,du\,dv+C\,du^2=0.$$

Darboux[3]) has called (10) the *differential equation of the characteristics* of (8).

There is only one such function φ when

$$(11)\qquad AC-B^2=0.$$

If we take it for u', equation (9) is reducible to the form

$$\frac{\partial^2\theta}{\partial v'^2}+a'\frac{\partial\theta}{\partial u'}+b'\frac{\partial\theta}{\partial v'}=0.$$

Let S be a surface in 3-space whose cartesian coordinates x are functions of any two parameters u and v. We can find by differentiation an equation of the form (8) satisfied by the three coordinates and by any function of them, say $F(x^1, x^2, x^3)$. Then

[3]) Leçons, vol. 1, p. 193.

the curves defined by (10) form a net, which is determined by the character of F; or if (11) is satisfied, a family of asymptotic lines [§ 77].

If S is a surface in 4-space[4]), an equation of the form (8) can be found which is satisfied by the four coordinates, and this equation is unique to within a factor. Consequently there is a unique net on S, unless (11) is satisfied, in which case equation (10) defines a self-conjugate family of curves.

When S is a surface in a space of order higher than the fourth, it is not always possible to find an equation of the form (8) satisfied by all of the coordinates of S. Consequently in such spaces there are surfaces upon which there are not any nets.

4. Parallel nets. When the points of two surfaces are in a one-to-one correspondence of any sort, and two corresponding systems of curves are taken as parametric, the parameters can be chosen so that u and v have the same values on the two surfaces at corresponding points. It is understood that this plan will be followed hereafter whenever we are dealing with point-to-point correspondence between two surfaces.

We inquire under what conditions the tangents to the curves of the parametric systems at corresponding points on two surfaces are parallel. When these conditions are satisfied we say that the two systems are *parallel*. The coordinates x and x' of the two systems, expressed as functions of the parameters u and v, must satisfy the equations

$$(12) \qquad \frac{\partial x'}{\partial u} = h \frac{\partial x}{\partial u}, \qquad \frac{\partial x'}{\partial v} = l \frac{\partial x}{\partial v},$$

where h and l are functions of u and v such that the conditions

$$\frac{\partial}{\partial v}\left(\frac{\partial x'}{\partial u}\right) = \frac{\partial}{\partial u}\left(\frac{\partial x'}{\partial v}\right)$$

are satisfied. These equations show that the x's satisfy an equation of the form (1), where now a and b are given by

[4]) When we speak of a surface in n-space, it is meant that the surface is not contained in any space of order less than n.

(13) $$\frac{\partial h}{\partial v} = (l-h)\frac{\partial \log a}{\partial v}, \qquad \frac{\partial l}{\partial u} = (h-l)\frac{\partial \log b}{\partial u}$$ [5]).

Hence a necessary condition that a system admit a parallel system is that it be a *net*. Evidently the parallel system also forms a net. In fact, it follows from (12) that the coordinates x' are solutions of the equation

(14) $$\frac{\partial^2 \theta'}{\partial u \partial v} = \frac{l}{h}\frac{\partial \log a}{\partial v}\frac{\partial \theta'}{\partial u} + \frac{h}{l}\frac{\partial \log b}{\partial u}\frac{\partial \theta'}{\partial v},$$

which may be written in the form

(15) $$\frac{\partial^2 \theta'}{\partial u \partial v} = \frac{\partial \log a'}{\partial v}\frac{\partial \theta'}{\partial u} + \frac{\partial \log b'}{\partial u}\frac{\partial \theta'}{\partial v},$$

where

(16) $$a' = ah, \quad b' = bl.$$

Assume that we have a net whose equation is (1). Each pair of functions satisfying (13) gives by quadratures (12) a parallel net. If θ is any solution of (1), the function θ' given by the quadratures

(17) $$\frac{\partial \theta'}{\partial u} = h\frac{\partial \theta}{\partial u}, \quad \frac{\partial \theta'}{\partial v} = l\frac{\partial \theta}{\partial v}$$

is a solution of (14); we call θ and θ' *corresponding solutions* of (1) and (14).

The analytical problem of finding parallel nets may be given another form. If we define a function φ by

(18) $$h - l = \varphi,$$

equations (13) may be replaced by

(19) $$\frac{\partial l}{\partial u} = \varphi\frac{\partial \log b}{\partial u}, \quad \frac{\partial l}{\partial v} = -\varphi\frac{\partial}{\partial v}\log a\varphi.$$

---

[5]) A particular solution of these equations is $h = l = \text{const.}$, in which case the surfaces are homothetic transforms of one another with respect to the origin, to within a translation. We exclude this case hereafter.

The condition of integrability of these equations leads directly to

$$(20)\quad \frac{\partial^2\varphi}{\partial u\,\partial v}+\frac{\partial\log a}{\partial v}\frac{\partial\varphi}{\partial u}+\frac{\partial\log b}{\partial u}\frac{\partial\varphi}{\partial v}+\varphi\frac{\partial^2}{\partial u\,\partial v}\log ab=0.$$

Each solution of this equation leads by a quadrature (19) and by (18) to a pair of solutions of equations (13), and consequently to the determination of a parallel net.

Equation (20) is by definition the *adjoint* of equation (1). Hence we have the theorem:

The determination of nets parallel to a given net N is equivalent to the solution of the adjoint of the point equation of N.

The functions h and l are determined by (18) and (19) only to within the same additive constant k. Hence if h and l are one set of solutions of (18) and (19), and x' the corresponding solution of (12), the other solutions $h+k$, $l+k$ lead to $x'+kx$.

Suppose now that we have two nets N and N' such that the tangents to the curves of parameter u at corresponding points are parallel. We shall show that N and N' are parallel, unless they are planar nets.

By hypothesis the first of equations (12) holds. Differentiating it with respect to v and making use of the fact that x satisfies (1) and x' (15), we get

$$\frac{\partial\log b'}{\partial u}\frac{\partial x'}{\partial v}=h\frac{\partial}{\partial v}\log\frac{ha}{a'}\frac{\partial x}{\partial u}+h\frac{\partial\log b}{\partial u}\frac{\partial x}{\partial v}.$$

If the coefficient of $\frac{\partial x}{\partial u}$ is zero, the theorem is established. If it is not equal to zero, we express the condition of integrability of this equation and the first of (12). The resulting equation is reducible to the form

$$\frac{\partial^2 x}{\partial u^2}=A\frac{\partial x}{\partial u}+B\frac{\partial x}{\partial v}.$$

Expressing the condition of integrability of this equation and (1), we get an equation of the form

$$\frac{\partial^2 x}{\partial v^2}=C\frac{\partial x}{\partial u}+D\frac{\partial x}{\partial v}.$$

In § 40 it will be shown that at most two linearly independent functions can satisfy two such equations and (1). Hence:

If two non-planar nets correspond and the tangents to the parametric curves in one family are parallel, the nets are parallel.

If $N(x)$ and $N'(x')$ are parallel nets, the coordinates of any point on the line L joining corresponding points are of the form

$$x + t(x' - x).$$

In consequence of (12) the derivatives of this expression are reducible to

$$\frac{\partial x}{\partial u}(1 + th - t) + \frac{\partial t}{\partial u}(x' - x),$$

$$\frac{\partial x}{\partial v}(1 + tl - t) + \frac{\partial t}{\partial v}(x' - x).$$

Hence the points for which t has the respective values

$$t_1 = \frac{1}{1-h}, \quad t_2 = \frac{1}{1-l}$$

describe surfaces Σ_1 and Σ_2 such that the lines L are tangent to the curves $v = \text{const.}$ on Σ_1 and $u = \text{const.}$ on Σ_2. The coordinates y and z of Σ_1 and Σ_2 are

$$y = \frac{x' - hx}{1-h}, \quad z = \frac{x' - lx}{1-l}. \tag{21}$$

A one-parameter family of straight lines tangent to a curve or meeting in a point, or having constant direction-parameters is called a *developable surface*[6]). Any other one-parameter family of lines constitutes a *skew ruled surface*. In a two-parameter family of lines each relation between the parameters determines a surface, developable or skew. Each line of the family belongs to an infinity of these surfaces. In space of three dimensions two of these surfaces are developable [§ 163]. In spaces of higher order there

[6]) cf. [§ 27]. As in 3-space we use the terms *cone* and *cylinder* for the second and third types here mentioned.

are not necessarily two developables of the family through each line. We call a *congruence* in n-space a two-parameter family of lines such that through each line pass two developable surfaces of the family. Hereafter it is understood that the parameters u and v of the congruence are such that these developables are given by $u =$ const. and $v =$ const.

The preceding results may be stated thus:

The lines joining corresponding points on two parallel nets form a congruence whose developables meet the surfaces on which the nets lie in the nets.

The points, F_1 and F_2, whose coordinates are given by (21) are called the *first and second focal points* of the line of the congruence on which they lie; that is, the point at which the line is tangent to the curve of parameter u is called the first focal point. The focal points are also spoken of as being of the *first and second rank.* The surfaces, Σ_1 and Σ_2, the loci of F_1 and F_2 respectively, are called the *first and second focal surfaces* of the congruence.

We remark that the tangent planes of the second focal surface are the osculating planes of the curves of parameter u of the first focal surface, and the tangent planes of the first focal surface are the osculating planes of the curves of parameter v of the second focal surface [cf. § 163].

By differentiating equations (21), we obtain

$$(22)\quad \begin{cases} \dfrac{\partial y}{\partial u} = \dfrac{x'-x}{(1-h)^2}\dfrac{\partial h}{\partial u}, \quad \dfrac{\partial y}{\partial v} = \dfrac{l-h}{1-h}\left(\dfrac{\partial x}{\partial v} + \dfrac{x'-x}{1-h}\dfrac{\partial \log a}{\partial v}\right), \\[2ex] \dfrac{\partial z}{\partial u} = \dfrac{h-l}{1-l}\left(\dfrac{\partial x}{\partial u} + \dfrac{x'-x}{1-l}\dfrac{\partial \log b}{\partial u}\right), \quad \dfrac{\partial z}{\partial v} = \dfrac{x'-x}{(1-l)^2}\dfrac{\partial l}{\partial v}, \end{cases}$$

and

$$(23)\quad \begin{cases} \dfrac{\partial^2 y}{\partial u\,\partial v} = \dfrac{\partial}{\partial v}\log\left(\dfrac{a}{1-h}\dfrac{\partial h}{\partial u}\right)\dfrac{\partial y}{\partial u} + \dfrac{\partial}{\partial u}\log\left(b\,\dfrac{l-h}{1-h}\right)\dfrac{\partial y}{\partial v}, \\[2ex] \dfrac{\partial^2 z}{\partial u\,\partial v} = \dfrac{\partial}{\partial v}\log\left(a\,\dfrac{h-l}{1-l}\right)\dfrac{\partial z}{\partial u} + \dfrac{\partial}{\partial u}\log\left(\dfrac{b}{1-l}\dfrac{\partial l}{\partial v}\right)\dfrac{\partial z}{\partial v}. \end{cases}$$

From these equations it is seen that the parametric curves on Σ_1 and Σ_2 form nets [cf. § 163]. In the next section we show that any congruence consists of the joins of corresponding points on two parallel nets. Hence:

The developables of a congruence meet each of the focal surfaces in a net.

Following Guichard, we say that a net and a congruence are *conjugate* when the developables of the congruence meet the surface of the net in the curves of the net, provided that the surface is not a focal surface of the congruence. Accordingly we may state the next to the last theorem in the form:

The lines joining corresponding points of two parallel nets form a congruence conjugate to these nets.

5. Congruences conjugate to a net. We consider a net $N(x)$ and a congruence G of direction-parameters X passing through points of the net. We seek the general conditions to be satisfied by the parameters X in order that N and G shall be conjugate.

A necessary and sufficient condition that N and G be conjugate is that on each line of G there be two points defined by equations of the form

$$y = x - \lambda X, \qquad z = x - \mu X, \tag{24}$$

such that as u and v vary respectively the corresponding point moves tangentially to the line. This is expressed analytically by

$$\frac{\partial y}{\partial u} = \sigma X, \qquad \frac{\partial z}{\partial v} = \tau X, \tag{25}$$

where σ and τ are determinate functions. Substituting the above values, we arrive at equations of the form

$$\frac{\partial x}{\partial u} = \lambda \frac{\partial X}{\partial u} + \nu X, \qquad \frac{\partial x}{\partial v} = \mu \frac{\partial X}{\partial v} + \varrho X. \tag{26}$$

Expressing the condition of integrability of these equations, we find that the parameters X must satisfy an equation of the form

$$\frac{\partial^2 \theta}{\partial u \partial v} = \frac{\partial \log A}{\partial v} \frac{\partial \theta}{\partial u} + \frac{\partial \log B}{\partial u} \frac{\partial \theta}{\partial v} + C\theta. \tag{27}$$

Hence we have the theorem:

The direction-parameters of a congruence referred to its developables satisfy an equation of Laplace.

We call (27) the *direction equation of the congruence.*

When now we require that the point M of coordinates x describe a net whose equation is (1), we find on differentiating equations (26) with respect to v and u respectively that the coefficients in (27) have the respective values

(28)
$$A=\frac{a}{\lambda},\quad \frac{\partial \log B}{\partial u}=\frac{1}{\lambda}\left(\mu\frac{\partial \log b}{\partial u}-\nu\right),\quad C=\frac{\nu}{\lambda}\left(\frac{\partial}{\partial v}\log\frac{a}{\nu}+\frac{\varrho}{\nu}\frac{\partial \log b}{\partial u}\right).$$

and

(29)
$$\frac{\partial \log A}{\partial v}=\frac{1}{\mu}\left(\lambda\frac{\partial \log a}{\partial v}-\varrho\right),\quad B=\frac{b}{\mu},\quad C=\frac{\varrho}{\mu}\left(\frac{\partial}{\partial u}\log\frac{b}{\varrho}+\frac{\nu}{\varrho}\frac{\partial \log a}{\partial v}\right).$$

If these two sets of values of the coefficients be equated, we get the following equations of condition:

(30)
$$\begin{cases}\dfrac{\partial}{\partial v}\dfrac{1}{\lambda}+\dfrac{\varrho}{\lambda\mu}+\dfrac{\partial \log a}{\partial v}\left(\dfrac{1}{\lambda}-\dfrac{1}{\mu}\right)=0,\\[2ex] \dfrac{\partial}{\partial u}\dfrac{1}{\mu}+\dfrac{\nu}{\lambda\mu}+\dfrac{\partial \log b}{\partial u}\left(\dfrac{1}{\mu}-\dfrac{1}{\lambda}\right)=0,\end{cases}$$
$$\frac{\partial}{\partial v}\frac{\nu}{\lambda}=\frac{\partial}{\partial u}\frac{\varrho}{\mu}\text{ [7]}.$$

If the last of these equations be replaced by

(31)
$$\frac{\nu}{\lambda}=\frac{\partial \log t}{\partial u},\quad \frac{\varrho}{\mu}=\frac{\partial \log t}{\partial v},$$

where t is thus defined, the first two are reducible to

(32)
$$\begin{cases}\dfrac{\partial}{\partial v}\dfrac{t}{\lambda}+\dfrac{\partial \log a}{\partial v}\left(\dfrac{t}{\lambda}-\dfrac{t}{\mu}\right)=0,\\[2ex] \dfrac{\partial}{\partial u}\dfrac{t}{\mu}+\dfrac{\partial \log b}{\partial u}\left(\dfrac{t}{\mu}-\dfrac{t}{\lambda}\right)=0.\end{cases}$$

[7] We note that if we put $\frac{1}{\lambda}=h$, $\frac{1}{\mu}=l$, $\nu=\rho=0$, equations (26) and (30) reduce to (12) and (13).

Moreover, equations (26) can be written

$$\frac{\partial x}{\partial u}=\frac{\lambda}{t}\frac{\partial}{\partial u}(Xt),\quad \frac{\partial x}{\partial v}=\frac{\mu}{t}\frac{\partial}{\partial v}(Xt). \tag{33}$$

Comparing these equations with (12), we see that the locus of the point whose coordinates x' are given by

$$x'=Xt \tag{34}$$

is a net parallel to N. Hence by a quadrature (31) we can determine direction-parameters of the congruence which are the cartesian coordinates of a net N' parallel to N, and we have the theorem:

If a net N is conjugate to a congruence G, a net N' parallel to N can be found by quadratures whose cartesian coordinates are direction-parameters of the congruence.

Conversely, if N' is any net parallel to N and through points of the latter we draw lines parallel to lines joining the origin to corresponding points of N', that is, lines with direction-parameters x', the coordinates of any point P on such a line are of the form

$$x-rx'. \tag{35}$$

The first derivatives of this expression are of the form

$$\frac{\partial x}{\partial u}(1-rh)-\frac{\partial r}{\partial u}x',\quad \frac{\partial x}{\partial v}(1-rl)-\frac{\partial r}{\partial v}x'. \tag{36}$$

When r takes the values $1/h$ and $1/l$ respectively, the points are focal points of the line, and hence the lines form a congruence. The coordinates of the focal points are of the form

$$y=x-\frac{1}{h}x',\quad z=x-\frac{1}{l}x'. \tag{37}$$

From these results follows the theorem:

Any congruence conjugate to a given net N can be obtained by drawing through points of N lines parallel to lines joining the origin to corresponding points of a net N' parallel to the given net; and every parallel net determines in this way a congruence conjugate to N.

It is evident from the above investigation that lines joining any fixed point to N' determine the directions of a congruence conjugate to N.

If two congruences with corresponding direction-parameters equal or proportional are said to be *parallel*, we have, as a corollary of the above results, the theorem:

If two nets are parallel, every congruence conjugate to one is parallel to a congruence conjugate to the other.

From (36) it follows that the point P with coordinates (35) describes a net parallel to N when r is a constant, and only in this case. Hence we have the theorem:

A congruence conjugate to a net N is conjugate to an infinity of nets parallel to N.

Combining this result with the third theorem of § 4, we have also:

Any congruence conjugate to a net N consists of the joins of corresponding points of N and of a parallel net.

6. Focal Surfaces of a congruence. From (37) we have by differentiation and reduction by means of (12):

$$(38)\quad \begin{cases} \dfrac{\partial y}{\partial u}=\dfrac{1}{h^2}\dfrac{\partial h}{\partial u}x', & \dfrac{\partial y}{\partial v}=\left(1-\dfrac{l}{h}\right)\left(\dfrac{\partial x}{\partial v}-\dfrac{x'}{h}\dfrac{\partial \log a}{\partial v}\right),\\[2ex] \dfrac{\partial z}{\partial u}=\left(1-\dfrac{h}{l}\right)\left(\dfrac{\partial x}{\partial u}-\dfrac{x'}{l}\dfrac{\partial \log b}{\partial u}\right), & \dfrac{\partial z}{\partial v}=\dfrac{1}{l^2}\dfrac{\partial l}{\partial v}x', \end{cases}$$

and

$$(39)\quad \begin{cases} \dfrac{\partial^2 y}{\partial u\,\partial v}=\dfrac{\partial}{\partial v}\log\left(\dfrac{a}{h}\dfrac{\partial h}{\partial u}\right)\dfrac{\partial y}{\partial u}+\dfrac{\partial}{\partial u}\log\left(b\dfrac{h-l}{h}\right)\dfrac{\partial y}{\partial v},\\[2ex] \dfrac{\partial^2 z}{\partial u\,\partial v}=\dfrac{\partial}{\partial v}\log\left(a\dfrac{l-h}{l}\right)\dfrac{\partial z}{\partial u}+\dfrac{\partial}{\partial u}\log\left(\dfrac{b}{l}\dfrac{\partial l}{\partial v}\right)\dfrac{\partial z}{\partial v}. \end{cases}$$

From these equations we see again that the developables meet the focal surfaces in nets.

In order that the point midway between the focal points shall describe the net $N(x)$ conjugate to the congruence, we must have, as follows from (37),

$$(40)\qquad l=-h.$$

From (13) and (16) it follows that in all generality we may take

$$a = b = \frac{1}{\sqrt{h}}, \tag{41}$$

$$a' = -b' = \sqrt{h}. \tag{42}$$

We recall that for an equation of the Laplace form

$$\frac{\partial^2 \theta}{\partial u \, \partial v} = a \frac{\partial \theta}{\partial u} + b \frac{\partial \theta}{\partial v} + c\theta \tag{43}$$

the functions

$$H = -\frac{\partial a}{\partial u} + ab + c, \quad K = -\frac{\partial b}{\partial v} + ab + c, \tag{44}$$

are called the *invariants* of the equation, since these functions are invariant when equation (43) is transformed into an equation of the same form in θ_1, where $\theta_1 = \lambda\theta$, λ being any function of u and v.

From (41) and (42) we have for n-space the theorem announced by Ribaucour for 3-space:

A necessary condition that the developables of a congruence meet the middle surface in a net is that the direction equation of the congruence have equal invariants; in this case the point equation of the net on the middle surface also has equal invariants.

We are in position now to establish the theorem:

When two congruences are conjugate to a net, the joins of corresponding focal points of the same rank form a congruence conjugate to the nets described by these focal points.

Let $N(x)$ be the net, and let the direction-parameters of the congruences be the coordinates x' and x'' of nets N' and N'' parallel to N, determined by solutions h, l and h_1, l_1 of (13). The coordinates of the focal points of the congruences are of the respective forms (37) and

$$y_1 = x - \frac{x''}{h_1}, \quad z_1 = x - \frac{x''}{l_1}. \tag{45}$$

The coordinates of any point on the line joining the focal points of coordinates y and y_1 are of the form $y + t(y - y_1)$. If we differentiate this expression with respect to u and v and make use of (38) and similar equations for y_1, we find that its first derivatives are proportional to the corresponding first derivatives of y when $t = h_1$. Consequently the points of coordinates y and

$$(46) \qquad y + h_1 (y - y_1)$$

generate parallel nets, and hence by the third theorem of § 4 the congruence is conjugate to these nets. In like manner we can show that it is conjugate to the net of coordinates y_1.

7. Laplace transforms. In [§ 165] we have derived for 3-space the expressions for the cartesian coordinates of the second focal surface of the congruence of tangents to the curves $v =$ const. or $u =$ const. of a net. The method followed is equally valid for spaces of higher order. If (1) is the point equation of the net, the coordinates of these respective second focal nets are of the form

$$(47) \qquad x_{-1} = x - \frac{1}{\frac{\partial \log b}{\partial u}} \frac{\partial x}{\partial u}, \qquad x_1 = x - \frac{1}{\frac{\partial \log a}{\partial v}} \frac{\partial x}{\partial v}.$$

In fact we have

(48)
$$\frac{\partial x_{-1}}{\partial v} = \frac{b}{\frac{\partial b}{\partial u}} \frac{\partial}{\partial v} \log \left(\frac{\frac{\partial b}{\partial u}}{ab} \right) \frac{\partial x}{\partial u}, \qquad \frac{\partial x_1}{\partial u} = \frac{a}{\frac{\partial a}{\partial v}} \frac{\partial}{\partial u} \log \left(\frac{\frac{\partial a}{\partial v}}{ab} \right) \frac{\partial x}{\partial v}.$$

The nets N_1 and N_{-1} with the respective coordinates x_1 and x_{-1} are called the *first Laplace transform* of N and the *minus first Laplace transform* respectively. If the point equation of N_{-1} is written in the form

$$(49) \qquad \frac{\partial^2 \theta_{-1}}{\partial u \partial v} = \frac{\partial}{\partial v} (\log a_{-1}) \frac{\partial \theta_{-1}}{\partial u} + \frac{\partial}{\partial u} (\log b_{-1}) \frac{\partial \theta_{-1}}{\partial v},$$

we find that

$$(50) \qquad a_{-1} = \frac{ab}{\frac{\partial b}{\partial u}}, \qquad b_{-1} = b \frac{\partial}{\partial v} \log \frac{\frac{\partial b}{\partial u}}{ab} = - \frac{bK}{\frac{\partial \log b}{\partial u}}.$$

The Laplace transforms of a net parallel to N are defined by equations of the form

$$(51)\qquad x'_{-1} = x' - \frac{1}{\frac{\partial \log b'}{\partial u}}\frac{\partial x'}{\partial u}, \qquad x'_1 = x' - \frac{1}{\frac{\partial \log a'}{\partial v}}\frac{\partial x'}{\partial v}.$$

From these, (14) and (48) we have

$$(52)\qquad \begin{cases} \dfrac{\partial x'_{-1}}{\partial u} = l\dfrac{\partial x_{-1}}{\partial u}, & \dfrac{\partial x'_{-1}}{\partial v} = \dfrac{l^2K'}{hK}\dfrac{\partial x_{-1}}{\partial v}, \\ \dfrac{\partial x'_1}{\partial u} = \dfrac{h^2H'}{lH}\dfrac{\partial x_1}{\partial u}, & \dfrac{\partial x'_1}{\partial v} = h\dfrac{\partial x_1}{\partial v}, \end{cases}$$

where H' and K' are the invariants of (15).

Hence we have the theorem:

If N and N' are parallel nets, their respective Laplace transforms are parallel.

8. Transformations of Levy. By means of (38) equations (37) can be written in the form

$$x = y - \frac{\frac{1}{h}}{\frac{\partial}{\partial u}\frac{1}{h}}\frac{\partial y}{\partial u}, \qquad x = z - \frac{\frac{1}{l}}{\frac{\partial}{\partial v}\frac{1}{l}}\frac{\partial z}{\partial v}.$$

It is readily shown that $1/h$ and $1/l$ are solutions of the respective equations (39). By a change of notation the second of these equations may be written

$$y = x - \frac{\theta}{\frac{\partial \theta}{\partial v}}\frac{\partial x}{\partial v},$$

where now the congruence consists of the tangents to the curves $u =$ const. of $N(x)$ and θ is a solution of its point equation, and the y's are the coordinates of a net conjugate to this congruence. In like manner the first of the above equations may be written

$$z = x - \frac{\theta}{\frac{\partial \theta}{\partial u}}\frac{\partial x}{\partial u}.$$

Since $N(x)$ in (37) may be any net conjugate to the tangents to the curves $u =$ const. of $N(y)$ or $v =$ const. of $N(z)$, we have the first part of the following theorem of Levy:

The coordinates of any net conjugate to the congruence of tangents to the curves $u =$ const. or $v =$ const. of a net $N(x)$ whose point equation is (1) *may be expressed in the respective forms*

$$(53)\qquad y = x - \frac{\theta}{\frac{\partial \theta}{\partial v}} \frac{\partial x}{\partial v}, \qquad z = x - \frac{\theta}{\frac{\partial \theta}{\partial u}} \frac{\partial x}{\partial u},$$

where θ is a solution of (1). *Conversely, every solution of* (1) *gives two nets conjugate to the congruences of tangents.*

In order to prove the latter part of this theorem, we note that if θ is a solution of (1), we have from (53):

$$(54)\qquad \frac{\partial y}{\partial u} = \frac{\partial \log B}{\partial u}(y - z), \qquad \frac{\partial z}{\partial v} = \frac{\partial \log A}{\partial v}(z - y),$$

where

$$(55)\qquad A = \frac{a\theta}{\frac{\partial \theta}{\partial u}}, \qquad B = \frac{b\theta}{\frac{\partial \theta}{\partial v}}.$$

From (54) we have by differentiation

$$(56)\qquad \begin{cases} \dfrac{\partial^2 y}{\partial u \partial v} = \dfrac{\partial}{\partial v} \log\left(A \dfrac{\partial \log B}{\partial u}\right) \dfrac{\partial y}{\partial u} + \dfrac{\partial \log B}{\partial u} \dfrac{\partial y}{\partial v}, \\[2ex] \dfrac{\partial^2 z}{\partial u \partial v} = \dfrac{\partial \log A}{\partial v} \dfrac{\partial z}{\partial u} + \dfrac{\partial}{\partial u} \log\left(B \dfrac{\partial \log A}{\partial v}\right) \dfrac{\partial z}{\partial v}. \end{cases}$$

Hence the points of coordinates (53) describe nets. We call these nets the *Levy transforms of N by means of θ.*

As a corollary of the above theorem we have:

There are nets conjugate to any congruence.

It is evident that, if θ is a solution of (1), the function

$$\theta_{-1} = \theta - \frac{1}{\frac{\partial \log b}{\partial u}} \frac{\partial \theta}{\partial u}$$

is a solution of (49), the point equation of the minus first Laplace transform of N. We call θ_{-1} the minus first Laplace transform of θ. From these equations, (47), (48) and (53), we have

$$x_{-1} - \frac{\theta_{-1}}{\frac{\partial \theta_{-1}}{\partial v}} \frac{\partial x_{-1}}{\partial v} = x - \frac{\theta}{\frac{\partial \theta}{\partial u}} \frac{\partial x}{\partial u}.$$

Consequently the net of coordinates z in (53) is the Levy transform of the minus first Laplace transform of N by means of θ_{-1}. Similar results follow when we consider the net of coordinates y. Hence:

The Levy transforms of a net determined by a solution θ of the point equation of N are Levy transforms of the minus first and first Laplace transforms of N by means of the corresponding Laplace transforms of θ.

9. Determination of congruences. We saw in § 5 that the direction-parameters X of a congruence are solutions of an equation of the form (27). If in (27) we put

$$X = x' \theta,$$

we obtain

$$\frac{\partial^2 x'}{\partial u \partial v} = \frac{\partial}{\partial v} \log\left(\frac{A}{\theta}\right) \frac{\partial x'}{\partial u} + \frac{\partial}{\partial u} \log\left(\frac{B}{\theta}\right) \frac{\partial x'}{\partial v} + C' x', \tag{57}$$

where

$$C' = \frac{1}{\theta}\left(\frac{\partial \log A}{\partial v} \frac{\partial \theta}{\partial u} + \frac{\partial \log B}{\partial u} \frac{\partial \theta}{\partial v} + C\theta - \frac{\partial^2 \theta}{\partial u \partial v}\right). \tag{58}$$

Hence a necessary and sufficient condition that the quantities x' are the cartesian coordinates of a net is that θ be a solution of (27).

By the above corollary of the theorem of Levy there are nets conjugate to any congruence. From the second theorem of § 5 it follows that any one of these nets is parallel to a net whose coordinates are direction-parameters of the congruence. Hence:

In order to obtain a congruence with a given set of direction-parameters X, we find a solution θ of the equation of Laplace satisfied by the X's; then the quantities

$$x' = \frac{X}{\theta} \tag{59}$$

are the coordinates of a net N'; through points of a net N parallel to N' draw lines with parameters X; these lines form a congruence conjugate to N; all congruences with direction-parameters X can be found in this way.

From (38) we find by means of (12) and (16), that the direction-parameters of the tangents to the curves $u=$ const. and $v=$ const. respectively, on the first and second focal surfaces defined by (37) are expressible in the form

$$\frac{\partial x'}{\partial v}-x'\frac{\partial \log a'}{\partial v}, \quad \frac{\partial x'}{\partial u}-x'\frac{\partial \log b'}{\partial u}.$$

When x' is replaced by the value (59), the resulting expressions are reducible to the same form in terms of X and the coefficients of (27) to within the factor $1/\theta$. Hence:

If the direction-parameters X of a congruence G are solutions of an equation (27), *the functions*

$$\frac{\partial X}{\partial v}-\frac{\partial \log A}{\partial v}X, \quad \frac{\partial X}{\partial u}-\frac{\partial \log B}{\partial u}X \tag{60}$$

are direction-parameters of the tangents to the curves $u=$ const. *and* $v=$ const., *respectively, on the first and second focal surfaces of* G.

We say that these congruences of tangents are the *first derived* and *minus first derived congruences* of G, and we denote them by G_1 and G_{-1}.

As a corollary of this theorem we have:

When two congruences are parallel, their focal nets of the same rank are parallel.

Let $M_0(x_0)$ be a generic point on the middle surface of a congruence with direction-parameters X, the parameters u and v being those of the developables of the congruence. The coordinates of the focal points are of the form

$$y=x_0+\varrho X, \quad z=x_0-\varrho X. \tag{61}$$

Expressing that these values must satisfy (25), we have equations of the form (26). In order that these equations be consistent, they must reduce, on the assumption that the X's satisfy (27), to

$$\left\{\begin{aligned} \frac{\partial x_0}{\partial u}&=-\varrho\frac{\partial X}{\partial u}+2\varrho X\frac{\partial}{\partial u}\log B\sqrt{\varrho}, \\ \frac{\partial x_0}{\partial v}&=\varrho\frac{\partial X}{\partial v}-2\varrho X\frac{\partial}{\partial v}\log A\sqrt{\varrho}, \end{aligned}\right. \tag{62}$$

and ϱ must satisfy the equation

$$(63)\quad \frac{\partial^2 \varrho}{\partial u\, \partial v} + \frac{\partial \log A}{\partial v}\frac{\partial \varrho}{\partial u} + \frac{\partial \log B}{\partial u}\frac{\partial \varrho}{\partial v} + \left(\frac{\partial^2}{\partial u\, \partial v}\log AB - C\right)\varrho = 0,$$

which is the adjoint of equation (27).

Conversely, each solution of (63) and n linearly independent solutions of (27) determine a congruence for which the surface of coordinates x_0 is the middle surface.

As a consequence of these results and the preceding corollary we have:

The determination of nets parallel to the focal nets of a congruence is equivalent to the integration of the adjoint of the direction equation of the congruence.

10. Congruences harmonic to a net. From (54) it follows that the points of coordinates y and z defined by (53) are the focal points of first and second rank respectively of the congruence of lines joining these points. Hence:

The two Levy transforms of a net N by means of the same solution θ of the point equation of N are the focal points of the congruence of the joins of corresponding points of the transforms; that is, the points defined by (53) *are Laplace transforms of one another.*

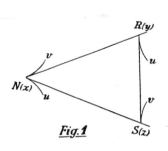

Fig. 1

The mutual arrangement of N and the congruence is shown in fig. 1 where u and v indicate the parameter varying along the curve; this notation is used in all subsequent figures.

A net and a congruence are said to be *harmonic* when the foci of the congruence lie on the tangents of the net, and the developables of the congruence correspond to the curves of the net. As a consequence of the above theorem and the first one of § 8 we have:

When a net N is conjugate to a congruence G, the congruence of tangents to one family of curves of N is harmonic to one of the focal nets of G and the congruence of tangents of the other family of curves is harmonic to the other focal net of G.

This situation is illustrated by fig. 2. We have also the theorem:

If N is conjugate to a congruence G, the osculating planes of the curves of parameter $u(v)$ of the first (second) focal net of G are determined by the lines of G and the tangents of the curves $u(v)$ of N.

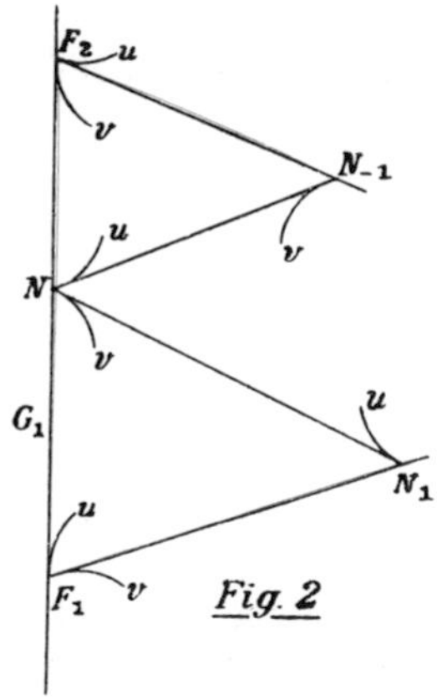

Fig. 2

Suppose that we have a net N and a congruence whose lines lie in tangent planes of N and the developables of G correspond to the curves of N, taken as parametric. As u varies, the corresponding focus of a line of the congruence must lie on the characteristic of the developable of the tangent planes along a curve $v=$ const.[8]). Since these characteristics are tangent to the curves $u=$ const., we have the theorem:

If lines of a congruence lie in tangent planes of a net and developables of the congruence correspond to the curves of the net, the congruence is harmonic to the net.

We shall prove that any congruence harmonic to a net $N(x)$ may be obtained as in the first theorem of this section. In fact, the coordinates z and y of the foci R and S of a congruence harmonic to $N(x)$ are of the form

$$z = x - r\frac{\partial x}{\partial u}, \quad y = x - t\frac{\partial x}{\partial v}. \tag{64}$$

Now

$$\frac{\partial z}{\partial v} = -r\frac{\partial x}{\partial u}\frac{\partial \log r a}{\partial v} + \frac{\partial x}{\partial v}\left(1 - r\frac{\partial \log b}{\partial u}\right).$$

Expressing the condition that this is proportional to $r\dfrac{\partial x}{\partial u} - t\dfrac{\partial x}{\partial v}$, we get

$$\frac{\partial}{\partial v}\frac{1}{r} = \frac{1}{r}\frac{\partial \log a}{\partial v} + \frac{1}{t}\frac{\partial \log b}{\partial u} - \frac{1}{rt}. \tag{65}$$

8) This can be shown analytically by making use of the fact that the x's cannot satisfy (1) and two equations of the form referred to in § 4.

In similar manner the condition that the expression for $\frac{\partial y}{\partial u}$ shall be proportional to $r\frac{\partial x}{\partial u}-t\frac{\partial x}{\partial v}$ is

$$\frac{\partial}{\partial u}\frac{1}{t}=\frac{1}{r}\frac{\partial \log a}{\partial v}+\frac{1}{t}\frac{\partial \log b}{\partial u}-\frac{1}{tr}.$$

Hence there must exist a function θ such that

$$\frac{1}{r}=\frac{1}{\theta}\frac{\partial \theta}{\partial u},\quad \frac{1}{t}=\frac{1}{\theta}\frac{\partial \theta}{\partial v}.$$

Substituting these values in (65), we find that θ is a solution of equation (1), and consequently equations (64) become equivalent to (53). Hence we have the theorem:

A necessary and sufficient condition that a congruence be harmonic to a net $N(x)$ is that the focal nets of the congruence be Levy transforms of N by means of the same solution θ of the point equation of N.

Since the direction-parameters of the harmonic congruence are of the form

$$\frac{\partial \theta}{\partial u}\frac{\partial x}{\partial v}-\frac{\partial \theta}{\partial v}\frac{\partial x}{\partial u},$$

it follows that if a second harmonic congruence, determined by a function θ_1, is to be parallel to the given one, θ_1 must be a function of θ. Since both must satisfy (1), θ_1 is a linear function of θ with constant coefficients. Hence we have:

A necessary and sufficient condition that two congruences, harmonic to a given net N and determined by solutions θ and θ_1 of the point equation of N, be parallel is that θ_1 be a linear function of θ with constant coefficients.

Consider now a congruence G and two nets N_1 and N_2 harmonic to G. Corresponding tangents to N_1 and N_2 meet in a point of a focal net of G, and the congruences of these tangents are conjugate to this focal net, by the theorem of Levy. These two congruences and the nets N_1 and N_2 are in the relation discussed in the last theorem of § 6. Hence we have the theorem:

If two nets are harmonic to a congruence, the joins of corresponding points of the nets form a congruence conjugate to the nets.

11. Derived nets. Derivant nets. Let G_1 and G_2 be congruences harmonic to a net N, determined by solutions θ_1 and θ_2 of the point equation (1) of N, it being understood that θ_2 is not a linear function of θ_1. The function

$$\varphi = \theta_2 - \frac{\theta_1}{\frac{\partial \theta_1}{\partial u}} \frac{\partial \theta_2}{\partial u}$$

is a solution of the second of equations (56) with θ replaced by θ_1, that is, the point equation of the first focal net of G_1. The coordinates of the Levy transform $\overline{N}(\overline{x})$ of this focal net by means of φ conjugate to G_1 are of the form

$$\overline{x} = z - \frac{\varphi}{\frac{\partial \varphi}{\partial v}} \frac{\partial z}{\partial v},$$

which in consequence of (53) and (54) is reducible to

$$\text{(66)} \qquad \overline{x} = x - \frac{\left(\theta_1 \frac{\partial \theta_2}{\partial v} - \theta_2 \frac{\partial \theta_1}{\partial v}\right) \frac{\partial x}{\partial u} - \left(\theta_1 \frac{\partial \theta_2}{\partial u} - \theta_2 \frac{\partial \theta_1}{\partial u}\right) \frac{\partial x}{\partial v}}{\frac{\partial \theta_1}{\partial u} \frac{\partial \theta_2}{\partial v} - \frac{\partial \theta_1}{\partial v} \frac{\partial \theta_2}{\partial u}}.$$

The coordinates y_2 and z_2 of the focal points of G_2 are given by (53) when θ is replaced by θ_2. The point equation of the first focal surface of G_2 admits the solution $\theta_1 - \theta_2 \frac{\partial \theta_1}{\partial u} \Big/ \frac{\partial \theta_2}{\partial u}$, which determines a Levy transform of this surface conjugate to G_2. The expressions for the coordinates of this transform are reducible to (66). Hence:

If two congruences are harmonic to a net N, the point of intersection of corresponding lines of the two congruences describes a net conjugate to the two congruences.

This result is illustrated by fig. 3, where L_{1u} and L_{1v} are Levy transforms

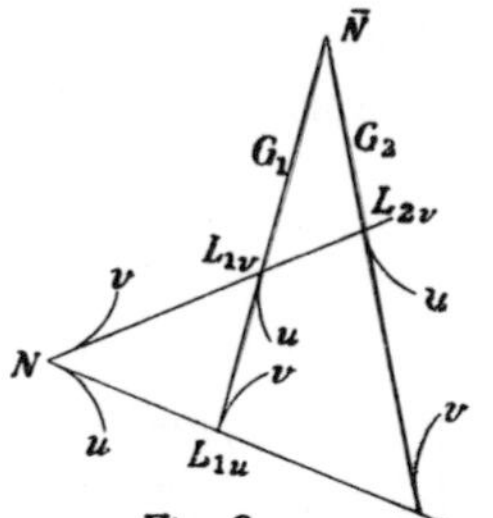

Fig. 3

of N by means of θ_1 and L_{2u} and L_{2v} by means of θ_2. $\overline{N}$ is called the corresponding *derived net* by Guichard.

We shall prove the following converse of the above theorem:

If two congruences are conjugate to a net N, the planes determined by pairs of corresponding lines of the congruences envelop a net harmonic to the congruences.

Let the coordinates of the focal points of the congruences be taken in the forms (37) and (45). We have seen that the point of coordinates (46) describes a net parallel to the net of coordinates y, and is conjugate to the congruence $\overline{G}$ of the lines joining the points of coordinates y and y_1. If the expression (46) is differentiated with respect to v, the resulting expression is reducible by means of (12) and (38) to $\overline{l}\frac{\partial y}{\partial v}$, where

$$\overline{l} = 1 + \frac{h l_1 - h_1 l}{h - l}.$$

If we apply the formulas (21) to his congruence $\overline{G}$, we find that the coordinates of the second focal net are in the form

$$\frac{y + h_1(y - y_1) - \overline{l} y}{1 - \overline{l}}$$

which is reducible to

$$x + \frac{x'(l_1 - h_1) - x''(l - h)}{h_1 l - h l_1}. \tag{67}$$

In like manner we find that the coordinates of the first focal point of the congruence conjugate to the nets of coordinates z and z_1 are of the form (67). Hence the above theorem is proved. We say that the net of coordinates (67) is the *derivant* net of N.

From (66) we have by differentiation

$$\text{(68a)} \begin{cases} \dfrac{\partial \overline{x}}{\partial u} = \dfrac{\theta_1 \dfrac{\partial \theta_2}{\partial v} - \theta_2 \dfrac{\partial \theta_1}{\partial v}}{\dfrac{\partial \theta_2}{\partial u}\dfrac{\partial \theta_1}{\partial v} - \dfrac{\partial \theta_2}{\partial v}\dfrac{\partial \theta_1}{\partial u}} \cdot \\ \left[\dfrac{\partial^2 x}{\partial u^2} + \dfrac{\left(\dfrac{\partial^2 \theta_1}{\partial u^2}\dfrac{\partial \theta_2}{\partial v} - \dfrac{\partial^2 \theta_2}{\partial u^2}\dfrac{\partial \theta_1}{\partial v}\right)\dfrac{\partial x}{\partial u} - \left(\dfrac{\partial^2 \theta_1}{\partial u^2}\dfrac{\partial \theta_2}{\partial u} - \dfrac{\partial^2 \theta_2}{\partial u^2}\dfrac{\partial \theta_1}{\partial u}\right)\dfrac{\partial x}{\partial v}}{\dfrac{\partial \theta_2}{\partial u}\dfrac{\partial \theta_1}{\partial v} - \dfrac{\partial \theta_2}{\partial v}\dfrac{\partial \theta_1}{\partial u}} \right], \end{cases}$$

$$(68\text{b})\left\{\begin{aligned}
\frac{\partial \bar{x}}{\partial v} &= -\frac{\theta_1\frac{\partial\theta_2}{\partial u}-\theta_2\frac{\partial\theta_1}{\partial u}}{\frac{\partial\theta_2}{\partial u}\frac{\partial\theta_1}{\partial v}-\frac{\partial\theta_2}{\partial v}\frac{\partial\theta_1}{\partial u}}\cdot\\
&\left[\frac{\partial^2 x}{\partial v^2}+\frac{\left(\frac{\partial^2\theta_1}{\partial v^2}\frac{\partial\theta_2}{\partial v}-\frac{\partial^2\theta_2}{\partial v^2}\frac{\partial\theta_1}{\partial v}\right)\frac{\partial x}{\partial u}-\left(\frac{\partial^2\theta_1}{\partial v^2}\frac{\partial\theta_2}{\partial u}-\frac{\partial^2\theta_2}{\partial v^2}\frac{\partial\theta_1}{\partial u}\right)\frac{\partial x}{\partial v}}{\frac{\partial\theta_2}{\partial u}\frac{\partial\theta_1}{\partial v}-\frac{\partial\theta_2}{\partial v}\frac{\partial\theta_1}{\partial u}}\right].
\end{aligned}\right.$$

We remark that if we replace θ_2 by $\theta_2 + \text{const.}$ the expressions in the parentheses are unaltered. Consequently:

The ∞^1 *derived nets of* N *determined by* θ_1 *and* $\theta_2 + c$, *where* c *is a parameter, are parallel to one another and conjugate to the congruence harmonic to* N *determined by* θ_1.

12. Determination of nets harmonic to a given congruence. We establish the following theorem which may be looked upon as a limiting case of the second theorem of the preceding section:

If two congruences are parallel, the point of intersection of lines joining corresponding focal points generates a net harmonic to the congruences.

Let $N(x)$ and $N'(x')$ be the first focal nets of the congruences. The second focal nets are the minus first Laplace transforms of N and N', and their coordinates are given by (47) and (51). From these expressions we find that the coordinates of the points of intersection of the lines joining the focal points of the first and second ranks respectively are of the form $\frac{x'-lx}{1-l}$. By (21) this is the second focal point of the lines joining corresponding points on N and N'. In like manner it can be shown that it is the first focal point of the congruence conjugate to N_{-1} and N'_{-1}.

From these two theorems it follows that the problem of finding nets harmonic to a given congruence G is equivalent to the determination of congruences conjugate to a net conjugate to G, or of congruences parallel to G, or of nets parallel to either focal net of G. In this section we give another means of finding nets harmonic to G, arising from the solution of the last problem.

If G and G' are parallel congruences, and we use the notation of the above paragraph, we have from (47), (51), (52) and (14),

(69) $$\bar{x} = x - \frac{x'}{l} = x_{-1} - \frac{x'_{-1}}{l},$$

where $\bar{x}$ is thus defined. Consequently for the congruences conjugate to N and N_{-1} with direction-parameters x' and x'_{-1} corresponding lines meet in the points of coordinates $\bar{x}$, which is the second and first focal point respectively of these two congruences, in consequence of (52). Hence:

If G and G' are parallel congruences, and through the focal points of G lines are drawn parallel to the lines joining a fixed point to the corresponding focal points of G', these lines are tangent to the curves of a net harmonic to G.

From these results and the last theorem of § 9 we have:

The determination of nets harmonic to a congruence is equivalent to the integration of the adjoint of the direction equation of the congruence.

13. Congruences harmonic to point nets. If y and z are the coordinates of the first and second focal points of a congruence, we have

(70) $$\frac{\partial y}{\partial u} = \frac{\partial \log q}{\partial u}(z - y), \qquad \frac{\partial z}{\partial v} = \frac{\partial \log p}{\partial v}(y - z),$$

where p and q are determinate functions. These equations are reducible to the normal form (6), if we put

(71) $$\alpha = zp, \qquad \beta = yq$$

with

(72) $$\frac{\partial p}{\partial v} = qn, \qquad \frac{\partial q}{\partial u} = pm.$$

Hence we have the theorem:

The lines joining the origin to the foci of a congruence constitute a point net.

We say that the congruence is *harmonic* to the point net.

The direction-parameters of the congruence are given by

(73) $$Z = \alpha q - \beta p.$$

Conversely, suppose we have any point net of parameters α and β, and a pair of solutions p and q of the equations (6). The functions y and z given by (71) satisfy the conditions (70). Hence the joins of the points whose coordinates are y and z form a congruence for which these are the focal points, and consequently the congruence is harmonic to the point net. Accordingly we have the theorem:

If the parameters of a point net are in the normal form, each pair of solutions of the corresponding equations (6) *gives directly a congruence harmonic to the point net, and all such harmonic congruences are so determined.*

It is readily seen that if the parameters are not in the normal form the determination of harmonic congruences reduces to the solution of the equations (4) of the parameters.

Consider a net N with normal parameters of its tangents given by (6). If p and q are a pair of solutions of (6), it follows from (5) that θ, given by the quadrature

$$\frac{\partial \theta}{\partial u} = ap, \qquad \frac{\partial \theta}{\partial v} = bq, \tag{74}$$

is a solution of the point equation (1) of N. Making use of this function θ, we get a family of parallel congruences harmonic to N whose direction-parameters are of the form

$$\frac{\partial x}{\partial u}\frac{\partial \theta}{\partial v} - \frac{\partial x}{\partial v}\frac{\partial \theta}{\partial u} = ab\,(\alpha q - \beta p).$$

From (73) it is seen that these congruences are parallel to those harmonic to the parallel point net determined by p and q.

Conversely, when a congruence harmonic to a net N is known, we have by a quadrature at most a solution of the point equation of N in consequence of the theorem of Levy (§ 8). If the parameters of the tangents of N are in the normal form, then p and q given by (74) satisfy the corresponding equations (6). Hence:

When the congruences harmonic to a point net are known, all the congruences harmonic to a parallel net can be found by quadratures; when a congruence harmonic to any net is known, by a quadrature at most a congruence harmonic to the parallel point net can be found.

Because of this theorem and the second one of § 12 we have:

If N is a net harmonic to a congruence G, and lines be drawn through the focal points of a parallel congruence G' parallel to the corresponding tangents to N, these lines are tangent to a net harmonic to G'.

We have also:

Of all the parallel nets harmonic to the family of congruences parallel to a given congruence, one is the point net of the family.

Since the direction-parameters of any congruence harmonic to a net can be given the form (73), we have:

Each pair of solutions p, q of equations (4) satisfied by the direction-parameters of the tangents to a net N determine a congruence harmonic to N; its direction-parameters are of the form $\alpha' q - \beta' p$; all congruences harmonic to N can be obtained in this way.

From (73) we have by differentiation, and with the aid of (6) and (72),

$$\frac{\partial Z}{\partial u} = \frac{\partial \alpha}{\partial u} q - \frac{\partial p}{\partial u} \beta, \quad \frac{\partial Z}{\partial v} = \frac{\partial q}{\partial v} \alpha - \frac{\partial \beta}{\partial v} p,$$

$$\frac{\partial^2 Z}{\partial u \partial v} = \frac{\partial q}{\partial v}\frac{\partial \alpha}{\partial u} - \frac{\partial p}{\partial u}\frac{\partial \beta}{\partial v} + mnZ.$$

Hence the direction equation of the congruence is

$$(75) \qquad \frac{\partial^2 Z}{\partial u \partial v} = \frac{\partial \log q}{\partial v}\frac{\partial Z}{\partial u} + \frac{\partial \log p}{\partial u}\frac{\partial Z}{\partial v} + \left(mn - \frac{\partial \log p}{\partial u} \cdot \frac{\partial \log q}{\partial v}\right) Z.$$

This is of the form (27), where now

$$(76) \qquad q = AU, \quad p = BV, \quad mn - \frac{\partial \log p}{\partial u} \cdot \frac{\partial \log q}{\partial v} = C,$$

U and V being functions of u and v alone respectively. Hence:

The direction-parameters of any congruence whose direction equation is (27) are expressible in the form

$$(77) \qquad Z = \alpha A U - \beta B V,$$

where α and β are normal parameters of a net harmonic to the congruence.

14. Radial transformations. Suppose we have a net whose point equation is (1) and let θ be any solution of (1). From (57), and (58) it follows that the locus of the points of coordinates $\bar{x}$ given by

$$\bar{x} = \frac{x}{\theta}, \tag{78}$$

is a net $\bar{N}$, whose point equation is

$$\frac{\partial^2 \bar{\theta}}{\partial u \partial v} = \frac{\partial}{\partial v} \log \frac{a}{\theta} \frac{\partial \bar{\theta}}{\partial u} + \frac{\partial}{\partial u} \log \frac{b}{\theta} \frac{\partial \bar{\theta}}{\partial v}. \tag{79}$$

Conversely it follows from (58) that only when θ is a solution of (1) does the point $\bar{x}$ describe a net. We call $\bar{N}$ the *radial transform* of N by means of θ.

The tangents to the curves $v =$ const. at corresponding points on N and $\bar{N}$ meet in the point whose coordinates are

$$x - \frac{\theta - 1}{\frac{\partial \theta}{\partial u}} \frac{\partial x}{\partial u} = \bar{x} + \frac{1 - \frac{1}{\theta}}{\frac{\partial}{\partial u}\left(\frac{1}{\theta}\right)} \frac{\partial \bar{x}}{\partial u},$$

and the curves $u =$ const. in the point

$$x - \frac{\theta - 1}{\frac{\partial \theta}{\partial v}} \frac{\partial x}{\partial v} = \bar{x} + \frac{1 - \frac{1}{\theta}}{\frac{\partial}{\partial v}\left(\frac{1}{\theta}\right)} \frac{\partial \bar{x}}{\partial v}.$$

These points generate the Levy transforms of N by means of the function $\theta - 1$, and of $\bar{N}$ by $1 - 1/\theta$. Hence we have the theorem:

The lines of intersection of the tangent planes of two nets N and $\bar{N}$ in the relation of a radial transformation generate a congruence harmonic to both nets.

Exercises.

1. The coordinates of any point on a line joining two points of coordinates x^i_1 and x^i_2 are expressible in the form $(l_1 x^i_1 + l_2 x^i_2)/(l_1 + l_2)$.

2. The coordinates of any point of a plane determined by three points of coordinates x^i_1, x^i_2, x^i_3 are expressible in the form $(l_1 x^i_1 + l_2 x^i_2 + l_3 x^i_3)/(l_1 + l_2 + l_3)$.

3. The tangents to the curves $v = \text{const.}$ of all nets conjugate to a given congruence at points of the same line of the congruence are coplanar; likewise for the tangents to the curves $u = \text{const.}$

4. A necessary and sufficient condition that a point P on the join of corresponding points of two parallel nets describe a net parallel to them is that P divide the segment between points of the nets in constant ratio.

5. Show that if h in (12) is a function V of v alone, then (1) must be of the form

$$\frac{\partial^2\theta}{\partial u\,\partial v} = \rho V' \frac{\partial\theta}{\partial u} + \frac{\partial \log\rho}{\partial u}\frac{\partial\theta}{\partial v},$$

one of whose invariants is zero. In this case $l = V + 1/\rho$.

6. When in equation (1) we have $a = U$ and $b = V$, where U and V are functions of u and v alone respectively, the point equation is $\frac{\partial^2\theta}{\partial u\,\partial v} = 0$. In this case we say that $N(x)$ is a *net of translation* [cf. § 81]. Show that all nets parallel to a net of translation are nets of translation.

7. The curves on the surface S of a net N which are defined by $E\,du^2 + 2F\,du\,dv + G\,dv^2 = 0$ are called the *minimal curves* of S [cf. § 35]. When the curves of N are the minimal curves of S, N is called a *minimal net*. Show that every net parallel to a minimal net is a minimal net.

8. If a net $N'(x')$ has equal point invariants, that is $b' = a'$, the equations

$$\frac{\partial x}{\partial u} = \frac{1}{a'^2}\frac{\partial x'}{\partial u}, \quad \frac{\partial x}{\partial v} = -\frac{1}{a'^2}\frac{\partial x'}{\partial v}$$

are consistent, and the x's are coordinates of a net N. The congruence conjugate to N and of direction-parameters x' has for focal points $x - x'/a'^2$, $x + x'/a'^2$. Consequently N lies on the middle surface of the congruence.

9. If N and N' are parallel nets, and θ and θ' are corresponding solutions of their point equations (§ 4), the point of coordinates $(x\theta' - x'\theta)/(\theta' - \theta)$ describes a net conjugate to the congruence of the lines joining corresponding points on N and N'.

10. If N and N' are parallel nets, and θ and θ' are corresponding solutions of their point equations (§ 4), the corresponding Levy transforms of N and N' by means of these respective functions are parallel nets; also the lines joining corresponding Levy transforms meet in the points of the net of Ex. 9.

Martin, Comptes Rendus, vol. 139 (1904), p. 32.

11. If θ_1 is a solution of (1), then $\theta_1 - \theta\frac{\partial\theta_1}{\partial v}\Big/\frac{\partial\theta}{\partial v}$ and $\theta_1 - \theta\frac{\partial\theta_1}{\partial u}\Big/\frac{\partial\theta}{\partial u}$ are solutions of the respective equations (56); and the former admits the latter as its minus first Laplace transform.

12. To each solution φ of the first of equations (56) there correspondends a solution θ_1 of (1) such that $\varphi = \theta_1 - \theta\frac{\partial\theta_1}{\partial v}\Big/\frac{\partial\theta}{\partial v}$.

13. If $\overline{N}$ is a derived net of a net N, the osculating planes of the curves of parameter u and v of N pass through the corresponding points of the minus first and first Laplace transforms of $\overline{N}$.

14. If $\overline{N}$ is a derived net of a net N, the first and minus first Laplace transforms of $\overline{N}$ are derived nets of the first and minus first Laplace transforms respectively of N. Tzitzeica, Comptes Rendus, vol. 156 (1913), p. 374.

15. If $\overline{N}$ is the derived net of N by means of solutions θ_1 and θ_2 of (1), the quantities $\overline{x}' = \left(\frac{\partial x}{\partial u}\frac{\partial \theta_1}{\partial v} - \frac{\partial x}{\partial v}\frac{\partial \theta_1}{\partial u}\right) \Big/ \left(\frac{\partial \theta_2}{\partial u}\frac{\partial \theta_1}{\partial v} - \frac{\partial \theta_2}{\partial v}\frac{\partial \theta_1}{\partial u}\right)$ are the coordinates of a net parallel to $\overline{N}$.

16. A necessary and sufficient condition that a net N and a parallel net N' defined by (12) be radial transforms of one another, to within a translation of either net, is that $h = l =$ const., say c; then if N' is a radial transform, $x' = cx$.

17. A necessary and sufficient condition that two nets, N' and N'', parallel to N and determined by pairs of solutions h_1, l_1, and h_2, l_2 of (13) be radial transforms of one another, to within a translation of either, is that $\frac{h_2}{h_1} = \frac{l_2}{l_1} =$ const.

18. If more than two ruled surfaces of a congruence are developable, all the ruled surfaces are developable and the lines of the congruence are concurrent.

19. If $\overline{N}$ is a radial transform of a net N by means of a solution θ of the point equation (1) of N, the minus first and first Laplace transforms of $\overline{N}$ are radial transforms of the corresponding Laplace transforms of N. the respective functions being

$$\theta - \frac{b}{\frac{\partial b}{\partial u}}\frac{\partial \theta}{\partial u}, \qquad \theta - \frac{a}{\frac{\partial a}{\partial v}}\frac{\partial \theta}{\partial v}.$$

20. If $\overline{N}$ is a radial transform of a net N by means of a solution θ of the point equation of N, and θ_1 is any other solution of this equation, then θ_1/θ is a solution of the point equation of $\overline{N}$. Show that the Levy transforms of N and $\overline{N}$ by means of θ_1 and θ_1/θ are radial transforms of one another.

21. If G and G_1 are parallel congruences and lines be drawn through the focal points of each parallel to the lines joining the corresponding foci of the other to the origin, the two nets determined by the intersections of these pairs of lines are in the relation of a radial transformation.

Chapter II.

Transformations F.

15. Fundamental equations. In this chapter we are concerned with the determination of all nets N_1 such that for a net N_1 and a given net N the lines joining corresponding points form a congruence G conjugate to N and N_1[9]. These transformations of N into nets N_1 are fundamental in a general theory of nets, and we call them the *fundamental transformations*, or for the sake of brevity *transformations* F. We say also that N and N_1 are in *relation* F. We call G the *conjugate congruence* of the transformation[10]. An example of this relation is afforded by two parallel nets and the lines joining corresponding points (§ 4). Also the second theorem of § 6 and the last theorem of § 10 may be stated as follows:

When two congruences are conjugate to a net, corresponding focal nets are in relation F, or are radial transforms of one another.

When two nets are harmonic to a congruence, they are in relation F, or are radial transforms of one another.

We turn now to the general study of this relation. From the second theorem of § 5 it follows that if N and N_1 are in relation F, the direction-parameters of the conjugate congruence of the transformation are proportional to the coordinates x' of a net N' parallel to N, and also to the coordinates x_1' of a net N_1' parallel to N_1. Hence these coordinates must satisfy a relation of the form

$$x_1' = \frac{x'}{\theta'}, \tag{1}$$

[9]) A statement of the history of these transformations is given in the Preface.

[10]) Two nets in the relation of a radial transformation (§ 14) satisfy this requirement, since all the lines of the congruence meet in a point, and then every ruled surface of the congruence is developable. However, we exclude this exceptional case from the definition of transformations F.

where, as follows from § 14, θ' is necessarily a solution of the point equation of N'.

The coordinates x_1 of N_1 are necessarily of the form

$$x_1 = x - \frac{\theta}{\theta'} x', \tag{2}$$

where θ is to be determined. The coordinates x' are given by equations of the form (cf. I, 12)

$$\frac{\partial x'}{\partial u} = h \frac{\partial x}{\partial u}, \quad \frac{\partial x'}{\partial v} = l \frac{\partial x}{\partial v}. \tag{3}$$

Hence the first derivatives of x_1 are reducible to the forms

$$\left\{\begin{aligned} \frac{\partial x_1}{\partial u} &= \left(\frac{\theta'}{h} - \theta\right) \frac{\partial x_1'}{\partial u} + x_1' \left(\frac{1}{h} \frac{\partial \theta'}{\partial u} - \frac{\partial \theta}{\partial u}\right), \\ \frac{\partial x_1}{\partial v} &= \left(\frac{\theta'}{l} - \theta\right) \frac{\partial x_1'}{\partial v} + x_1' \left(\frac{1}{l} \frac{\partial \theta'}{\partial v} - \frac{\partial \theta}{\partial v}\right). \end{aligned}\right. \tag{4}$$

From these expressions it follows that N_1 is parallel to N_1', if, and only if, θ and θ' satisfy

$$\frac{\partial \theta'}{\partial u} = h \frac{\partial \theta}{\partial u}, \quad \frac{\partial \theta'}{\partial v} = l \frac{\partial \theta}{\partial v}. \tag{5}$$

Expressing the condition of integrability of these equations, we find from (I, 13) that θ is a solution of the point equation of N, namely

$$\frac{\partial^2 \theta}{\partial u \partial v} = \frac{\partial \log a}{\partial v} \frac{\partial \theta}{\partial u} + \frac{\partial \log b}{\partial u} \frac{\partial \theta}{\partial v}. \tag{6}$$

Moreover, from (5) it follows that θ' is the corresponding solution of the point equation of N' (cf. § 4). Conversely, if θ is any solution of (6) and θ' the corresponding solution of the point equation of N', then (2) defines an F transform of N. Hence:

Any transformation F of a net N is determined by a net N' parallel to N, such that the joins of corresponding points of N and N' are not concurrent, and by a solution of the point equation of N; and any such net N' and a solution determine an F transform.

In consequence of (5) equations (4) may be written

$$(7)\qquad \frac{\partial x_1}{\partial u} = -\frac{\tau}{h}\frac{\partial x_1'}{\partial u}, \qquad \frac{\partial x_1}{\partial v} = -\frac{\sigma}{l}\frac{\partial x_1'}{\partial v},$$

where we have put

$$(8)\qquad \tau = h\theta - \theta', \qquad \sigma = l\theta - \theta'.$$

By means of (1), (3), and (5) equations (7) are reducible to

$$(9)\quad \frac{\partial x_1}{\partial u} = \frac{\tau}{\theta'^2}\left(x'\frac{\partial \theta}{\partial u} - \theta'\frac{\partial x}{\partial u}\right), \quad \frac{\partial x_1}{\partial v} = \frac{\sigma}{\theta'^2}\left(x'\frac{\partial \theta}{\partial v} - \theta'\frac{\partial x}{\partial v}\right),$$

which, in consequence of (2), are equivalent to

$$(10)\qquad \left\{\begin{aligned} \frac{\partial x_1}{\partial u} &= -\frac{\tau}{\theta\theta'}\left[(x_1 - x)\frac{\partial \theta}{\partial u} + \theta\frac{\partial x}{\partial u}\right], \\ \frac{\partial x_1}{\partial v} &= -\frac{\sigma}{\theta\theta'}\left[(x_1 - x)\frac{\partial \theta}{\partial v} + \theta\frac{\partial x}{\partial v}\right]. \end{aligned}\right.$$

From (9) it follows that the point equation of N_1 is reducible to

$$(11)\qquad \frac{\partial^2 \theta_1}{\partial u\,\partial v} = \frac{\partial \log a_1}{\partial v}\frac{\partial \theta_1}{\partial u} + \frac{\partial \log b_1}{\partial u}\frac{\partial \theta_1}{\partial v},$$

where

$$(12)\qquad a_1 = a\frac{\tau}{\theta'}, \qquad b_1 = b\frac{\sigma}{\theta'}.$$

This equation may also be put in the form

$$(13)\quad \frac{\partial^2 \theta_1}{\partial u\,\partial v} = \frac{\sigma}{\tau}\left(\frac{\partial \log a}{\partial v} - \frac{h}{\theta'}\frac{\partial \theta}{\partial v}\right)\frac{\partial \theta_1}{\partial u} + \frac{\tau}{\sigma}\left(\frac{\partial \log b}{\partial u} - \frac{l}{\theta'}\frac{\partial \theta}{\partial u}\right)\frac{\partial \theta_1}{\partial v}.$$

In consequence of (I, 37) equations (2) can also be given the forms

$$(14)\qquad x_1 = -\frac{\tau}{\theta'}x + \frac{\theta h y}{\theta'} = -\frac{\sigma}{\theta'}x + \frac{\theta l z}{\theta'}.$$

From (8) and (I, 18) follows

$$\tau - \sigma = \varphi \theta. \tag{15}$$

Incidentally we observe that τ and σ satisfy

$$\tag{16} \begin{cases} \dfrac{\partial \tau}{\partial u} = \theta \varphi \dfrac{\partial}{\partial u} \log b \varphi, & \dfrac{\partial \tau}{\partial v} = \theta \varphi \dfrac{\partial}{\partial v} \log \dfrac{\theta}{a}, \\ \dfrac{\partial \sigma}{\partial u} = - \theta \varphi \dfrac{\partial}{\partial u} \log \dfrac{\theta}{b}, & \dfrac{\partial \sigma}{\partial v} = - \theta \varphi \dfrac{\partial}{\partial v} \log a \varphi. \end{cases}$$

Suppose we have any congruence G. There is a net N conjugate to G (§ 8), and a net N' parallel to N whose coordinates x' are direction-parameters of G (§ 5). Each radial transform of N', say N_1', determines an F transform N_1 of N, and N_1 is parallel to N_1'. Since there is an infinity of parallel nets N_1 satisfying this condition (§ 5), we have the theorem:

If the coordinates of a net are the direction-parameters of a congruence, there are an infinity of nets parallel to the former net and conjugate to the congruence.

As a corollary we have:

If two congruences are parallel, every net conjugate to the one is parallel to ∞^1 nets conjugate to the other.

For, if N is a net conjugate to the first congruence, there is a net N', parallel to N, whose coordinates are direction-parameters of both congruences, and by the theorem there are ∞^1 nets conjugate to the second congruence and parallel to N'.

16. Inverse of a transformation F. Parallel transformations F. Evidently N can be looked upon as a transform of N_1 and now we seek the functions θ^{-1} and $(\theta')^{-1}$ giving this transformation. Since the roles of N' and N_1' are interchanged it follows from (1) that

$$(\theta')^{-1} = \frac{1}{\theta'}. \tag{17}$$

Hence if we make (2) conform to

$$x = x_1 - \frac{\theta^{-1}}{(\theta')^{-1}} x_1', \tag{18}$$

we find that

$$\theta^{-1} = -\frac{\theta}{\theta'}. \tag{19}$$

It is readily verified that equations (7) are satisfied by these values of θ^{-1} and $(\theta')^{-1}$. Hence θ^{-1} is a solution of (11). Moreover, we have

$$\begin{cases} \frac{\partial}{\partial u}\left(\frac{1}{\theta^{-1}}\right) = \tau \frac{\partial}{\partial u}\left(\frac{1}{\theta}\right), \\ \frac{\partial}{\partial v}\left(\frac{1}{\theta^{-1}}\right) = \sigma \frac{\partial}{\partial v}\left(\frac{1}{\theta}\right). \end{cases} \tag{20}$$

Hence equations (9) can be written

$$\begin{cases} \frac{\partial}{\partial u}\left(\frac{x_1}{\theta^{-1}}\right) = \tau \frac{\partial}{\partial u}\left(\frac{x}{\theta}\right), \\ \frac{\partial}{\partial v}\left(\frac{x_1}{\theta^{-1}}\right) = \sigma \frac{\partial}{\partial v}\left(\frac{x}{\theta}\right). \end{cases} \tag{21}$$

From these equations follows:

If N and N_1 are in the relation F determined by a solution θ of the point equation of N, and θ^{-1} is the solution of the point equation of N_1 likewise determining the transformation, the radial transforms of N and N_1 by means of θ and θ^{-1} respectively are parallel.

We have observed in § 15 that two parallel nets are in relation F, since they are conjugate to the congruence of lines joining corresponding points. We wish to find the form of equation (2) in this case.

From (9) we see that:

A necessary and sufficient condition that N_1 be parallel to N is that θ be a constant.

Now θ' also is a constant, which must be different from zero. Hence the equations of the parallel transforms are of the form

$$x_1 = x - cx',$$

where c is an arbitrary constant.

In a general transformation F the function θ corresponding to a given θ' is determined by (5) only to within an additive constant. Suppose we consider the transforms N_1 and N_2, corresponding to the values θ and $\theta + c$, where c is a constant and to the same θ'. Now the coordinates of N_1 are given by (2) and those of N_2 by

$$x_2 = x - \frac{\theta + c}{\theta'} x'.$$

From these follows

$$x_2 = x_1 - c x_1'.$$

In consequence of the above results we have:

When the conjugate congruence of two transformations is the same, and the two functions θ differ by an additive constant while θ' is the same, the two transforms are parallel to one another.

In the definition of transformations F we have required that N' be not a radial transform of N. It is readily shown that in order that N', parallel to N, be a radial transform of N it is necessary and sufficient that $x' = cx$, where c is a constant. In this case corresponding solutions θ and θ' of the point equations of N and N' are in the relation $\theta' = c\theta + d$. Substituting in (2), we have

$$x_1 = \frac{xd}{c\theta + d},$$

that is N_1 is a radial transform of N. Conversely, in order that (2) define a radial transform of N it is necessary that N' be a radial transform of N. Consequently, if the restriction is removed from the definition of transformations F, radial transformations form a sub-group of transformations F. But we shall retain the restriction and thus distinguish between the two types of transformations.

17. Harmonic congruence of a transformation F. From (20) and (21) we have

$$\text{(22)} \qquad \left\{ \begin{aligned} x_1 - \frac{\theta^{-1}}{\dfrac{\partial \theta^{-1}}{\partial u}} \frac{\partial x_1}{\partial u} &= x - \frac{\theta}{\dfrac{\partial \theta}{\partial u}} \frac{\partial x}{\partial u}, \\ x_1 - \frac{\theta^{-1}}{\dfrac{\partial \theta^{-1}}{\partial v}} \frac{\partial x_1}{\partial v} &= x - \frac{\theta}{\dfrac{\partial \theta}{\partial v}} \frac{\partial x}{\partial v}. \end{aligned} \right.$$

Hence the corresponding tangents to the curves $u =$ const. of the nets N and N_1 meet in points of a net which is a Levy transform of N by θ and N_1 by θ^{-1}, and likewise the tangents to the curves $v = \text{const.}$ Furthermore as follows from the theorem of Levy (§ 8) the line joining these points of intersection generates a congruence harmonic to the nets N and N_1. Hence we have the following converse of the second theorem of § 15:

When two nets N, N_1 are in the relation of a transformation F, their corresponding tangent planes meet in a line generating the congruence harmonic to N determined by the function θ and harmonic to N_1 determined by θ^{-1}.

We call this the *harmonic congruence* of the transformation.

From the above theorem and the second of § 15 follows:

If N is a net and G a congruence harmonic to it, the nets harmonic to G are obtainable from N by transformations F involving the same function θ, or by radial transformations of N.

Since θ' is determined by (5) only to within an additive constant, we have as a corollary to this theorem:

All the nets N_1 obtained from N by transformations F determined by the same function θ, and differing only in the additive constant of θ', are harmonic to the same congruence, and consequently their tangent planes form linear pencils.

The coordinates of the point of intersection of the conjugate congruence of a transformation F and the hyperplane $x^i = 0$ (cf. § 1) are of the form

$$x - \frac{x^i}{x^{i'}} x'.$$

Since x^i and $x^{i'}$ are corresponding solutions of the point equations of N and N', we have the result:

The developables of any congruence meet a hyperplane in a net.

In the above case the ith coordinate of N_1' is *1*, as follows from (1). Consequently N_1' also is a net in a hyperplane.

18. Transformations F and radial transformations. Let $\overline{N}(\overline{x})$ be a radial transform of $N(x)$ by means of a solution ω of the point equation (6) of N, so that $\overline{x} = x/\omega$. From § 14 we have that the point equation of $\overline{N}$ is

$$\frac{\partial^2 \overline{\theta}}{\partial u \partial v} = \frac{\partial}{\partial v} \log \frac{a}{\omega} \frac{\partial \overline{\theta}}{\partial u} + \frac{\partial}{\partial u} \log \frac{b}{\omega} \frac{\partial \overline{\theta}}{\partial v}. \tag{23}$$

If θ is any other solution of (6), then $\bar{\theta} = \theta/\omega$ is a solution of (23). Also it can be shown that if φ is a solution of the adjoint of (6), then $\bar{\varphi} = \varphi\omega$ is a solution of the adjoint of (23).

From (16) it follows that if τ and σ are functions of the transformation F of N by means of θ and φ, these functions, τ and σ, serve also for the transformation F of $\bar{N}$ into a net $\bar{N}_1(\bar{x}_1)$, determined by $\bar{\theta}$ and $\bar{\varphi}$. Hence similarly to (20) and (21) we have

$$\text{(24)} \quad \frac{\partial}{\partial u}\left(\frac{1}{\bar{\theta}^{-1}}\right) = \tau\frac{\partial}{\partial u}\left(\frac{1}{\bar{\theta}}\right) = \tau\frac{\partial}{\partial u}\left(\frac{\omega}{\theta}\right), \quad \frac{\partial}{\partial v}\left(\frac{1}{\bar{\theta}^{-1}}\right) = \sigma\frac{\partial}{\partial v}\left(\frac{\omega}{\theta}\right),$$

$$\text{(25)} \quad \frac{\partial}{\partial u}\left(\frac{\bar{x}_1}{\bar{\theta}^{-1}}\right) = \tau\frac{\partial}{\partial u}\left(\frac{\bar{x}}{\bar{\theta}}\right) = \tau\frac{\partial}{\partial u}\left(\frac{x}{\theta}\right), \quad \frac{\partial}{\partial v}\left(\frac{\bar{x}_1}{\bar{\theta}^{-1}}\right) = \sigma\frac{\partial}{\partial v}\left(\frac{x}{\theta}\right).$$

From these equations and (21) we have

$$\text{(26)} \qquad \frac{\bar{x}_1}{\bar{\theta}^{-1}} = \frac{x_1}{\theta^{-1}},$$

to within an additive constant of integration. If we define a function ω_1 by

$$\bar{\theta}^{-1}\omega_1 = \theta^{-1},$$

equations (24) become

$$\text{(27)} \qquad \frac{\partial}{\partial u}\left(\frac{\omega_1}{\theta^{-1}}\right) = \tau\frac{\partial}{\partial u}\left(\frac{\omega}{\theta}\right), \quad \frac{\partial}{\partial v}\left(\frac{\omega_1}{\theta^{-1}}\right) = \sigma\frac{\partial}{\partial v}\left(\frac{\omega}{\theta}\right).$$

Comparing these equations with (21), we note that ω_1 is a solution of the point equation of N_1. Hence from (26) it follows that $\bar{N}_1$ is the radial transform of N_1 by means of ω_1. Thus by the quadrature (27) we obtain a net $\bar{N}_1$ which is an F transform of $\bar{N}$. Moreover, there are an infinity of such nets $\bar{N}_1$, since $\omega_c = \omega_1 + c\theta^{-1}$, where c is an arbitrary constant, satisfies (27). Hence:

If N and $\bar{N}$ are nets in the relation of a radial transformation, and N_1 is an F transform of N, there can be found by a quadrature ∞^1 nets $\bar{N}_1$, which are F transforms of $\bar{N}$ and radial transforms of N_1.

When in particular $\theta = \omega$, then $\bar{\theta} = 1$ and consequently $\bar{N}$ and the nets $\bar{N}_1$ are parallel, the functions ω_1 being $c\theta^{-1}$. Hence:

A transformation F is equivalent to the combination of a radial, a parallel and a radial transformation[11]).

19. Transformations F with a common conjugate congruence. Suppose we have two solutions θ_1 and θ_2 of equation (6). We seek the two nets obtained from N by transformations F determined by these respective functions and by a net N' parallel to N. We denote these nets by $N_{1,1}$ and $N_{2,1}$[12]).

The point coordinates of $N_{1,1}$ and $N_{2,1}$ are expressible in the forms

$$(28) \qquad x_{1,1} = x - \frac{\theta_1}{\theta_1'} x', \qquad x_{2,1} = x - \frac{\theta_2}{\theta_2'} x',$$

where θ_1, θ_1' and θ_2, θ_2' are pairs of corresponding solutions of the point equations of N and N', that is θ_1' and θ_2' are obtained from θ_1 and θ_2 respectively by quadratures of the form (5).

We consider the functions

$$(29) \qquad \theta_2 - \frac{\theta_1}{\theta_1'} \theta_2', \qquad \frac{\theta_2'}{\theta_1'}.$$

From (2) and (1) it follows that these functions are solutions of the point equations of $N_{1,1}$ and $N_{1,1}'$ respectively, and their derivatives are in relations analogous to (7). Hence a transformation of $N_{1,1}$ is given by

$$(30) \qquad x_{1,1} - \frac{\theta_2 \theta_1' - \theta_1 \theta_2'}{\theta_2'} x_{1,1}'.$$

By substitution we find that this expression is reducible to that of $x_{2,1}$, given by (28). Hence $N_{2,1}$ is the transform of $N_{1,1}$ by means of $N_{1,1}'$, and the functions (29). It follows then from § 16 that $N_{1,1}$ is obtained from $N_{2,1}$ by the functions $\theta_1 - \theta_2 \theta_1'/\theta_2'$ and θ_1'/θ_2'.

20. Transformations F determined by the same function θ. Let N' and N'' be two nets parallel to a given net N

---

11) In fact Jonas developed the transformations from this point of view (see Preface); this theorem follows also from the first of § 16.

12) In this notation the first subscripts refer to the subscripts of θ_1 and θ_2 and the second to the subscript of common function, φ_1, determining the conjugate congruence.

which are not radial transforms of one another. The coordinates x' and x'' of N' and N'' respectively are given by quadratures of the form

$$(31)\quad \begin{cases} \dfrac{\partial x'}{\partial u} = h_1 \dfrac{\partial x}{\partial u}, & \dfrac{\partial x'}{\partial v} = l_1 \dfrac{\partial x}{\partial v}, \\[2ex] \dfrac{\partial x''}{\partial u} = h_2 \dfrac{\partial x}{\partial u}, & \dfrac{\partial x''}{\partial v} = l_2 \dfrac{\partial x}{\partial v}, \end{cases}$$

where h_1, l_1 and h_2, l_2 are pairs of solutions of equations (I, 13). The coordinates x' and x'' are the direction-parameters of two congruences, G' and G'' respectively, conjugate to N. By means of them and a solution θ_1 of the point equation of N we obtain two transforms $N_{1,1}$ and $N_{1,2}$ of N, whose point coordinates are of the respective forms

$$(32)\quad x_{1,1} = x - \frac{\theta_1}{\theta_1'} x', \qquad x_{1,2} = x - \frac{\theta_1}{\theta_1''} x''.$$

It is our purpose to show that $N_{1,1}$ and $N_{1,2}$ are in relation F.

There is a net which is the F transform of N'' by means of θ_1'' and N'. Its coordinates are of the form

$$(33)\quad x_{1,1}''' = x'' - \frac{\theta_1''}{\theta_1'} x'.$$

Differentiating and making use of (19), (31) and similar equations for θ_1' and θ_1'', we get

$$(34)\quad \begin{cases} \dfrac{\partial x_{1,1}'''}{\partial u} = (h_1 \theta_1'' - h_2 \theta_1') \dfrac{1}{\tau_1} \cdot \dfrac{\partial x_{1,1}}{\partial u}, \\[2ex] \dfrac{\partial x_{1,1}'''}{\partial v} = (l_1 \theta_1'' - l_2 \theta_1') \dfrac{1}{\sigma_1} \cdot \dfrac{\partial x_{1,1}}{\partial v}. \end{cases}$$

Hence $N_{1,1}'''$ as defined by (33) is parallel to $N_{1,1}$ [13]).

We have seen that the solution of the point equation of $N_{1,1}$ giving N by the inverse transformation is $-\theta_1/\theta_1'$. When $x_{1,1}$ in (34) is replaced by this value, we have by a quadrature a solution of the point equation of $N_{1,1}'''$. By means of (20) we find that the

[13]) We have used the notation $x_{1,1}'''$ to mean that the net is parallel to $N_{1,1}$ and determines a congruence G''' conjugate to $N_{1,1}$.

corresponding solution of (34) is $-\theta_1''/\theta_1'$. Hence a transformation F of $N_{1,1}$ is given by equations of the form

$$x_{1,1} - \frac{\theta_1}{\theta_1''} x_{1,1}'''. \tag{35}$$

By substituting the above values we find that this expression is reducible to the second of (32). Thus $N_{1,2}$ is a transform of $N_{1,1}$ by means of the same function, $-\theta_1/\theta_1'$, which gives the transformation of $N_{1,1}$ into N. Hence we have the theorem:

If a net N is transformed into two nets $N_{1,1}$ and $N_{1,2}$ by means of the same function θ_1, the latter two nets are in the relation of a transformation F; moreover, in the triad of nets N, $N_{1,1}$ and $N_{1,2}$, any two are the transforms of the third by means of the same solution of its point equation.

Hereafter we say that three nets so related form a *triad under transformations F*. Now equation (33) may be interpreted as follows:

If the nets N, N_1, and N_2 form a triad, and if N' and N'' are the nets parallel to N determining the transformations from N to N_1 and N_2 respectively, the net $N_{1,1}'''$ determining the congruence of the transformation from N_1 to N_2 can be so placed in space that it is an F transform of N'', the conjugate congruence of the latter transformation being determined by N'.

As a particular case of this result, suppose we use for θ_1 the coordinate $x^{(n)}$. Then the two transforms are the nets in which the hyperplane $x^{(n)} = 0$ is met by the lines of the two congruences, and in accordance with the above theorem these two nets in the hyperplane $x^{(n)} = 0$ are in the relation of a transformation F. In general, we have:

If a net N is conjugate to two congruences G' and G'', the developables of these congruences meet any hyperplane in two nets in the relation F.

We shall prove the converse of the above theorem:

If two nets N_1 and N_2, transforms of a net N by means of congruences G' and G'', are F transforms of one another, the three nets form a triad, unless N_1 and N_2 are parallel transforms of N.

Let the coordinates of x_1 and x_2 of N_1 and N_2 be given by

$$x_1 = x - \frac{\theta_1}{\theta_1'} x', \quad x_2 = x - \frac{\theta_2}{\theta_2''} x''.$$

If these nets are to be in relation F, it is necessary and sufficient that on the lines joining corresponding points there be focal points, that is that there exist functions λ_1, λ_2, μ_1, μ_2 such that

$$\frac{\partial}{\partial u}[x_1 + \lambda_1(x_1 - x_2)] = \mu_1(x_1 - x_2),$$

$$\frac{\partial}{\partial v}[x_1 + \lambda_2(x_1 - x_2)] = \mu_2(x_1 - x_2).$$

When the above values are substituted in these equations, we get equations of the form

$$A_1 x' + B_1 x'' + C_1 \frac{\partial x}{\partial u} = 0, \qquad A_2 x' + B_2 x'' + C_2 \frac{\partial x}{\partial v} = 0.$$

Evidently we must have

$$A_1 = B_1 = C_1 = A_2 = B_2 = C_2 = 0.$$

These conditions are equivalent to

$$(1 + \lambda_1)\tau_1 \theta_2'' - \lambda_1 \tau_2 \theta_1' = 0, \qquad (1 + \lambda_1)\sigma_1 \theta_2'' - \lambda_1 \sigma_2 \theta_1' = 0,$$

$$\lambda_1 \tau_2 \frac{\partial \theta_1}{\partial u} + \theta_1 \theta_2'' \left(\mu_1 - \frac{\partial \lambda_1}{\partial u}\right) = 0, \quad \lambda_1 \tau_2 \frac{\partial \theta_2}{\partial u} + \theta_2 \theta_2'' \left(\mu_1 - \frac{\partial \lambda_1}{\partial u}\right) = 0,$$

$$\lambda_2 \sigma_2 \frac{\partial \theta_1}{\partial v} + \theta_1 \theta_2'' \left(\mu_2 - \frac{\partial \lambda_2}{\partial v}\right) = 0, \quad \lambda_2 \sigma_2 \frac{\partial \theta_2}{\partial v} + \theta_2 \theta_2'' \left(\mu_2 - \frac{\partial \lambda_2}{\partial v}\right) = 0.$$

If $\tau_1 = \sigma_1 = \tau_2 = \sigma_2 = 0$, then $h_1 = l_1 =$ const. and $h_2 = l_2 =$ const. (§ 4), and consequently G' and G'' are not distinct. If θ_1 and θ_2 are constants, then N_1 and N_2 are parallel (§ 16). Excluding these cases, we find that the above equations necessitate $\theta_2/\theta_1 =$ const., that is N, N_1, N_2 form a triad.

21. The theorem of permutability of transformations F. The equations (1) and (2) apply to any pairs of solutions of the point equations of N and $N_{1,1}$. Making use of (1), (2) and (18) we can show that any solution of the point equation of $N_{1,1}$ is expressible in the form

$$\theta_{12} = \theta_2 - \frac{\theta_1}{\theta_1'} \theta_2', \tag{36}$$

where θ_2 is a solution of (6). Incidentally we remark that from (21) it follows that

$$(37)\qquad \begin{cases} \dfrac{\partial}{\partial u}\left(\theta_{12}\dfrac{\theta_1'}{\theta_1}\right) = -\tau_1\dfrac{\partial}{\partial u}\left(\dfrac{\theta_2}{\theta_1}\right), \\ \dfrac{\partial}{\partial v}\left(\theta_{12}\dfrac{\theta_1'}{\theta_1}\right) = -\sigma_1\dfrac{\partial}{\partial v}\left(\dfrac{\theta_2}{\theta_1}\right). \end{cases}$$

This function θ_{12} determines a transform of $N_{1,1}$ such that its points lie on the lines joining corresponding points on $N_{1,1}$ and $N_{1,2}$, that is, G''' is the conjugate congruence. From (33) it is seen that the corresponding function θ_{12}''' is given by

$$(38)\qquad \theta_{12}''' = \theta_2'' - \frac{\theta_1''}{\theta_1'}\theta_2'.$$

Hence the coordinates of the transform N_{12} are of the form

$$(39)\qquad x_{12} = x_{1,1} - \frac{\theta_2\theta_1' - \theta_1\theta_2'}{\theta_2''\theta_1' - \theta_1''\theta_2'}x_{1,1}'''.$$

The function θ_2 and the congruences G' and G'' define two transforms of N, namely $N_{2,1}$ and $N_{2,2}$, whose coordinates are respectively of the forms

$$(40)\qquad x_{2,1} = x - \frac{\theta_2}{\theta_2'}x', \qquad x_{2,2} = x - \frac{\theta_2}{\theta_2''}x''.$$

Corresponding points of the nets N, $N_{1,2}$ and $N_{2,2}$ lie on a line, and from (29), (32) and (40) we have that $N_{2,2}$ is a transform of $N_{1,2}$ by means of the function

$$(41)\qquad \theta_2 - \frac{\theta_1}{\theta_1''}\theta_2''.$$

In like manner it follows from (29) and (35) that N_{12} is obtainable from $N_{1,2}$ by means of the function $\theta_{12} - \theta_1\theta_{12}'''/\theta_1''$. But by means of (36) and (38) we show that this expression is reducible to (41). Hence $N_{2,2}$ and N_{12}, being transforms of $N_{1,2}$ by means of the same solution of the latter's point equation are themselves in relation F. We wish to show further that N_{12} bears to $N_{2,2}$ and $N_{2,1}$ a relation analogous to that born to $N_{1,1}$ and $N_{1,2}$ used to determine N_{12}.

Since $N_{2,2}$ and $N_{2,1}$ are obtained from N by θ_2, they are in relation F. The corresponding net parallel to $N_{2,2}$ is defined by equations of the form (cf. (33))

$$x_{2,2}'''' = x' - \frac{\theta_2'}{\theta_2''} x'' \quad (42)$$

[14]).

A solution of the point equation of $N_{2,2}$ is

$$\theta_{21} = \theta_1 - \frac{\theta_2}{\theta_2''}\theta_1'', \quad (43)$$

and the corresponding function θ_{21}'''' is given by

$$\theta_{21}'''' = \theta_1' - \frac{\theta_2'}{\theta_2''}\theta_1''. \quad (44)$$

The net N_{21} obtained by this transformation is defined by equations of the form

$$x_{21} = x_{2,2} - \frac{\theta_1\theta_2'' - \theta_2\theta_1''}{\theta_1'\theta_2'' - \theta_2'\theta_1''} x_{2,2}''''. \quad (45)$$

Making use of the above values, we find

$$x_{12} - x = x_{21} - x = \frac{(\theta_1''\theta_2 - \theta_2''\theta_1)x' + (\theta_2'\theta_1 - \theta_1'\theta_2)x''}{\theta_1'\theta_2'' - \theta_1''\theta_2'}. \quad (46)$$

Hence the nets N_{12} and N_{21} coincide and the congruences G' and G'''' are conjugate to $N_{2,1}$[15]).

In view of the above results we have that when two nets N' and N'' parallel to N are known, and two solutions θ_1 and θ_2 of equation (6) are given, the four functions θ_1', θ_1'', θ_2' and θ_2'' (each involving an additive constant of integration) can be found by as many quadratures. When these are known, we have a group of

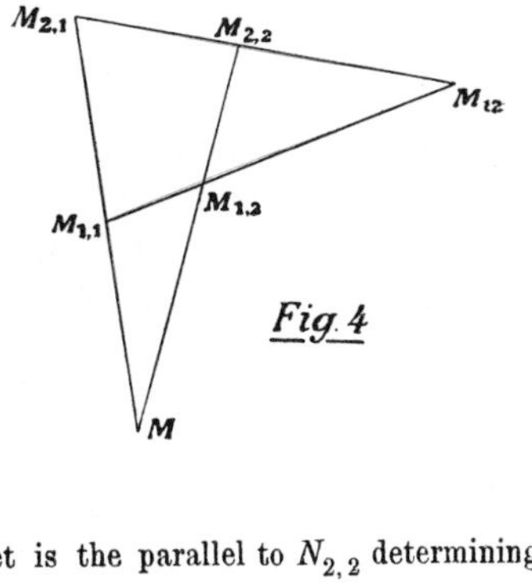

Fig. 4

[14]) The mark $''''$ indicates that the net is the parallel to $N_{2,2}$ determining the conjugate congruence G''''.

[15]) Cf. Jonas, Sitzungsberichte Berl. Math. Gesell., vol. 14 (1915), p. 103; also Transactions, vol. 18 (1917), p. 111.

six nets pictured schematically in the fig. 4 by corresponding points of these nets. We say that any four nets as N, $N_{1,1}$, $N_{2,2}$, N_{12}, such that the first and fourth are in relations F with each of the second and third form a *quatern.*

We note that $N_{1,1}$ and $N_{2,2}$ determine the additive constants in θ_1' and θ_2'', but that the additive constants of θ_2' and θ_1'' are arbitrary and consequently there are ∞^2 transforms N_{12} of a given $N_{1,1}$ and $N_{2,2}$. However, it follows from (33) and (42) that when one of these constants is fixed, the ∞^1 transforms N_{12} are conjugate to the same congruence.

We may gather together the foregoing results into the following fundamental *theorem of permutability:*

If $N_{1,1}$ and $N_{2,2}$ are two transforms of N by means of functions θ_1 and θ_2 and congruences G' and G'', there exist ∞^2 nets N_{12}, each of which is an F transform of $N_{1,1}$ and $N_{2,2}$, their determination involving two quadratures; there are obtained incidentally two other nets $N_{2,1}$ and $N_{1,2}$ such that $N_{2,1}$, $N_{1,1}$, $N_{2,2}$, $N_{1,2}$ is a quatern, and also N, $N_{2,1}$, $N_{1,2}$, N_{12}, Moreover, the six nets can be associated into the triads N, $N_{1,1}$, $N_{1,2}$; N, $N_{2,1}$, $N_{2,2}$; $N_{1,2}$, $N_{2,2}$, N_{12}; $N_{2,1}$, $N_{1,1}$, N_{12}.

Any set of corresponding points in the above configuration are the vertices of the complete quadrilateral formed by corresponding lines of the four conjugate congruences of the transformations. Each point generates a net which may be taken in place of N as the given net from which the configuration is obtained.

With each net there are associated two parallel nets whose coordinates are direction-parameters of the two congruences conjugate to the former net. These twelve auxiliary nets may be so chosen that they may be constituted into four groups such that corresponding points of the three nets of a group lie on a line through the origin (cf. (1)). These four groups are N', $N_{1,1}'$, $N_{2,1}'$; N'', $N_{1,2}''$, $N_{2,2}''$; $N_{1,1}'''$, $N_{1,2}'''$, N_{12}'''; $N_{2,1}''''$, $N_{2,2}''''$, N_{12}''''[16]).

In consequence of (32), (36), (38), (40) and (43) equation (46) can be written

$$(47)\quad \theta_{12}'''\, x_{12} = \theta_2''\left(\frac{\theta_{21}}{\theta_1}\, x_{1,1} + \frac{\theta_{12}}{\theta_2}\, x_{2,2}\right) + \left(\theta_{12}''' - \frac{\theta_2''}{\theta_1}\,\theta_{21} - \frac{\theta_2''}{\theta_2}\,\theta_{12}\right) x.$$

---

[16]) In this notation $N_{i,j}'''$ means that the radius vector is parallel to a line of G''' and the net is parallel to $N_{i,j}$.

From the expressions (36), (38), (43) and (44) we find

$$(48)\qquad \theta_1'\,\theta_{12}''' = \theta_2''\,\theta_{21}'''' = \frac{\theta_1'\,\theta_2''}{\theta_1\,\theta_2}(\theta_2\,\theta_{21} + \theta_1\,\theta_{12} - \theta_{12}\,\theta_{21}).$$

Hence the above equation may be written

$$(49)\qquad \theta_1\,\theta_{12}'''\,x_{12} = \frac{\theta_2''}{\theta_2}(\theta_2\,\theta_{21}\,x_{1,1} + \theta_1\,\theta_{12}\,x_{2,2} - \theta_{12}\,\theta_{21}\,x).$$

From (34) it follows that the functions h_{12} and l_{12} of the parallel transformation determining G_1''' the congruence conjugate to $N_{1,1}$ and N_{12}, have the values

$$(50)\qquad h_{12} = \frac{h_1\,\theta_1'' - h_2\,\theta_1'}{\tau_1},\qquad l_{12} = \frac{l_1\,\theta_1'' - l_2\,\theta_1'}{\sigma_1}.$$

The functions τ_{12}, σ_{12}, φ_{12} of the transformations from $N_{1,1}$ into N_{12} are given by equations similar to (8) and (15), namely

$$(51)\quad \tau_{12} = h_{12}\,\theta_{12} - \theta_{12}''',\quad \sigma_{12} = l_{12}\,\theta_{12} - \theta_{12}''',\quad \varphi_{12}\,\theta_{12} = \tau_{12} - \sigma_{12}.$$

In consequence of the above values these functions have the expressions

$$(52)\qquad \begin{cases} \tau_{12} = -\dfrac{1}{\tau_1}\dfrac{\theta_1'}{\theta_1}\dfrac{\theta_2''}{\theta_2}\left(\dfrac{\theta_2}{\theta_1'}\,\theta_{21}\tau_1 + \dfrac{\theta_1}{\theta_2''}\,\theta_{12}\tau_2 + \theta_{12}\,\theta_{21}\right), \\[2ex] \sigma_{12} = -\dfrac{1}{\sigma_1}\dfrac{\theta_1'}{\theta_1}\dfrac{\theta_2''}{\theta_2}\left(\dfrac{\theta_2}{\theta_1'}\,\theta_{21}\sigma_1 + \dfrac{\theta_1}{\theta_2''}\,\theta_{12}\sigma_2 + \theta_{12}\,\theta_{21}\right), \\[2ex] \varphi_{12} = \dfrac{1}{\sigma_1\tau_1}\dfrac{\theta_1'}{\theta_2}(\tau_1\sigma_2 - \tau_2\sigma_1 + \varphi_1\,\theta_2''\,\theta_{21}). \end{cases}$$

In an analogous manner the functions h_{21} and l_{21} of the transformation from $N_{2,2}$ to N_{12} are of the form

$$(53)\qquad h_{21} = \frac{h_2\,\theta_2' - h_1\,\theta_2''}{\tau_2}.\qquad l_{21} = \frac{l_2\,\theta_2' - l_1\,\theta_2''}{\sigma_2},$$

and the values of the corresponding functions τ_{21}, σ_{21}, φ_{21}, defined by

$$(54)\quad \tau_{21} = h_{21}\,\theta_{21} - \theta_{21}'''',\quad \sigma_{21} = l_{21}\,\theta_{21} - \theta_{21}'''',\quad \varphi_{21}\,\theta_{21} = \tau_{21} - \sigma_{21},$$

are reducible to

$$(55)\quad \begin{cases} \tau_2\tau_{21} = \tau_1\tau_{12}, & \sigma_2\sigma_{21} = \sigma_1\sigma_{12}, \\ \varphi_{21} = \dfrac{1}{\sigma_2\tau_2}\dfrac{\theta_2''}{\theta_1}(\tau_2\sigma_1 - \tau_1\sigma_2 + \varphi_2\theta_1'\theta_{12}). \end{cases}$$

Consider in particular the case when $N_{2,2}$ is a parallel transform of N. If we take

$$\theta_2 = \theta_2'' = 1, \quad \theta_2' = 0,$$

then

$$\theta_{12} = \theta_{12}''' = 1,$$

and consequently N_{12} is a parallel transform of $N_{1,1}$. From (43) we have

$$\theta_{21} = \theta_1 - \theta_1'',$$

and consequently from (49)

$$(56)\quad \theta_1(x_{12} - x_{2,2}) = (\theta_1 - \theta_1'')(x_{1,1} - x).$$

Since θ_1'' involves an additive arbitrary constant, we have the theorem:

If N_1 is any transform of a net N and N_2 is parallel to N, there are ∞^1 transforms N_{12} of N_1 and N_2 which are parallel to N_1; corresponding points of these nets lie on the line through M_2 parallel to MM_1.

Consider also the case where $\theta_2 = \theta_1 + c$, c being a constant. We have accordingly

$$(57)\quad \begin{cases} \theta_2' = \theta_1' + c', \quad \theta_2'' = \theta_1'' + c'', \\ \theta_{12} = c - \dfrac{\theta_1}{\theta_1'}c', \quad \theta_{21} = -c + \dfrac{\theta_2}{\theta_2''}c'', \quad \theta_{12}''' = c'' - \dfrac{\theta_1''}{\theta_1'}c', \end{cases}$$

where c' and c'' are constants. If $c' = 0$, θ_{12} is constant; it follows from § 16 that N_{12} is parallel to $N_{1,1}$. Also $N_{2,2}$ is parallel to N_{12} if $c'' = 0$.

In order to determine the effect of the additive arbitrary constants of θ_2' and θ_1'', we replace them by $\theta_2' + (c-1)$ and $\theta_1'' + (e-1)$ in (33) and (36). If we denote the new functions by $x_{e,1}'''$ and θ_{c2}, we find in consequence of (1) and (19)

$$(58)\quad x_{e,1}''' = x_{1,1}''' - (e-1)x_1', \qquad \theta_{c2} = \theta_{12} + (c-1)\theta_1^{-1}.$$

Hence the ∞^1 nets N_{12} obtained by varying c and holding e fixed are conjugate to the same congruence conjugate to $N_{1,1}$ also; similarly as e varies and c remains fixed the ∞^1 nets N_{12} and $N_{2,2}$ are conjugate to the same congruence.

The foregoing formulas are interesting also in another connection. Thus if we look upon N and a net N_{12} as F transforms of $N_{2,2}$, there are ∞^2 nets, including $N_{1,1}$, each of which forms a quatern with $N_{2,2}$, N and N_{12}. The above results lead to a means of finding these nets $N_{c,e}$. In fact we replace $N_{1,1}$ by the transform of N by means of the functions

$$(59) \qquad \theta_c = \theta_1 + (c-1)\,\theta_2, \qquad x^{(e)} = x' + (e-1)\,x'',$$

the quantities $x^{(e)}$ being taken as direction-parameters of the congruence of the transformation. Now we have

$$(60) \qquad \frac{\partial x^{(e)}}{\partial u} = h_e \frac{\partial x}{\partial u}, \qquad \frac{\partial x^{(e)}}{\partial v} = l_e \frac{\partial x}{\partial v},$$

where

$$(61) \qquad h_e = h_1 + (e-1)\,h_2, \qquad l_e = l_1 + (e-1)\,l_2;$$

also

$$(62) \qquad \begin{gathered} \theta_2^{(e)} = \theta_2' + (e-1)\,\theta_2'', \qquad \theta_c'' = \theta_1'' + (c-1)\,\theta_2'', \\ \theta_c^{(e)} = \theta_1' + (c-1)\,\theta_2' + (e-1)\,\theta_1'' + (c-1)(e-1)\,\theta_2''. \end{gathered}$$

When these values are substituted in the following expression which is the analogue of the right-hand member of (46), it is found that the result is reducible to the latter:

$$(63) \qquad \frac{(\theta_c''\theta_2 - \theta_2''\theta_c)\,x^{(e)} + (\theta_2^{(e)}\theta_c - \theta_c^{(e)}\theta_2)\,x''}{\theta_c^{(e)}\theta_2'' - \theta_c''\theta_2^{(e)}}.$$

Hence:

Let $N_{1,1}$ and $N_{2,2}$ be F transforms of N by means of functions θ_1 and θ_2, x' and x'' being the direction-parameters of the congruences of the transformations; if $N_{c,e}$ is the transform of N by means of $\theta_1 + (c-1)\,\theta_2$ and a congruence of direction-parameters $x' + (e-1)x''$, c and e being constants, the ∞^2 nets N_{12} forming quaterns with N, $N_{1,1}$ and $N_{2,2}$ form quaterns also with N, $N_{c,e}$ and $N_{2,2}$ whatever be c and e.

22. Derived nets and transformations F. If $N(x)$ is a net with the point equation (6), and θ_1 and θ_2 are solutions of (6), they determine a derived net $\overline{N}(\overline{x})$ of N (cf. § 11), whose equations may be written

$$\overline{x} = x + p\frac{\partial x}{\partial u} + q\frac{\partial x}{\partial v}, \tag{64}$$

where

$$\left\{\begin{aligned} p &= \frac{1}{\varDelta}\left(\theta_1\frac{\partial \theta_2}{\partial v} - \theta_2\frac{\partial \theta_1}{\partial v}\right), \\ q &= \frac{1}{\varDelta}\left(\theta_2\frac{\partial \theta_1}{\partial u} - \theta_1\frac{\partial \theta_2}{\partial u}\right), \quad \varDelta = \frac{\partial \theta_2}{\partial u}\frac{\partial \theta_1}{\partial v} - \frac{\partial \theta_2}{\partial v}\frac{\partial \theta_1}{\partial u}. \end{aligned}\right. \tag{65}$$

Let θ_3 be another solution of (6), and N' a net parallel to N. An F transform N_3 of N is given by

$$x_3 = x - \frac{\theta_3}{\theta_3'}x'. \tag{66}$$

The functions θ_{31} and θ_{32} defined by

$$\theta_{3i} = \theta_i - \frac{\theta_3}{\theta_3'}\theta_i' \quad (i = 1, 2), \tag{67}$$

where

$$\frac{\partial \theta_i'}{\partial u} = h\frac{\partial \theta_i}{\partial u}, \quad \frac{\partial \theta_i'}{\partial v} = l\frac{\partial \theta_i}{\partial v} \quad (i = 1, 2, 3), \tag{68}$$

are solutions of the point equation of N_3. They determine a derived net $\overline{N}_3$ of N_3, whose coordinates are of the form

$$\overline{x}_3 = x_3 + p_3\frac{\partial x_3}{\partial u} + q_3\frac{\partial x_3}{\partial v}, \tag{69}$$

where p_3 and q_3 are given by (65) when θ_1 and θ_2 are replaced by θ_{31} and θ_{32} respectively.

From (66) and (67) we have

$$\frac{\partial x_3}{\partial u} = \frac{\theta_3 h - \theta_3'}{\theta_3'^2}\left(x'\frac{\partial \theta_3}{\theta u} - \theta_3'\frac{\partial x}{\partial u}\right),$$

$$\frac{\partial x_3}{\partial v} = \frac{\theta_3 l - \theta_3'}{\theta_3'^2}\left(x'\frac{\partial \theta_3}{\partial v} - \theta_3'\frac{\partial x}{\partial v}\right),$$

$$\frac{\partial \theta_{3i}}{\partial u} = \frac{\theta_3 h - \theta_3'}{\theta_3'^2}\left(\theta_i' \frac{\partial \theta_3}{\partial u} - \theta_3' \frac{\partial \theta_i}{\partial u}\right),$$

$$\frac{\partial \theta_{3i}}{\partial v} = \frac{\theta_3 l - \theta_3'}{\theta_3'^2}\left(\theta_i' \frac{\partial \theta_3}{\partial v} - \theta_3' \frac{\partial \theta_i}{\partial v}\right), \quad (i = 1, 2).$$

On substituting these expressions in (69), the resulting expression in reducible to

(70)
$$\bar{x}_3 = x + \frac{1}{A}\left\{x' \begin{vmatrix} \theta_1 & \theta_2 & \theta_3 \\ \frac{\partial \theta_1}{\partial u} & \frac{\partial \theta_2}{\partial u} & \frac{\partial \theta_3}{\partial u} \\ \frac{\partial \theta_1}{\partial v} & \frac{\partial \theta_2}{\partial v} & \frac{\partial \theta_3}{\partial v} \end{vmatrix} + \frac{\partial x}{\partial u} \begin{vmatrix} \theta_1' & \theta_2' & \theta_3' \\ \theta_1 & \theta_2 & \theta_3 \\ \frac{\partial \theta_1}{\partial v} & \frac{\partial \theta_2}{\partial v} & \frac{\partial \theta_3}{\partial v} \end{vmatrix} - \frac{\partial x}{\partial v} \begin{vmatrix} \theta_1' & \theta_2' & \theta_3' \\ \theta_1 & \theta_2 & \theta_3 \\ \frac{\partial \theta_1}{\partial u} & \frac{\partial \theta_2}{\partial u} & \frac{\partial \theta_3}{\partial u} \end{vmatrix}\right\},$$

where

$$A = \theta_1' \left(\frac{\partial \theta_2}{\partial v}\frac{\partial \theta_3}{\partial u} - \frac{\partial \theta_2}{\partial u}\frac{\partial \theta_3}{\partial v}\right) + \theta_2' \left(\frac{\partial \theta_3}{\partial v}\frac{\partial \theta_1}{\partial u} - \frac{\partial \theta_3}{\partial u}\frac{\partial \theta_1}{\partial v}\right)$$
$$+ \theta_3' \left(\frac{\partial \theta_1}{\partial v}\frac{\partial \theta_2}{\partial u} - \frac{\partial \theta_1}{\partial u}\frac{\partial \theta_2}{\partial v}\right).$$

Since θ_1' and θ_2' are solutions of the point equation of N', a derived net $\overline{N}'$ of N' is given by equations of the form

$$\bar{x}' = x' + p' \frac{\partial x'}{\partial u} + q' \frac{\partial x'}{\partial v},$$

where p' and q' are obtained from (65) by replacing θ_1 and θ_2 by θ_1' and θ_2'. From equations analogous to (I, 68), we find

$$\frac{\partial \bar{x}'}{\partial u} = \bar{h} \frac{\partial \bar{x}}{\partial u}, \qquad \frac{\partial \bar{x}'}{\partial v} = \bar{l} \frac{\partial \bar{x}}{\partial v},$$

where

$$\bar{h} = \frac{\theta_1' \frac{\partial \theta_2}{\partial v} - \theta_2' \frac{\partial \theta_1}{\partial v}}{\theta_1 \frac{\partial \theta_2}{\partial v} - \theta_2 \frac{\partial \theta_1}{\partial v}}, \qquad \bar{l} = \frac{\theta_1' \frac{\partial \theta_2}{\partial u} - \theta_2' \frac{\partial \theta_1}{\partial u}}{\theta_1 \frac{\partial \theta_2}{\partial u} - \theta_2 \frac{\partial \theta_1}{\partial u}}.$$

Consequently $\overline{N}'$ is parallel to $\overline{N}$.

The functions $\overline{\theta}_3$ and $\overline{\theta}_3'$ defined by

$$\overline{\theta}_3 = \theta_3 + p\frac{\partial \theta_3}{\partial u} + q\frac{\partial \theta_3}{\partial v}, \qquad \overline{\theta}_3' = \theta_3' + p'\frac{\partial \theta_3'}{\partial u} + q'\frac{\partial \theta_3'}{\partial v}$$

are corresponding solutions of the point equations of $\overline{N}$ and $\overline{N}'$. Hence quantities of the form

$$\overline{x} - \frac{\overline{\theta}_3}{\overline{\theta}_3'}\overline{x}'$$

are the coordinates of an F transform of $\overline{N}$. When the above expressions are substituted in this quantity, it is reducible to (70). Since θ_1' and θ_2', as given by (68) involve additive arbitrary constants, there are ∞^2 nets $\overline{N}_3$. Hence we have the theorem:

If $\overline{N}$ is a derived net of N and N_3 is any F transform of N, there can be found by two quadratures ∞^2 nets $\overline{N}_3$, each of which is a derived net of N_3 and an F transform of $\overline{N}$.

23. Derivant net and derived net of two transformations F. We note that the corresponding points of six nets in the relation of the theorem of permutability are coplanar. From the second theorem of § 11 it follows that these planes envelope a derivant net $\hat{N}$ of N. Since the four congruences of the configuration are harmonic to $\hat{N}$, it is a derivant net of each of the six nets. By means of (32), (40) and equations similar to (8) and (15) the expressions (I, 67) for the coordinates of $\hat{N}$ are reducible to

$$(71)\qquad \left\{\begin{aligned} &\left(\frac{\tau_1\sigma_2 - \tau_2\sigma_1}{\theta_1\theta_2} + \frac{\theta_2''}{\theta_2}\varphi_1 - \frac{\theta_1'}{\theta_1}\varphi_2\right)\hat{x} \\ &= \frac{\tau_1\sigma_2 - \tau_2\sigma_1}{\theta_1\theta_2}x + \frac{\theta_2''}{\theta_2}\varphi_1 x_{2,2} - \frac{\theta_1'}{\theta_1}\varphi_2 x_{1,1}. \end{aligned}\right.$$

From § 17 it follows that corresponding tangent planes of N, $N_{1,1}$ and $N_{2,2}$ meet in the point which generates the derived net $\overline{N}$ of N determined by the solutions θ_1 and θ_2 of the point equation of N. We shall show that the corresponding tangent planes of the ∞^2 nets N_{12} pass through this point. In fact from (I, 66) it follows that the coordinates $\overline{x}$ of this point may be given the form

$$\overline{x} = x + \frac{\frac{\partial}{\partial v}\left(\frac{\theta_2}{\theta_1}\right)\frac{\partial x}{\partial u} - \frac{\partial}{\partial u}\left(\frac{\theta_2}{\theta_1}\right)\frac{\partial x}{\partial v}}{\theta_1\left[\frac{\partial}{\partial u}\left(\frac{1}{\theta_1}\right)\frac{\partial}{\partial v}\left(\frac{\theta_2}{\theta_1}\right) - \frac{\partial}{\partial v}\left(\frac{1}{\theta_1}\right)\frac{\partial}{\partial u}\left(\frac{\theta_2}{\theta_1}\right)\right]}.$$

Consider now the net $N_{1,1}$ and look upon N and a net N_{12} as F transforms of it by means of $\theta_1^{-1} = -\theta_1/\theta_1'$ and θ_{12}. The corresponding formula for this case is

$$x_1 - \frac{\theta_1'}{\theta_1} \frac{\frac{\partial}{\partial v}\left(\theta_{12}\frac{\theta_1'}{\theta_1}\right)\frac{\partial x_1}{\partial u} - \frac{\partial}{\partial u}\left(\theta_{12}\frac{\theta_1'}{\theta_1}\right)\frac{\partial x_1}{\partial v}}{\frac{\partial}{\partial u}\left(\frac{1}{\theta_1^{-1}}\right)\frac{\partial}{\partial v}\left(\theta_{12}\frac{\theta_1'}{\theta_1}\right) - \frac{\partial}{\partial v}\left(\frac{1}{\theta_1^{-1}}\right)\frac{\partial}{\partial u}\left(\theta_{12}\frac{\theta_1'}{\theta_1}\right)}.$$

By means of (9), (20) and (37) this is reducible to the preceding form. Hence:

The corresponding tangent planes of N, $N_{1,1}$, $N_{2,2}$ and the ∞^2 nets N_{12} meet in the point which generates the derived net of N by means of the functions θ_1 and θ_2 of the transformations of N into $N_{1,1}$ and $N_{2,2}$.

24. The extended theorem of permutability. In this section we extend the theorem of permutability so as to involve three transforms of N. Let N_1, N_2 and N_3 be these transforms of N by means of the functions θ_i and w_i $(i = 1, 2, 3)$, where

$$w_1 = \frac{\theta_1'}{\theta_1}, \quad w_2 = \frac{\theta_2''}{\theta_2}, \quad w_{12} = \frac{\theta_{12}'''}{\theta_{12}}, \quad w_{21} = \frac{\theta_{21}''''}{\theta_{21}}, \quad \cdots\cdots$$

Applying the theorem of permutability to the three pairs of these nets, we get three families of nets N_{12}, N_{23} and N_{31}, since $N_{ij} = N_{ji}$. From (48) and (49) we have

$$(72)\quad \begin{cases} \theta_i\,\theta_{ij}\,w_{ij} = w_j\,(\theta_j\,\theta_{ji} + \theta_i\,\theta_{ij} - \theta_{ij}\,\theta_{ji}), \\ \theta_i\theta_{ij}w_{ij}x_{ij} = w_j\,(\theta_j\,\theta_{ji}\,x_i + \theta_i\,\theta_{ij}\,x_j - \theta_{ij}\,\theta_{ji}\,x) \quad (i \neq j). \end{cases}$$

Since a net N_{12} and a net N_{13} are transforms of N_1, there exist ∞^2 nets $\overline{N}$ for each of which N_1, N_{12}, N_{13} and $\overline{N}$ form a quatern. It is our purpose to show that one of these nets $\overline{N}$ is such that N_2, N_{12}, N_{23}, $\overline{N}$ form a quatern; and likewise N_3, N_{13}, N_{23} and $\overline{N}$.

We denote by $\overline{\theta}_{ij}$ and $\overline{w}_{ij}$ the functions by means of which N_{ij} is transformed into $\overline{N}$; from their definition it follows that $\overline{\theta}_{ij} = \overline{\theta}_{ji}$ and $\overline{w}_{ij} = \overline{w}_{ji}$. According as we look upon $\overline{N}$ as belonging to the one or the other of the quaterns, N_1, N_{12}, N_{13}, $\overline{N}$; N_2, N_{12}, N_{23}, $\overline{N}$, the coordinates $\overline{x}$ of $\overline{N}$ are given by the respective equations

$$(73)\qquad \begin{cases} \theta_{12}\bar{\theta}_{12}\bar{w}_{12}\bar{x} = w_{13}(\theta_{13}\bar{\theta}_{13}x_{12} + \theta_{12}\bar{\theta}_{12}x_{13} - \bar{\theta}_{12}\bar{\theta}_{13}x_1), \\ \theta_{21}\bar{\theta}_{21}\bar{w}_{21}\bar{x} = w_{23}(\theta_{23}\bar{\theta}_{23}x_{12} + \theta_{21}\bar{\theta}_{21}x_{23} - \bar{\theta}_{21}\bar{\theta}_{23}x_2), \end{cases}$$

which are analogous to (72). When we equate these two values for $\bar{x}$, the resulting equation is reducible by means of (72) to an equation of the form $Ax_1 + Bx_2 + Cx = 0$. Since A, B and C are necessarily equal to zero, we have the following equations of condition:

$$\theta_1 w_{12}\bar{\theta}_{12}\left(\theta_1 w_{13}\bar{\theta}_{13} - \theta_3 w_3 \frac{\theta_{12}\theta_{31}}{\theta_{13}}\right) - \theta_1 w_{13}\bar{\theta}_{13}\theta_2 w_2 \frac{\theta_{21}\theta_{13}}{\theta_{12}} + \theta_2 w_{23}\bar{\theta}_{23}\theta_1 w_2\theta_{23} = 0,$$

$$\theta_1 w_{12}\bar{\theta}_{12}\left(\theta_2 w_{23}\bar{\theta}_{23} - \theta_3 w_3 \frac{\theta_{21}\theta_{32}}{\theta_{23}}\right) - \theta_2 w_{23}\bar{\theta}_{23}\theta_1 w_2\theta_{23} + \theta_1 w_{13}\bar{\theta}_{13}\theta_2 w_2 \frac{\theta_{21}\theta_{13}}{\theta_{12}} = 0,$$

$$\theta_1 w_{12}\bar{\theta}_{12}(\theta_1 w_3\theta_{32} - \theta_2 w_3\theta_{31}) - \theta_1 w_{13}\bar{\theta}_{13}\theta_2 w_2 \frac{\theta_{13}\theta_{21}}{\theta_{12}} + \theta_2 w_{23}\bar{\theta}_{23}\theta_1 w_2\theta_{23} = 0.$$

By subtracting the last of these equations from the first and adding it to the second we find that the above system is equivalent to

$$(74)\qquad \begin{cases} \theta_1\theta_{12}w_{12}\bar{\theta}_{12} = w_2(\theta_2\theta_{21}\theta_{13} + \theta_1\theta_{12}\theta_{23} - \theta_3\theta_{12}\theta_{21}), \\ \theta_1\theta_{13}w_{13}\bar{\theta}_{13} = w_3(\theta_3\theta_{31}\theta_{12} + \theta_1\theta_{13}\theta_{32} - \theta_2\theta_{13}\theta_{31}), \\ \theta_2\theta_{23}w_{23}\bar{\theta}_{23} = w_3(\theta_3\theta_{32}\theta_{21} + \theta_2\theta_{23}\theta_{31} - \theta_1\theta_{23}\theta_{32}). \end{cases}$$

From (38) and (44) it follows that

$$(75)\qquad w_1 w_{12}\theta_1\theta_{12} = w_2 w_{21}\theta_2\theta_{21},$$

so that the above equations are consistent with the requirement that $\bar{\theta}_{ij} = \bar{\theta}_{ji}$. When equations (74) are compared with the second of (72), it is found that $\bar{\theta}_{ij}$ is a solution of the point equation of N_{ij}, which is a necessary condition. The analogue of the first of (72) is

$$\theta_{12}\bar{\theta}_{12}\bar{w}_{12} = w_{13}(\theta_{13}\bar{\theta}_{13} + \theta_{12}\bar{\theta}_{12} - \bar{\theta}_{12}\bar{\theta}_{13}).$$

Substituting in the right-hand member the expressions for $\bar{\theta}_{12}$ and $\bar{\theta}_{13}$ from (74), we have

$$\Phi = \frac{\theta_1 \theta_{12} w_{12} \overline{\theta}_{12} \overline{w}_{12}}{w_2 w_3} = \theta_1 (\theta_{12}\theta_{23} + \theta_{13}\theta_{32} - \theta_{32}\theta_{23}) + \theta_2 (\theta_{23}\theta_{31} + \theta_{21}\theta_{13} - \theta_{13}\theta_{31}) + \theta_3 (\theta_{31}\theta_{12} + \theta_{32}\theta_{21} - \theta_{21}\theta_{12}) - \theta_{12}\theta_{23}\theta_{31} - \theta_{21}\theta_{13}\theta_{32},$$

which in consequence of (75) is consistent with the requirement that $\overline{w}_{ij} = \overline{w}_{ji}$. By means of these results equations (73) reduce to

$$(76)\quad \begin{cases} \Phi \overline{x} = x_1 (\theta_2 \theta_{23}\theta_{31} + \theta_3\theta_{32}\theta_{21} - \theta_1\theta_{23}\theta_{32}) \\ \qquad + x_2 (\theta_3\theta_{31}\theta_{12} + \theta_1\theta_{13}\theta_{32} - \theta_2\theta_{31}\theta_{13}) \\ \qquad + x_3 (\theta_1\theta_{12}\theta_{23} + \theta_2\theta_{21}\theta_{13} - \theta_3\theta_{12}\theta_{21}) \\ \qquad - x (\theta_{12}\theta_{23}\theta_{31} + \theta_{21}\theta_{13}\theta_{32}). \end{cases}$$

Since this expression is symmetrical in the functions involved, it follows that $\overline{N}$ defined by (76) forms a quatern with N_2, N_{12} and N_{23} and also with N_3, N_{13} and N_{23}.

25. Transformations K. We inquire under what conditions a net N and a transform N_1 meet the lines of the congruence in points harmonic to the focal points. From (I, 37) and (2) we have that the necessary and sufficient condition is that

$$(77)\qquad \theta' = \tfrac{1}{2}(h + l)\,\theta.$$

When we require that this function satisfy (5), the resulting equations are reducible, in consequence of (I, 13, 18), to

$$(78)\qquad \frac{\partial}{\partial u} \log \frac{\theta}{\varphi} = 2 \frac{\partial \log b}{\partial u}, \qquad \frac{\partial}{\partial v} \log \frac{\theta}{\varphi} = 2 \frac{\partial \log a}{\partial v}.$$

From this it follows that the point equation of N is necessarily of the form

$$(79)\qquad \frac{\partial^2 \theta}{\partial u \partial v} = \frac{\partial \log \sqrt{\varrho}}{\partial v} \frac{\partial \theta}{\partial u} + \frac{\partial \log \sqrt{\varrho}}{\partial u} \frac{\partial \theta}{\partial v},$$

where ϱ is defined by

$$(80)\qquad \varrho \varphi = 2\theta.$$

Then from (I, 18) and (77) we have

$$h = \frac{\theta}{\varrho} + \frac{\theta'}{\theta}, \quad l = -\frac{\theta}{\varrho} + \frac{\theta'}{\theta}. \tag{81}$$

Now the equations (5) may be written

$$\frac{\partial}{\partial u}\left(\frac{\theta'}{\theta}\right) = \frac{1}{\varrho}\frac{\partial \theta}{\partial u}, \qquad \frac{\partial}{\partial v}\left(\frac{\theta'}{\theta}\right) = -\frac{1}{\varrho}\frac{\partial \theta}{\partial v}. \tag{82}$$

From (8) it follows that

$$\tau = -\sigma = \frac{\theta^2}{\varrho}. \tag{83}$$

Hence equations (10) become

$$\left\{\begin{aligned} \frac{\partial x_1}{\partial u} &= -\frac{1}{\varrho}\frac{\theta}{\theta'}\left((x_1 - x)\frac{\partial \theta}{\partial u} + \theta\frac{\partial x}{\partial u}\right), \\ \frac{\partial x_1}{\partial v} &= \frac{1}{\varrho}\frac{\theta}{\theta'}\left((x_1 - x)\frac{\partial \theta}{\partial v} + \theta\frac{\partial x}{\partial v}\right), \end{aligned}\right. \tag{84}$$

and the point equation of N_1 is

$$\frac{\partial^2 \theta_1}{\partial u \partial v} = \frac{\partial \log \sqrt{\varrho_1}}{\partial v}\frac{\partial \theta_1}{\partial u} + \frac{\partial \log \sqrt{\varrho_1}}{\partial u}\frac{\partial \theta_1}{\partial v}, \tag{85}$$

where

$$\sqrt{\varrho_1} = \frac{\theta^2}{\sqrt{\varrho\theta'}}. \tag{86}$$

We note that the invariants H and K of equation (79) are equal, or, in other words, N has *equal point invariants.* Since the same in true of N_1, as shown by (85), we have the theorem:

In order that a net N and a F transform N_1 meet the lines of the conjugate congruence in points harmonic to the focal points, it is necessary that both N and N_1 have equal point invariants.

Koenigs solved this problem for 3-space[17]). Accordingly we call a transformation of this sort for space of any order a *transformation K.*

---

[17]) Comptes Rendus, vol. 113 (1891), p. 1022.

When two nets in the relation of the above transformation are parallel we say they are *associate*[18]. In all generality equations (84) are in this case

$$(87) \qquad \frac{\partial x_1}{\partial u} = -\frac{1}{\varrho}\frac{\partial x}{\partial u}, \qquad \frac{\partial x_1}{\partial v} = \frac{1}{\varrho}\frac{\partial x}{\partial v}.$$

Suppose now that N has equal point invariants. The knowledge of a parallel net N' gives h and l, and consequently a solution φ of the adjoint (I, 20) of the point equation which in this case is reducible to

$$(88) \qquad \frac{\partial^2}{\partial u \partial v}(\varphi\sqrt{\varrho}) = \sqrt{\varrho}\frac{\partial^2}{\partial u \partial v}\left(\frac{1}{\sqrt{\varrho}}\right)\cdot(\varphi\sqrt{\varrho}).$$

Since equation (79) can be written

$$(89) \qquad \frac{\partial^2}{\partial u \partial v}\left(\frac{\theta}{\sqrt{\varrho}}\right) = \sqrt{\varrho}\frac{\partial^2}{\partial u \partial v}\left(\frac{1}{\sqrt{\varrho}}\right)\cdot\frac{\theta}{\sqrt{\varrho}},$$

a solution of this equation is given by (80). It is readily shown that θ' given by (77) satisfies (5), and thus we have:

When N has equal point invariants, each parallel net N' determines without quadrature a transformation K into a net N_1, the function θ of the transformation having the value $\varphi\cdot\varrho/2$, θ' being given by (77).

In particular, $\varphi = \frac{2}{\varrho}$ is a solution of (88). In this case $\theta = 1$ from (80) and consequently N_1 is associate to N.

Suppose conversely that we have a solution θ of the point equation. From (88) and (89) it follows that $\varphi = 2\theta/\varrho$ is a solution of the adjoint equation. From § 4 we know that by means of φ we find ∞^1 nets N' parallel to N, of the form $x' + kx$, where x' are the coordinates of one of these nets and k is a constant. Accordingly we have the theorem:

When N has equal point invariants, each solution of the point equation determines by a quadrature, an infinity of transformations K,

---

[18]) This is a generalization of the idea of associate surfaces in 3-space [§ 155 and Ex. 22, p. 425].

such that corresponding lines of the conjugate congruences of the transformations which pass through a point of N are coplanar.

26. Theorem of permutability of transformations K. If N_1 and N_2 are two nets, each in the relation of a transformation K with a given net N, we apply the theorem of permutability of general transformations F, and seek the nets N_{12}, which are K transforms of N_1 and N_2. For this case we must have

$$\tau_{12} = -\sigma_{12}, \qquad \tau_{21} = -\sigma_{21}.$$

Since

$$\tau_1 = -\sigma_1 = \frac{\theta_1^2}{\varrho}, \qquad \tau_2 = -\sigma_2 = \frac{\theta_2^2}{\varrho}, \tag{90}$$

these conditions are equivalent, in consequence of (52), to

$$\theta_{21}\frac{\theta_2''}{\theta_2} + \theta_{12}\frac{\theta_1'}{\theta_1} = 0. \tag{91}$$

In consequence of (90) equations (37) for the case of transformations K are reducible to

$$\left\{\begin{aligned} \frac{\partial}{\partial u}\left(\theta_{12}\frac{\theta_1'}{\theta_1}\right) &= \frac{1}{\varrho}\left(\theta_2\frac{\partial\theta_1}{\partial u} - \theta_1\frac{\partial\theta_2}{\partial u}\right), \\ \frac{\partial}{\partial v}\left(\theta_{12}\frac{\theta_1'}{\theta_1}\right) &= -\frac{1}{\varrho}\left(\theta_2\frac{\partial\theta_1}{\partial v} - \theta_1\frac{\partial\theta_2}{\partial v}\right). \end{aligned}\right. \tag{92}$$

From these equations and similar ones in θ_{21} we find that the left-hand member of (91) is necessarily constant. Since each term of this expression is determined to within an additive constant, there are ∞^1 sets of solutions satisfying (91). In fact, in consequence of (36) and (43) we can put (91) in the form

$$\frac{\theta_2''\theta_1}{\theta_2} - \theta_1'' + \frac{\theta_1'\theta_2}{\theta_1} - \theta_2' = 0. \tag{93}$$

From (52), (86) and (93) it follows that

$$\varphi_{12} = 2\frac{\theta_{12}}{\varrho_1}, \qquad \varphi_{21} = 2\frac{\theta_{21}}{\varrho_2}.$$

Hence each N_{12} for which (93) is satisfied is a K transform of N_1 and N_2.

Now equations (48) and (49) become

$$
(94)\quad \begin{cases} \theta_1 \theta_{12}''' = \theta_{12}\left(\theta_1 \dfrac{\theta_2''}{\theta_2} - \theta_2 \dfrac{\theta_1'}{\theta_1} + \theta_{12}\dfrac{\theta_1'}{\theta_1}\right), \\ \theta_1 \theta_{12}''' x_{12} = \theta_{12}\left(\theta_1 \dfrac{\theta_2''}{\theta_2} x_{2,2} - \theta_2 \dfrac{\theta_1'}{\theta_1} x_{1,1} + \theta_{12}\dfrac{\theta_1'}{\theta_1} x\right). \end{cases}
$$

By means of these results the coordinates (71) of the point of contact $\hat{M}$ of the plane of the quatern with its envelope are reducible to

$$
\hat{x} = \frac{\theta_2''\theta_1^2 x_{2,2} - \theta_1'\theta_2^2 x_{1,1}}{\theta_2''\theta_1^2 - \theta_1'\theta_2^2} = \frac{\theta_{12}'''\theta_1^2 x_{12} - \theta_1'\theta_{12}^2 x}{\theta_{12}'''\theta_1^2 - \theta_1'\theta_{12}^2}.
$$

Hence $\hat{M}$ is the intersection of the lines MM_{12} and M_1M_2; consequently the points M_{12} of the ∞^1 nets lie on a line, MM_{12}. Therefore in consequence of the theorem of permutability of general transformations F (§§ 21, 23), we have the following theorem of permutability of transformations K:

If N_1 and N_2 are K transforms of a net N with equal point invariants, there can be found by a quadrature ∞^1 nets N_{12} which are K transforms of N_1 and N_2; corresponding points M_{12} of these nets N_{12} lie on a line l through the corresponding point M of N and in the plane π determined by M and the corresponding points M_1 and M_2 of N_1 and N_2; the plane π touches its envelope at the intersection of l and the line M_1M_2; the parametric lines on the envelope form a net to which are harmonic the congruences generated by the lines MM_1, MM_2, M_1M_{12}, M_2M_{12}, and the tangents to this net are harmonic to l and M_1M_2.

27. Transformations F of applicable nets. We say that a net N in n-space and a net $\overline{N}$ in p-space are *applicable*, when their coordinates x and $\overline{x}$ satisfy the condition

$$
\sum_1^n dx^2 = \sum_1^p d\overline{x}^2,
$$

which is equivalent to

$$
E = \sum_1^n \left(\frac{\partial x}{\partial u}\right)^2 = \sum_1^p \left(\frac{\partial \overline{x}}{\partial u}\right)^2, \quad F = \sum_1^n \frac{\partial x}{\partial u}\frac{\partial x}{\partial v} = \sum_1^p \frac{\partial \overline{x}}{\partial u}\frac{\partial \overline{x}}{\partial v},
$$

$$
G = \sum_1^n \left(\frac{\partial x}{\partial v}\right)^2 = \sum_1^p \left(\frac{\partial \overline{x}}{\partial v}\right)^2.
$$

From (I, 3) it follows that the point equations of the two nets are the same. Hence a pair of solutions h and l of equations (I, 13) determine a net $\bar{N}'$ parallel to $\bar{N}$, as well as a net N' parallel to N. Moreover, it is evident that N' and $\bar{N}'$ are applicable. Hence:

If N and $\bar{N}$ are applicable nets, the knowledge of a net parallel to either enables one to find by quadratures a net parallel to the other, to which it is applicable.

Suppose now that we subject N to a transformation F determined by a parallel net N' and a solution θ of the point equation of N. From (9) it follows that the fundamental coefficients of the new net N_1 are given by

$$E_1 = \frac{\tau^2}{\theta'^4}\left(\sum x'^2 \cdot \left(\frac{\partial \theta}{\partial u}\right)^2 - 2\sum x' \frac{\partial x}{\partial u}\, \theta' \frac{\partial \theta}{\partial u} + \theta'^2 E\right),$$

$$F_1 = \frac{\tau\sigma}{\theta'^4}\left(\sum x'^2 \cdot \frac{\partial \theta}{\partial u}\frac{\partial \theta}{\partial v} - \sum x' \frac{\partial x}{\partial u}\, \theta' \frac{\partial \theta}{\partial v} - \sum x' \frac{\partial x}{\partial v}\, \theta' \frac{\partial \theta}{\partial u} + \theta'^2 F\right),$$

$$G_1 = \frac{\sigma^2}{\theta'^4}\left(\sum x'^2 \cdot \left(\frac{\partial \theta}{\partial v}\right)^2 - 2\sum x' \frac{\partial x}{\partial v}\, \theta' \frac{\partial \theta}{\partial v} + \theta'^2 G\right).$$

We transform $\bar{N}$ by means of the net $\bar{N}'$, applicable to N', and the same function θ used above. In order that $\bar{N}_1$ and N_1 shall be applicable, the expressions for the fundamental coefficients for $\bar{N}_1$ must be equal to the above. Equating the corresponding expressions, we get three equations, which in fact are equivalent to the two

$$\left(\sum x'^2 - \sum \bar{x}'^2\right) \frac{\partial \theta}{\partial u} = 2\left(\sum x' \frac{\partial x}{\partial u} - \sum \bar{x}' \frac{\partial \bar{x}}{\partial u}\right) \theta',$$

$$\left(\sum x'^2 - \sum \bar{x}'^2\right) \frac{\partial \theta}{\partial v} = 2\left(\sum x' \frac{\partial x}{\partial v} - \sum \bar{x}' \frac{\partial \bar{x}}{\partial v}\right) \theta'.$$

By integration we find, to within a negligible constant factor,

$$\theta' = \sum x'^2 - \sum \bar{x}'^2. \tag{95}$$

It is readily shown that this function is a solution of the common point equation of the applicable nets N' and $\bar{N}'$. Consequently the F transforms of N and $\bar{N}$ by means of θ' and θ given by the quadrature

$$\frac{\partial \theta}{\partial u} = 2\left(\sum x' \frac{\partial x}{\partial u} - \sum \overline{x}' \frac{\partial \overline{x}}{\partial u}\right), \quad \frac{\partial \theta}{\partial v} = 2\left(\sum x' \frac{\partial x}{\partial v} - \sum \overline{x}' \frac{\partial \overline{x}}{\partial v}\right),$$

are applicable. Hence[19]):

If N and $\overline{N}$ are applicable nets, each net parallel to N determines a pair of applicable nets N_1 and $\overline{N}_1$ which are respectively F transforms of N and $\overline{N}$.

We shall establish a theorem of permutability of these transformations. Let two applicable nets N and $\overline{N}$ be transformed into pairs of applicable nets N_1, $\overline{N}_1$ and N_2, $\overline{N}_2$ be means of parallel nets N', $\overline{N}'$ and N'', $\overline{N}''$ and functions θ_1' and θ_2'' given by

$$\theta_1' = \sum x'^2 - \sum \overline{x}'^2, \quad \theta_2'' = \sum x''^2 - \sum \overline{x}''^2. \tag{96}$$

We apply the results of § 21 to this case and seek whether N_{12} and $\overline{N}_{12}$ are applicable. To this end we take

$$\theta_{12}''' = \sum x_1'''^2 - \sum \overline{x}_1'''^2, \quad \theta_{21}'''' = \sum x_2''''^2 - \sum \overline{x}_2''''^2.$$

Substituting the values of these functions from §§ 20, 21, we get

$$\theta_1'' + \theta_2' - 2\left(\sum x' x'' - \sum \overline{x}' \overline{x}''\right) = 0. \tag{97}$$

In consequence of (96) we find by differentiation that the left-hand member of (97) is constant. We have observed that in the general case θ_1'' and θ_2' involve additive arbitrary constants. Hence they can be chosen in an infinity of ways to satisfy (97), and we have:

Of the ∞^2 transforms N_{12} and $\overline{N}_{12}$, ∞^1 pairs are applicable, these cases arising when the constants in θ_1'' and θ_2' are chosen so that (97) *is satisfied.*

28. Nets corresponding with orthogonality of linear elements. Two nets in n-space are said to *correspond with orthogonality of linear elements,* if corresponding directions on the surfaces of these nets are orthogonal to one another. We say that two such nets are in *relation O.* A necessary and sufficient condition that $N(x)$ and $\overline{N}(\overline{x})$ are in relation O is [cf. § 153]

$$\sum \frac{\partial x}{\partial u}\frac{\partial \overline{x}}{\partial u} = 0, \quad \sum \frac{\partial x}{\partial u}\frac{\partial \overline{x}}{\partial v} + \sum \frac{\partial x}{\partial v}\frac{\partial \overline{x}}{\partial u} = 0, \quad \sum \frac{\partial x}{\partial v}\frac{\partial \overline{x}}{\partial v} = 0. \tag{98}$$

---

[19]) Transactions, vol. 19 (1918) p. 170.

Let (6) be the point equation of $N(x)$ and let

$$\frac{\partial^2 \theta}{\partial u \partial v} = \frac{\partial \log \bar{a}}{\partial v} \frac{\partial \theta}{\partial u} + \frac{\partial \log \bar{b}}{\partial u} \frac{\partial \theta}{\partial v}$$

be the point equation of $\bar{N}(\bar{x})$. If the first and third of (98) be differentiated with respect to v and u respectively, we have in consequence of the second of (98) that N and $\bar{N}$ have the same point equation. Hence:

When N and $\bar{N}$ are two nets in relation O, they have the same point equation.

From this result and § 4 it follows that if h and l are a pair of solutions of

$$(99) \qquad \frac{\partial h}{\partial v} = (l-h) \frac{\partial \log a}{\partial v}, \quad \frac{\partial l}{\partial u} = (h-l) \frac{\partial \log b}{\partial u},$$

the nets $N'(x')$ and $\bar{N}'(\bar{x}')$, whose coordinates are given by

$$(100) \quad \frac{\partial x'}{\partial u} = h \frac{\partial x}{\partial u}, \quad \frac{\partial x'}{\partial v} = l \frac{\partial x}{\partial v}; \qquad \frac{\partial \bar{x}'}{\partial u} = h \frac{\partial \bar{x}}{\partial u}, \quad \frac{\partial \bar{x}'}{\partial v} = l \frac{\partial \bar{x}}{\partial v}$$

are parallel to N and $\bar{N}$ respectively. Moreover, from (98) it follows that N' and $\bar{N}'$ are in relation O. If we say that N' and $\bar{N}'$ are *corresponding* parallel nets of N and $\bar{N}$, we have:

If N and $\bar{N}$ are two nets in relation O, corresponding parallel nets are in relation O.

We seek transformations F of nets N and $\bar{N}$ in relation O into nets N_1 and $\bar{N}_1$ in relation O. Let N' and $\bar{N}'$ be two corresponding parallel nets of N and $\bar{N}$, and let θ and θ' be corresponding solutions of the point equations of N and N' respectively, that is

$$(101) \qquad \frac{\partial \theta'}{\partial u} = h \frac{\partial \theta}{\partial u}, \quad \frac{\partial \theta'}{\partial v} = l \frac{\partial \theta}{\partial v}.$$

The equations of the transformations are

$$(102) \qquad x_1 = x - \frac{\theta}{\theta'} x', \quad \bar{x}_1 = \bar{x} - \frac{\theta}{\theta'} \bar{x}'.$$

From the first we have by differentiation equations (9) and similar expressions for $\frac{\partial \bar{x}_1}{\partial u}$ and $\frac{\partial \bar{x}_1}{\partial v}$.

When we express the condition that these quantities satisfy equations of the form (98), the resulting equations give, to within a negligible constant factor,

$$\theta' = \sum x' \bar{x}'. \tag{103}$$

Since N' and $\bar{N}'$ are in the relation O, this function θ' satisfies their common point equation.

Hence:

If $N(x)$ and $\bar{N}(\bar{x})$ are nets in relation O, and $N'(x')$ and $\bar{N}'(\bar{x}')$ are two corresponding parallel nets, the nets N_1 and $\bar{N}_1$ which are F transforms of N and $\bar{N}$ respectively by means of the equations

$$x_1 = x - \frac{\theta}{\sum x' \bar{x}'} x', \quad \bar{x}_1 = \bar{x} - \frac{\theta}{\sum x' \bar{x}'} \bar{x}', \tag{104}$$

where θ is given by

$$\frac{\partial \theta}{\partial u} = \frac{1}{h} \frac{\partial}{\partial u} \sum x' \bar{x}', \quad \frac{\partial \theta}{\partial v} = \frac{1}{l} \frac{\partial}{\partial v} \sum x' \bar{x}', \tag{105}$$

are in relation O.

We shall establish a theorem of permutability of these transformations. Let two nets N and $\bar{N}$ in relation O be transformed into pairs of nets N_1, $\bar{N}_1$ and N_2, $\bar{N}_2$ by means of parallel nets N', $\bar{N}'$ and N'', $\bar{N}''$ and the functions θ_1' and θ_2'' given by

$$\theta_1' = \sum x' \bar{x}', \quad \theta_2'' = \sum x'' \bar{x}''. \tag{106}$$

We apply the results of § 21 to this case and seek under what condition N_{12} and $\bar{N}_{12}$ are in relation O. For this to be the case we must have

$$\theta_{12}''' = \sum x_1''' \bar{x}_1''', \quad \theta_{21}'''' = \sum x_2'''' \bar{x}_2'''',$$

where x_1''' and x_2'''' are given by (33) and (42) and $\bar{x}_1'''$ and $\bar{x}_2''''$ have analogous expressions. Substituting the values of θ_{12}''' and θ_{21}'''' from § 21, we have

$$\theta_1'' + \theta_2' - \sum (x'' \bar{x}' + x' \bar{x}'') = 0. \tag{107}$$

In consequence of (106) we find by differentiation that the left-hand member of (107) is constant. We have observed (§ 21) that in the general case of the theorem of permutability the functions θ_1'' and θ_2 are determined to within additive arbitrary constants. Since these can be chosen in an infinity of ways so that (107) holds, we have:

Of the ∞^2 F transforms N_{12} and $\overline{N}_{12}$ arising from the theorem of permutability of any nets N and $\overline{N}$ in relation O, there are ∞^1 pairs in relation O; they arise when the constants in θ_2' and θ_1'' are chosen so that (107) *is satisfied; all these ∞^1 pairs of transforms can be found by two quadratures, when N_1, $\overline{N}_1$ and N_2, $\overline{N}_2$ are known.*

Exercises.

1. If N is a net of translation (cf. I, Ex. 6), the only F transforms of N which are nets of translation are parallel to N.

2. If N is a minimal net (cf. I, Ex. 7), the only F transforms of N which are minimal nets are parallel to N.

3. If N is any net and N_1 is the F transform defined by (2), and $(N)_1$, $(N_1)_1$ and $(N')_1$ are the first Laplace transforms of N, N_1 and N' respectively, then

$$(x_1)_1 = (x)_1 - \frac{(\theta)_1}{(\theta')_1}(x')_1,$$

where

$$(\theta)_1 = \theta - \frac{1}{\frac{\partial \log a}{\partial v}} \frac{\partial \theta}{\partial v}, \quad (\theta')_1 = \theta' - \frac{1}{\frac{\partial \log a h}{\partial v}} \frac{\partial \theta'}{\partial v}.$$

4. If N_1 is an F transform of a net N, any Laplace transform of N admits as F transform the corresponding Laplace transform of N_1, the equations of the transformation being

$$(x_1)_r = (x)_r - \frac{(\theta)_r}{(\theta')_r}(x')_r$$

where $(\theta)_r$, $(\theta')_r$ and $(x')_r$ are the rth Laplace transforms of θ, θ' and x'.

5. If N and N_1 are in relation F, and φ and φ_1 are corresponding solutions of their point equations, the Levy transforms of N and N_1 on the tangents to the curves $v =$ const. of N and N_1 are in relation F, and also the Levy transform on the tangents to the curves $u =$ const.; moreover, the lines of the conjugate congruences of these transformations are tangent to the net which is the F transform of N by φ conjugate to the congruence of the transformation from N into N_1.

6. By means of Ex. 5 and § 11 show that if N and N_1 are nets in relation F, and φ, φ_1 and ψ, ψ_1 are corresponding pairs of solutions of the point equations of N and N_1, the derived net of N by φ and ψ is in relation F with the derived net of N_1 by φ_1 and ψ_1.

7. If N and N_1 are nets in relation F, and N_2 and N_{12} are parallel to N and N_1 respectively in accordance with the second theorem of § 21, corresponding lines of the congruences of parameters x_2 and x_{12} conjugate to N and N_1 meet in a point describing a net forming a triad with N and N_1.

8. Show that if in § 24 we take $\theta_3 = w_3 = 1$, $\theta_3' = \theta_3'' = 0$, the nets N_3, N_{13}, N_{23}, $\overline{N}$ are parallel to N, N_1, N_2, N_{12} respectively.

9. If N, N_1, N_2, N_{12} are nets of a quatern, the respective functions θ_2, θ_{12}, $-\theta_2/\theta_2''$, $-\theta_{12}/\theta_{12}'''$ determine radial transforms $\overline{N}$, $\overline{N}_1$, $\overline{N}_2$, $\overline{N}_{12}$, forming a quatern under transformations F. Transactions, vol. 18 (1917), p. 123.

10. If N is a net and θ any solution of its point equation, the equations $x_1 = x - c\theta$, where the c's are constants define a net N_1 which is a transform of N, the congruence of the transformation consisting of parallel lines. The tangent planes to N and N_1 meet in the harmonic congruence of N determined by θ.

11. If N and $\overline{N}$ are applicable nets, the equations $x_1 = x - c\theta$, $\overline{x}_1 = \overline{x} - \overline{c}\,\theta$ determine applicable nets N_1 and $\overline{N}_1$, if $\theta = 2\,(\Sigma \overline{c}\,\overline{x} - \Sigma cx)/(\Sigma \overline{c}^2 - \Sigma c^2)$.

12. When the functions a and b in equation (6) satisfy the condition

$$\text{(i)}\qquad a\frac{\partial^2 a}{\partial u\,\partial v} - b\frac{\partial^2 b}{\partial u\,\partial v} = \left(\frac{a}{b} - \frac{b}{a}\right)\frac{\partial a}{\partial v}\frac{\partial b}{\partial u},$$

the equations

$$\frac{\partial \log \sqrt{\rho}}{\partial u} = \frac{1}{a}\frac{\partial b}{\partial u}, \qquad \frac{\partial \log \sqrt{\rho}}{\partial v} = \frac{1}{b}\frac{\partial a}{\partial v}$$

are consistent, and the functions

$$\text{(ii)}\qquad h_1 = \frac{\sqrt{\rho}}{a}, \quad l_1 = \frac{\sqrt{\rho}}{b}; \quad h_2 = \frac{1}{\sqrt{\rho}\,a}, \quad l_2 = -\frac{1}{\sqrt{\rho}\,b}$$

satisfy equations (I, 13). The two nets N and N_0 parallel to a net N' with equation (6) determined by the solutions (ii) have equal point invariants, and are associate (§ 25) to one another.

Conversely, if a net N' with point equation (6) admits a parallel net with equal point invariants equation (i) must be satisfied.

13. When the condition (i) of Ex. 12 is satisfied, equation (6) admits the solution $\theta' = \frac{1}{4}(a^2 - b^2)$. If we put $\theta = \frac{1}{2}\sqrt{\rho}\,(a - b)$, we have $\frac{\partial \theta'}{\partial u} = \frac{a}{\sqrt{\rho}}\frac{\partial \theta}{\partial u}$, $\frac{\partial \theta'}{\partial v} = \frac{b}{\sqrt{\rho}}\frac{\partial \theta}{\partial v}$. These values satisfy (81), and consequently θ and θ' and the congruence conjugate to N whose direction-parameters are the coordinates x' of N' determine a K transform of N.

14. Let M, M_1, M_2, M_{12} be corresponding points of four nets N, N_1, N_2, N_{12} of a quatern under transformations F. Show that a necessary and sufficient condition that another net N_{12} obtained by varying the additive constants of θ_1'' and θ_2 be such that its points lie on the corresponding lines MM_{12} is that the transformations be K.

15. If N is a net with equal point invariants, N_1, N_2, N_3 are K transforms of N, and N_{12}, N_{13}, N_{23} are the nets with equal point invariants which together with the respective groups N, N_1, N_2; N, N_1, N_3; N, N_2, N_3 form quaterns under transformations K, then $\overline{N}$ defined by (76) is a K transform of N_{12}, N_{13}, N_{23}.

Transactions, vol. 16 (1915), p. 296.

16. Determine whether transformations K are the only transformations F of a net with equal point invariants into nets with equal point invariants.

17. In order that the Levy transforms conjugate to the tangents to the curves of parameter u of a net N with the point equation (6) and determined by solutions θ and θ_1 of (6) be K transforms of one another, it is necessary that $\theta\theta_1 = b^2 V$, where V is a function of v alone.

18. If N and N_1 are two nets in relation K, their respective associates can be so placed in space that they shall be in relation K.

19. If in (46) θ_1'' and θ_2' are replaced by $\theta_1'' + c$ and $\theta_2' - c$, where c is a parameter, the corresponding points of the ∞^1 nets N_{12} lie on a conic which passes through the corresponding points of N, N_1 and N_2; this conic is degenerate when the transformations are K, and only in this case (cf. Ex. 14).

Chapter III.

Sequences of Laplace.

29. Homogeneous point coordinates. If the cartesian coordinates of a point P are $x^1, \ldots . x^n$, the $n+1$ quantities y, of which $y^{n+1} \neq 0$, satisfying the conditions

$$x^1 = \frac{y^1}{y^{n+1}} \ldots . x^n = \frac{y^n}{y^{n+1}}$$

are called *homogeneous cartesian coordinates* of P. If the coordinates y are given, P is determined, but if the cartesian coordinates x are given, the homogeneous coordinates y are defined only to within a factor.

In homogeneous coordinates the equation of a hyperplane is of the form (§ 1)

$$a^1 y^1 + \ldots . + a^{n+1} y^{n+1} = 0.$$

Now $y^i = 0$ $(i = 1, \ldots ., n)$ is the equation of a coordinate hyperplane. Also $y^{n+1} = 0$ is taken as the equation of a hyperplane, namely the *hyperplane at infinity*. This hyperplane likewise is a coordinate hyperplane in homogeneous coordinates. Thus we have $n+1$ hyperplanes forming a coordinate $(n+1)$-hedron. Moreover, a point all of whose homogeneous coordinates save one, say y^i, are zero lies in all of these hyperplanes except the hyperplane $y^i = 0$; it is a *vertex* of the coordinate $(n+1)$-hedron.

Suppose now that we have any $n+1$ hyperplanes, say

$$a_i^1 y^1 + a_i^2 y^2 + \ldots . + a_i^{n+1} y^{n+1} = 0 \qquad (i = 1, \ldots ., n+1),$$

subject to the single condition that they do not have a point in common, that is, the determinant of the a's is not equal to zero; thus $|a_i^j| \neq 0$. If we put

$$\varrho z^i = a_i^1 y^1 + \ldots . + a_i^{n+1} y^{n+1} \qquad (i = 1, \ldots ., n+1),$$

where ϱ is a factor independent of i, the quantities z^i serve also as point coordinates. For when the y's are given for a point the z's are uniquely determined except for a factor. Conversely, when the z's are given, the determination of the corresponding y's requires the solution of a linear system of equations, whose determinant is different from zero. We call the z's *general homogeneous point coordinates,* and as such they are distinguished from the particular system of y's, corresponding to the case where n of the coordinate planes are mutually perpendicular, and the other is at infinity. As in the case of tetrahedral coordinates in 3-space, the transformation is not completely determined by the $(n+1)$-hedron, but is defined when it is required that a particular point, not on the faces of the new $(n+1)$-hedron is to have the coordinates $(1, 1, \ldots, 1)$ in the new system.

Since the steps used in the preceding are reversible, we have that there exist linear transformations P_0 by means of which from a general system of homogeneous coordinates z we pass to a system y so that $y^1/y^{n+1} \ldots y^n/y^{n+1}$ are cartesian coordinates. Hereafter we understand that when homogeneous coordinates are used they are of the general type.

We are prepared to prove the theorem:

The homogeneous coordinates of any point on the line joining two points $P_1(z_1)$ and $P_2(z_2)$ *are of the form*

$$\lambda z_1 + \mu z_2$$

and conversely.

Consider the point with these coordinates and apply a transformation P_0 (referred to above). The resulting expressions will be of the form $\lambda y_1 + \mu y_2$. Hence the cartesian coordinates of the point are

$$\frac{\lambda y_1^i + \mu y_2^i}{\lambda y_1^{n+1} + \mu y_2^{n+1}} = \frac{\lambda y_1^{n+1} x_1^i + \mu y_2^{n+1} x_2^i}{\lambda y_1^{n+1} + \mu y_2^{n+1}} \qquad (i = 1, 2, \ldots n),$$

which shows that the point lies on $P_1 P_2$ (cf. I, Ex. 1). Evidently the converse also is true.

In like manner it can be shown (cf. I, Ex. 2) that:

The homogeneous coordinates of any point on the plane through three points $P_1(z_1)$, $P_2(z_2)$ $P_3(z_3)$ *are of the form*

$$\lambda z_1 + \mu z_2 + \nu z_3,$$

and conversely.

From § 1 the locus of a point whose homogeneous coordinates z are functions of a parameter u is a curve. We wish to prove: *The homogeneous coordinates of any point on the tangent to a curve $z(u)$ are of the form*

$$\lambda z + \mu \frac{dz}{du}$$

and conversely.

If the coordinates of a point are in this form, and we apply a transformation P_0 we get for the new coordinates of the point $\lambda y + \mu \dfrac{dy}{du}$. Hence the cartesian coordinates of the point are

$$\frac{\lambda y^i + \mu \dfrac{dy^i}{du}}{\lambda y^{n+1} + \mu \dfrac{dy^{n+1}}{du}} = x^i + \frac{\dfrac{dx^i}{du}}{\dfrac{\lambda}{\mu} + \dfrac{d}{du}\log y^{n+1}}.$$

As these are of the form $x + \lambda \dfrac{dx}{du}$, the point lies on the tangent (§ 1). Conversely, the cartesian coordinates of any point on the tangent being of this form are readily transformable into the form of the theorem.

Consider a point on the tangent to a curve with its coordinates in the form $\lambda z + \mu \dfrac{dz}{du}$. Two functions ϱ and t are defined by

$$\varrho \frac{dt}{du} = \lambda, \quad \varrho t = \mu.$$

In terms of ϱ and t the coordinates of the point are of the form $\varrho \dfrac{d}{du}(tz)$. Hence we have:

The homogeneous point coordinates z of a curve can be chosen so that the coordinates of a given point on the tangent other than the point of contact are of the form $\dfrac{dz}{du}$.

The *osculating plane* of a curve $z(u)$ at a representative point is by definition the locus of points whose coordinates are of the form

$\lambda z + \mu \frac{dz}{du} + \nu \frac{d^2 z}{du^2}$. If we apply a transformation P_0 to the coordinates and proceed as above, we can show that the cartesian coordinates of any point of the osculating plane are of the form

$$x + \lambda \frac{dx}{du} + \mu \frac{d^2 x}{du^2}$$

We observe that this is the result previously found for 3-space [§ 7].

30. Laplace transformations. We have seen in § 2 that a necessary and sufficient condition that a system of parametric curves be a net is that any point on the tangent to a curve $v =$ const. of a system moves in the tangent plane to the surface as v varies. Given a net N with $n + 1$ homogeneous coordinates x. The coordinates of any point P on the tangent to a curve $v =$ const. are of the form $\lambda x + \mu \frac{\partial x}{\partial u}$. As v varies, the point moves in the tangent plane, provided $\frac{\partial}{\partial v}\left(\lambda x + \mu \frac{\partial x}{\partial u}\right)$ is expressible linearly in terms of x, $\frac{\partial x}{\partial u}$, and $\frac{\partial x}{\partial v}$. Hence a net is characterised analytically by the condition that its homogeneous coordinates are solutions of the same equation of the form

$$\text{(1)} \qquad \frac{\partial^2 \theta}{\partial u \partial v} = \frac{\partial \log a}{\partial v} \frac{\partial \theta}{\partial u} + \frac{\partial \log b}{\partial u} \frac{\partial \theta}{\partial v} + c\theta.$$

We call this the *point equation of the net.*

If, in particular, the point P moves tangentially to the tangent to $v =$ const., that is if P describes the minus first Laplace transform of N, we must have

$$\lambda + \mu \frac{\partial \log b}{\partial u} = 0.$$

Since similar results follow for the first Laplace transform, we have:

The coordinates of the minus first and first Laplace transforms of a net with the point equation (1) *can be taken in the form*

$$\text{(2)} \qquad x_{-1} = \frac{\partial x}{\partial u} - \frac{\partial \log b}{\partial u} x, \quad x_1 = \frac{\partial x}{\partial v} - \frac{\partial \log a}{\partial v} x.$$

In consequence of the fourth theorem of § 29 the equations of a Laplace transformation can be put in the simple form indicated in the following theorem:

The homogeneous coordinates z^i and y^i of the focal points of a congruence can be chosen so that

$$\frac{\partial z}{\partial u} = my, \qquad \frac{\partial y}{\partial v} = nz. \tag{3}$$

From (2) we have by differentiation

$$\frac{\partial x_{-1}}{\partial v} = \frac{\partial \log a}{\partial v} x_{-1} + Kx, \qquad \frac{\partial x_1}{\partial u} = \frac{\partial \log b}{\partial u} x_1 + Hx, \tag{4}$$

where H and K are the invariants of (1) namely

$$\left\{ \begin{aligned} H &= -\frac{\partial^2 \log a}{\partial u \partial v} + \frac{\partial \log a}{\partial v} \frac{\partial \log b}{\partial u} + c, \\ K &= -\frac{\partial^2 \log b}{\partial u \partial v} + \frac{\partial \log a}{\partial v} \frac{\partial \log b}{\partial u} + c. \end{aligned} \right. \tag{5}$$

If $K = 0$, we get on integration $x_{-1} = Ua$, where U is an arbitrary function of u alone. As the arbitrary function U varies with the integral but a remains the same, the point M_{-1} describes a curve, and not a net; we say that N_{-1} is degenerate. Substituting in the first of (2) and integrating the resulting equation, we find

$$x = b\left(V + \int \frac{Ua}{b} du\right), \tag{6}$$

V being an arbitrary function of v alone.

In like manner, if $H = 0$, the integral of (1) can be given the form

$$x = a\left(U + \int \frac{Vb}{a} dv\right). \tag{7}$$

Hence we have the theorem:

When either invariant of an equation of Laplace is equal to zero, the equation can be integrated by quadratures.

31. Sequences of Laplace. When the invariants H and K of (1) are different from zero, by the iteration of the first Laplace transformation upon a net N with (1) for its point equation, and also of the minus first transformation, we get a sequence of nets

$$\ldots . N_{-j},\ N_{-(j-1)},\ \ldots . N_{-1},\ N,\ N_1,\ \ldots ,\ N_i,\ \ldots .$$

such that any net of the sequence is a first Laplace transform of its predecessor (sense being from left to right), and a minus first transform of its successor. We say that these nets form *a sequence of Laplace.*

We are interested in finding the Laplace equation of each net of the sequence. In order to write these equations and others associated with (1) in abbreviated form, we denote by

$$[\theta_i;\ a_i,\ b_i,\ e_i] \tag{8}$$

the equation

$$\left\{\begin{aligned} &\frac{\partial^2\theta_i}{\partial u\,\partial v}=\frac{\partial \log a_i}{\partial v}\frac{\partial \theta_i}{\partial u}+\frac{\partial \log b_i}{\partial u}\frac{\partial \theta_i}{\partial v}\\ &+\left(\frac{\partial^2}{\partial u\,\partial v}\log e_i-\frac{\partial \log a_i}{\partial v}\frac{\partial \log b_i}{\partial u}+\frac{\partial \log a}{\partial v}\frac{\partial \log b}{\partial u}+c\right)\theta_i.\end{aligned}\right. \tag{9}$$

Then from (5) it follows that

$$\left\{\begin{aligned} H_i&=\frac{\partial^2}{\partial u\,\partial v}\log\frac{e_i}{a_i}+\frac{\partial \log a}{\partial v}\frac{\partial \log b}{\partial u}+c,\\ K_i&=\frac{\partial^2}{\partial u\,\partial v}\log\frac{e_i}{b_i}+\frac{\partial \log a}{\partial v}\frac{\partial \log b}{\partial u}+c.\end{aligned}\right. \tag{10}$$

If in equation (1) we put

$$x=\frac{x'}{\lambda}, \tag{11}$$

where λ is a function of u and v, the Laplace equation satisfied by x' is denoted by

$$[\theta';\ a\lambda,\ b\lambda,\ \lambda]. \tag{12}$$

Then from (10) we have $H'=H$, $K'=K$, showing that H and K are invariants of (1) for transformations of the form (11).

In order to find the Laplace equation of N_1, we differentiate the second of (4) with respect to v. Making use of (2), we find that the Laplace equation of N_1 is denoted by

$$\left[\theta_1;\ aH,\ b,\ \frac{b}{a}\right] \tag{13}$$

and that

$$H_1 = H - \frac{\partial^2}{\partial u\,\partial v}\log\frac{aH}{b},\qquad K_1 = H. \tag{14}$$

Proceeding in a like manner with the first of (4), we find that the Laplace equation of N_{-1} is denoted by

$$\left[\theta_{-1};\ a,\ bK,\frac{a}{b}\right] \tag{15}$$

and that

$$H_{-1} = K,\ K_{-1} = K - \frac{\partial^2}{\partial u\,\partial v}\log\frac{bK}{a}. \tag{16}$$

The coordinates x_2 of N_2 are given by the equations

$$x_2 = \frac{\partial x_1}{\partial v} - x_1\frac{\partial}{\partial v}\log aH \tag{17}$$

analogous to (2), and the point of equation of N_2 is denoted by

$$\left[\theta_2;\ aHH_1,\ b,\ \frac{b^2}{a^2H}\right]. \tag{18}$$

In general the coordinates of N_r are given by

$$x_r = \frac{\partial x_{r-1}}{\partial v} - \frac{\partial}{\partial v}\log(aHH_1\ldots\ldots H_{r-2})\,x_{r-1}, \tag{19}$$

and the point equation is

$$\left[\theta_r;\ aHH_1\ldots\ldots H_{r-1},\ b,\ \frac{b^r}{a^r H^{r-1}H_1^{r-2}\ldots\ldots H_{r-2}}\right]. \tag{20}$$

The equations analogous to (4) and (17) are

$$(21)\qquad \begin{cases} \dfrac{\partial x_r}{\partial u} = \dfrac{\partial \log b}{\partial u} x_r + H_{r-1} x_{r-1}, \\[2ex] \dfrac{\partial x_r}{\partial v} = \dfrac{\partial}{\partial v} \log (a H \ldots . H_{r-1})\, x_r + x_{r+1}. \end{cases}$$

The coordinates of N_{-r} are given by

$$(22)\qquad x_{-r} = \frac{\partial x_{-r+1}}{\partial u} - \frac{\partial}{\partial u} \log (b K K_{-1} \ldots . K_{-r+2})\, x_{-r+1},$$

and the point equation is

$$(23)\qquad \left[\theta_{-r};\ a,\ b K K_{-1} \ldots . K_{-r+1},\ \frac{a^r}{b^r K^{r-1} K_{-1}^{r-2} \ldots . K_{-r+2}}\right].$$

Also we have

$$(24)\qquad \begin{cases} \dfrac{\partial x_{-r}}{\partial u} = \dfrac{\partial}{\partial u} \log (b K \ldots . K_{-r+1})\, x_{-r} + x_{-r-1}, \\[2ex] \dfrac{\partial x_{-r}}{\partial v} = \dfrac{\partial \log a}{\partial v} x_{-r} + K_{-r+1} \cdot x_{-r+1}. \end{cases}$$

32. Periodic sequences of Laplace. Ordinarily a sequence of Laplace is unlimited in both directions. If H_r or K_{-r} is zero, the sequence terminates in the positive or negative sense (cf. III, Ex. 5). In the present section we are concerned with the case when the sequence is *periodic*, that is when a certain net N_p coincides with N. In this case we must have

$$(25)\qquad x_p = m x,$$

where m is at most a function of u and v which is the same for all n coordinates x^i. Since n is at least equal to 3, the coefficients of (12) and (20) for $r = p$ must be equal. Hence we must have

$$(26)\qquad \frac{\partial}{\partial v} \log \frac{H \ldots . H_{p-1}}{m} = 0, \qquad \frac{\partial}{\partial u} \log m = 0,$$

$$(27)\qquad \frac{\partial^2}{\partial u\, \partial v} \log \frac{b^p}{a^p H^{p-1} H_1^{p-2} \ldots . H_{p-2}} = 0.$$

Differentiating the first of (26) with respect to u and making use of the second, we find that

$$HH_1 \dots . H_{p-1} = UV, \tag{28}$$

where U and V are functions of u and v respectively. If we change the independent variables in accordance with the equations

$$u = \varphi(u'), \qquad v = \psi(v'),$$

we find that the invariants $H', H_1', \dots . H_p'$ of the transformed equations of the nets $N, N_1, \dots . N_p$ are given by

$$H' = \varphi'(u')\psi'(v')H, \quad H_i' = \varphi'(u')\psi'(v')H_i \quad (i = 1, \dots . p),$$

where φ' and ψ' denote the derivates of φ and ψ. Hence φ and ψ can be chosen so that (28) becomes

$$HH_1 \dots . H_{p-1} = 1. \tag{29}$$

Then from (26) it follows that m in (25) is constant[20]).

Suppose now that (27) and (29) are satisfied for equation (1). Applying (10) to (20) for $r = p-1$, we get, in consequence of (27),

$$(30) \quad \begin{cases} H_{p-1} = H - \dfrac{\partial^2}{\partial u \partial v} \log \dfrac{a^{p-1} H^{p-1} H_1^{p-2} \dots . H_{p-2}}{b^{p-1}} \\ \quad = H - \dfrac{\partial^2}{\partial u \partial v} \log \dfrac{b}{a} = K. \end{cases}$$

In like manner, making use of (27), (29) and (30), we obtain

$$H_{p-2} = H - \frac{\partial^2}{\partial u \partial v} \log \frac{a^{p-2} H^{p-2} \dots . H_{p-3}}{b^{p-2}}$$

$$= H - \frac{\partial^2}{\partial u \partial v} \log \frac{b^2 H_{p-1}}{a^2} = K - \frac{\partial^2}{\partial u \partial v} \log \frac{bK}{a} = K_{-1}.$$

---

20) Cf. Tzitzeica, Comptes Rendus, vol. 157 (1913), p. 908; also Hammond, Annals of Mathematics, ser. 2, vol. 22 (1921), p. 245.

Hence in general we have

$$H_{p-i} = K_{-i+1}. \tag{31}$$

If we differentiate (25) with respect to u, and make use of (2) and (21), we can reduce the resulting equation to

$$H_{p-1}\, x_{p-1} = m x_{-1} \tag{32}$$

which gives the analytical form of the condition that the nets N_{p-1} and N_{-1} coincide. Again differentiating (32) with respect to u, we get, in consequence of (21), (24), (30) and (32),

$$H_{p-1} H_{p-2}\, x_{p-2} = m x_{-2}.$$

And in general because of (31) we have

$$H_{p-1} H_{p-2} \ldots H_{p-i}\, x_{p-i} = m x_{-i}, \tag{33}$$

which in consequence of (29) is equivalent to

$$x_{p-i} = m H H_1 \ldots H_{p-i-1}\, x_{-i}. \tag{34}$$

Finally we have

$$x = m x_{-p}, \tag{35}$$

showing that N and N_{-p} coincide.

Conversely if we differentiate (35) with respect to v we get (34) with $i = p - 1$. In general, if we differentiate (34) with respect to v, we get (34) with i replaced by $i - 1$. Hence according as we differentiate (33) or (34) with respect to u or v we increase or diminish i by 1. In order to point out the significance of this observation, we note that the expressions (19) and (22) for x_r and x_{-r} are expressible in the forms

$$x_r = \frac{\partial^r x}{\partial v^r} + A_{r,r-1} \frac{\partial^{r-1} x}{\partial v^{r-1}} + \ldots + A_{r,o}\, x,$$

$$x_{-r} = \frac{\partial^r x}{\partial u^r} + B_{r,r-1} \frac{\partial^{r-1} x}{\partial u^{r-1}} + \ldots + B_{r,o}\, x,$$

where A's and B's are determinate functions of the derivates of a, b and c obtained by repeated use of (19) and (22). Hence equation (33) involves the derivatives of x with respect to v of orders $1, \ldots, p-i$, and of x with respect to u of orders $1, \ldots i$. If this equation is differentiated with respect to u and all derivatives with respect to u and v are eliminated by means of (1) and the equations obtained by differentiating (1), we obtain an equation involving derivatives of x with respect to v of orders $1, \ldots p-i-1$ and with respect to u of orders $1, \ldots i+1$, which necessarily is (33) with i replaced by $i-1$.

Suppose now that we consider a periodic net of odd order, and write $p = 2n+1$. If in (34) we put $i = n$ and in (33) $i = n+1$, we get

$$\text{(36)} \qquad \left\{ \begin{aligned} x_{n+1} &= mHH_1 \ldots H_n x_{-n}, \\ x_{-n-1} &= \frac{1}{m} H_{2n} H_{2n-1} \ldots H_n x_n. \end{aligned} \right.$$

These two equations express $\frac{\partial^{n+1} x}{\partial v^{n+1}}$ and $\frac{\partial^{n+1} x}{\partial u^{n+1}}$ linearly in terms of the $2n+1$ quantities

$$\text{(37)} \qquad \frac{\partial^n x}{\partial u^n}, \ldots, \frac{\partial x}{\partial u}, \frac{\partial^n x}{\partial v^n}, \ldots, \frac{\partial x}{\partial v}, x.$$

We have seen that the consistency of (36) and (1) leads to other equations of the series (33) and (34), by means of which and (1) we can express all the derivatives of order higher than n in terms of (37). Since m does not appear in (27) and (29), for each value of m there exist p independent solutions of (1), (33) and (34) including the condition (25); and not more than p independent solutions.

When p is even, and we put $p = 2n$, we have in place of (36),

$$x_n = mHH_1 \ldots H_{n-1} x_{-n}, \quad x_{-n-1} = \frac{1}{m} H_{2n-1} \ldots H_{n-1} x_{n-1}.$$

Then all the derivatives of order n and higher are expressible linearly in terms of the p quantities

$$\frac{\partial^n x}{\partial u^n}, \ldots, \frac{\partial x}{\partial u}, \frac{\partial^{n-1} x}{\partial v^{n-1}}, \ldots \frac{\partial x}{\partial v}, x.$$

Hence we have the theorem:

When an equation of Laplace (1) *satisfies the conditions* (27) *and* (29), *an infinity of sequences of Laplace of period p exist in space of period p* — 1.

33. Harmonic congruences. We wish to establish the theorem:

The homogeneous coordinates x of a net N can be so chosen that homogeneous coordinates of the focal points of any harmonic congruence are $\frac{\partial x}{\partial u}$ *and* $\frac{\partial x}{\partial v}$ *respectively.*

Let $N(x)$ be a net with homogeneous coordinates x satisfying (1). Let F_1 and F_2 be the foci of any harmonic congruence, these points being on the tangents to the curves $v =$ const., $u =$ const., respectively. Evidently x can be chosen so that the coordinates of F_1 are $\frac{\partial x}{\partial u}$ (§ 29). Then the coordinates of F_2 according as it is looked upon as on the tangent to the curves $u =$ const. at M or on the tangent to the curves $u =$ const. at F_1 are of the respective forms $\lambda x + \mu \frac{\partial x}{\partial v}$, $\sigma \frac{\partial x}{\partial u} + \tau \frac{\partial^2 x}{\partial u \partial v}$. These forms must be proportional to one another in consequence of x being a solution of the corresponding equation (1). Expressing this requirement, we find that both of these must be proportional to $\frac{\partial \log b}{\partial u} \frac{\partial x}{\partial v} + cx$. Evidently $\frac{\partial \log b}{\partial u} \neq 0$, otherwise F_2 and M coincide. Looking upon F_1 as the minus first Laplace transform of F_2 we must have

$$\frac{\partial x}{\partial u} = l\left(\frac{\partial \log b}{\partial u} \frac{\partial x}{\partial v} + cx\right) + m \frac{\partial}{\partial u}\left(\frac{\partial \log b}{\partial u} \frac{\partial x}{\partial v} + cx\right).$$

As this equation must be satisfied identically, we must have either $c = 0$, or $V' \frac{\partial \log b}{\partial u} = Vc$, where V is a function of v alone and V' its derivative with respect to v. In the latter case the coordinates of F_2 can be chosen of the form $\frac{\partial}{\partial v}(Vx)$. Replacing Vx by x, which does not change the form $\frac{\partial x}{\partial u}$ of the coordinates of F_1, we have the result stated in the theorem.

Furthermore, when the coordinates of F_1 and F_2 are of the form $\frac{\partial x}{\partial u}$ and $\frac{\partial x}{\partial v}$, in the point equation of N we have $c = 0$. If we put $\theta = \theta_1 \theta_0$ where θ_0 is any function of u and v, in equation (1), the function θ_1 satisfies an equation of the type (1), and for this new equation $c = 0$ in case θ_0 is a solution of (1) and only in this case. As a result we have the corollary:

The homogeneous coordinates of the focal points of any congruence harmonic to a net $N(x)$ are expressible in the form

$$\frac{\partial}{\partial u}\left(\frac{x}{\theta}\right), \quad \frac{\partial}{\partial v}\left(\frac{x}{\theta}\right), \tag{38}$$

in which case θ is a solution of the point equation of N.

We have also the converse theorem:

If θ is any solution of the point equation (1) *of a net N, the points whose coordinates are of the form* (38) *are the focal points of a congruence harmonic to N.*

For, as v varies the direction-parameters of the path of the first of these points are of the form

$$\frac{\partial}{\partial v}\left(\frac{\partial}{\partial u}\left(\frac{x}{\theta}\right)\right) = \frac{\partial}{\partial v}\log\frac{a}{\theta}\cdot\frac{\partial}{\partial u}\left(\frac{x}{\theta}\right) + \frac{\partial}{\partial u}\log\frac{b}{\theta}\cdot\frac{\partial}{\partial v}\left(\frac{x}{\theta}\right),$$

which evidently are the parameters of the line joining the two points; similarly when u varies.

We have also the theorem:

When $\theta = \sum a_i x^i$, where the a's are constants, the points of coordinates (38) *lie in the hyperplane $\sum a_i x^i = 0$.*

34. Levy sequences of the first order. If θ is any solution of the point equation (1) of a net N, from (2) it follows that the functions

$$\theta_{-1} = \frac{\partial \theta}{\partial u} - \frac{\partial \log b}{\partial u}\theta, \quad \theta_1 = \frac{\partial \theta}{\partial v} - \frac{\partial \log a}{\partial v}\theta \tag{39}$$

are solutions of the point equations of N_{-1} and N_1 respectively. We call them the minus first and first Laplace transforms of θ.

The points of coordinates (38) are the Levy transforms of N by means of θ (cf. I, 53). In consequence of (2) and (39), we can take as homogeneous coordinates of these respective points

$$(40) \qquad x_{-1,1} = x - \frac{\theta}{\theta_{-1}} x_{-1}, \quad x_{o,1} = x_1 - \frac{\theta_1}{\theta} x.$$

Moreover, the net of coordinates $x_{o,1}$ is the first Laplace transform of the net of coordinates $x_{-1,1}$.

By differentiation and reduction by means of (2), (4) and (39), we find that the point equations of these nets are denoted by (cf. § 31)

$$(41) \qquad \left[\theta_{-1,1};\ \frac{a\theta}{\theta_{-1}},\ b,\ \frac{a}{\theta_{-1}}\right],$$

$$(42) \qquad \left[\theta_{o,1};\ \frac{a\theta_1}{\theta},\ b,\ \frac{b}{\theta}\right].$$

From the form of (40) it follows that $N_{-1,1}$ and $N_{o,1}$ are Levy transforms of N_{-1} and N_1 by means of θ_{-1} and θ_1. Moreover, from § 10 we have that the tangents to the curves of parameter v of $N_{o,1}$ are harmonic to N_1, and consequently this harmonic congruence G_1 is determined by the solution θ_1 of the point equation of N_1. Its focal point of the first order generates a Levy transform $N_{1,1}$ of N_1 whose coordinates are given (analogously to (40)) by

$$(43) \qquad x_{1,1} = x_2 - \frac{\theta_2}{\theta_1} x_1,$$

where θ_2 is the second Laplace transform of θ. In like manner the function θ_{-1} determines a congruence G_{-1} harmonic to N_{-1} whose focal nets are $N_{-1,1}$ and $N_{-2,1}$, where

$$(44) \qquad x_{-2,1} = x_{-1} - \frac{\theta_{-1}}{\theta_{-2}} x_{-2},$$

θ_{-2} being the minus second Laplace transform of θ.

Continuing this process we obtain a sequence of Laplace whose focal nets are Levy transforms of the nets of the Laplace sequence arising from N. We call it the *first Levy sequence* of N determined by θ. The coordinates of the nets $N_{r,1}$ for positive and negative values of r are of the form

$$x_{r,1} = x_{r+1} - \frac{\theta_{r+1}}{\theta_r} x_r, \tag{45}$$

where θ_r is the rth Laplace transform of θ.

35. Levy sequences of higher order. Derived sequences. Let θ and θ' be two solutions of the point equation (1) of N linearly independent of the coordinates of N. By means of θ and θ' we determine two first Levy sequences $N_{r,1}$ and $N'_{r,1}$. These nets are the focal nets of two sequences of congruences G_r and G'_r harmonic to the nets N_r respectively of the Laplace sequence obtained from N. From § 11 it follows that the point of intersection of corresponding lines of G_r and G'_r describe a derived net of N_r. Moreover, from the results of § 11 it follows that these derived nets form first Levy sequences of the sequences of $N_{r,1}$ and $N'_{r,1}$ and consequently we call them *Levy sequences of the second order*. We shall obtain the analytical expressions for their coordinates.

We consider first the derived net of N by means of θ and θ'. The functions $\theta_{-1,1}$ and $\theta_{0,1}$ defined by

$$\theta_{-1,1} = \theta' - \frac{\theta}{\theta_{-1}} \theta_{-1}, \qquad \theta_{0,1} = \theta'_1 - \frac{\theta_1}{\theta} \theta', \tag{46}$$

where θ'_{-1} and θ'_1 are the minus first and first Laplace transforms of θ', are evidently corresponding solutions of $N_{-1,1}$ and $N_{0,1}$, which as we have seen are Laplace transforms of one another. Hence the coordinates of the Levy transform of $N_{-1,1}$ by means of $\theta_{-1,1}$ are the form

$$x_{-1,2} = x_{0,1} - \frac{\theta_{0,1}}{\theta_{-1,1}} x_{-1,1}. \tag{47}$$

In consequence of (40) and (46) this is equivalent to

$$x_{-1,2} = \frac{1}{\theta_{-1}\,\theta_{-1,1}} \begin{vmatrix} \theta_{-1} & \theta'_{-1} & x_{-1} \\ \theta & \theta' & x \\ \theta_1 & \theta_1 & x_1 \end{vmatrix} \equiv \frac{1}{\theta_{-1}\,\theta_{-1,1}} \,|\, \theta_{-1} \;\; \theta' \;\; x_1 \,|,$$

if we make use of the following lemma concerning determinants:

If $D = \| a_{lm} \| \, (l, m = 1, \ldots . n)$ is any determinant of the nth order, and we write

$$a_{r+1,s} - \frac{a_{r+1,1}\, a_{r,s}}{a_{r,1}} = A_{r,s},$$

then

$$D = a_{11} \begin{vmatrix} A_{1,2} & A_{1,3} \ldots\ldots A_{1,n} \\ A_{2,2} & A_{2,3} \ldots\ldots A_{2,n} \\ \text{— — —} & \text{— — —} \\ A_{n-1,2}, \ldots\ldots & A_{n-1,n} \end{vmatrix}. \tag{48}$$

Hence the coordinates of $N_{-1,2}$ can be taken in the form

$$x_{-1,2} = | \theta_{-1}\ \theta'\ x_1 |. \tag{49}$$

From the symmetry of this expression it follows that $N_{-1,2}$ is also a Levy transform of $N'_{-1,1}$, which shows that it is the derived net of N for the functions θ and θ'. Evidently the derived net of N_1 for θ_1 and θ_1' and of N_{-1} for θ_{-1} and θ'_{-1} are given by

$$x_{0,2} = | \theta\ \theta_1'\ x_2 |, \quad x_{-2,2} = | \theta_{-2}\ \theta'_{-1}\ x |. \tag{50}$$

Since $N_{-1,2}$ and $N_{0,2}$ are the Levy transforms of $N_{0,1}$ determined by $\theta_{0,1}$ they are Laplace transforms of one another; similarly $N_{-2,2}$ and $N_{-1,2}$ are the Levy transforms of $N_{-1,1}$ determined by $\theta_{-1,1}$. Hence the solutions θ and θ' determine a Laplace sequence of nets $N_{r,2}$ which are derived nets of the nets N_{r+1}, and a first Levy sequence of the nets $N_{r,1}$. The coordinates of $N_{r,2}$ are of the form

$$x_{r,2} = | \theta_r\ \theta'_{r+1}\ x_{r+2} |, \tag{51}$$

for r positive and negative, and where $N_0 = N$.

If θ'' is another solution of (1) independent θ, θ' and the coordinates of N, the functions

$$\theta'_{-1,1} = \theta' - \frac{\theta}{\theta_{-1}} \theta'_{-1}, \quad \theta''_{-1,1} = \theta'' - \frac{\theta}{\theta_{-1}} \theta''_{-1},$$

solutions of the point equation of $N_{-1,1}$, determine a derived net of $N_{-1,1}$. Analogously to (49) we have that the coordinates of this net are of the form

$$| \theta'_{-2,1}\ \theta''_{-1,1}\ x_{0,1} |.$$

Applying the lemma to this case, we have that the coordinates of the net may be taken in the form

$$(52) \qquad x_{-2,3} = |\theta_{-2}\ \theta'_{-1}\ \theta''\ x_1|.$$

Hence the functions θ, θ' and θ'' determine a sequence of Laplace whose coordinates are of the form

$$(53) \qquad x_{r,3} = |\theta_r\ \theta'_{r+1}\ \theta''_{r+2}\ x_{r+3}|.$$

We remark that from the symmetry of (52) it follows that the net $N_{-2,3}$ is a derived net also of the Levy transforms $N'_{-1,1}$ and $N''_{-1,1}$ determined by θ' and θ'' respectively.

In general m independent solutions $\theta, \theta', \ldots. \theta^{(m-1)}$ of (1) determine a Levy sequence of order m whose coordinates are of the form

$$(54) \qquad x_{r,m} = |\theta_r\ \theta'_{r+1}\ \theta''_{r+2} \ldots \theta^{(m-1)}_{r+m-1},\quad x_{r+m}|,$$

for positive and negative values of r[21]).

36. Periodic Levy sequences. Suppose that we have a Laplace sequence of period p. We seek under what condition the Levy sequence of the first order determined by a solution θ of (1) is also of period p. It is necessary that $x_{p,1} = \lambda x_{0,1}$, where λ is at most a function of u and v. In consequence of (40) and (45) this condition is equivalent to

$$(55) \qquad x_{p+1} - \frac{\theta_{p+1}}{\theta_p} x_p = \lambda \left(x_1 - \frac{\theta_1}{\theta} x \right).$$

From (19), (25) and (29) we have

$$(56) \qquad x_{p+1} = m x_1, \qquad \theta_{p+1} = \frac{\partial \theta_p}{\partial v} - \frac{\partial}{\partial v} \log a \cdot \theta_p.$$

Consequently from (55) it follows that

$$\lambda = m, \qquad \frac{\partial}{\partial v} \log \frac{\theta_p}{\theta} = 0.$$

---

[21]) Cf. Hammond, l. c., p. 252.

In like manner the condition $x_{p-1,1} = \mu x_{-1,1}$ is equivalent in consequence of (21) and (32) to

$$\mu = m, \qquad \frac{\partial}{\partial u} \log \frac{\theta_p}{\theta} = 0.$$

Hence we must have

(57) $$\theta_p = m_1 \theta,$$

where m_1 is a constant. We have seen that equation (1) admits solutions of this type. If we have such a solution, the Laplace transforms of θ satisfy equations (33) and (34) with m replaced by m_1. Hence we have

(58) $$x_{p-i,1} = x_{p-i+1} - \frac{\theta_{p-i+1}}{\theta_{p-i}} x_{p-i} = mH \ldots . H_{p-i}\, x_{-i,1}.$$

Therefore:

If N is a net of period p in $(p-1)$-space such that $x_p = mx$ and θ is a solution of the point equation of N such that $\theta_p = m_1 \theta$, where m_1 is a constant, the Levy sequence determined by θ is of period p; when $m_1 = m$, θ is necessarily a linear function of the x's and the nets of the Levy sequence lie in $(p-2)$-space.

The latter part of the theorem is a consequence of the last theorem of § 33.

If we take two solutions θ and θ' of (1) satisfying the conditions $\theta_p = m_1 \theta$, $\theta_p = m_2 \theta'$, the first Levy sequences determined by θ and θ' are periodic. Also in consequence of (56) and (33) we have from (51)

$$x_{p,2} = m m_1 m_2 x_{o,2},$$
$$x_{p-i,2} = m m_1 m_2 (H H_1 \ldots . H_{p-i-1})^3 H_{p-i}^2 H_{p-i+1}\, x_{-i,2}.$$

Consequently the second Levy sequence determined by θ and θ' is of period p.

Similar results hold for the Levy sequences of higher order. Consider in particular, the case of the Levy sequence of order p determined by the p independent solutions $\theta, \theta', \ldots . \theta^{(p-1)}$ of (1) for which $\theta_p^{(i)} = m_1 \theta^{(i)} (i = 0, \ldots . p-1)$. From (54) we have

$$x_{o,p} = |\theta\ \theta_1'\ \theta_2'' \ldots . \theta_{p-1}^{(p-1)} x_p| = (m - m_1) |\theta\ \theta_1 \ldots . \theta_{p-1}^{(p-1)}|\, x.$$

Similar results hold for $x_{r,p}$. Hence:

If N is a net of period p in $(p-1)$-space, such that $x_p = m x$ and $\theta, \theta', \theta'', \ldots \theta^{(p-1)}$ are p independent solutions of the point equation of N such that $\theta_p^{(i)} = m_1 \theta^{(i)}\,(i = 0, \ldots p-1)$, the pth Levy sequence coincides with the given sequence[22]).

37. Transformations F in homogeneous coordinates. When two nets N and N_1 are in the relation F, the tangents to the curves $u =$ const. and $v =$ const. at corresponding points M and M_1 meet in the focal points of a congruence harmonic to both N and N_1 (§ 17). In accordance with the first theorem of § 33 the coordinates of N and N_1 can be chosen so that we have

$$(59)\qquad \frac{\partial x_1}{\partial u} = \tau_0 \frac{\partial x}{\partial u}, \quad \frac{\partial x_1}{\partial v} = \sigma_0 \frac{\partial x}{\partial v},$$

where τ_0 and σ_0 are functions of u and v. Hence the equations of any transformation F can be given this form. As previously remarked, in this case $c = 0$ in (1) and likewise $c_1 = 0$ in the point equation of N_1.

When $c \neq 0$ in (1), the equation can be reduced to this special form by replacing x by $x\theta$, where θ is any solution of (1). Hence when the point equation of the net N has the general form (1), the equations of a transformation F are

$$(60)\qquad \frac{\partial x_1}{\partial u} = \tau \frac{\partial}{\partial u}\left(\frac{x}{\theta}\right), \quad \frac{\partial x_1}{\partial v} = \sigma \frac{\partial}{\partial v}\left(\frac{x}{\theta}\right).$$

In order that the conditions of integrability of (60) be satisfied for any solutions x and θ of (1), it is necessary and sufficient that τ and σ be solutions of

$$(61)\qquad \frac{\partial \tau}{\partial v} = (\tau - \sigma) \frac{\partial}{\partial v} \log \frac{\theta}{a}, \quad \frac{\partial \sigma}{\partial u} = (\sigma - \tau) \frac{\partial}{\partial u} \log \frac{\theta}{b},$$

or in other form

$$(62)\qquad \frac{\partial}{\partial v} \log \frac{\tau a}{\theta} = \frac{\sigma}{\tau} \frac{\partial}{\partial v} \log \frac{a}{\theta}, \quad \frac{\partial}{\partial u} \log \frac{\sigma b}{\theta} = \frac{\tau}{\sigma} \frac{\partial}{\partial u} \log \frac{b}{\theta}.$$

---

22) Cf. Hammond, l. c., p. 256.

If we put

$$(63) \qquad \tau - \sigma = \varphi\theta,$$

we get equations (II, 16), and find that φ is a solution of the adjoint of (1), which is denoted by (cf. § 31)

$$(64) \qquad \left[\varphi; \frac{1}{a}, \frac{1}{b}, \frac{1}{ab}\right].$$

Suppose we have any pair of solutions of (61), and the net N_1 whose coordinates x_1 are given by the corresponding equations (60). The points F_1 and F_2 whose coordinates y and z are of the forms

$$(65) \qquad y = x_1 - \tau\frac{x}{\theta}, \qquad z = x_1 - \sigma\frac{x}{\theta},$$

lie on the line joining corresponding points of the nets N and N_1. Moreover, as u, or v, varies the point F_1, or F_2, moves tangentially to this line. Hence F_1 and F_2 are the focal points of the congruences of these lines, and N and N_1 are in relation F.

With the aid of (61) we show that the point equation of N_1 is

$$(66) \qquad \frac{\partial^2\theta_1}{\partial u\,\partial v} = \frac{\partial}{\partial v}\log\frac{\tau a}{\theta}\frac{\partial\theta_1}{\partial u} + \frac{\partial}{\partial u}\log\frac{\sigma b}{\theta}\frac{\partial\theta_1}{\partial v}.$$

When we put $\theta = 1$ in (61), we get the conditions of integrability of (59), namely

$$(67) \qquad \frac{\partial\tau_0}{\partial v} = (\sigma_0 - \tau_0)\frac{\partial}{\partial v}\log a, \qquad \frac{\partial\sigma_0}{\partial u} = (\tau_0 - \sigma_0)\frac{\partial}{\partial u}\log b.$$

As a consequence of these results we have:

Whenever the homogeneous coordinates of two nets are in either of the relations (59) *or* (60), *the nets are in relation* F.

From the manner in which equations (59) were obtained it is evident that the transformations F obtained by taking all possible solutions of (67) possess the property that all the corresponding tangent planes of the nets pass through the line of the congruence whose focal points have the coordinates $\frac{\partial x}{\partial u}$ and $\frac{\partial x}{\partial v}$. Hence in order to obtain general transformations F, especially in dealing with two such transformations, it is desirable to take the equations in the form (60). However, when a solution of (1) is known, we can write (60) in the form (59), and then the analysis of the transformations F in homogeneous coordinates is the same as that of parallel nets in cartesian coordinates.

38. Transformations F with the same conjugate congruence. Triads of nets. Suppose we have a transformation in the form (59), so that the new net $N'(x')$ is given by

$$\frac{\partial x'}{\partial u} = \tau_0 \frac{\partial x}{\partial u}, \qquad \frac{\partial x'}{\partial v} = \sigma_0 \frac{\partial x}{\partial v}. \tag{68}$$

Now the point equation of N is necessarily of the form (1) with $c=0$. If θ is any solution of this equation and θ' is given by the quadratures

$$\frac{\partial \theta'}{\partial u} = \tau_0 \frac{\partial \theta}{\partial u}, \qquad \frac{\partial \theta'}{\partial v} = \sigma_0 \frac{\partial \theta}{\partial v}, \tag{69}$$

then the functions x_1, defined by

$$x_1 = x - \frac{\theta}{\theta'} x', \tag{70}$$

are the homogeneous coordinates of a net N_1, since

$$\left\{\begin{aligned} \frac{\partial}{\partial u}\left(\frac{x_1 \theta'}{\theta}\right) &= (\theta' - \tau_0 \theta) \frac{\partial}{\partial u}\left(\frac{x}{\theta}\right), \\ \frac{\partial}{\partial v}\left(\frac{x_1 \theta'}{\theta}\right) &= (\theta' - \sigma_0 \theta) \frac{\partial}{\partial v}\left(\frac{x}{\theta}\right). \end{aligned}\right. \tag{71}$$

From the form of (70) it follows that corresponding points M, M', M_1 on the three nets N, N', N_1 are collinear. Hence not only is N_1 an F transform of N, but also of N'. In the latter respect it differs from the case of § 15 (cf. III, Ex. 24).

As an application of the foregoing results we prove the theorem[23]):

[23]) This theorem for 3-space is due to Ribaucour, Comptes Rendus, vol. 74 (1872), p. 1491.

If a net N lies on a hyperquadric

$$\sum_{i,k} a_{ik} x^{(i)} x^{(k)} = 0,$$

each congruence conjugate to N meets the hyperquadric again in a net, which consequently is an F transform of N.

We assume that the given conjugate congruence is conjugate to a net N' whose coordinates are given by (68). From the above equation we have by differentiation

$$\sum a_{ik} \left(\frac{\partial x^{(i)}}{\partial u} \frac{\partial x^{(k)}}{\partial v} + \frac{\partial x^{(i)}}{\partial v} \frac{\partial x^{(k)}}{\partial u} \right) = 0,$$

since the coordinates x satisfy (1) with $c = 0$. In consequence of this result it follows readily that θ given by

$$\theta = \sum a_{ik} (x^{(i)} x'^{(k)} + x^{(k)} x'^{(i)})$$

is a solution of (1), and that θ' where

$$\theta' = \sum a_{ik} x'^{(i)} x'^{(k)}$$

satisfies (69). If N_1 denotes the corresponding transform of N with the equations (70), it is found that N_1 lies on the quadric.

If τ_1, σ_1 and τ_2, σ_2 are two sets of solutions of (61) for the same θ, by means of equations of the form (60), we get by quadratures two nets, N_1 and N_2, transforms of N. From their equations we find

$$\frac{\partial x_2}{\partial u} = \frac{\tau_2}{\tau_1} \frac{\partial x_1}{\partial u}, \qquad \frac{\partial x_2}{\partial v} = \frac{\sigma_2}{\sigma_1} \frac{\partial x_1}{\partial v}.$$

Consequently N_1 and N_2 are in relation F, and form with N a triad (§ 20).

39. Theorem of permutability. In view of the remarks of the preceding section it follows that the results of §§ 20, 21 can be translated at once into analogous forms for transformations F in homogeneous coordinates.

Suppose then that we have two solutions θ_1, θ_2 of (1) and two solutions φ_1, φ_2 of the adjoint of (1), so that by quadratures of the form (II, 16) two pairs of functions $\tau_1, \sigma_1; \tau_2, \sigma_2$ are to be found. Transforms $N_1(x_1)$ and $N_2(x_2)$ are given by

$$(72)\qquad \frac{\partial x_i}{\partial u} = \tau_i \frac{\partial}{\partial u}\left(\frac{x}{\theta_i}\right), \quad \frac{\partial x_i}{\partial v} = \sigma_i \frac{\partial}{\partial v}\left(\frac{x}{\theta_i}\right), \quad (i = 1, 2).$$

Solutions of the point equations of N_1 and N_2 are given by

$$(73)\qquad \frac{\partial \theta_{ij}}{\partial u} = \tau_i \frac{\partial}{\partial u}\left(\frac{\theta_j}{\theta_i}\right), \quad \frac{\partial \theta_{ij}}{\partial v} = \sigma_i \frac{\partial}{\partial v}\left(\frac{\theta_j}{\theta_i}\right) \quad \left(\begin{matrix} i = 1, 2, \\ j = 1, 2, \end{matrix}\; i \neq j\right).$$

The coordinates of the transform $N_{12}(x_{12})$ are given by (it being understood that N_{12} and N_{21} are the same net)

$$(74)\qquad \frac{\partial x_{ij}}{\partial u} = \tau_{ij} \frac{\partial}{\partial u}\left(\frac{x_i}{\theta_{ij}}\right), \quad \frac{\partial x_{ij}}{\partial v} = \sigma_{ij} \frac{\partial}{\partial v}\left(\frac{x_i}{\theta_{ij}}\right) \quad \left(\begin{matrix} i = 1, 2, \\ j = 1, 2, \end{matrix}\; i \neq j\right).$$

Comparing these results with (60), (71) and with (II, 21, 37) we have from (II, 52, 49)

$$(75)\qquad \begin{cases} \tau_1 \tau_{12} = \tau_2 \tau_{21} = \dfrac{\theta_2 \theta_{21} \tau_1}{\theta_1} + \dfrac{\theta_1 \theta_{12} \tau_2}{\theta_2} - \theta_{12}\theta_{21}, \\ \sigma_1 \sigma_{12} = \sigma_2 \sigma_{21} = \dfrac{\theta_2 \theta_{21} \sigma_1}{\theta_1} + \dfrac{\theta_1 \theta_{12} \sigma_2}{\theta_2} - \theta_{12}\theta_{21}, \\ \qquad\qquad \varphi_{12} = \dfrac{\theta_1}{\theta_2 \sigma_1 \tau_1} (\theta_{21}\theta_2 \varphi_1 + \sigma_1 \tau_2 - \sigma_2 \tau_1), \end{cases}$$

and

$$(76)\qquad \theta_1 \theta_{12} x_{12} = \theta_2 \theta_{21} x_1 + \theta_1 \theta_{12} x_2 - \theta_{12}\theta_{21} x \; ^{24)}.$$

Exercises.

1. The homogeneous point coordinates of any point of the tangent plane to a surface are expressible in the form

$$\lambda x + \mu \frac{\partial x}{\partial u} + \nu \frac{\partial x}{\partial v}.$$

2. Show that equations (3) hold for the special homogeneous coordinates such that y^i/y^{n+1} and z^i/z^{n+1} are cartesian coordinates of the foci; also that if the direction-parameters of the congruence are taken in the form

---

[24]) In making this comparison it must be noted that the quantities $x_i\theta_i'/\theta_i$, $\theta_{ij}\theta_j'/\theta_i$, $x_{12}\theta_{12}'''/\theta_{12}$ of Chapter II must be replaced by $-x_i$, $-\theta_{ij}$, $-x_{12}$ respectively in order to conform to the usages of the present chapter.

$$X^i = \frac{y^i}{y^{n+1}} - \frac{z^i}{z^{n+1}},$$

we have

$$\frac{\partial^2 X}{\partial u \partial v} + \frac{\partial \log y^{n+1}}{\partial v} \frac{\partial X}{\partial u} + \frac{\partial \log z^{n+1}}{\partial u} \frac{\partial X}{\partial v} + CX = 0.$$

3. The invariants of the Laplace transforms N_1 and N_{-1} of a net N are given by

$$H_1 = 2H - K - \frac{\partial^2}{\partial u \partial v} \log H, \qquad K_1 = H;$$

$$H_{-1} = K, \qquad K_{-1} = 2K - H - \frac{\partial^2}{\partial u \partial v} \log K.$$

Darboux, Leçons, vol. 2, p. 28.

4. The invariants of the Laplace transforms N_r and N_{-r} of a net N are given by

$$H_r = H_{r-1} + H - K - \frac{\partial^2}{\partial u \partial v} \log H \ldots. H_{r-1}, \qquad K_r = H_{r-1};$$

$$H_{-r} = K_{-r+1}, \qquad K_{-r} = K_{-r+1} + K - H - \frac{\partial^2}{\partial u \partial v} \log K \ldots. K_{-r+1}.$$

Darboux, Leçons, vol. 2, p. 30.

5. If $H_i = 0$ for a Laplace sequence, then

$$x = A\left(U + \int V\beta\, dv\right) + A_1\left(U' + \int V \frac{\partial \beta}{\partial u} dv\right) + \ldots. + A_i\left(U^{(i)} + \int V \frac{\partial^i \beta}{\partial u^i} dv\right),$$

where β, $A, \ldots. A_i$ are determinat functions; U and V are functions of u and v respectively, and $U^{(i)}$ is the ith derivative of U with respect to u.

Darboux, Leçons, vol. 2, p. 33.

6. When an equation of Laplace admits a solution of the form

$$x = AU + A_1 U' + \ldots. + A_i U^{(i)},$$

where the A's are functions of u and v and $U^{(i)}$ is the ith derivative with respect to u of a function U of u, then $H_i = 0$. Darboux, Leçons, vol. 2, p. 35.

7. If $H_i = 0$ and $K_{-j} = 0$ for a sequence of Laplace, the point equation for N admits solutions of the form

$$x = AU + \ldots. + A_i U^{(i)} + BV + \ldots. + B_j V^{(j)},$$

where the A's and B's are determinate functions; U and V are arbitrary functions of u and v respectively, and $U^{(i)}$ and $V^{(i)}$ denote i^{th} derivatives with respect to u and v.

Darboux, Leçons, vol. 2, p. 38.

8. A necessary and sufficient condition that the point coordinates of a net can be chosen so that the coordinates of the minus first and first Laplace transforms are $\frac{\partial x}{\partial u}$ and $\frac{\partial x}{\partial v}$ respectively is that the point equation of the net have equal invariants.

9. If the parametric curves on a surface S form a net N, the tangents to the curves defined by $A\,du^2 + B\,dv^2 = 0$ meet the lines joining the points M_{-1} and M_1 of the Laplace transforms of N in points harmonic to M_{-1} and M_1.

10. Show that if a point equation (1) satisfies the conditions (27) and (29), it satisfies also the conditions

$$KK_{-1}\ldots.K_{-p+1}=1,\ \frac{\partial^2}{\partial u\,\partial v}\log\frac{a^p}{b^pK^{p-1}K_{-1}^{p-2}\ldots.K_{-p+2}}=0.$$

11. Show that if equation (1) admits solutions of period p, so also does its adjoint equation [cf. § 37]. Hammond, Annals, vol. 22 (1921), p. 260.

12. The point equation of $N_{1,1}$ defined by (43) is denoted by

$$\left[\theta_{1,1};\ aH\frac{\theta_2}{\theta_1},\ b,\ \frac{b^2}{a\theta_1}\right].$$

This may be obtained from (13) by multiplying the second term by θ_2/θ_1, retaining the third term, and multiplying together the third and fourth terms of (13) and dividing by θ_1. Show that the same method applied to (1), denoted by $[\theta; a, b, 1]$ gives (42).

13. Apply the method of the preceding exercise to (20) and obtain for the point equation of $N_{r,1}$ the following

$$\left[\theta_{r,1};\ aHH_1\ldots.H_{r-1}\frac{\theta_{r+1}}{\theta_r},\ b,\ \frac{b^{r+1}}{a^rH^{r-1}H_1^{r-2}\ldots.H_{r-2}\theta_r}\right].$$

Verify this result directly for $r=2$. Hammond, l. c. p. 249.

14. The point equation of $N_{-2,1}$ is denoted by

$$\left[\theta_{-2,1};\ a\frac{\theta_{-1}}{\theta_{-2}},\ bK,\ \frac{a^2}{b\theta_{-2}}\right].$$

This may be obtained from (15), by multiplying the second term of the latter by θ_{-1}/θ_{-2}, retaining the third term and taking for the fourth term the product of the second and fourth of (15) divided by θ_{-2}. Show that (41) is obtained from (1) by the same method.

15. Apply the method of the preceding exercise to (23) and obtain for the point equation of $N_{-(r+1),1}$

$$\left[\theta_{-(r+1),1};\ \frac{a\theta_{-r}}{\theta_{-r-1}},\ bKK_{-1}\ldots.K_{-r+1},\ \frac{a^{r+1}}{b^rK^{r-1}\ldots.K_{-r+2}\theta_{-r-1}}\right].$$

Hammond, l. c.

16. Show that for the derived net $N_{-s,m}$ for $m>s$ the coordinates are expressible in the form

$$x_{-s,m}=\left[\frac{\partial^s\theta}{\partial u^s},\ \frac{\partial^{s-1}\theta'}{\partial u^{s-1}},\ \ldots,\ \theta^{(s)},\ \ldots,\ \frac{\partial^{m-s-1}\theta^{(m-1)}}{\partial v^{m-s-1}},\ \frac{\partial^{m-s}x}{\partial v^{m-s}}\right].$$

Tzitzeica, Comptes Rendus, vol. 156 (1913), p. 375.

17. If two nets N and N_1 are in relation F so also are the nets resulting from a projective transformation of N and N_1.

18. Show that equation (66) is denoted by

$$\left[\theta_1;\ \frac{a\tau}{\theta},\ \frac{b\sigma}{\theta},\ \frac{1}{\theta}\right].$$

19. From (65) we have

$$\frac{\partial y}{\partial u} = -x\varphi_{-1},\quad \frac{\partial y}{\partial v} = -(x)_1\varphi;\quad \frac{\partial z}{\partial u} = (x)_{-1}\varphi,\quad \frac{\partial z}{\partial v} = x\varphi_1,$$

where $(x)_1$ and $(x)_{-1}$ denote coordinates of the first and minus first Laplace transforms of N, and φ_1 and φ_{-1} are first and minus first Laplace transforms of φ with respect to (64). Show that the coordinates of the first Laplace transform of F_1 and the minus first of F_2 are of the forms

$$(x)_1\varphi + y\frac{\partial}{\partial v}\log a\varphi_{-1},\quad (x)_{-1}\varphi - z\frac{\partial}{\partial u}\log b\varphi_1.$$

20. If N and N_1 are nets in relation F, the lines joining corresponding points of their first Laplace transforms (minus first Laplace transforms) meet the corresponding lines of the conjugate congruence of the transformation in the focal points of the first (second) order (cf. Ex. 19).

21. When two nets N and N_1 are in relation F, so also are their Laplace transforms of the same orders; the equations of these transformations are

$$\frac{\partial}{\partial u}(x_1)_r = \tau_r\frac{\partial}{\partial u}\left(\frac{(x)_r}{\theta_r}\right),\quad \frac{\partial}{\partial v}(x_1)_r = \sigma_r\frac{\partial}{\partial v}\left(\frac{(x)_r}{\theta_r}\right),$$

where

$$\tau_r = \tau_{r-1} + \frac{\theta_r\varphi_{-r}}{HH_1\ldots.H_{r-1}},\quad \sigma_r = \tau_{r-1},$$

for r positive. Hammond, l. c., p. 260.

22. If the coordinates of a net N of period p satisfy (25), and θ is a solution of its point equation (1) such that $\theta_p = m_1\theta$ and φ is a solution of the adjoint (64) of (1) such that $\varphi = n\varphi_{-p}$, where m_1 and n are constants, the F transform of N by means of θ and φ is a periodic net of the same period as N.

Hammond, l. c., p. 261.

23. If $N(x)$ and $N_1(x_1)$ are nets in relation F on the hyperquadric $\sum_{i,k} a_{ik}x^{(i)}x^{(k)} = o$, then $\sum_{i,k} a_{ik}(x^{(i)}x_1^{(k)} + x^{(k)}x_1^{(i)}) = k$, where k is a constant. When $k = 0$, the congruence of the transformation consists of generators of the hyperquadric [cf. § 38].

24. Show that if corresponding points of three nets in relation F are collinear the relation between their coordinates may be put in the form (70).

25. Show that for a net with the point equation (1) with $a = b = \sqrt{\rho}$ the equations of a transformation K (§ 25) are

$$\frac{\partial x_1}{\partial u} = \frac{\theta^2}{\rho}\frac{\partial}{\partial u}\left(\frac{x}{\theta}\right),\quad \frac{\partial x_1}{\partial v} = -\frac{\theta^2}{\rho}\frac{\partial}{\partial v}\left(\frac{x}{\theta}\right).$$

26. Let N be a net in 3-space and N_1 an F transform of N given by (60). Let corresponding points M and M_1 of these nets and the two focal points F_1

and F_2 of the harmonic congruence of the transformation be taken as the vertices of a tetrahedron of reference of homogeneous coordinates x, y, z, w such

$$M(0,1,0,0),\quad M_1(0,0,0,1),\quad F_1(1,0,0,0),\quad F_2(0,0,1,0).$$

Show that the pencil of conics tangent to the lines MF_1 and MF_2 at the points $(M)_{-1}$ and $(M)_1$ of the Laplace transforms $(N)_{-1}$ and $(N)_1$ of N are given by

$$2\lambda xz = \left(\frac{\partial}{\partial u}\log\frac{\theta}{b}\cdot x - \frac{y}{\theta} + \frac{\partial}{\partial v}\log\frac{\theta}{a}\cdot z\right)^2,$$

where λ is a parameter; also that according as λ is K, or H, the conic osculates the curve $u=$ const. of $(N)_{-1}$ at $(M)_{-1}$ or $v=$ const. of $(N)_1$ at $(M)_1$.

Annals, vol. 18 (1916), p. 11.

27. A necessary and sufficient condition that a conic of the pencil of Ex. 26 osculate the curve $u=$ const. at $(M)_{-1}$ and $v=$ const. at $(M)_1$ is that N have equal point invariants. Darboux, Lecons, vol. 4, p. 38.

28. Show that the pencil of conics tangent to the lines M_1F_1 and M_1F_2 at the points of the Laplace transforms of N_1 are defined, in the coordinates of Ex. 26, by

$$2xz = \lambda_1\left(\frac{x}{\sigma}\frac{\partial}{\partial u}\log\frac{b}{\theta} + \frac{z}{\tau}\frac{\partial}{\partial v}\log\frac{a}{\theta} + \frac{w}{\theta^2}\right)^2;$$

that this pencil and the pencil of Ex. 26 determine involutions on the line F_1F_2; and that a necessary and sufficient condition that the two involutions be identical is that the transformation F be K. Annals, l. c., p. 12.

29. If N and N_1 are two nets in relation K, any two conics of the two pencils of Exs. 26 and 28, meeting on the line F_1F_2 determine a pencil of quadrics which cut the line MM_1 in an involution whose double points are the focal points of this line for the congruence of these lines, and the two cones of the pencil are the quadrics tangent to MM_1 at these focal points.

Annals, l. c. p. 15.

30. If N and N_1 are nets in relation K, the doubly osculating conics of the pencils of Exs. 26 and 28 meet on the line F_1F_2, and the vertices of the two cones in the pencil of quadrics determined by these conics are the corresponding focal points of the conjugate congruence of the transformation.

Tzitzeica, Comptes Rendus, vol. 147 (1908), p. 1036; also Annals, l. c., p. 16.

Chapter IV.

Surfaces and congruences in 3-space.

40. Nets in 2-space. It is evident that any three functions of two parameters, u and v, satisfy an equation of the form

$$(1) \qquad \frac{\partial^2 \theta}{\partial u \partial v} = \frac{\partial \log a}{\partial v} \frac{\partial \theta}{\partial u} + \frac{\partial \log b}{\partial u} \frac{\partial \theta}{\partial v} + c\theta.$$

Consequently any two families of curves in 2-space form a net. It is likewise true that we can find two equations of the form

$$(2) \qquad \begin{cases} \dfrac{\partial^2 \theta}{\partial u^2} = a_1 \dfrac{\partial \theta}{\partial u} + b_1 \dfrac{\partial \theta}{\partial v} + c_1 \theta, \\[2ex] \dfrac{\partial^2 \theta}{\partial v^2} = a_2 \dfrac{\partial \theta}{\partial u} + b_2 \dfrac{\partial \theta}{\partial v} + c_2 \theta. \end{cases}$$

which the three given functions satisfy.

Conversely, we seek the conditions which must be satisfied by the coefficients in (1) and (2) in order that they admit three linearly independent solutions. To this end the following conditions of integrability must be satisfied:

$$\frac{\partial}{\partial v}\left(\frac{\partial^2 \theta}{\partial u^2}\right) = \frac{\partial}{\partial u}\left(\frac{\partial^2 \theta}{\partial u \partial v}\right), \qquad \frac{\partial}{\partial v}\left(\frac{\partial^2 \theta}{\partial u \partial v}\right) = \frac{\partial}{\partial u}\left(\frac{\partial^2 \theta}{\partial v^2}\right).$$

Reducing the resulting expressions by means of (1) and (2), we get two equations of the form

$$(3) \quad A_1 \frac{\partial \theta}{\partial u} + B_1 \frac{\partial \theta}{\partial v} + C_1 \theta = 0, \qquad A_2 \frac{\partial \theta}{\partial u} + B_2 \frac{\partial \theta}{\partial v} + C_2 \theta = 0,$$

where $A_1, B_1 \ldots . C_2$ are determinate functions, which must vanish, if equations (2) are to hold for three linearly independent solutions. Putting them equal to zero, we get the following conditions:

$$
(4)\begin{cases}
a_2 b_1 + \dfrac{\partial a_1}{\partial v} = \dfrac{\partial \log a}{\partial v}\dfrac{\partial \log b}{\partial u} + c + \dfrac{\partial^2 \log a}{\partial u\, \partial v}, \\
a_1 \dfrac{\partial \log b}{\partial u} + b_1 b_2 + c_1 + \dfrac{\partial b_1}{\partial v} = \dfrac{\partial \log a}{\partial v} b_1 + \left(\dfrac{\partial \log b}{\partial u}\right)^2 + \dfrac{\partial^2 \log b}{\partial u^2}, \\
a_1 c + b_1 c_2 + \dfrac{\partial c_1}{\partial v} = \dfrac{\partial \log a}{\partial v} c_1 + \dfrac{\partial \log b}{\partial u} c + \dfrac{\partial c}{\partial u}, \\
a_2 b_1 + \dfrac{\partial b_2}{\partial u} = \dfrac{\partial \log a}{\partial v}\dfrac{\partial \log b}{\partial u} + c + \dfrac{\partial^2 \log b}{\partial u\, \partial v}; \\
b_2 \dfrac{\partial \log a}{\partial v} + a_1 a_2 + c_2 + \dfrac{\partial a_2}{\partial u} = \dfrac{\partial \log b}{\partial u} a_2 + \left(\dfrac{\partial \log a}{\partial v}\right)^2 + \dfrac{\partial^2 \log a}{\partial v^2}, \\
b_2 c + a_2 c_1 + \dfrac{\partial c_2}{\partial u} = \dfrac{\partial \log b}{\partial u} c_2 + \dfrac{\partial \log a}{\partial v} c + \dfrac{\partial c}{\partial v}.
\end{cases}
$$

When these conditions are satisfied, the system (1) and (2) is completely integrable and there are at most three linearly independent solutions. For, the derivatives of the second and higher orders of θ are linearly expressible in terms of $\dfrac{\partial \theta}{\partial u}, \dfrac{\partial \theta}{\partial v}$, and θ. Hence all the integrals are expressible as linear functions, with constant coefficients, of three solutions. Therefore we have the theorem:

When the homogeneous coordinates of a net satisfy equations of the form (2), *the net is in 2-space; and all nets whose homogeneous coordinates satisfy the same equations* (1) *and* (2) *are projective transforms of one another.*

41. Tangential coordinates of a surface in 3-space. Let x, y, z, w be the homogeneous point coordinates of a surface S in 3-space referred to any system of parametric curves $u =$ const., $v =$ const. Since the tangents to the parameteric curves at a point of the surface lie in the tangent plane to the surface at that point, the equation of the tangent plane must be satisfied not only by x, y, z, and w, but also by the coordinates of any point on these tangents, that is by expressions of the form

$$\lambda_1 x + \mu_1 \frac{\partial x}{\partial u}, \quad \lambda_2 x + \mu_2 \frac{\partial x}{\partial v},$$

for any values of λ_1, μ_1, λ_2 and μ_2. Hence there exist four functions, X, Y, Z, W, of u and v, the *tangential coordinates* of the surface, [cf. § 67] satisfying identically the three conditions

$$(5)\qquad \begin{cases} Xx + Yy + Zz + Ww = 0, \\ \sum X \dfrac{\partial x}{\partial u} = 0, \qquad \sum X \dfrac{\partial x}{\partial v} = 0, \end{cases}$$

where $\sum$ indicates the sum of four terms obtained by replacing x and X by y and Y; z and Z; w and W respectively.

In consequence of the last two we have, on differentiating the first, the two equations

$$(6)\qquad \sum x \frac{\partial X}{\partial u} = 0, \qquad \sum x \frac{\partial X}{\partial v} = 0.$$

42. Asymptotic lines. An asymptotic line on a surface is characterized by the property that its osculating plane at a point is tangent to the surface at that point [§ 55]. Hence along an asymptotic line $\dfrac{dv}{du}$ must equal such a function of u and v that the equation of the tangent plane is satisfied by $\lambda x + \mu dx + \nu d^2 x$, for all values of λ, μ, and ν [cf. § 30]. Hence we must have

$$\sum X d^2 x = 0.$$

Eliminating X, Y, Z, and W from this equation and (5), we have

$$(7)\qquad L du^2 + 2 M du\, dv + N dv^2 = 0,$$

where

$$(8)\qquad L = \begin{vmatrix} x & \dfrac{\partial x}{\partial u} & \dfrac{\partial x}{\partial v} & \dfrac{\partial^2 x}{\partial u^2} \\ y & \dfrac{\partial y}{\partial u} & \dfrac{\partial y}{\partial v} & \dfrac{\partial^2 y}{\partial u^2} \\ z & \dfrac{\partial z}{\partial u} & \dfrac{\partial z}{\partial v} & \dfrac{\partial^2 z}{\partial u^2} \\ w & \dfrac{\partial w}{\partial u} & \dfrac{\partial w}{\partial v} & \dfrac{\partial^2 w}{\partial u^2} \end{vmatrix}, \quad M = \begin{vmatrix} x & \dfrac{\partial x}{\partial u} & \dfrac{\partial x}{\partial v} & \dfrac{\partial^2 x}{\partial u \partial v} \\ y & - & - & - \\ z & - & - & - \\ w & - & - & - \end{vmatrix}, \quad N = \begin{vmatrix} x & \dfrac{\partial x}{\partial u} & \dfrac{\partial x}{\partial v} & \dfrac{\partial^2 x}{\partial v^2} \\ y & - & - & - \\ z & - & - & - \\ w & - & - & - \end{vmatrix}$$

This is the equation of the asymptotic lines on S. We have immediately the theorem [cf. § 77]:

A necessary and sufficient condition that four functions x, y, z, w be the homogeneous point coordinates of a surface referred to its asymptotic lines is that x, y, z, w be four linearly independent solutions of two partial differential equations of the form

$$(9)\quad \begin{cases} \dfrac{\partial^2\theta}{\partial u^2} = a_1\dfrac{\partial\theta}{\partial u} + b_1\dfrac{\partial\theta}{\partial v} + c_1\theta, \\[2ex] \dfrac{\partial^2\theta}{\partial v^2} = a_2\dfrac{\partial\theta}{\partial u} + b_2\dfrac{\partial\theta}{\partial v} + c_2\theta. \end{cases}$$

We seek now the conditions upon the coefficients of equations (9) so that two equations (9) shall have four linearly independent solutions. It is necessary that the following condition be satisfied:

$$\frac{\partial^2}{\partial v^2}\left(\frac{\partial^2\theta}{\partial u^2}\right) = \frac{\partial^2}{\partial u^2}\left(\frac{\partial^2\theta}{\partial v^2}\right).$$

When the above expressions are substituted, the resulting equation is reducible by means of (9) to an equation of the form

$$A\frac{\partial^2\theta}{\partial u\,\partial v} + B\frac{\partial\theta}{\partial u} + C\frac{\partial\theta}{\partial v} + D\theta = 0,$$

where A, B, C and D are determinate functions of the coefficients of (9) and their derivatives. These functions must be equal to zero, otherwise we can have at most three linearly independent solutions of (9) [cf. § 40].

Putting them equal to zero, we obtain the four equations of condition

$$(10)\quad \begin{cases} \dfrac{\partial a_1}{\partial v} - \dfrac{\partial b_2}{\partial u} = 0, \\[2ex] \dfrac{\partial^2 a_2}{\partial u^2} - \dfrac{\partial^2 a_1}{\partial v^2} + \dfrac{\partial}{\partial u}(a_1 a_2) + b_2\dfrac{\partial a_1}{\partial v} - a_2\dfrac{\partial b_1}{\partial v} - \dfrac{\partial}{\partial v}(a_2 b_1) + 2\dfrac{\partial c_2}{\partial u} = 0, \\[2ex] \dfrac{\partial^2 b_1}{\partial v^2} - \dfrac{\partial^2 b_2}{\partial u^2} + \dfrac{\partial}{\partial v}(b_1 b_2) + a_1\dfrac{\partial b_2}{\partial u} - b_1\dfrac{\partial a_2}{\partial u} - \dfrac{\partial}{\partial u}(a_2 b_1) + 2\dfrac{\partial c_1}{\partial v} = 0, \\[2ex] \dfrac{\partial^2 c_2}{\partial u^2} - \dfrac{\partial^2 c_1}{\partial v^2} + 2c_1\dfrac{\partial a_2}{\partial u} + a_2\dfrac{\partial c_1}{\partial u} - a_1\dfrac{\partial c_2}{\partial u} - 2c_2\dfrac{\partial b_1}{\partial v} - b_1\dfrac{\partial c_2}{\partial v} + b_2\dfrac{\partial c_1}{\partial v} = 0. \end{cases}$$

When these conditions are satisfied, the system is completely integrable, and as all the higher derivatives are expressible linearly in terms of x, $\frac{\partial x}{\partial u}$, $\frac{\partial x}{\partial v}$ and $\frac{\partial^2 x}{\partial u\,\partial v}$, there are four linearly independent solutions, and only four. Hence we have the theorem:

A necessary and sufficient condition that a system (9) *admit four linearly independent solutions is that the coefficients satisfy* (10). *All surfaces whose four point coordinates satisfy the same system* (9) *are projective transforms of one another.*

When the surface S is subjected to a polar transformation with respect to the quadric

$$x^2 + y^2 + z^2 + w^2 = 0, \tag{11}$$

the point and tangential coordinates of S are tangential and point coordinates respectively of the transform S'. Since asymptotic lines are transformed into asymptotic lines on S' [cf. § 84], we have the theorem:

Any four linearly independent solutions of the system (9) *are tangential coordinates of a surface referred to its asymptotic lines; all surfaces whose tangential coordinates satisfy the same system of equations* (9) *are projective transforms of one another.*

43. Nets in 3-space. Point coordinates. Consider a surface S referred to any system of curves, $u=$ const., $v=$ const., and upon it a net, or conjugate system. Any point P on a tangent at M to a curve of a family of the net has homogeneous point coordinates of the form

$$\bar{x} = \lambda x + \mu\left(\frac{\partial x}{\partial u}\,du + \frac{\partial x}{\partial v}\,dv\right).$$

A necessary and sufficient condition (§ 2) that two families of curves determined by $\frac{dv}{du}$ and $\frac{\delta v}{\delta u}$ form a net is that, as M moves along the curve of the second family through it, P moves in the tangent plane to the surface at M. Hence the point whose coordinates are of the form $\bar{x} + \delta\bar{x} = \bar{x} + \frac{\partial \bar{x}}{\partial u}\,\delta u + \frac{\partial \bar{x}}{\partial v}\,\delta v$ must lie in the tangent plane. This gives the equation of condition

$$X\delta\bar{x} + Y\delta\bar{y} + Z\delta\bar{z} + W\delta\bar{w} = 0.$$

Combining this equation with the identities (5), we get

$$(12) \qquad L\,du\,\delta u + M(du\,\delta v + \delta u\,dv) + N\,dv\,\delta v = 0,$$

where L, M and N are given by (8). This is in keeping with (7) which defines the asymptotic or self-conjugate directions, and could have been inferred directly from (7), since these differential equations in the parameters are independent of the point coordinates and consequently should be equivalent to the similar equations found when cartesian rectangular coordinates are used [cf. §§ 54, 55]. As an immediate consequence of these observations and the results of [§ 56] we have:

A necessary and sufficient condition that the curves defined by $R\,du^2 + 2\,S\,du\,dv + T\,dv^2 = 0$ *form a conjugate system is*

$$(13) \qquad RN + TL - 2SM = 0.$$

From this result, and from (12) also, it follows that a necessary and sufficient condition that the parametric curves form a net is that $M = 0$. But from (8) this means merely that x, y, z and w are linearly independent solutions of an equation of the form (1). In this case the equation of the asymptotic lines is of the form

$$(14) \qquad du^2 + r\,dv^2 = 0,$$

where $r = N/L$ is a function of u and v. Comparing this equation with (7), we have in consequence of (8),

$$\begin{vmatrix} x & \dfrac{\partial x}{\partial u} & \dfrac{\partial x}{\partial v} & r\dfrac{\partial^2 x}{\partial u^2} - \dfrac{\partial^2 x}{\partial v^2} \\ y & & & \\ z & & & \\ w & & & \end{vmatrix} = 0.$$

Hence we have the theorem:

The homogeneous point coordinates of a net in 3-space are simultaneous solutions of two equations of the form (1) *and*

$$(15) \qquad \frac{\partial^2 \theta}{\partial v^2} = r\frac{\partial^2 \theta}{\partial u^2} + a'\frac{\partial \theta}{\partial u} + b'\frac{\partial \theta}{\partial v} + c'\theta.$$

Conversely, we shall show that two equations of the form (1) and (15) admit at most four linearly independent solutions. In the first place in order that they admit a common solution it is necessary that they satisfy the condition of integrability

$$\frac{\partial}{\partial v}\left(\frac{\partial^2 \theta}{\partial u \partial v}\right) = \frac{\partial}{\partial u}\left(\frac{\partial^2 \theta}{\partial v^2}\right).$$

When the expression from (1) and (15) are substituted, the resulting equation is reducible to

$$(16) \qquad \frac{\partial^3 \theta}{\partial u^3} = A_1 \frac{\partial^2 \theta}{\partial u^2} + B_1 \frac{\partial \theta}{\partial u} + C_1 \frac{\partial \theta}{\partial v} + D_1 \theta,$$

where

$$(17)\left\{\begin{aligned} A_1 &= \frac{\partial}{\partial u}\log\frac{b}{r} - \frac{a'}{r}, \quad B_1 = \frac{1}{r}\left(\frac{1}{a}\frac{\partial^2 a}{\partial v^2} + a'\frac{\partial}{\partial u}\log\frac{b}{a'} - b'\frac{\partial \log a}{\partial v} - c'\right), \\ C_1 &= \frac{1}{r}\left(K + 2\frac{\partial^2 \log b}{\partial u \partial v} - \frac{\partial b'}{\partial u}\right), \\ D_1 &= \frac{1}{r}\left(c\frac{\partial \log a}{\partial v} + c'\frac{\partial \log b}{\partial u} + \frac{\partial c}{\partial v} - cb' - \frac{\partial c'}{\partial u}\right), \end{aligned}\right.$$

where K is one of the invariants of (1) [cf. I, 44].

From (1) we have also by differentiation

$$(18) \qquad \frac{\partial^3 \theta}{\partial u^2 \partial v} = A_2 \frac{\partial^2 \theta}{\partial u^2} + B_2 \frac{\partial \theta}{\partial u} + C_2 \frac{\partial \theta}{\partial v} + D_2 \theta,$$

where

(19)

$$A_2 = \frac{\partial \log a}{\partial v}, \quad B_2 = H + 2\frac{\partial^2 \log a}{\partial u \partial v}, \quad C_2 = \frac{1}{b}\frac{\partial^2 b}{\partial u^2}, \quad D_2 = c\frac{\partial}{\partial u}\log bc.$$

Also from (15) we obtain $\dfrac{\partial^3 \theta}{\partial u \partial v^2}$ and $\dfrac{\partial^3 \theta}{\partial v^3}$ expressed linearly in terms of θ, $\dfrac{\partial \theta}{\partial u}$, $\dfrac{\partial \theta}{\partial v}$ and $\dfrac{\partial^2 \theta}{\partial u^2}$. There remains the condition

$$\frac{\partial}{\partial u}\left(\frac{\partial^3 \theta}{\partial u^2 \partial v}\right) = \frac{\partial}{\partial v}\left(\frac{\partial^3 \theta}{\partial u^3}\right).$$

By means of (16) and (18) this condition is reducible to the form

$$P\frac{\partial^2\theta}{\partial u^2}+Q\frac{\partial\theta}{\partial u}+R\frac{\partial\theta}{\partial v}+S\theta=0, \tag{20}$$

where P, Q, R and S are determinate functions. If the coefficients in (1) and (15) are not such that

$$P=Q=R=S=0, \tag{21}$$

we have a system to be satisfied similar to (1) and (2), which, as we saw in § 40, admits at most three linearly independent solutions. Hence we must have (21) satisfied, in which case the third and higher derivatives in θ are linearly expressible in terms of θ, $\frac{\partial\theta}{\partial u}$, $\frac{\partial\theta}{\partial v}$, $\frac{\partial^2\theta}{\partial u^2}$. Since all further conditions of integrability are satisfied, we see that there are at most four linearly independent solutions of a completely integrable system of equations of the type (1) and (15). Accordingly we have the theorem:

The homogeneous point coordinates of a net in 3-space satisfy a system of equations of the form (1) *and* (15); *conversely, a net whose coordinates satisfy such a system lies in 3-space. Any four linearly independent solutions of the same system of equations* (1) *and* (15) *are the homogeneous point coordinates of a net projective with the given net.*

When the expressions P, Q, R and S in (20) are calculated, it is found that equations (21) reduce to

$$\left\{\begin{aligned}
&\frac{\partial A_1}{\partial v}+C_1 r=\frac{\partial A_2}{\partial u}+B_2,\\
&\frac{\partial B_1}{\partial v}+A_1B_2+a'C_1=\frac{\partial B_2}{\partial u}+C_2\frac{\partial\log a}{\partial v}+D_2,\\
&\frac{\partial C_1}{\partial v}+A_1C_2+B_1\frac{\partial\log b}{\partial u}+b'C_1+D_1=\frac{\partial C_2}{\partial u}+A_2C_1+C_2\frac{\partial\log b}{\partial u},\\
&\frac{\partial D_1}{\partial v}+A_1D_2+B_1c+C_1c'=\frac{\partial D_2}{\partial u}+A_2D_1+C_2c.
\end{aligned}\right. \tag{22}$$

When the point coordinates of a net N are cartesian, we have from (14) and [(40) § 55] that $r = D''/D$. Consequently by the elimination of X from the first and third of the Gauss equations [(7) § 64] we find that the cartesian coordinates of N satisfy an equation of the form (15) with

$$a' = \begin{Bmatrix} 22 \\ 1 \end{Bmatrix} - r \begin{Bmatrix} 11 \\ 1 \end{Bmatrix} \quad b' = \begin{Bmatrix} 22 \\ 2 \end{Bmatrix} - r \begin{Bmatrix} 11 \\ 2 \end{Bmatrix}, \quad c' = 0.$$

From (14) and [§ 82] it follows that a necessary and sufficient condition that N be isothermal-conjugate is that $r = U/V$, where U and V are functions of u and v alone respectively. As a consequence of the preceding theorem, we have:

An isothermal-conjugate net is transformed into an isothermal-conjugate net by a projective transformation.

44. Ray congruence and ray curves. Consider a net N in n-space, and the system of lines joining corresponding points of the first and minus first Laplace transforms of N. If this system of lines is to form a congruence, there must be two points of a line generating curves to which the line is tangent. The coordinates of any point are of the form $\lambda x_{-1} + \mu x_1$. Hence it must be possible for u and v to vary in such a way that $d(\lambda x_{-1} + \mu x_1)$ is a linear function of x_{-1} and x_1. From (III, 2, 4) we have

$$(23) \quad \begin{cases} \dfrac{\partial x_{-1}}{\partial u} = \dfrac{\partial^2 x}{\partial u^2} - \dfrac{1}{b}\dfrac{\partial^2 b}{\partial u^2} x - \dfrac{\partial \log b}{\partial u} x_{-1}, & \dfrac{\partial x_{-1}}{\partial v} = \dfrac{\partial \log a}{\partial v} x_{-1} + Kx, \\ \dfrac{\partial x_1}{\partial u} = \dfrac{\partial \log b}{\partial u} x_1 + Hx, & \dfrac{\partial x_1}{\partial v} = \dfrac{\partial^2 x}{\partial v^2} - \dfrac{1}{a}\dfrac{\partial^2 a}{\partial v^2} x - \dfrac{\partial \log a}{\partial v} x_1, \end{cases}$$

where H and K are the invariants of (1). Expressing the above condition, we get equations of the following form to be satisfied by the coordinates x:

$$(24) \quad \begin{cases} \lambda\left[\left(\dfrac{\partial^2 x}{\partial u^2} - \dfrac{1}{b}\dfrac{\partial^2 b}{\partial u^2} x\right) du + xK\,dv\right] + \mu\left[xH\,du + \left(\dfrac{\partial^2 x}{\partial v^2} - \dfrac{1}{a}\dfrac{\partial^2 a}{\partial v^2} x\right) dv\right] \\ \qquad + \nu\left(\dfrac{\partial x}{\partial u} - \dfrac{\partial \log b}{\partial u} x\right) + \sigma\left(\dfrac{\partial x}{\partial v} - \dfrac{\partial \log a}{\partial v} x\right) = 0, \end{cases}$$

where ν and σ are to be determined.

Equation (24) is linear in $\frac{\partial^2 x}{\partial u^2}, \frac{\partial^2 x}{\partial v^2}, \frac{\partial x}{\partial u}, \frac{\partial x}{\partial v}$ and x. If $n > 3$, this equation must be satisfied by five or more linearly independent functions x, which is possible only when the coefficients of the quantities $\frac{\partial^2 x}{\partial u^2}, \ldots, x$ are zero. This gives $\lambda\, du = \mu\, dv = 0$, which from (24) is seen to be impossible.

When $n = 3$, by means of (15), (24) is reducible to an expression linear in $\frac{\partial^2 x}{\partial u^2}, \frac{\partial x}{\partial u}, \frac{\partial x}{\partial v}, x$. The coefficients of the latter expression must then be zero, which gives the four equations of condition

$$(25)\quad \begin{cases} \lambda\, du + \mu r\, dv = 0, \quad \mu a'\, dv + \nu = 0, \quad \mu b'\, dv + \sigma = 0, \\ \lambda \left(\frac{1}{b}\frac{\partial^2 b}{\partial u^2}\, du - K\, dv\right) + \mu\left[-H\, du + \left(\frac{1}{a}\frac{\partial^2 a}{\partial v^2} - c'\right) dv\right] \\ \qquad + \nu \frac{\partial \log b}{\partial u} + \sigma \frac{\partial \log a}{\partial v} = 0. \end{cases}$$

Eliminating λ, μ, ν and σ from these equations, we obtain

$$(26)\qquad H\, du^2 + R\, du\, dv - r K\, dv^2 = 0,$$

where

$$(27)\qquad R = \frac{r}{b}\frac{\partial^2 b}{\partial u^2} - \frac{1}{a}\frac{\partial^2 a}{\partial v^2} + c' + a'\frac{\partial \log b}{\partial u} + b'\frac{\partial \log a}{\partial v}.$$

Hence the system of lines forms a congruence. Following Wilczynski[25]) we call it the *ray congruence* of the net N, and the curves on the surface of the net defined by (26) the *ray curves*. Since any one parameter family of lines in a plane has an envelope, the developables of such a congruence for nets in 2-space have no significance. Hence we have the theorem:

The lines joining corresponding points of the first and minus first Laplace transforms of a net form a congruence only when the net lies in 3-space.

From (13), (14) and (26) we have the theorem of Wilczynski[26]):

---

25) Transactions of the American Mathematical Society, vol. 16 (1915), p. 318.

26) L. c. p. 319.

A necessary and sufficient condition that the ray curves for a net N form a net is that N have equal point invariants.

In consequence of the fourth theorem of § 10 we have:

The ray congruence of a net with equal point invariants is harmonic to the corresponding net of ray curves.

45. Nets *R*. We determine the condition that the tangents to the curves $v=$ const. of a net N form a W congruence, that is the asymptotic lines on the surface of N and its minus first Laplace transform correspond [§ 172].

From (23) we have by differentiation, making use of (16),

$$(28)\quad \begin{cases} \dfrac{\partial^2 x_{-1}}{\partial u^2} = \left(A_1 - \dfrac{\partial \log b}{\partial u}\right)\dfrac{\partial x_{-1}}{\partial u} + (B_1 - C_2)\dfrac{\partial x}{\partial u} + C_1 \dfrac{\partial x}{\partial v} \\ \qquad + \left(A_1 C_2 - \dfrac{\partial C_2}{\partial u} + D_1\right) x + \left(A_1 \dfrac{\partial \log b}{\partial u} - \dfrac{\partial^2 \log b}{\partial u^2}\right) x_{-1}, \\ \dfrac{\partial^2 x_{-1}}{\partial v^2} = \dfrac{\partial \log a}{\partial v}\dfrac{\partial x_{-1}}{\partial v} + K \dfrac{\partial x}{\partial v} + \dfrac{\partial K}{\partial v} x + \dfrac{\partial^2 \log a}{\partial v^2} x_{-1}. \end{cases}$$

If we replace x and $\dfrac{\partial x}{\partial u}$ by the linear expressions for them obtained from (III, 2, 4) and then eliminate $\dfrac{\partial x}{\partial v}$ from these two equations, we obtain for the net N_{-1} an equation of the form (15), where r_{-1} has the value K/C_1.

From this result and (14) it follows that a necessary and sufficient condition that the asymptotic lines correspond on the two surfaces is that $C_1 r = K$, which by (17) is equivalent to

$$(29)\qquad 2\frac{\partial^2 \log b}{\partial u \partial v} - \frac{\partial b'}{\partial u} = 0.$$

In like manner a necessary and sufficient condition that the tangents to the curves $u=$ const. of N form a W congruence is

$$(30)\qquad 2\frac{\partial^2 \log a}{\partial u \partial v} + \frac{\partial}{\partial v}\left(\frac{a'}{r}\right) = 0.$$

Tzitzeica[27]) has defined an R *net* to be one for which the tangents to the curves of both families form W congruences. Equations (29) and (30) are the analytical condition that N be an R net. When these conditions are satisfied, the first of (22) reduces to $\frac{\partial^2}{\partial u \partial v} \log r = 0$. Hence we have the theorem of Tzitzeica:

An R net is isothermal-conjugate.

By means of the first of equations (22) we establish the converse theorem due to Demoulin[28]):

If the tangents to the curves in either family of an isothermal-conjugate net form a W congruence, it is an R net.

Since an R net is isothermal-conjugate, the parameters can be chosen so that $r = -1$. Since a and b in (1) are determined only to within factors, which are functions of u and v respectively, these can be chosen so that (29) and (30) may be replaced by

$$b' = 2\frac{\partial \log b}{\partial v}, \qquad a' = 2\frac{\partial \log a}{\partial u}.$$

Hence:

The two differential equations satisfied by the homogeneous point coordinates of an R net are reducible to the form

$$(31) \qquad \begin{cases} \dfrac{\partial^2 \theta}{\partial u \partial v} = \dfrac{\partial \log a}{\partial v}\dfrac{\partial \theta}{\partial u} + \dfrac{\partial \log b}{\partial u}\dfrac{\partial \theta}{\partial v} + c\theta, \\[2ex] \dfrac{\partial^2 \theta}{\partial v^2} + \dfrac{\partial^2 \theta}{\partial u^2} = 2\dfrac{\partial \log a}{\partial u}\dfrac{\partial \theta}{\partial u} + 2\dfrac{\partial \log b}{\partial v}\dfrac{\partial \theta}{\partial v} + c'\theta. \end{cases}$$

We return to the consideration of the net N_{-1}. From (23) we have by differentiation

$$(32) \qquad \begin{cases} \dfrac{\partial^2 x_{-1}}{\partial u \partial v} = \dfrac{\partial \log a}{\partial v}\dfrac{\partial x_{-1}}{\partial u} + \dfrac{\partial}{\partial u}\log K b \dfrac{\partial x_{-1}}{\partial v} \\[2ex] \qquad + \left(\dfrac{\partial^2 \log \frac{a}{b}}{\partial u \partial v} - \dfrac{\partial \log K}{\partial u}\dfrac{\partial \log a}{\partial v} + c\right) x_{-1}. \end{cases}$$

---

27) Comptes Rendus, vol. 152 (1911), p. 1077.

28) Comptes Rendus, vol. 153 (1911), p. 592.

Since $r=-1$, it follows from (17) that $C_1=-K$. Making use of (III, 2, 4) and the third of (22), we find from (28)

$$(33)\qquad \begin{cases} \dfrac{\partial^2 x_{-1}}{\partial v^2}+\dfrac{\partial^2 x_{-1}}{\partial u^2} \\ =2\dfrac{\partial \log a}{\partial u}\dfrac{\partial x_{-1}}{\partial u}+2\dfrac{\partial \log Kb}{\partial v}\dfrac{\partial x_{-1}}{\partial v}+c'_{-1}x_{-1}, \end{cases}$$

where c'_{-1} is a determinate function. Comparing equations (31) and (33), we see that N_{-1} is an R net. Similar results hold for the first Laplace transform of N. Consequently:

The Laplace transforms of an R net are R nets.

Making use of the terminology of [§ 165], we have:

If either of the first derived congruences of a W congruence is a W congruence, then all of the derived congruences are W[29]).

46. W congruences. Let S be a surface referred to its asymptotic lines $\alpha=$ const., $\beta=$ const. The cartesian coordinates, $x^{(1)}$, $x^{(2)}$, $x^{(3)}$, of S are given by the Lelieuvre formulas of the form [§ 79]

$$(34)\qquad \frac{\partial x^{(1)}}{\partial \alpha}=\begin{vmatrix} \nu_2 & \nu_3 \\ \dfrac{\partial \nu_2}{\partial \alpha} & \dfrac{\partial \nu_3}{\partial \alpha}\end{vmatrix},\qquad \frac{\partial x^{(1)}}{\partial \beta}=\begin{vmatrix} \nu_2 & \nu_3 \\ \dfrac{\partial \nu_2}{\partial \beta} & \dfrac{\partial \nu_3}{\partial \beta}\end{vmatrix},$$

where ν_1, ν_2, ν_3 are proportional to the direction-cosines of the normal to S, such that the total curvature of S is given by

$$(35)\qquad K=-\frac{1}{(\nu_1^2+\nu_2^2+\nu_3^2)^2}=-\frac{1}{\varrho^2}.$$

The functions ν_i are solutions of an equation of the form

$$(36)\qquad \frac{\partial^2\theta}{\partial\alpha\,\partial\beta}=M\theta,$$

where M is a function of α and β.

---

[29]) Cf. Demoulin, l. c., p. 591.

If θ_1 is any solution of (36), the equations [cf. § 172]

$$\text{(37)}\qquad \frac{\partial(\theta_1\bar{\nu}_i)}{\partial\alpha} = -\begin{vmatrix} \theta_1 & \nu_i \\ \frac{\partial\theta_1}{\partial\alpha} & \frac{\partial\nu_i}{\partial\alpha} \end{vmatrix}, \qquad \frac{\partial(\theta_1\bar{\nu}_i)}{\partial\beta} = \begin{vmatrix} \theta_1 & \nu_i \\ \frac{\partial\theta_1}{\partial\beta} & \frac{\partial\nu_i}{\partial\beta} \end{vmatrix}$$

are consistent, and the functions $\bar{\nu}_i$ are solutions of

$$\text{(38)}\qquad \frac{\partial^2\bar{\theta}}{\partial\alpha\,\partial\beta} = \theta_1 \frac{\partial^2}{\partial\alpha\,\partial\beta}\left(\frac{1}{\theta_1}\right)\bar{\theta}.$$

The equations of the form

$$\text{(39)}\qquad \bar{x}^{(1)} = x^{(1)} + \nu_2\bar{\nu}_3 - \nu_3\bar{\nu}_2$$

define the coordinates, $\bar{x}^{(i)}$, of a surface $\bar{S}$, such that S and $\bar{S}$ are the focal surfaces of the congruence of lines joining corresponding points on S and $\bar{S}$; this is a W congruence, since the asymptotic lines are parametric on $\bar{S}$. Moreover, any W congruence with S as a focal surface may be obtained in this way. We shall give this result another form.

From (9) and the first of equations (10) it follows that the coordinates $x^{(i)}$ satisfy equations of the form

$$\text{(40)}\qquad \frac{\partial^2\theta}{\partial\alpha^2} = \frac{\partial\varphi}{\partial\alpha}\frac{\partial\theta}{\partial\alpha} + b\frac{\partial\theta}{\partial\beta}, \qquad \frac{\partial^2\theta}{\partial\beta^2} = a_1\frac{\partial\theta}{\partial\alpha} + \frac{\partial\varphi}{\partial\beta}\frac{\partial\theta}{\partial\beta}.$$

Differentiating (34), we obtain

$$\text{(41)}\qquad \frac{\partial^2 x^{(1)}}{\partial\alpha^2} = \begin{vmatrix} \nu_2 & \nu_3 \\ \frac{\partial^2\nu_2}{\partial\alpha^2} & \frac{\partial^2\nu_3}{\partial\alpha^2} \end{vmatrix}, \qquad \frac{\partial^2 x^{(1)}}{\partial\beta^2} = -\begin{vmatrix} \nu_2 & \nu_3 \\ \frac{\partial^2\nu_2}{\partial\beta^2} & \frac{\partial^2\nu_3}{\partial\beta^2} \end{vmatrix}.$$

The functions ν_i satisfy three equations of the form (1) and (2). From (36), (40), (41) and the first, second and fifth of equations (4), it follows that these equations are

$$(42)\quad \begin{cases} \dfrac{\partial^2 \nu_i}{\partial \alpha^2} = \dfrac{\partial \varphi}{\partial \alpha}\dfrac{\partial \nu_i}{\partial \alpha} - b\dfrac{\partial \nu_i}{\partial \beta} + \left(b\dfrac{\partial \varphi}{\partial \beta} + \dfrac{\partial b}{\partial \beta}\right)\nu_i, \\ \dfrac{\partial^2 \nu_i}{\partial \alpha\,\partial \beta} = \left(\dfrac{\partial^2 \varphi}{\partial \alpha\,\partial \beta} + a_1 b\right)\nu_i, \\ \dfrac{\partial^2 \nu_i}{\partial \beta^2} = -a_1\dfrac{\partial \nu_i}{\partial \alpha} + \dfrac{\partial \varphi}{\partial \beta}\dfrac{\partial \nu_i}{\partial \beta} + \left(a_1\dfrac{\partial \varphi}{\partial \alpha} + \dfrac{\partial a_1}{\partial \alpha}\right)\nu_i. \end{cases}$$

We write

$$(43)\qquad \theta_1 \bar{\nu}_i = k\nu_i + l\frac{\partial \nu_i}{\partial \alpha} + m\frac{\partial \nu_i}{\partial \beta}$$

and seek the conditions which k, l and m must satisfy in order that this expression may satisfy equations (37) for $i = 1, 2, 3$. By means of (42) we find

$$(44)\qquad \frac{\partial l}{\partial \beta} - a_1 m = 0, \qquad \frac{\partial m}{\partial \alpha} - bl = 0,$$

$$(45)\quad \begin{cases} k = -\dfrac{1}{2}\left(\dfrac{\partial l}{\partial \alpha} + \dfrac{\partial m}{\partial \beta} + l\dfrac{\partial \varphi}{\partial \alpha} + m\dfrac{\partial \varphi}{\partial \beta}\right), \\ \theta_1 = -\dfrac{1}{2}\left(\dfrac{\partial l}{\partial \alpha} - \dfrac{\partial m}{\partial \beta} + l\dfrac{\partial \varphi}{\partial \alpha} - m\dfrac{\partial \varphi}{\partial \beta}\right) \end{cases}$$

and

$$(46)\quad \begin{cases} \dfrac{\partial k}{\partial \alpha} - \dfrac{\partial \theta_1}{\partial \alpha} + l\left(b\dfrac{\partial \varphi}{\partial \beta} + \dfrac{\partial b}{\partial \beta}\right) + m\left(\dfrac{\partial^2 \varphi}{\partial \alpha\,\partial \beta} + a_1 b\right) = 0, \\ \dfrac{\partial k}{\partial \beta} + \dfrac{\partial \theta_1}{\partial \beta} + l\left(\dfrac{\partial^2 \varphi}{\partial \alpha\,\partial \beta} + a_1 b\right) + m\left(a_1\dfrac{\partial \varphi}{\partial \alpha} + \dfrac{\partial a_1}{\partial \alpha}\right) = 0. \end{cases}$$

Conversely, if l and m are any pair of solutions of (44), the functions k and θ_1, defined by (45) satisfy (46). Furthermore, if equations (46) are differentiated with respect to β and α respectively, and the resulting equations are substracted, we find that θ_1 is a solution of the second of equations (42), in consequence of (46) and the equations for (42) analogous to the third and last of (4). Hence[30]):

The determination of the W congruences with a given focal surface S is equivalent to the solution of equations (44), *in which* a_1

[30]) Cf. Jonas, Jahresbericht der deutschen Mathematiker-Vereinigung, vol. 29 (1920), p. 52.

and b are the functions appearing in the equations (40) *of the surface; when a pair of solutions is known, the coordinates* $\bar{x}^{(i)}$ *of the other focal surface of the congruence are given by*

$$\bar{x}^{(i)} = x^{(i)} + 2\,\frac{l\,\dfrac{\partial x^{(i)}}{\partial \alpha} - m\,\dfrac{\partial x^{(i)}}{\partial \beta}}{\dfrac{\partial m}{\partial \beta} - \dfrac{\partial l}{\partial \alpha} - l\,\dfrac{\partial \varphi}{\partial \alpha} + m\,\dfrac{\partial \varphi}{\partial \beta}}. \tag{47}$$

This expression follows from (39), (43), (45) and (34).

47. *R* surfaces. In § 45 we established the conditions to be satisfied by a net N in order that it be an R net. A surface is said to be an R *surface* when it contains an R net. In this section we establish an analytical characterization of R surfaces.

Let S be a surface referred to its asymptotic lines $\alpha =$ const., $\beta =$ const. Its cartesian coordinates satisfy equations of the form (40). Any isothermal-conjugate system of curves on S is defined by [cf. § 82]

$$u = A(\alpha) + B(\beta), \qquad v = A(\alpha) - B(\beta), \tag{48}$$

when A and B are arbitrary functions of α and β respectively. If we effect the transformation of variables (48), equations (40) become

$$\frac{\partial^2 \theta}{\partial u^2} + \frac{\partial^2 \theta}{\partial v^2} = (K+L)\frac{\partial \theta}{\partial u} + (M+N)\frac{\partial \theta}{\partial v},$$

$$\frac{\partial^2 \theta}{\partial u\,\partial v} = \frac{1}{2}(K-L)\frac{\partial \theta}{\partial u} + \frac{1}{2}(M-N)\frac{\partial \theta}{\partial v},$$

where

$$K = \frac{1}{2}\frac{1}{A'^2}\left(\frac{\partial \varphi}{\partial \alpha}A' + bB' - A''\right), \quad L = \frac{1}{2B'^2}\left(a_1 A' + \frac{\partial \varphi}{\partial \beta}B' - B''\right),$$

$$M = \frac{1}{2}\frac{1}{A'^2}\left(\frac{\partial \varphi}{\partial \alpha}A' - bB' - A''\right), \quad N = \frac{1}{2B'^2}\left(a_1 A' - \frac{\partial \varphi}{\partial \beta}B' + B''\right),$$

the primes indicating differentiation.

From (31) it follows that a necessary and sufficient condition that the net of parameters u and v be an R net is that

$$\frac{\partial}{\partial v}(K+L) = \frac{\partial}{\partial u}(K-L), \quad \frac{\partial}{\partial v}(M-N) = \frac{\partial}{\partial u}(M+N),$$

or in terms α and β

$$\frac{1}{B'}\frac{\partial K}{\partial \beta}-\frac{1}{A'}\frac{\partial L}{\partial \alpha}=0, \quad \frac{1}{B'}\frac{\partial M}{\partial \beta}+\frac{1}{A'}\frac{\partial N}{\partial \alpha}=0.$$

Substituting the above expressions for K, L, M, N, we are brought to the single condition

$$(49) \qquad B'^2\frac{\partial b}{\partial \beta}+B'B''b=A'^2\frac{\partial a_1}{\partial \alpha}+A'A''a_1$$ [31].

Since the quadrics are characterized by the condition that $a_1=b=0$, we have the theorem[32]):

Every isothermal-conjugate net on a quadric is an R net.

If the condition (49) is satisfied for two sets of functions A, B and A_1, B_1, it is satisfied also by $\overline{A}$, $\overline{B}$, where

$$\overline{A}'^2=A'^2+kA_1^2, \quad \overline{B}'^2=B'^2+kB_1'^2,$$

k being a constant. Hence we have the theorem of Demoulin[33]):

If a surface is an R surface in two ways, it is an R surface in an infinity of ways; that is an infinity of nets R lie upon it.

If the condition (49) is satisfied by a surface, the parameters of the asymptotic lines can be chosen so that $A=\alpha$, $B=\beta$. Consequently:

A necessary and sufficient condition that a surface be an R surface is that its cartesian coordinates satisfy equations of the form

$$(50) \qquad \begin{cases} \dfrac{\partial^2 \theta}{\partial \alpha^2}=\dfrac{\partial \varphi}{\partial \alpha}\dfrac{\partial \theta}{\partial \alpha}+\dfrac{\partial \psi}{\partial \alpha}\dfrac{\partial \theta}{\partial \beta}, \\ \dfrac{\partial^2 \theta}{\partial \beta^2}=\dfrac{\partial \psi}{\partial \beta}\dfrac{\partial \theta}{\partial \alpha}+\dfrac{\partial \varphi}{\partial \beta}\dfrac{\partial \theta}{\partial \beta}. \end{cases}$$

When the conditions (10) are applied to (50) we obtain the equations to be satisfied by φ and ψ, whose solution gives the complete determination of R surfaces.

---

31) Cf. Demoulin, Comptes Rendus, vol. 153 (1911), p. 799.
32) Cf. Bianchi, Rendiconti dei Lincei, ser. 5, vol. 22^2, (1913), p. 5.
33) L. c.

For this case equations (44) become

$$\frac{\partial l}{\partial \beta}-\frac{\partial \psi}{\partial \beta}m=0, \quad \frac{\partial m}{\partial \alpha}-\frac{\partial \psi}{\partial \alpha}l=0,$$

of which a solution is $l=m=e^{\psi}$. Making use of (45), the equation (43) becomes in this case

$$(51)\quad \left\{\begin{aligned} &\left[\frac{\partial}{\partial \alpha}(\varphi+\psi)-\frac{\partial}{\partial \beta}(\varphi+\psi)\right]\bar{\nu}_i= \\ &\left[\frac{\partial}{\partial \alpha}(\varphi+\psi)+\frac{\partial}{\partial \beta}(\varphi+\psi)\right]\nu_i-2\frac{\partial \nu_i}{\partial \alpha}-2\frac{\partial \nu_i}{\partial \beta}.\end{aligned}\right.$$

48. R Congruences. Transformations θ_1. By definition the W congruence of tangents to the curves of either family of an R net is an *R congruence.* In this section we show that when an R surface is known, a congruence R can be found by quadratures, whose lines are parallel to the normals to the given surface R[34]).

Equations (50) can be written

$$(52)\quad \frac{\partial}{\partial \alpha}\left(e^{-\varphi}\frac{\partial \theta}{\partial \alpha}\right)=e^{-\varphi}\frac{\partial \psi}{\partial \alpha}\frac{\partial \theta}{\partial \beta}, \quad \frac{\partial}{\partial \beta}\left(e^{-\varphi}\frac{\partial \theta}{\partial \beta}\right)=e^{-\varphi}\frac{\partial \psi}{\partial \beta}\frac{\partial \theta}{\partial \alpha}.$$

Hence if we put

$$(53)\quad \bar{\eta}_i+\eta_i=2e^{-\varphi}\frac{\partial x^{(i)}}{\partial \alpha}, \quad \bar{\eta}_i-\eta_i=2e^{-\varphi}\frac{\partial x^{(i)}}{\partial \beta},$$

we have

$$(54)\quad \frac{\partial}{\partial \alpha}(\bar{\eta}_i+\eta_i)=\frac{\partial \psi}{\partial \alpha}(\bar{\eta}_i-\eta_i), \quad \frac{\partial}{\partial \beta}(\bar{\eta}_i-\eta_i)=\frac{\partial \psi}{\partial \beta}(\bar{\eta}_i+\eta_i).$$

Differentiating these equations with respect to β and α respectively, we find that

$$(55)\quad \frac{\partial^2 \eta_i}{\partial \alpha\,\partial \beta}=e^{\psi}\frac{\partial^2 e^{-\psi}}{\partial \alpha\,\partial \beta}\eta_i, \quad \frac{\partial^2 \bar{\eta}_i}{\partial \alpha\,\partial \beta}=e^{-\psi}\frac{\partial^2 e^{\psi}}{\partial \alpha\,\partial \beta}\bar{\eta}_i.$$

---

[34]) Demoulin, Comptes Rendus, vol. 153 (1911), p. 798; also, Jonas, l. c., pp. 67 et seq.

Since equations (54) may be written in the form (37) with θ_1 replaced by $e^{-\psi}$ and ν_i, $\bar{\nu}_i$ by η_i, $\bar{\eta}_i$, it follows that the surfaces Σ and $\bar{\Sigma}$ of coordinates $\xi^{(i)}$ and $\bar{\xi}^{(i)}$ given by equations of the form (34) in η_i and analogously to (39) by equations of the form

$$\bar{\xi}^{(1)} = \xi^{(1)} + \eta_2 \bar{\eta}_3 - \eta_3 \bar{\eta}_2 \tag{56}$$

are the focal surfaces of a W congruence Γ. In consequence of (53) we have

$$\sum (\bar{\xi}^{(i)} - \xi^{(i)}) \frac{\partial x^{(i)}}{\partial \alpha} = \sum (\bar{\xi}^{(i)} - \xi^{(i)}) \frac{\partial x^{(i)}}{\partial \beta} = 0.$$

Consequently the lines of the W congruence are parallel to the normals to the given R surface.

From (53) we have

$$\eta_i = e^{-\varphi} \left(\frac{\partial x^{(i)}}{\partial \alpha} - \frac{\partial x^{(i)}}{\partial \beta} \right). \tag{57}$$

If we differentiate this equation with respect to α and β and add the resulting equations, we find in consequence of (50) and (53)

$$\begin{aligned} \frac{\partial \eta_i}{\partial \alpha} + \frac{\partial \eta_i}{\partial \beta} + \frac{1}{2} \eta_i \left[\frac{\partial}{\partial \alpha} (\varphi + \psi) + \frac{\partial}{\partial \beta} (\varphi + \psi) \right] \\ = \frac{1}{2} \bar{\eta}_i \left[\frac{\partial}{\partial \alpha} (\varphi + \psi) - \frac{\partial}{\partial \beta} (\varphi + \psi) \right]. \end{aligned} \tag{58}$$

Comparing this result with an equation analogous to (43) written

$$\vartheta_1 \bar{\eta}_i = k \eta_i + \lambda \frac{\partial \eta_i}{\partial \alpha} + \mu \frac{\partial \eta_i}{\partial \beta}, \tag{59}$$

we see that $\lambda = \mu$, and hence from equations analogous to (44) and (49) it follows that Σ is an R surface, and consequently the congruence Γ is R. Moreover, from (57) it is seen that the normals to Σ and $\bar{\Sigma}$ are parallel to the tangents to the curves of the R net $\alpha - \beta = \text{const.}$, $\alpha + \beta = \text{const.}$ on S.

The equations for Σ analogous to (50) for S are obtained from (50) by replacing φ and ψ by functions φ_1 and ψ_1, where $\lambda = \mu = e^{\psi_1}$, as follows from equations analogous to (44). From (58) and equations similar to (51), we find that φ_1 can be chosen so that

$$\varphi_1+\psi_1+\varphi+\psi=0.$$

Also from (54) we have that $\vartheta_1=\frac{1}{2}e^{-\psi}$. Hence equations (53) can be written

$$\vartheta_1(\bar{\eta}_i+\eta_i)=e^{\varphi_1+\psi_1}\frac{\partial x^{(i)}}{\partial \alpha},\qquad \vartheta_1(\bar{\eta}_i-\eta_i)=e^{\varphi_1+\psi_1}\frac{\partial x^{(i)}}{\partial \beta}.$$

Suppose conversely that we have an R congruence for which one of the focal surfaces is S whose point coordinates $x^{(i)}$ satisfy (50), and for which the functions $\bar{\nu}_i$ are given by (51). In consequence of (37) and (51), the equations

$$\frac{\partial \xi^{(i)}}{\partial \alpha}=\theta_1(\bar{\nu}_i+\nu_i)e^{-(\varphi+\psi)},\qquad \frac{\partial \xi^{(i)}}{\partial \beta}=\theta_1(\bar{\nu}_i-\nu_i)e^{-(\psi+\varphi)},$$

are consistent, and $\xi^{(i)}$ are solutions of

$$\frac{\partial^2\theta}{\partial\alpha^2}=\frac{\partial}{\partial\alpha}(\log\theta_1-\varphi-\psi)\frac{\partial\theta}{\partial\alpha}-\frac{\partial\log\theta_1}{\partial\alpha}\frac{\partial\theta}{\partial\beta},$$

$$\frac{\partial^2\theta}{\partial\beta^2}=-\frac{\partial\log\theta_1}{\partial\beta}\frac{\partial\theta}{\partial\alpha}+\frac{\partial}{\partial\beta}(\log\theta_1-\varphi-\psi)\frac{\partial\theta}{\partial\beta}.$$

Hence $\xi^{(i)}$ are the coordinates of a surface R.

Accordingly we have the theorem of Demoulin:

When an R surface is known, an associated R congruence can be found by quadratures, and conversely; the lines of the congruence are parallel to the normals of the associated R surface, and the normals to the focal surfaces of the congruence are parallel to the tangents to the R net on the R surface.

Demoulin has called this reciprocal relation a *tranformation* θ_1.

49. Reciprocally derived nets. Transformations W of nets R. In § 11 we remarked that if θ_1 and θ_2 are solutions of the point equation

$$\frac{\partial^2\theta}{\partial u\,\partial v}=\frac{\partial\log a}{\partial v}\frac{\partial\theta}{\partial u}+\frac{\partial\log b}{\partial u}\frac{\partial\theta}{\partial v}\tag{60}$$

of the cartesian coordinates of a net $N(x)$, they determine a derived net $\overline{N}(\overline{x})$ of N, whose coordinates are given by equations of the form

$$(61)\qquad \overline{x} = x + p\frac{\partial x}{\partial u} + q\frac{\partial x}{\partial v},$$

where

$$(62)\qquad \begin{cases} p = \dfrac{1}{\Delta}\left(\theta_1\dfrac{\partial \theta_2}{\partial v} - \theta_2\dfrac{\partial \theta_1}{\partial v}\right), \quad q = \dfrac{1}{\Delta}\left(\theta_2\dfrac{\partial \theta_1}{\partial u} - \theta_1\dfrac{\partial \theta_2}{\partial u}\right), \\ \Delta = \dfrac{\partial \theta_2}{\partial u}\dfrac{\partial \theta_1}{\partial v} - \dfrac{\partial \theta_2}{\partial v}\dfrac{\partial \theta_1}{\partial u}. \end{cases}$$

From these equations we have

$$(63)\qquad \theta_1 + p\frac{\partial \theta_1}{\partial u} + q\frac{\partial \theta_1}{\partial v} = 0, \quad \theta_2 + p\frac{\partial \theta_2}{\partial u} + q\frac{\partial \theta_2}{\partial v} = 0.$$

Ordinarily N is not a derived net of $\overline{N}$. When it is, we say that N and $\overline{N}$ are *reciprocally derived nets*[35]). If N and $\overline{N}$ are reciprocally derived nets, the tangents planes at corresponding points, M and $\overline{M}$, must pass through $\overline{M}$ and M respectively. Hence the surfaces, S and $\overline{S}$, on which N and $\overline{N}$ lie are the focal surfaces of the congruence $\overline{G}$ of lines $M\overline{M}$. Since the lines of $\overline{G}$ are not tangents to the curves of N or $\overline{N}$, there exist upon S and $\overline{S}$ corresponding nets to which these lines are tangent, namely the focal nets. Consequently S and $\overline{S}$ are surfaces in 3-space (§ 3), and since two nets on S correspond to two nets on $\overline{S}$, the asymptotic lines correspond on S and $\overline{S}$. Hence $\overline{G}$ is a W congruence.

Since θ_1 and θ_2 are solutions of (60), we have from (62)

$$(64)\qquad \begin{cases} \dfrac{\partial p}{\partial u} = -1 - q\dfrac{\partial \log a}{\partial v} + \dfrac{p}{\Delta}\left(\dfrac{\partial^2 \theta_1}{\partial u^2}\dfrac{\partial \theta_2}{\partial v} - \dfrac{\partial^2 \theta_2}{\partial u^2}\dfrac{\partial \theta_1}{\partial v}\right), \\ \dfrac{\partial p}{\partial v} = -p\dfrac{\partial \log a}{\partial v} + \dfrac{1}{\Delta}\left(\theta_1\dfrac{\partial^2 \theta_2}{\partial v^2} - \theta_2\dfrac{\partial^2 \theta_1}{\partial v^2}\right) - \dfrac{p}{\Delta}\left(\dfrac{\partial \theta_2}{\partial u}\dfrac{\partial^2 \theta_1}{\partial v^2} - \dfrac{\partial \theta_1}{\partial u}\dfrac{\partial^2 \theta_2}{\partial v^2}\right), \\ \dfrac{\partial q}{\partial u} = -q\dfrac{\partial \log b}{\partial u} + \dfrac{1}{\Delta}\left(\theta_2\dfrac{\partial^2 \theta_1}{\partial u^2} - \theta_1\dfrac{\partial^2 \theta_2}{\partial u^2}\right) - \dfrac{q}{\Delta}\left(\dfrac{\partial \theta_1}{\partial v}\dfrac{\partial^2 \theta_2}{\partial u^2} - \dfrac{\partial \theta_2}{\partial v}\dfrac{\partial^2 \theta_1}{\partial u^2}\right), \\ \dfrac{\partial q}{\partial v} = -1 - p\dfrac{\partial \log b}{\partial u} + \dfrac{q}{\Delta}\left(\dfrac{\partial^2 \theta_2}{\partial v^2}\dfrac{\partial \theta_1}{\partial u} - \dfrac{\partial^2 \theta_1}{\partial v^2}\dfrac{\partial \theta_2}{\partial u}\right). \end{cases}$$

35) Cf. Tzitzeica, Comptes Rendus, vol. 156 (1913), p. 666.

With the aid of these expressions we show that the point equation of $\overline{N}$ is

$$(65)\qquad \frac{\partial^2 \theta}{\partial u \partial v} = \frac{\partial}{\partial v} \log a p \frac{\partial \theta}{\partial u} + \frac{\partial}{\partial u} \log b q \frac{\partial \theta}{\partial v}.$$

If N is to be a derived net of $\overline{N}$, we must have

$$(66)\qquad x = \overline{x} + \overline{p}\frac{\partial \overline{x}}{\partial u} + \overline{q}\frac{\partial \overline{x}}{\partial v},$$

and the point equation of N is, analogously to (65),

$$(67)\qquad \frac{\partial^2 \theta}{\partial u \partial v} = \frac{\partial}{\partial v} \log a p \overline{p} \frac{\partial \theta}{\partial u} + \frac{\partial}{\partial u} \log b q \overline{q} \frac{\partial \theta}{\partial v}.$$

Comparing this equation with (60), we have

$$(68)\qquad p\overline{p} = U, \quad q\overline{q} = V,$$

where U and V are functions of u and v alone. From (61) and (66) it is seen that the parameters can be chosen so that

$$(69)\qquad p\overline{p} = q\overline{q} = -\frac{1}{c},$$

where c is a constant.

When the expression (61) for $\overline{x}$ is substituted in (66), the result is reducible to

$$(70)\qquad \frac{\partial^2 x}{\partial u^2} + \frac{\partial^2 x}{\partial v^2} = a' \frac{\partial x}{\partial u} + b' \frac{\partial x}{\partial v},$$

where

$$(71)\qquad \left\{\begin{aligned} -a' &= -cp + \frac{1}{p} + \frac{\partial \log p}{\partial u} + \left(\frac{q}{p} + \frac{p}{q}\right)\frac{\partial \log a}{\partial v} + \frac{1}{q}\frac{\partial p}{\partial v}, \\ -b' &= -cq + \frac{1}{q} + \frac{\partial \log q}{\partial v} + \left(\frac{p}{q} + \frac{q}{p}\right)\frac{\partial \log b}{\partial u} + \frac{1}{p}\frac{\partial q}{\partial u}. \end{aligned}\right.$$

By means of (64) equations (71) are reducible to

$$\frac{\partial \theta_2}{\partial v}\left(\frac{\partial^2 \theta_1}{\partial u^2} + \frac{\partial^2 \theta_1}{\partial v^2} - a' \frac{\partial \theta_1}{\partial u} - c\theta_1\right) = \frac{\partial \theta_1}{\partial v}\left(\frac{\partial^2 \theta_2}{\partial u^2} + \frac{\partial^2 \theta_2}{\partial v^2} - a' \frac{\partial \theta_2}{\partial u} - c\theta_2\right),$$

$$\frac{\partial \theta_2}{\partial u}\left(\frac{\partial^2 \theta_1}{\partial u^2} + \frac{\partial^2 \theta_1}{\partial v^2} - b' \frac{\partial \theta_1}{\partial v} - c\theta_1\right) = \frac{\partial \theta_1}{\partial u}\left(\frac{\partial^2 \theta_2}{\partial u^2} + \frac{\partial^2 \theta_2}{\partial v^2} - b' \frac{\partial \theta_2}{\partial v} - c\theta_2\right),$$

from which it follows that θ_1 and θ_2 are solutions of

$$(72)\qquad \frac{\partial^2\theta}{\partial u^2}+\frac{\partial^2\theta}{\partial v^2}=a'\frac{\partial\theta}{\partial u}+b'\frac{\partial\theta}{\partial v}+c\,\theta.$$

In order that equations (60) and (70) shall admit four independent solutions, we must have equations (22) satisfied with $c=c'=0$. When we make use of these results in obtaining equation (20) for the system (60) and (72), we find that $P=Q=R=0$ and consequently $S=0$. But this is the last of (22) and it reduces to

$$\frac{\partial b'}{\partial u}-2\frac{\partial^2\log b}{\partial u\,\partial v}=0.$$

Then from the first of (22) we have

$$\frac{\partial a'}{\partial v}-2\frac{\partial^2\log a}{\partial u\,\partial v}=0.$$

From the results of § 45 it follows that N is an R net, whose cartesian coordinates satisfy equations which can be written in the forms

$$(73)\qquad \begin{cases} \dfrac{\partial^2\theta}{\partial u^2}+\dfrac{\partial^2\theta}{\partial v^2}=2\dfrac{\partial\log a}{\partial u}\dfrac{\partial\theta}{\partial u}+2\dfrac{\partial\log b}{\partial v}\dfrac{\partial\theta}{\partial v}, \\[2ex] \dfrac{\partial^2\theta}{\partial u\,\partial v}=\dfrac{\partial\log a}{\partial v}\dfrac{\partial\theta}{\partial u}+\dfrac{\partial\log b}{\partial u}\dfrac{\partial\theta}{\partial v}. \end{cases}$$

Now equation (72), to be satisfied by θ_1 and θ_2, is

$$(74)\qquad \frac{\partial^2\theta}{\partial u^2}+\frac{\partial^2\theta}{\partial v^2}=2\frac{\partial\log a}{\partial u}\frac{\partial\theta}{\partial u}+2\frac{\partial\log b}{\partial v}\frac{\partial\theta}{\partial v}+c\theta.$$

Since (60) and (74) satisfy the corresponding equations (22), they admit four independent solutions.

If in (61) the expression (66) for x is substituted, we find in consequence of (69) and (71) that $\bar{x}$ is a solution of

$$(75)\qquad \frac{\partial^2\theta}{\partial u^2}+\frac{\partial^2\theta}{\partial v^2}=2\frac{\partial}{\partial u}\log ap\,\frac{\partial\theta}{\partial u}+2\frac{\partial}{\partial v}\log bq\,\frac{\partial\theta}{\partial v}.$$

Hence $\bar{N}$ is an R net whose equations are (65) and (75).

In § 50 it is shown that, if θ_3 and θ_4 are two solutions of (60) and (74) independent of θ_1 and θ_2, the functions $\overline{\theta}_3$ and $\overline{\theta}_4$, defined by

$$\overline{\theta}_i = \theta_i + p\frac{\partial \theta_i}{\partial u} + q\frac{\partial \theta_i}{\partial v} \quad (i = 3, 4) \tag{76}$$

are solutions of (65), and that, moreover, the functions $\overline{p}$ and $\overline{q}$ in (66) are expressible in terms of $\overline{\theta}_3$ and $\overline{\theta}_4$ in the form analogous to (62). Hence N is a derived net of $\overline{N}$, and consequently is reciprocally derived. We say that $\overline{N}$ is obtained from N by a *transformation* W_c. Since any solution of (60) and (74) is expressible linearly in terms of four independent solutions, it follows from the form of (62) that there are ∞^5 transformations W_c for each value of c, different from zero, in (74). Hence:

Any R net admits of ∞^5 transformations W_c into R nets, for each value of the constant c different from zero[36].

50. Theorem of permutability of transformations *W*. Let θ_3 and θ_4 be two solutions of the equation (60) and

$$\frac{\partial^2 \theta}{\partial u} + \frac{\partial^2 \theta}{\partial v^2} = 2\frac{\partial \log a}{\partial u}\frac{\partial \theta}{\partial u} + 2\frac{\partial \log b}{\partial v}\frac{\partial \theta}{\partial v} + c'\theta,$$

and consider the functions (76). Analogously to (I, 68) we have

$$\tag{77} \left\{ \begin{aligned} \frac{\partial \overline{\theta}_i}{\partial u} &= p\left\{\frac{\partial^2 \theta_i}{\partial u^2} + \frac{1}{\Delta}\left[\frac{\partial \theta_i}{\partial u}\left(\frac{\partial \theta_2}{\partial v}\frac{\partial^2 \theta_1}{\partial u^2} - \frac{\partial \theta_1}{\partial v}\frac{\partial^2 \theta_2}{\partial u^2}\right)\right.\right. \\ &\qquad \left.\left. - \frac{\partial \theta_i}{\partial v}\left(\frac{\partial \theta_2}{\partial u}\frac{\partial^2 \theta_1}{\partial u^2} - \frac{\partial \theta_1}{\partial u}\frac{\partial^2 \theta_2}{\partial u^2}\right)\right]\right\}, \\ \frac{\partial \overline{\theta}_i}{\partial v} &= q\left\{\frac{\partial^2 \theta_i}{\partial v^2} + \frac{1}{\Delta}\left[\frac{\partial \theta_i}{\partial u}\left(\frac{\partial \theta_2}{\partial v}\frac{\partial^2 \theta_1}{\partial v^2} - \frac{\partial \theta_1}{\partial v}\frac{\partial^2 \theta_2}{\partial v^2}\right)\right.\right. \\ &\qquad \left.\left. - \frac{\partial \theta_i}{\partial v}\left(\frac{\partial \theta_2}{\partial u}\frac{\partial^2 \theta_1}{\partial v^2} - \frac{\partial \theta_1}{\partial u}\frac{\partial^2 \theta_2}{\partial v^2}\right)\right]\right\}, \\ &= q\left\{-\frac{1}{p}\frac{\partial \overline{\theta}_i}{\partial u} + (c' - c)\,\theta_i + c\,\overline{\theta}_i\right\}. \end{aligned} \right.$$

[36] Annals of Mathematics, vol. 22 (1921), p. 170; these transformations are given in a different form by Demoulin, Bulletin de la Classe des Sciences, Académie Royale de Belgique, 1920, p. 226, and by Jonas, Jahresbericht, vol. 29 (1920), p. 58.

Differentiating the first of these equations with respect to u, we get

$$\frac{\partial^2 \overline{\theta}_i}{\partial u^2} = \frac{\partial \overline{\theta}_i}{\partial u}\left[\frac{\partial}{\partial u}\log p\, a^2 b + \frac{1}{\Delta}\left(\frac{\partial \theta_2}{\partial v}\frac{\partial^2 \theta_1}{\partial u^2} - \frac{\partial \theta_1}{\partial v}\frac{\partial^2 \theta_2}{\partial u^2}\right)\right]$$

$$+ p\,(c' - c)\frac{\partial \theta_i}{\partial u} - p\frac{\partial \log b}{\partial u}\left[c'\theta_i + c\left(p\frac{\partial \theta_i}{\partial u} + q\frac{\partial \theta_i}{\partial v}\right)\right].$$

Making use of the expression (64) for $\frac{\partial p}{\partial u}$ and (76), we reduce this to

$$\frac{\partial^2 \overline{\theta}_i}{\partial u^2} = \frac{\partial \overline{\theta}_i}{\partial u}\left[\frac{\partial}{\partial u}\log p^2 a^2 b + \frac{1}{p} + \frac{q}{p}\frac{\partial \log a}{\partial v}\right] + p\,(c' - c)\frac{\partial \theta_i}{\partial u}$$

$$- p\frac{\partial \log b}{\partial u}\left[(c' - c)\,\theta_i + c\overline{\theta}_i\right].$$

Also we find that

$$\frac{\partial^2 \overline{\theta}_i}{\partial u\, \partial v} = \frac{\partial}{\partial v}\log a p\frac{\partial \overline{\theta}_i}{\partial u} + \frac{\partial}{\partial u}\log b q\frac{\partial \overline{\theta}_i}{\partial v}.$$

From the second of (77) we get

$$\frac{\partial^2 \overline{\theta}_i}{\partial v^2} = -\frac{q}{p}\frac{\partial \log a}{\partial v}\frac{\partial \overline{\theta}_i}{\partial u} + \left(\frac{\partial \log q}{\partial v} - \frac{q}{p}\frac{\partial \log b q}{\partial u} + c q\right)\frac{\partial \overline{\theta}_i}{\partial v} + q\,(c' - c)\frac{\partial \theta_i}{\partial v}.$$

With the aid of (71) and (77) we obtain

$$\frac{\partial^2 \overline{\theta}_i}{\partial u^2} + \frac{\partial^2 \overline{\theta}_i}{\partial v^2} = 2\frac{\partial \log a p}{\partial u}\frac{\partial \overline{\theta}_i}{\partial u} + 2\frac{\partial \log b q}{\partial v}\frac{\partial \overline{\theta}_i}{\partial v} + c'\overline{\theta}_i.$$

Hence the functions $\overline{\theta}_i$ determine a $W_{c'}$ transformation of $\overline{N}$. The coordinates of the transform $\hat{N}$ are of the form

(78) $$\hat{x} = \overline{x} + \overline{p}\frac{\partial \overline{x}}{\partial u} + \overline{q}\frac{\partial \overline{x}}{\partial v},$$

where (cf. I, 68)

$$\frac{\partial \bar{x}}{\partial u}=p\left\{\frac{\partial^2 x}{\partial u^2}+\frac{1}{\varDelta}\left[\frac{\partial x}{\partial u}\left(\frac{\partial \theta_2}{\partial v}\frac{\partial^2\theta_1}{\partial u^2}-\frac{\partial \theta_1}{\partial v}\frac{\partial^2\theta_2}{\partial u^2}\right)\right.\right.$$
$$\left.\left.-\frac{\partial x}{\partial v}\left(\frac{\partial \theta_2}{\partial u}\frac{\partial^2\theta_1}{\partial u^2}-\frac{\partial \theta_1}{\partial u}\frac{\partial^2\theta_2}{\partial u^2}\right)\right]\right\},$$

$$\frac{\partial \bar{x}}{\partial v}=q\left[-\frac{1}{p}\frac{\partial \bar{x}}{\partial u}+c\left(p\frac{\partial x}{\partial u}+q\frac{\partial x}{\partial v}\right)\right],$$

and

$$(79)\quad\begin{cases}\bar{p}=\dfrac{1}{\bar{\varDelta}}\left(\bar{\theta}_3\dfrac{\partial \bar{\theta}_4}{\partial v}-\bar{\theta}_4\dfrac{\partial \bar{\theta}_3}{\partial v}\right), \qquad \bar{q}=\dfrac{1}{\bar{\varDelta}}\left(\bar{\theta}_4\dfrac{\partial \bar{\theta}_3}{\partial u}-\bar{\theta}_3\dfrac{\partial \bar{\theta}_4}{\partial u}\right),\\[2ex] \bar{\varDelta}=\left(\dfrac{\partial \bar{\theta}_4}{\partial u}\dfrac{\partial \bar{\theta}_3}{\partial v}-\dfrac{\partial \bar{\theta}_4}{\partial v}\dfrac{\partial \bar{\theta}_3}{\partial u}\right).\end{cases}$$

From (77) and (63) we have

$$(80)\quad\begin{cases}\bar{\varDelta}=q\left[(c'-c)\left(\theta_3\dfrac{\partial \bar{\theta}_4}{\partial u}-\theta_4\dfrac{\partial \bar{\theta}_3}{\partial u}\right)+c\left(\bar{\theta}_3\dfrac{\partial \bar{\theta}_4}{\partial u}-\bar{\theta}_4\dfrac{\partial \bar{\theta}_3}{\partial u}\right)\right]\\[2ex] \quad=\dfrac{pq}{\varDelta}\left\{c'\left[\left(\dfrac{\partial \theta_2}{\partial u}\dfrac{\partial \theta_1}{\partial v}-\dfrac{\partial \theta_2}{\partial v}\dfrac{\partial \theta_1}{\partial u}\right)\left(\theta_3\dfrac{\partial^2\theta_4}{\partial u^2}-\theta_4\dfrac{\partial^2\theta_3}{\partial u^2}\right)\right.\right.\\[2ex] \qquad+\left(\theta_3\dfrac{\partial \theta_4}{\partial u}-\theta_4\dfrac{\partial \theta_3}{\partial u}\right)\left(\dfrac{\partial \theta_2}{\partial v}\dfrac{\partial^2\theta_1}{\partial u^2}-\dfrac{\partial \theta_1}{\partial v}\dfrac{\partial^2\theta_2}{\partial u^2}\right)\\[2ex] \qquad\left.-\left(\theta_3\dfrac{\partial \theta_4}{\partial v}-\theta_4\dfrac{\partial \theta_3}{\partial v}\right)\left(\dfrac{\partial \theta_2}{\partial u}\dfrac{\partial^2\theta_1}{\partial u^2}-\dfrac{\partial \theta_1}{\partial u}\dfrac{\partial^2\theta_2}{\partial u^2}\right)\right]\\[2ex] \qquad+c\left[\left(\dfrac{\partial \theta_4}{\partial u}\dfrac{\partial \theta_3}{\partial v}-\dfrac{\partial \theta_4}{\partial v}\dfrac{\partial \theta_3}{\partial u}\right)\left(\theta_1\dfrac{\partial^2\theta_2}{\partial u^2}-\theta_2\dfrac{\partial^2\theta_1}{\partial u^2}\right)\right.\\[2ex] \qquad+\left(\theta_1\dfrac{\partial \theta_2}{\partial u}-\theta_2\dfrac{\partial \theta_1}{\partial u}\right)\left(\dfrac{\partial \theta_4}{\partial v}\dfrac{\partial^2\theta_3}{\partial u^2}-\dfrac{\partial \theta_3}{\partial v}\dfrac{\partial^2\theta_4}{\partial u^2}\right)\\[2ex] \qquad\left.\left.-\left(\theta_1\dfrac{\partial \theta_2}{\partial v}-\theta_2\dfrac{\partial \theta_1}{\partial v}\right)\left(\dfrac{\partial \theta_4}{\partial u}\dfrac{\partial^2\theta_3}{\partial u^2}-\dfrac{\partial \theta_3}{\partial u}\dfrac{\partial^2\theta_4}{\partial u^2}\right)\right]\right\}\end{cases}$$

By means of the above formulas equation (78) is reducible to

$$\begin{aligned}\hat{x} &= x + q\frac{c'-c}{\bar{\Delta}}\left\{\left(p\frac{\partial x}{\partial u}+q\frac{\partial x}{\partial v}\right)\left(\theta_3\frac{\partial\bar{\theta}_4}{\partial u}-\theta_4\frac{\partial\bar{\theta}_3}{\partial u}\right)+(\bar{\theta}_3\,\theta_4-\bar{\theta}_4\,\theta_3)\frac{\partial\bar{x}}{\partial u}\right\}\\
&= x+\frac{c'-c}{\Delta\bar{\Delta}}pq\left\{\frac{\partial x}{\partial u}\left[\left(\theta_1\frac{\partial\theta_2}{\partial v}-\theta_2\frac{\partial\theta_1}{\partial v}\right)\left(\theta_3\frac{\partial^2\theta_4}{\partial u^2}-\theta_4\frac{\partial^2\theta_3}{\partial u^2}\right)\right.\right.\\
&\quad\left.-\left(\theta_3\frac{\partial\theta_4}{\partial v}-\theta_4\frac{\partial\theta_3}{\partial v}\right)\left(\theta_1\frac{\partial^2\theta_2}{\partial u^2}-\theta_2\frac{\partial^2\theta_1}{\partial u^2}\right)\right]\\
&\quad-\frac{\partial x}{\partial v}\left[\left(\theta_1\frac{\partial\theta_2}{\partial u}-\theta_2\frac{\partial\theta_1}{\partial u}\right)\left(\theta_3\frac{\partial^2\theta_4}{\partial u^2}-\theta_4\frac{\partial^2\theta_3}{\partial u^2}\right)\right.\\
&\quad\left.-\left(\theta_3\frac{\partial\theta_4}{\partial u}-\theta_4\frac{\partial\theta_3}{\partial u}\right)\left(\theta_1\frac{\partial^2\theta_2}{\partial u^2}-\theta_2\frac{\partial^2\theta_1}{\partial u^2}\right)\right]\\
&\quad+\frac{\partial^2 x}{\partial u^2}\left[\left(\theta_1\frac{\partial\theta_2}{\partial v}-\theta_2\frac{\partial\theta_1}{\partial v}\right)\left(\theta_4\frac{\partial\theta_3}{\partial u}-\theta_3\frac{\partial\theta_4}{\partial u}\right)\right.\\
&\quad\left.\left.-\left(\theta_1\frac{\partial\theta_2}{\partial u}-\theta_2\frac{\partial\theta_1}{\partial u}\right)\left(\theta_4\frac{\partial\theta_3}{\partial v}-\theta_3\frac{\partial\theta_4}{\partial v}\right)\right]\right\}.\end{aligned}$$

In consequence of (80) this expression is symmetrical in c and c', and the pairs of functions θ_1, θ_2 and θ_3, θ_4. Hence the net $\hat{N}$ can be obtained also by applying to N the $W_{c'}$ transformation determined by θ_3 and θ_4, and then to the resulting net $\bar{\bar{N}}$ the transformation determined by the functions

$$\bar{\theta}_i = \theta_i + \frac{\left(\theta_4\frac{\partial\theta_3}{\partial v}-\theta_3\frac{\partial\theta_4}{\partial v}\right)\frac{\partial\theta_i}{\partial u}-\left(\theta_4\frac{\partial\theta_3}{\partial u}-\theta_3\frac{\partial\theta_4}{\partial u}\right)\frac{\partial\theta_i}{\partial v}}{\frac{\partial\theta_3}{\partial u}\frac{\partial\theta_4}{\partial v}-\frac{\partial\theta_3}{\partial v}\frac{\partial\theta_4}{\partial u}}\quad(i=1,2),$$

which are analogous to (76).

If $c'=c$, the net $\hat{N}$ coincides with N. Hence if a net $\bar{N}$ is a W_c transform of N by means of functions θ_1 and θ_2, solutions of (60) and (72), and θ_3 and θ_4 are two other solutions linearly independent of θ_1 and θ_2, the functions (76) determine N as a W_c transform of $\bar{N}$.

When $c' \neq c$, we have that $\hat{N}$ is a $W_{c'}$ transform of $\bar{N}$ and a W_c transform of $\bar{\bar{N}}$. Hence:

If N is an R net, and N_1 and N_2 are obtained from N by transformations W_{c_1} and W_{c_2}, there can be found directly an R net N_{12} which is a W_{c_2} transform of N_1 and a W_{c_1} transform of N_2[37]).

Exercises.

1. If x_i $(i = 1, 2, 3, 4)$ satisfy equations of the form (9), from the first of (10) and the first and fourth of (4) it follows that x_1, x_2, x_3 satisfy an equation of the form (1) with equal invariants. Hence the projection from a point upon any plane of the asymptotic lines of a surface is a plane net with equal point invariants. Koenigs, Comptes Rendus, vol. 114 (1892), p. 55.

2. If x_1, x_2, x_3 are the coordinates of a planar net satisfying equations (2) and

$$\frac{\partial^2 \theta}{\partial u \partial v} = \frac{\partial \log \sigma}{\partial v}\frac{\partial \theta}{\partial u} + \frac{\partial \log \sigma}{\partial u}\frac{\partial \theta}{\partial v},$$

the equations

$$\frac{\partial y_1}{\partial u} = \frac{1}{\sigma^2}\left(x_2\frac{\partial x_3}{\partial u} - x_3\frac{\partial x_2}{\partial u}\right), \qquad \frac{\partial y_1}{\partial v} = -\frac{1}{\sigma^2}\left(x_2\frac{\partial x_3}{\partial v} - x_3\frac{\partial x_2}{\partial v}\right)$$

are consistent. In like manner we obtain by quadratures two functions y_2 and y_3 by permuting the subscripts of the x's cyclicly. Show that the function

$$x_4 = x_1 y_1 + x_2 y_2 + x_3 y_3$$

satisfies equations (2). Hence x_i $(i = 1, 2, 3, 4)$ are the coordinates of a surface S referred to its asymptotic lines. Annals, vol. 18 (1917), p. 224.

3. The functions $y_1, y_2, y_3, -1$ in Ex. 2 are the homogeneous point coordinates of the asymptotic lines of a surface which is the polar reciprocal of S with respect to the quadric $x_1^2 + x_2^2 + x_3^2 + x_4^2 = 0$. Annals, l. c., p. 225.

4. A necessary and sufficient condition that the surface S whose coordinates satisfy (9) be a ruled surface is that $a_2 = 0$ or $b_1 = 0$; in this case the curves $u =$ const. or $v =$ const. are straight lines.

5. If in accordance with the first of (10) we put $a_1 = 2\frac{\partial \log \lambda}{\partial u}$, $b_2 = 2\frac{\partial \log \lambda}{\partial v}$, then the coordinates $\bar{x}^i = x^i/\lambda$ satisfy equations of the form

$$\frac{\partial^2 \theta}{\partial u^2} = b_1 \frac{\partial \theta}{\partial v} + c_1 \theta, \qquad \frac{\partial^2 \theta}{\partial v^2} = a_2 \frac{\partial \theta}{\partial u} + c_2 \theta$$

called by Wilczynski the *canonical form* of (9). Trans., vol. 8 (1907), p. 247.

6. Let S be a ruled surface for which $u =$ const. are the straight lines and the equations are in the canonical form (Ex. 5). Now $a_2 = 0$, and from (10) we have $\frac{\partial c_2}{\partial u} = 0$. The tangents to the curved asymptotic lines at points of a generator $u =$ const. form a ruled surface R_u whose coordinates are given by

$$y = wx + \frac{\partial x}{\partial u}.$$

---

37) Annals, l. c., p. 172.

It is readily found that the y's satisfy the equations

$$\frac{\partial^2 y}{\partial v^2} = c_2 y, \qquad \frac{\partial^2 y}{\partial w^2} = 0.$$

Hence R_u is a quadric, which osculates S along the given generator.

7. If two surfaces S and $\bar{S}$ in 3-space are so related that each net on $\bar{S}$ is a radial transform of a net on S, then

$$\bar{x}^{(i)} = \frac{x^{(i)}}{\sum_j a_j x^{(j)} + d},$$

where a_j, d are constants.

8. If two parallel nets in 3-space have areas preserved, the total curvature is the same at corresponding points.

Guichard, Comptes Rendus, vol. 136, p. 151.

9. The focal points of a ray congruence are given by $\lambda x_{-1} + \mu x_1$, where $K\lambda^2 + R\lambda\mu - rH\mu^2 = 0$; they are the intersections of the lines of the congruence and the tangents to the curves

$$K\,du^2 + R\,du\,dv - rH\,dv^2 = 0.$$

10. A necessary and sufficient condition that the tangents to the ray curves of a net N pass through the corresponding focal points of the ray congruence is that N have equal point invariants.

Green, Amer. Journ., vol. 38 (1916), p. 313.

11. Let N be a net with equal points invariants on a surface S and N_0 its associate net on a surface S_0 (§ 25); also let Σ and Σ_0 be the surfaces corresponding with orthogonality of linear elements to S and S_0 as determined by N_0 and N respectively [§ 157]. If N_1 is a K transform of N, it is possible to place the associate, N_{10}, of N_1 so that N_0 and N_{10} are in relation K (II. Ex. 18). These nets determine surfaces Σ_1 and Σ_{10} corresponding to S_1 and S_{10} by orthogonality of linear elements. Show that the pairs of surfaces Σ, Σ_1; Σ, Σ_0; Σ_{10}, Σ_0 and Σ_{10} Σ_1 are the focal surfaces of W congruences; that is the K transformation from N into N_1 determines a quatern of W congruences. Trans., vol. 15 (1914), p. 415.

12. Four nets N, N_1, N_2, N_{12} forming a quatern under transformations K determine twelve W congruences, forming six quaterns. Trans. l. c., p. 416.

13. The focal nets of the congruence of normals to a surface of constant curvature are R nets. Tzitzeica, Comptes Rendus, vol. 152 (1911), p. 1078.

14. The lines of curvature of a surface of constant curvature and the normals to the surface are in relation θ_1. Demoulin, Comptes Rendus, vol. 153 (1911), p. 798.

15. An isothermal orthogonal system on a sphere and the normals to the minimal surface, whose lines of curvature admit this system for spherical representation, are in relation θ_1. Demoulin, l. c.

16. An R net N admits ∞^4 parallel nets determining congruences G of transformations F of N into R nets N_1; when such a parallel net is known, each solution θ of equations (60) and (74) defines a transform N_1.

Annals, vol. 22 (1921), p. 176.

17. If N is an R net, and N_1 and N_2 are two F transforms of N by means of functions θ_1 and θ_2 which are solutions of equations (60) and (74) for the same constant c, all of the ∞^2 nets N_{12} which are F transforms of N_1 and N_2 (§ 21) are R nets and their determination requires two quadratures; when the constant c in (74) is different for θ_1 and θ_2, there is a unique net N_{12} which is an R net and it can be found without quadratures. Annals, vol. 22 (1921), p. 178.

18. If $\bar{N}$ is a W transform of an R net N by means of solutions θ_1 and θ_2 of equations (60) and (74), and N_3 is an R net, which is an F transform of N by means of a solution θ_3 of (60) and (74) with c replaced by c', there can be found directly a unique net $\bar{N}_3$ which is a W transform of N_3 and an F transform of $\bar{N}$; when $c = c'$, there are ∞^2 such nets $\bar{N}_3$ obtained by two quadratures. Annals, vol. 22 (1921), p. 181.

19. From the equation (15) of a net $N(x)$ on a surface S it follows that the point of coordinates $z = \frac{\partial^2 x}{\partial u^2} + \frac{a'}{r}\frac{\partial x}{\partial u}$ lies on the intersection l of the osculating planes of the curves of N at the corresponding point. This line generates a congruence whose focal points are determined by functions λ and μ such that $d(\lambda x + \mu z)$ is a linear function of x and z. Proceeding as in § 44, we show that the developables of the congruence are determined by the equation

$$\text{(i)} \qquad r C_1\, du^2 + R\, du\, dv - r\left(B_2 + \frac{\partial}{\partial v}\left(\frac{a'}{r}\right)\right) dv^2 = 0,$$

where R is given by (27). The curves on S defined by (i) are called the *axis curves* and the congruence the *axis congruence* of N. By means of (22) equation (i) may be written

$$\text{(ii)} \qquad r C_1\, du^2 + R\, du\, dv - r\left(H - K + r C_1 - \frac{\partial^2}{\partial u\, \partial v} \log r\right) dv^2 = 0.$$

Wilczynski, Trans., vol. 16 (1915), p. 316;
Green, Amer. Journ., vol. 38 (1916), p. 308.

20. A necessary and sufficient condition that the axis curves form a conjugate system is

$$H - K - \frac{\partial^2}{\partial u\, \partial v} \log r = 0.$$

Green, l. c., p. 311.

21. When a net has equal point invariants and is isothermal-conjugate, the ray curves and the axis curves form nets; and conversely.

Green, l. c., p. 321.

22. When a net is subjected to a polar reciprocation the axis and ray congruences are interchanged. Wilczynski, l. c., p. 317.

23. Show that at any point on a surface S the tangents to the two systems of curves defined by the equations

$$a_1\, du^2 + 2 b_1\, du\, dv + c_1\, dv^2 = 0,$$
$$a_2\, du^2 + 2 b_2\, du\, dv + c_2\, dv^2 = 0,$$

are separated harmonically by the tangents to the curves of the system defined by

$$\begin{vmatrix} a_1\,du + b_1\,dv, & b_1\,du + c_1\,dv \\ a_2\,du + b_2\,dv, & b_2\,du + c_2\,dv \end{vmatrix} = 0.$$

24. If the parametric curves on a surface S form a net N with equations (1) and (15), the curves defined by

$$du^2 - r\,dv^2 = 0$$

form a net, whose tangents at a point separate harmonically the tangents of N and the asymptotic tangents.

25. A necessary and sufficient condition that a net $N(x)$ on a surface be isothermal-conjugate, that is $\frac{\partial^2}{\partial u\,\partial v}\log r = 0$, is that the tangents to the axis curves, the curves defined by Ex. 24 and the curves defined by $H\,du^2 - R\,du\,dv - rK\,dv^2 = 0$ be pairs of the same involution, provided that the double lines of the involution are not the tangents of the net.

Green, Amer. Journ., vol. 38 (1916), p. 323.
Wilczynski, Amer. Journ., vol. 42 (1920), p. 216.

Chapter V.

Transformations Ω. W Congruences.

51. Tangential coordinates of a net. Laplace transforms in tangential coordinates. In [§ 84] we found that a necessary and sufficient condition that the parametric curves on a surface in 3-space form a net is that the tangential coordinates X, Y, Z, W satisfy a Laplace equation

$$\frac{\partial^2 \lambda}{\partial u \partial v} = \frac{\partial \log \alpha}{\partial v} \frac{\partial \lambda}{\partial u} + \frac{\partial \log \beta}{\partial u} \frac{\partial \lambda}{\partial v} + \gamma \lambda. \tag{1}$$

From [22, § 66] and [34, § 67] it follows that the tangential coordinates satisfy also the equation

$$\frac{\partial^2 \lambda}{\partial v^2} = r \frac{\partial^2 \lambda}{\partial u^2} + \alpha' \frac{\partial \lambda}{\partial u} + \beta' \frac{\partial \lambda}{\partial v} + \gamma' \lambda, \tag{2}$$

where in terms of the spherical representation of the net

$$r = \frac{D''}{D}, \quad \alpha' = \begin{Bmatrix} 22 \\ 1 \end{Bmatrix}' - r \begin{Bmatrix} 11 \\ 1 \end{Bmatrix}', \quad \beta' = \begin{Bmatrix} 22 \\ 2 \end{Bmatrix}' - r \begin{Bmatrix} 11 \\ 2 \end{Bmatrix}'. \tag{3}$$

Conversely, if two equations of the form (1) and (2) admit four linearly independent solutions, the latter may be taken as the tangential coordinates of a net N, whose homogeneous point coordinates x, y, z, w are given directly by the equations

$$\sum X x = 0, \quad \sum \frac{\partial X}{\partial u} x = 0, \quad \sum \frac{\partial X}{\partial v} x = 0. \tag{4}$$

We have also the following theorem analogous to the third theorem of § 43:

Any four linearly independent solutions of equations (1) *and* (2) *are the tangential coordinates of a net which is a projective transform of the given net N.*

We call (1) the *tangential equation* of the net N. If this equation has equal invariants, we say that the net has *equal tangential* invariants.

The homogeneous point coordinates x, y, z, w and the tangential coordinates X, Y, Z, W of a net in 3-space, satisfy respectively equations (IV, 1) and (1), and also the relations (IV, 5). If the second and third of the latter be differentiated with respect to u and v, we have accordingly

$$(5)\qquad \begin{cases} \sum X\dfrac{\partial^2 x}{\partial u^2}+\sum\dfrac{\partial X}{\partial u}\dfrac{\partial x}{\partial u}=0, \\ \sum\dfrac{\partial X}{\partial u}\dfrac{\partial x}{\partial v}=0, \quad \sum\dfrac{\partial X}{\partial v}\dfrac{\partial x}{\partial u}=0, \\ \sum X\dfrac{\partial^2 x}{\partial v^2}+\sum\dfrac{\partial X}{\partial v}\dfrac{\partial x}{\partial v}=0. \end{cases}$$

From the first and last of (5) we have in consequence of (IV, 5)

$$(6)\qquad \sum\frac{\partial X}{\partial v}\frac{\partial x}{\partial v}-r\sum\frac{\partial X}{\partial u}\frac{\partial x}{\partial u}=0.$$

When the second and third of (5) are differentiated with respect to v and u respectively, the resulting equations are reducible by means of (1) and (5) to

$$(7)\qquad \begin{cases} \sum\left(\dfrac{\partial X}{\partial u}-\dfrac{\partial\log\beta}{\partial u}X\right)\dfrac{\partial^2 x}{\partial v^2}=0, \\ \sum\left(\dfrac{\partial X}{\partial v}-\dfrac{\partial\log\alpha}{\partial v}X\right)\dfrac{\partial^2 x}{\partial u^2}=0. \end{cases}$$

The minus first and first Laplace transforms of equation (1) are given by

$$(8)\qquad X_{-1}=\frac{\partial X}{\partial u}-\frac{\partial\log\beta}{\partial u}X, \qquad X_1=\frac{\partial X}{\partial v}-\frac{\partial\log\alpha}{\partial v}X.$$

From § 30, (5) and (7) we have

$$\sum X_{-1} x_1 = 0, \qquad \sum X_1 x_{-1} = 0,$$

$$\sum X_{-1} \frac{\partial x_1}{\partial u} = 0, \qquad \sum X_1 \frac{\partial x_{-1}}{\partial u} = 0,$$

$$\sum X_{-1} \frac{\partial x_1}{\partial v} = 0, \qquad \sum X_1 \frac{\partial x_{-1}}{\partial v} = 0.$$

Hence we have the theorem:

When the Laplace transformations are applied to the tangential coordinates of a net N, the resulting functions are the tangential coordinates of the Laplace transforms of N, but in opposite sense.

52. Transformations F in tangential coordinates. Since the analytical processes of § 37 are independent of their geometrical interpretation, it follows that if λ is a solution of (1) and μ a solution of its adjoint, namely

$$(9) \qquad \frac{\partial^2 \mu}{\partial u \partial v} = -\frac{\partial \log \alpha}{\partial v}\frac{\partial \mu}{\partial u} - \frac{\partial \log \beta}{\partial u}\frac{\partial \mu}{\partial v} + \left(\gamma - \frac{\partial^2}{\partial u \partial v}\log \alpha\beta\right)\mu,$$

there exist two functions $\bar{\tau}$ and $\bar{\sigma}$, defined to within additive constants by

$$(10) \qquad \begin{cases} \dfrac{\partial \bar{\tau}}{\partial u} = \lambda\mu \dfrac{\partial}{\partial u}\log \mu\beta, & \dfrac{\partial \bar{\tau}}{\partial v} = \lambda\mu \dfrac{\partial}{\partial v}\log \dfrac{\lambda}{\alpha}, \\[2ex] \dfrac{\partial \bar{\sigma}}{\partial u} = -\lambda\mu \dfrac{\partial}{\partial u}\log \dfrac{\lambda}{\beta}, & \dfrac{\partial \bar{\sigma}}{\partial v} = -\lambda\mu \dfrac{\partial}{\partial v}\log \mu\alpha. \end{cases}$$

Consider now a net N with tangential coordinates X, Y, Z, W satisfying (1). Then the functions X_1, Y_1, Z_1, W_1, given by quadratures of the form

$$(11) \qquad \frac{\partial X_1}{\partial u} = \bar{\tau}\frac{\partial}{\partial u}\left(\frac{X}{\lambda}\right), \qquad \frac{\partial X_1}{\partial v} = \bar{\sigma}\frac{\partial}{\partial v}\left(\frac{X}{\lambda}\right),$$

(which are consistent in consequence of (10)) satisfy the equation

$$(12) \qquad \frac{\partial^2 \lambda_1}{\partial u \partial v} + \frac{\bar{\sigma}}{\bar{\tau}}\frac{\partial}{\partial v}\log\frac{\lambda}{\alpha}\frac{\partial \lambda_1}{\partial u} + \frac{\bar{\tau}}{\bar{\sigma}}\frac{\partial}{\partial u}\log\frac{\lambda}{\beta}\frac{\partial \lambda_1}{\partial v} = 0,$$

and consequently are tangential coordinates of a net N_1. It is our purpose to show that N and N_1 are in the relation F, and furthermore to find λ in terms of the functions defining the transformation F, when N and N_1 are given in terms of homogeneous point coordinates, x and x_1.

On the supposition that N and N_1 are in the relation F, their homogeneous point coordinates are related as in (III, 65). Necessarily we must have

$$\sum x_1 \frac{\partial X_1}{\partial u} = 0, \qquad \sum x_1 \frac{\partial X_1}{\partial v} = 0, \tag{13}$$

which in consequence of (III, 65) and (11) lead to

$$\frac{\partial \log \lambda}{\partial u} = \frac{\sum y \frac{\partial X}{\partial u}}{\sum y X}, \qquad \frac{\partial \log \lambda}{\partial v} = \frac{\sum y \frac{\partial X}{\partial v}}{\sum y X}.$$

From (III, 60, 65) it follows that

$$\sum X \frac{\partial y}{\partial u} = 0, \qquad \sum X \frac{\partial y}{\partial v} = 0.$$

Hence, to within a constant factor, the integral of the above equations is

$$\lambda = \sum y X.$$

In consequence of (5) we have by differentiation

$$\frac{\partial \lambda}{\partial u} = \sum y \frac{\partial X}{\partial u}, \quad \frac{\partial \lambda}{\partial v} = \sum y \frac{\partial X}{\partial v}, \quad \frac{\partial^2 \lambda}{\partial u \partial v} = \sum y \frac{\partial^2 X}{\partial u \partial v},$$

so that λ is a solution of (1). From (III, 65) it follows that

$$\lambda = \sum y X = \sum z X. \tag{14}$$

The analogues of equations (III, 65) are

$$\overline{X}_1 = X_1 - \tau \frac{X}{\lambda}, \qquad \overline{X}_2 = X_1 - \sigma \frac{X}{\lambda}. \tag{15}$$

These functions $\overline{X}_1$ and $\overline{X}_2$ satisfy the equations

$$(16)\quad \begin{cases} \dfrac{\partial \overline{X}_1}{\partial u} = -X\mu\dfrac{\partial}{\partial u}\log \mu\beta, & \dfrac{\partial \overline{X}_1}{\partial v} = -X\mu\dfrac{\partial}{\partial v}\log\dfrac{X}{\alpha}, \\ \dfrac{\partial \overline{X}_2}{\partial u} = X\mu\dfrac{\partial}{\partial u}\log\dfrac{X}{\beta}, & \dfrac{\partial \overline{X}_2}{\partial v} = X\mu\dfrac{\partial}{\partial v}\log \mu\alpha. \end{cases}$$

We must have also

$$(17)\qquad \sum X_1\frac{\partial x_1}{\partial u} = 0, \qquad \sum X_1\frac{\partial x_1}{\partial v} = 0,$$

which by means of (III, 60) and (15) are reducible to

$$\frac{\partial \log\theta}{\partial u} = \frac{\sum \overline{X}_1\dfrac{\partial x}{\partial u}}{\sum \overline{X}_1 x}, \qquad \frac{\partial \log\theta}{\partial v} = \frac{\sum \overline{X}_1\dfrac{\partial x}{\partial v}}{\sum \overline{X}_1 x}.$$

From these we find that we may take

$$(18)\qquad \theta = \sum \overline{X}_1 x = \sum \overline{X}_2 x.$$

Moreover, this expression for θ satisfies equation (III, 1).

As a consequence of (13) and (17) we have that $\sum X_1 x_1$ is a constant. However, we wish it to be equal to zero. Substituting from (III, 65) and (15), we find with the aid of (14) and (18) that this is accomplished, if the additive constants of integration of $\overline{\tau}$ and $\overline{\sigma}$ are chosen so that

$$(19)\qquad \begin{cases} \tau + \overline{\tau} - \sum y\overline{X}_1 = 0, \\ \sigma + \overline{\sigma} - \sum z\overline{X}_2 = 0. \end{cases}$$

Thus we have established that the net N_1 whose tangential coordinates are given by (11) is in the relation F with N. Moreover, when the transformation is given in point coordinates, the functions λ and μ follow from (14), (11) and (10); and conversely, when the transformation is defined in terms of tangential coordinates.

In consequence of (III, 65) and (15) the expressions for λ and θ can be given also the forms

$$(20)\qquad \lambda = \sum X x_1, \qquad \theta = \sum X_1 x.$$

By making use of the results of § 39, we can obtain the equations of the theorem of permutability of transformations F from the standpoint of tangential coordinates. The functions λ_{12} and λ_{21} must satisfy

$$\frac{\partial \lambda_{ij}}{\partial u} = \bar{\tau}_i \frac{\partial}{\partial u}\left(\frac{\lambda_j}{\lambda_i}\right), \qquad \frac{\partial \lambda_{ij}}{\partial v} = \bar{\sigma}_i \frac{\partial}{\partial v}\left(\frac{\lambda_j}{\lambda_i}\right) \quad (i,j = 1, 2,\ i \neq j).$$

The functions $\bar{\sigma}_{12}$, $\bar{\sigma}_{21}$, $\bar{\tau}_{12}$, $\bar{\tau}_{21}$ are given by

$$(21) \qquad \begin{cases} \bar{\tau}_1 \bar{\tau}_{12} = \bar{\tau}_2 \bar{\tau}_{21} = \dfrac{\lambda_2 \lambda_{21} \bar{\tau}_1}{\lambda_1} + \dfrac{\lambda_1 \lambda_{12} \bar{\tau}_2}{\lambda_2} - \lambda_{12}\lambda_{21}, \\ \bar{\sigma}_1 \bar{\sigma}_{12} = \bar{\sigma}_2 \bar{\sigma}_{21} = \dfrac{\lambda_2 \lambda_{21} \bar{\sigma}_1}{\lambda_1} + \dfrac{\lambda_1 \lambda_{12} \bar{\sigma}_2}{\lambda_2} - \lambda_{12}\lambda_{21}, \end{cases}$$

and the tangential coordinates X_{12} of N_{12} are of the form

$$(22) \qquad \lambda_1 \lambda_{12} X_{12} = \lambda_2 \lambda_{21} X_1 + \lambda_1 \lambda_{12} X_2 - \lambda_{12} \lambda_{21} X.$$

If equations similar to (20) are to be satisfied, we must have

$$(23) \qquad \begin{cases} \lambda_{12} = \sum X_1 x_{12} = \sum X_1 x_2 - \theta_{21}, \\ \lambda_{21} = \sum X_2 x_{12} = \sum X_2 x_1 - \theta_{12}. \end{cases}$$

When these equations are differentiated, we find that the resulting equations are satisfied in virtue of the preceding formulas. Also we find that x_{12}, given by (III; 76), and X_{12} given by (22) satisfy the condition $\sum X_{12}\, x_{12} = 0$. Hence we may take λ_{12} and λ_{21} as just given.

Equations similar to (III, 65) and (15) are

$$\begin{aligned} y_{ij} &= x_{ij} - \frac{\tau_{ij}}{\theta_{ij}} x_i, & z_{ij} &= x_{ij} - \frac{\sigma_{ij}}{\theta_{ij}} x_i, \\ \bar{X}_{1,ij} &= X_{ij} - \frac{\bar{\tau}_{ij}}{\lambda_{ij}} X_i, & \bar{X}_{2,ij} &= X_{ij} - \frac{\bar{\sigma}_{ij}}{\lambda_{ij}} X_i, \end{aligned} \qquad (i,j = 1, 2,\ i \neq j).$$

From these equations, (20) and (23) we obtain

$$\sum \bar{X}_{1,ij}\, y_{ij} - \tau_{ij} - \bar{\tau}_{ij} = 0, \qquad \sum \bar{X}_{2,ij}\, z_{ij} - \sigma_{ij} - \bar{\sigma}_{ij} = 0.$$

Consequently when λ_{12} and λ_{21} have the values (23), the expressions (22) are the tangential coordinates of N_{12}, whose point coordinates are given by (III, 76). From the form of (22) we are led at once to the theorem of § 23, namely:

When N, N_1, N_2 aud N_{12} form a quatern under transformations F four corresponding tangent planes meet in a point.

When the point coordinates are cartesian, we make use of the preceding results by taking $w = -1$, and assuming that X Y, Z are direction-cosines. Then we have

$$Xx + Yy + Zz = W, \tag{24}$$

so that W is the distance of the tangent plane from the origin.

From (III, 60) and (II, 20) we have in this case $w_1 = \theta'/\theta$ and x_1 in the formulas of Chapter 3 must be replaced by $-x_1\theta'/\theta$, so as to obtain formulas of Chapter 2. From these results, (II, 2) and (20) we have $\lambda = \sum Xx'$ [38]), so that λ is the distance from the origin to the tangent plane to the net N' determining the conjugate congruence of the transformation. If we call it w and denote by w^{-1} the corresponding tangential coordinate of N_1', parallel to N_1, and determining the same congruence, we have

$$\lambda = \sum Xx' = w, \qquad \sum X_1 x_1' = w^{-1}, \tag{25}$$

where X_1, Y_1, Z_1 are the direction-cosines of the normal to N_1. If W_1 denotes the other tangential coordinate of N_1, we can write (11) in the form

$$\left\{\begin{aligned} \frac{\partial}{\partial u}\left(\frac{X_1}{w^{-1}}\right) &= \bar{\tau}\frac{\partial}{\partial u}\left(\frac{X}{w}\right), & \frac{\partial}{\partial v}\left(\frac{X_1}{w^{-1}}\right) &= \bar{\sigma}\frac{\partial}{\partial v}\left(\frac{X}{w}\right),\\ \frac{\partial}{\partial u}\left(\frac{W_1}{w^{-1}}\right) &= \bar{\tau}\frac{\partial}{\partial u}\left(\frac{W}{w}\right), & \frac{\partial}{\partial v}\left(\frac{W_1}{w^{-1}}\right) &= \bar{\sigma}\frac{\partial}{\partial v}\left(\frac{W}{w}\right).\end{aligned}\right. \tag{26}$$

In this case equations (15) become

$$\bar{X}_1 = \frac{X_1}{w^{-1}} - \bar{\tau}\frac{X}{w}, \qquad \bar{X}_2 = \frac{X_1}{w^{-1}} - \bar{\sigma}\frac{X}{w}. \tag{27}$$

---

[38]) When we are dealing with cartesian coordinates, the symbol Σ denotes the sum of the terms in x, y and z.

From these expressions it follows that if ε denotes the angle between the tangent planes of N and N_1, a necessary and sufficient condition that the harmonic congruence of the transformation be normal is that

$$(28)\qquad (w^{-1})^2\overline{\tau}\overline{\sigma} - w w^{-1}\cos\varepsilon(\overline{\tau}+\overline{\sigma}) + w^2 = 0.$$

53. Transformations Ω of nets with equal tangential invariants. From (15) it follows that a necessary and sufficient condition that the focal planes of the harmonic congruence of the transformation be harmonic with respect to the tangent planes to N and N_1 is that (cf. V, Ex. 8)

$$\overline{\tau}+\overline{\sigma} = 0.$$

In this case we have from (10)

$$\frac{\partial}{\partial u}\log\frac{\lambda}{\mu} = 2\frac{\partial}{\partial u}\log\beta, \qquad \frac{\partial}{\partial v}\log\frac{\lambda}{\mu} = 2\frac{\partial}{\partial v}\log\alpha.$$

Recalling that α and β are determined only to within factors which are respectively functions of u alone and v alone, we see that in all generality the tangential equation (1) can in this case be written

$$(29)\qquad \frac{\partial^2\lambda}{\partial u\,\partial v} + \frac{\partial\log\sqrt{\varrho}}{\partial v}\frac{\partial\lambda}{\partial u} + \frac{\partial\log\sqrt{\varrho}}{\partial u}\frac{\partial\lambda}{\partial v} + \gamma\lambda = 0.$$

If we put $\mu = -2\varrho w$, w being the solution of (29) determining the transformation, equations (10) can be integrated in the form

$$(30)\qquad \overline{\tau} = -\overline{\sigma} = -\varrho w^2.$$

Now the tangential equation of N_1 is

$$(31)\qquad \frac{\partial^2\lambda_1}{\partial u\,\partial v} - \frac{\partial}{\partial v}\log\sqrt{\varrho w}\,\frac{\partial\lambda_1}{\partial u} - \frac{\partial}{\partial u}\log\sqrt{\varrho w}\,\frac{\partial\lambda_1}{\partial v} = 0.$$

Thus the tangential equations of both N and N_1 have equal invariants. We say that N and N_1 are in the relation of a *transformation* Ω[39]).

[39]) Rendiconti di Palermo, vol. 39 (1915), p. 161; cf. also Demoulin, Bull. Acad. de Belgique, 1919, p. 273.

If we put

$$\vartheta = \lambda \sqrt{\varrho}, \quad \overline{\vartheta} = \frac{\lambda_1}{\sqrt{\varrho w}},$$

equations (29) and (31) are transformed into

$$\frac{\partial^2 \vartheta}{\partial u \partial v} = \left(\frac{1}{\sqrt{\varrho}} \frac{\partial^2 \sqrt{\varrho}}{\partial u \partial v} - \gamma\right) \vartheta, \quad \frac{\partial^2 \overline{\vartheta}}{\partial u \partial v} = \left(\sqrt{\varrho w} \frac{\partial^2}{\partial u \partial v} \frac{1}{\sqrt{\varrho w}}\right) \overline{\vartheta}.$$

These equations are satisfied respectively by

$$(32) \qquad \begin{cases} \nu_1 = \sqrt{\varrho} X, & \nu_2 = \sqrt{\varrho} Y, & \nu_3 = \sqrt{\varrho} Z, \\ \overline{\nu}_1 = \dfrac{X_1}{\sqrt{\varrho w}}, & \overline{\nu}_2 = \dfrac{Y_1}{\sqrt{\varrho w}}, & \overline{\nu}_3 = \dfrac{Z_1}{\sqrt{\varrho w}}. \end{cases}$$

In terms of these functions equations (11) are reducible to

$$(33) \qquad \begin{cases} \dfrac{\partial}{\partial u}(\overline{\nu}_i \vartheta) = -\left(\vartheta \dfrac{\partial \nu_i}{\partial u} - \nu_i \dfrac{\partial \vartheta}{\partial u}\right), \\ \dfrac{\partial}{\partial v}(\overline{\nu}_i \vartheta) = \left(\vartheta \dfrac{\partial \nu_i}{\partial v} - \nu_i \dfrac{\partial \vartheta}{\partial v}\right), \end{cases} \qquad (i = 1, 2, 3).$$

Since N has equal tangential invariants, its spherical representation is the spherical representation also of the asymptotic lines on a surface Σ whose point coordinates, ξ, η, ζ, are given by the Lelieuvre formulas [§ 79], namely

$$\frac{\partial \xi}{\partial u} = \nu_2 \frac{\partial \nu_3}{\partial u} - \nu_3 \frac{\partial \nu_2}{\partial u}, \qquad \frac{\partial \xi}{\partial v} = -\nu_2 \frac{\partial \nu_3}{\partial v} + \nu_3 \frac{\partial \nu_2}{\partial v}.$$

Similar equations in the functions $\overline{\nu}_i$ give the point coordinates ξ_1, μ_1, ζ_1, of a surface Σ_1 with the same spherical representation of its asymptotic lines as the curves of the net N_1. Moreover, equations (33) express the condition that Σ and Σ_1 are the focal surfaces of a W congruence [§ 172]. The surfaces Σ and Σ_1 are associate to the respective nets N and N_1 [§ 155].

From the theory of W congruences [§ 172] it follows that if X, Y, Z and X_1, Y_1, Z_1 are direction-cosines of the normals to Σ and Σ_1, then

(34) $$\nu_1 = \sqrt{\varrho} X, \qquad \overline{\nu}_1 = \sqrt{\varrho_1} X_1,$$

where $-1/\varrho^2$ and $-1/\varrho_1^2$ are the Gaussian total curvatures of Σ and Σ_1 respectively. From these expressions, (26) and (32), we have

(35) $$w^{-1} = \frac{1}{\sqrt{\varrho\varrho_1}\, w}.$$

Hence equations (26) become

(36) $$\begin{cases} \dfrac{\partial}{\partial u}(\sqrt{\varrho\varrho_1} w X_1) = -\varrho w^2 \dfrac{\partial}{\partial u}\left(\dfrac{X}{w}\right), & \dfrac{\partial}{\partial v}(\sqrt{\varrho\varrho_1} w X_1) = \varrho w^2 \dfrac{\partial}{\partial v}\left(\dfrac{X}{w}\right), \\ \dfrac{\partial}{\partial u}(\sqrt{\varrho\varrho_1} w W_1) = -\varrho w^2 \dfrac{\partial}{\partial u}\left(\dfrac{W}{w}\right), & \dfrac{\partial}{\partial v}(\sqrt{\varrho\varrho_1} w W_1) = \varrho w^2 \dfrac{\partial}{\partial v}\left(\dfrac{W}{w}\right), \end{cases}$$

and we have the theorem:

Each solution w of the tangential equation of a net with equal tangential invariants leads by quadratures (36) *to the determination of a net N_1 which is an Ω transform of N.*

From [72, § 172] we have that the coordinates of the surface Σ_1 associate to N_1 are given by equations of the form

(37) $$\xi_1 = \xi + \sqrt{\varrho\varrho_1}(YZ_1 - ZY_1).$$

In [§ 172] it is shown that direction-parameters of the normals to the focal surfaces of any W congruence satisfy equations of the form (33). Since these are of the form (11) with $\overline{\tau} + \overline{\sigma} = 0$, we have

If two nets N and N_1 with equal tangential invariants are in relation F, and if the surfaces Σ and Σ_1 with the same spherical representation of their asymptotic lines as the curves of N and N_1 respectively can be so placed in space that they are the focal surfaces of a W congruence, then N and N_1 are in relation Ω.

54. Theorems of permutability of transformations Ω and of W congruences. Let N be a net with equal tangential invariants, and N_1 and N_2 be Ω transforms of N by means of solutions w_1 and w_2 of equation (1).

The functions w_{12} and w_{21} defined by the quadratures

$$(38)\qquad \begin{cases} \dfrac{\partial}{\partial u}(\sqrt{\varrho\varrho_i}\, w_i\, w_{ij}) = -\varrho w_i^2 \dfrac{\partial}{\partial u}\left(\dfrac{w_j}{w_i}\right), \\ \dfrac{\partial}{\partial v}(\sqrt{\varrho\varrho_i}\, w_i\, w_{ij}) = \varrho w_i^2 \dfrac{\partial}{\partial v}\left(\dfrac{w_j}{w_i}\right), \end{cases} \qquad (i, j = 1, 2, i \neq j)$$

are evidently solutions of the tangential equations of N_1 and N_2 respectively. It is clear that w_{ij} as thus defined is determined to within the additive function $\dfrac{c_i}{\sqrt{\varrho\varrho_i}\, w_i}$. The constants c_i can be chosen so that there are ∞^1 pairs of functions w_{12} and w_{21} satisfying the condition

$$(39)\qquad \sqrt{\varrho\varrho_1}\, w_1 w_{12} + \sqrt{\varrho\varrho_2}\, w_2 w_{21} = 0\,[40].$$

By applying the results of § 52 we shall show that each pair of functions determines a net N_{12} which is an Ω transform of N_1 and N_2. In fact, the tangential coordinates X_{12}, Y_{12}, Z_{12}, W_{12} of N_{12} are given by the following equations analogous to (22):

$$(40)\qquad \sqrt{\varrho_{12}}\, X_{12} = \sqrt{\varrho}\left(X - \frac{w_2}{w_{12}} X_1 - \frac{w_1}{w_{21}} X_2\right),$$

where

$$(41)\qquad \varrho_{12} = \varrho\left(1 + \frac{w_2^2}{w_{12}^2} + \frac{w_1^2}{w_{21}^2} - 2\frac{w_2}{w_{12}}\cos\varepsilon_1 - 2\frac{w_1}{w_{21}}\cos\varepsilon_2 + 2\frac{w_1 w_2}{w_{12} w_{21}}\sum X_1 X_2\right).$$

It is readily shown that, in consequence of (36) and (39), the functions (40) satisfy the equations

$$(42)\qquad \begin{cases} \dfrac{\partial}{\partial u}(\sqrt{\varrho_i\varrho_{ij}}\, w_{ij} X_{12}) = -\varrho_i w_{ij}^2 \dfrac{\partial}{\partial u}\left(\dfrac{X_i}{w_{ij}}\right), \\ \dfrac{\partial}{\partial v}(\sqrt{\varrho_i\varrho_{ij}}\, w_{ij} X_{12}) = \varrho_i w_{ij}^2 \dfrac{\partial}{\partial v}\left(\dfrac{X_i}{w_{ij}}\right), \end{cases} \qquad (i, j = 1, 2, i \neq j).$$

Hence we have established the theorem:

If N has equal tangential invariants, and N_1 and N_2 are two Ω transforms of N, by a quadrature we can find ∞^1 nets N_{12}, which are Ω transforms of N_1 and N_2.

---

[40]) The reason for this choice is to be found in (21).

If Σ, Σ_1 and Σ_2 are the surfaces associate to N, N_1 and N_2 so that Σ and Σ_1 are the focal surfaces of a W congruence, and also Σ and Σ_2, the associate Σ_{12} of a net N_{12} can be so placed in space that Σ_1 and Σ_{12} are focal surfaces of a W congruence, and likewise Σ_2 and Σ_{12}. From equations analogous to (34) and (37) we have for the coordinates, ξ_{12}, η_{12}, ζ_{12}, of Σ_{12}

$$\xi_{12} = \xi - \sqrt{\varrho\varrho_1}\,\frac{w_1}{w_{21}}\,(Y_1 Z_2 - Y_2 Z_1). \tag{43}$$

Hence we have the theorem of Bianchi[41]):

If Σ and Σ_1 are focal surfaces of a W congruence and Σ and Σ_2 of a second W congruence, there can be found by quadratures an infinity of surfaces Σ_{12} such that Σ_1 and Σ_{12} are focal surfaces of a W congruence, and likewise Σ_2 and Σ_{12}.

55. Nets permanent in deformation. When the harmonic congruence of a transformation Ω is normal, the focal planes of the congruence are perpendicular, and consequently the angles between the tangent planes of the nets N and N_1 are bisected by these focal planes. Now from (28), (30) and (35) we have $\varrho = \varrho_1$. Hence:

A necessary and sufficient condition that the harmonic congruence of a transformation Ω be normal is that the associate surfaces Σ and Σ_1 of N and N_1 have the same total curvature at corresponding points; moreover, the focal planes of the congruence bisect the angles between the tangent planes of N and N_1.

If $\varrho = \varrho_1$, we have from (34)

$$\sum \nu_1 \bar{\nu}_1 = \varrho \cos\varepsilon, \qquad \sum \nu_1^2 = \sum \bar{\nu}_1^2 = \varrho. \tag{44}$$

Multiplying the first of (33) by ν_i and summing; and also by $\bar{\nu}_i$ and summing, we get

$$-\sum \nu_i \frac{\partial \bar{\nu}_i}{\partial u} = \frac{1}{2}\frac{\partial \varrho}{\partial u} + \varrho(\cos\varepsilon - 1)\frac{\partial \log \vartheta}{\partial u},$$

$$-\sum \bar{\nu}_i \frac{\partial \nu_i}{\partial u} = \frac{1}{2}\frac{\partial \varrho}{\partial u} + \varrho(1 - \cos\varepsilon)\frac{\partial \log \vartheta}{\partial u}.$$

---

[44]) Lezioni, vol. 2, pp. 71—74.

Adding, we have

$$\frac{\partial}{\partial u}\sum \nu_i \bar{\nu}_i = -\frac{\partial \varrho}{\partial u}.$$

Differentiating the first of (44), we get

$$\frac{\partial}{\partial u}\cos\varepsilon = -(1+\cos\varepsilon)\frac{\partial \log \varrho}{\partial u}. \tag{45}$$

In like manner from the second of (33) we get

$$\frac{\partial}{\partial v}\cos\varepsilon = (1-\cos\varepsilon)\frac{\partial \log \varrho}{\partial v}. \tag{46}$$

Expressing the condition of integrability of these two equations, we find that

$$\varrho = U + V, \tag{47}$$

where U and V are functions of u and v alone respectively. Now the integral of equations (45) and (46) is

$$\tan\frac{\varepsilon}{2} = \sqrt{\frac{U-c}{V+c}}, \tag{48}$$

where c is an arbitrary constant.

From [§ 141] it follows that in this case both N and N_1 are nets which admit an infinity of applicable nets, which we shall call *nets permanent in deformation*.

If D and D'' are the second fundamental coefficients of N, the coefficients D_k and D_k'' of the nets N_k applicable to N are given by [cf. § 141].

$$D_k = \tanh\varphi\, D, \qquad D_k'' = \coth\varphi\, D'', \tag{49}$$

where φ is defined by

$$\frac{\partial \varphi}{\partial u} = -\frac{\partial \log\sqrt{\varrho}}{\partial u}\tanh\varphi, \qquad \frac{\partial \varphi}{\partial v} = -\frac{\partial \log\sqrt{\varrho}}{\partial v}\coth\varphi. \tag{50}$$

Moreover,

$$(51)\qquad \frac{\partial \log \varrho}{\partial u} = -2\begin{Bmatrix}12\\2\end{Bmatrix}', \qquad \frac{\partial \log \varrho}{\partial v} = -2\begin{Bmatrix}12\\1\end{Bmatrix}',$$

the Christoffel symbols being formed with respect to the linear element of the spherical representation of N, namely

$$(52)\qquad d\sigma^2 = \mathfrak{E}\,du^2 + 2\,\mathfrak{F}\,du\,dv + \mathfrak{G}\,dv^2.$$

From the formulas of [§ 83], namely

$$\mathfrak{E} = \frac{GD^2}{H^2}, \qquad \mathfrak{F} = -\frac{FDD''}{H^2}, \qquad \mathfrak{G} = \frac{ED''^2}{H^2},$$

it follows that the coefficients $\mathfrak{E}_k$, $\mathfrak{F}_k$, $\mathfrak{G}_k$ of the linear element of the spherical representation of N_k are given by

$$(53)\qquad \mathfrak{E}_k = \tanh^2\varphi\,\mathfrak{E}, \qquad \mathfrak{F}_k = \mathfrak{F}, \qquad \mathfrak{G}_k = \coth^2\varphi\,\mathfrak{G}.$$

The integral of equations (50) for ϱ given by (47) is

$$(54)\qquad \tanh\varphi = \sqrt{\frac{1+kV}{1-kU}},$$

where k is a constant, such that when $k=0$ we have the net N, that is $N_0 = N$.

If we form the Christoffel symbols $\begin{Bmatrix}12\\1\end{Bmatrix}'_k$ and $\begin{Bmatrix}12\\2\end{Bmatrix}'_k$ with respect to (53), the equations analogous to (51) are

$$(55)\qquad \begin{cases} \dfrac{\partial \log \varrho_k}{\partial u} = -2\begin{Bmatrix}12\\2\end{Bmatrix}'_k = \dfrac{U'}{U+V}\,\dfrac{1+kV}{1-kU}, \\[2ex] \dfrac{\partial \log \varrho_k}{\partial v} = -2\begin{Bmatrix}12\\1\end{Bmatrix}'_k = \dfrac{V'}{U+V}\,\dfrac{1-kU}{1+kV}, \end{cases}$$

from which it follows that we may take

$$(56)\qquad \varrho_k = \frac{U+V}{(1-kU)(1+kV)} = \frac{1}{k}\left(\frac{1}{1-kU} - \frac{1}{1+kV}\right).$$

56. Transformations Ω of permanent nets for which $\mathfrak{E} \neq 0$ and $\mathfrak{G} \neq 0$.

We write the linear element of the sphere in the form

$$(57) \qquad d\sigma^2 = \mathfrak{E}\, du^2 + 2\sqrt{\mathfrak{E}\mathfrak{G}} \cos 2\omega \, du\, dv + \mathfrak{G}\, dv^2,$$

where 2ω is the angle between the parametric curves.

We denote by X', Y', Z'; X'', Y'', Z'' the direction-cosines of the bisectors of the angles between the parametric curves on the sphere, so that we have

$$(58) \qquad \begin{cases} \dfrac{\partial X}{\partial u} = \sqrt{\mathfrak{E}}(\sin\omega X' + \cos\omega X''), \\ \dfrac{\partial X}{\partial v} = \sqrt{\mathfrak{G}}(-\sin\omega X' + \cos\omega X''). \end{cases}$$

If these equations be differentiated with respect to v and u respectively and we make use of [(22) § 66], we find

$$(59) \qquad \begin{cases} \dfrac{\partial X'}{\partial u} = -AX'' - \sqrt{\mathfrak{E}} \sin\omega X, & \dfrac{\partial X'}{\partial v} = BX'' + \sqrt{\mathfrak{G}} \sin\omega X, \\ \dfrac{\partial X''}{\partial u} = AX' - \sqrt{\mathfrak{E}} \cos\omega X, & \dfrac{\partial X''}{\partial v} = -BX' - \sqrt{\mathfrak{G}} \cos\omega X, \end{cases}$$

where

$$(60) \qquad \begin{cases} A = \dfrac{\partial\omega}{\partial u} - \sqrt{\dfrac{\mathfrak{E}}{\mathfrak{G}}} \sin 2\omega \dfrac{\partial \log\sqrt{\varrho}}{\partial v}, \\ B = \dfrac{\partial\omega}{\partial v} - \sqrt{\dfrac{\mathfrak{G}}{\mathfrak{E}}} \sin 2\omega \dfrac{\partial \log\sqrt{\varrho}}{\partial u}. \end{cases}$$

The direction-cosines, X_1, Y_1, Z_1, of the normal to an Ω transform N_1 may be written in the form

$$(61) \qquad X_1 = X\cos\varepsilon + \sin\varepsilon(\sin\alpha X' - \cos\alpha X'').$$

Since $\varrho = \varrho_1$, equations (36) become

$$(62) \quad \frac{\partial}{\partial u}(\varrho w X_1) = -\varrho w^2 \frac{\partial}{\partial u}\left(\frac{X}{w}\right), \qquad \frac{\partial}{\partial v}(\varrho w X_1) = \varrho w^2 \frac{\partial}{\partial v}\left(\frac{X}{w}\right).$$

When the expressions (61) are substituted in (62), we find the following equations:

$$
(63)\quad \left\{
\begin{aligned}
&\frac{\partial \alpha}{\partial u} - \frac{\partial \omega}{\partial u} + \sqrt{\frac{\mathfrak{E}}{\mathfrak{G}}}\sin 2\omega \frac{\partial \log \sqrt{\varrho}}{\partial v} + \sqrt{\mathfrak{E}}\sin(\alpha+\omega)\cot\frac{\varepsilon}{2} = 0,\\
&\frac{\partial \alpha}{\partial v} + \frac{\partial \omega}{\partial v} - \sqrt{\frac{\mathfrak{G}}{\mathfrak{E}}}\sin 2\omega \frac{\partial \log \sqrt{\varrho}}{\partial u} - \sqrt{\mathfrak{G}}\sin(\alpha-\omega)\tan\frac{\varepsilon}{2} = 0,\\
&\qquad\frac{\partial \log w}{\partial u} - \cot\frac{\varepsilon}{2}\sqrt{\mathfrak{E}}\cos(\alpha+\omega) + \frac{1}{1-\cos\varepsilon}\,\frac{\partial \log \varrho}{\partial u} = 0,\\
&\qquad\frac{\partial \log w}{\partial v} + \tan\frac{\varepsilon}{2}\sqrt{\mathfrak{G}}\cos(\alpha-\omega) + \frac{1}{1+\cos\varepsilon}\,\frac{\partial \log \varrho}{\partial v} = 0.
\end{aligned}\right.
$$

The condition of integrability of the first two equations is satisfied, and by means of them we show that the last two are consistent, and that w satisfies the tangential equation of N, namely (29) with $\gamma = \sqrt{\mathfrak{E}\mathfrak{G}}\cos 2\omega$. Hence:

If N is a permanent net with the spherical representation (57), *each pair of functions α and w satisfying* (63) *leads by quadratures to an Ω transform N_1 which is a permanent net; and the associates surfaces Σ and Σ_1 of N and N_1 have the same total curvature at corresponding points and can be so placed in space that they are the focal surfaces of an W congruence*[42]).

From (37) it follows that the coordinates ξ_1, μ_1, ζ_1 of Σ_1 are of the form

$$
(64)\qquad \xi_1 = \xi + \sin\varepsilon(\cos\alpha X' + \sin\alpha X'').
$$

Since w in (63) is not a general solution of (29), we say that the permanent nets whose tangential coordinates are X, Y, Z and a function w defined by (63) is a *special permanent net.*

Suppose that N_1 and N_2 are two Ω transforms of N by means of functions $\alpha_i, w_i, \varepsilon_i$ $(i = 1, 2)$. In order that one of the ∞^1 Ω transforms N_{12} shall be a permanent net, it is necessary that $\varrho_{12} = \varrho$. From (39), (41) and (61) we have in this case

$$
w_{12}(\cos\varepsilon_1 - \cos\varepsilon_2) = w_2[1 - \cos\varepsilon_1\cos\varepsilon_2 - \sin\varepsilon_1\sin\varepsilon_2\cos(\alpha_1-\alpha_2)].
$$

It is readily shown that this function w_{12} satisfies the corresponding equations (38), namely

42) The existence of such W congruences was established by Bianchi Lezioni, vol. 2, pp. 74—80.

$$(65)\quad \frac{\partial}{\partial u}(\varrho w_1 w_{12}) = -\varrho w_1^2 \frac{\partial}{\partial u}\left(\frac{w_2}{w_1}\right), \quad \frac{\partial}{\partial v}(\varrho w_1 w_{12}) = \varrho w_1^2 \frac{\partial}{\partial v}\left(\frac{w_2}{w_1}\right).$$

Hence we have the following theorem of permutability:

If N is a permanent net and N_1 and N_2 are permanent nets which are Ω transforms of N by means of functions α_1, w_1, ε_1 and α_2, w_2, ε_2 $(\varepsilon_2 \neq \varepsilon_1)$, of the ∞^1 Ω transforms N_{12} one is a permanent net and it can be found without quadratures.

Incidentally we have established the theorem of Bianchi[43]):

If Σ and Σ_1 are focal surfaces of a W congruence and Σ and Σ_2 are focal surfaces of a second W congruence such that the total curvatures of Σ, Σ_1 and Σ_2 are the same, there can be found without quadratures a surface Σ_{12} of the same total curvature such that Σ_1 and Σ_{12} are focal surfaces of a W congruence, and likewise Σ_2 and Σ_{12}.

When in particular $\varrho = \text{const.}$, N is the net of geodesics on a surface of Voss [§ 141]. In this case ε is a constant. Each set of solutions of the corresponding equations (63) determines an Ω transform N_1 which is a net of geodesics on a surface of Voss. Moreover, these transformations admit a theorem of permutability. The associated W congruence is pseudospherical, and the preceding theorem is the theorem of permutability of transformations of Bäcklund [§ 121].

57. Transformations Ω of a sequence of permanent nets. In § 56 we saw that in order to obtain an Ω transformation of a permanent net N into a permanent net N_1, it is necessary and sufficient to take for the net N' parallel to N one of the special permanent nets determined by a pair of functions satisfying (63). Suppose now that we consider one of the deforms N_k of N (§ 55). The equations for the Ω transformations of N_k analogous to (63) are

$$(66)\quad \begin{cases} \dfrac{\partial \alpha_k}{\partial u} - \dfrac{\partial \omega}{\partial u} + \sqrt{\dfrac{\mathfrak{E}_k}{\mathfrak{G}_k}} \sin 2\omega \dfrac{\partial}{\partial v} \log \sqrt{\varrho_k} + \sqrt{\mathfrak{E}_k} \sin(\alpha_k + \omega) \cot \dfrac{\varepsilon_k}{2} = 0, \\ \dfrac{\partial \alpha_k}{\partial v} + \dfrac{\partial \omega}{\partial v} - \sqrt{\dfrac{\mathfrak{G}_k}{\mathfrak{E}_k}} \sin 2\omega \dfrac{\partial}{\partial u} \log \sqrt{\varrho_k} - \sqrt{\mathfrak{G}_k} \sin(\alpha_k - \omega) \tan \dfrac{\varepsilon_k}{2} = 0, \\ \dfrac{\partial \log w_k}{\partial u} - \cot \dfrac{\varepsilon_k}{2} \sqrt{\mathfrak{E}_k} \cos(\alpha_k + \omega) + \dfrac{1}{1 - \cos \varepsilon_k} \dfrac{\partial \log \varrho_k}{\partial u} = 0, \\ \dfrac{\partial \log w_k}{\partial v} + \tan \dfrac{\varepsilon_k}{2} \sqrt{\mathfrak{G}_k} \cos(\alpha_k - \omega) + \dfrac{1}{1 + \cos \varepsilon_k} \dfrac{\partial \log \varrho_k}{\partial v} = 0, \end{cases}$$

43) Lezioni, vol. 2, pp. 80—82.

where $\mathfrak{E}_k$, $\mathfrak{G}_k$ and ϱ_k are given by (53) and (56), and analogously to (48) we have

$$\tan\frac{\varepsilon_k}{2} = \sqrt{\frac{\frac{1}{kU-1}+kc_k}{\frac{1}{kV+1}-kc_k}}. \tag{67}$$

When the expressions for $\mathfrak{E}_k$, $\mathfrak{G}_k$ and ϱ_k are substituted in the first two of (66), we find that $\alpha_k = \alpha$ is a solution, if

$$\coth\varphi\cdot\tan\frac{\varepsilon_k}{2} = \tan\frac{\varepsilon}{2},$$

which is consistent with (67), if we take

$$kc_k(1-ck) = 1.$$

On this hypothesis the last two of (66) are reducible to

$$\left\{\begin{aligned} \frac{\partial\log w_k}{\partial u} &= \frac{\partial\log w}{\partial u} - \frac{1}{2}\frac{U'k}{1-kU}, \\ \frac{\partial\log w_k}{\partial v} &= \frac{\partial\log w}{\partial v} + \frac{1}{2}\frac{V'k}{1+kV}, \end{aligned}\right. \tag{68}$$

of which the integral is $w_k = \sigma w\sqrt{(1-kU)(1+kV)}$, where σ is a constant. We shall show that when $\sigma = (1-kc)^{-1}$ the corresponding net N_k' parallel to N_k is applicable to N'. To this end we remark that the second fundamental coefficients $(D_k)'$ and $(D_k'')'$ of the net with the spherical representation (53) and determined by w_k are given by [cf. § 67]

$$\left\{\begin{aligned} (D_k)' &= -\frac{\partial^2 w_k}{\partial u^2} + \begin{Bmatrix}11\\1\end{Bmatrix}_k' \frac{\partial w_k}{\partial u} + \begin{Bmatrix}11\\2\end{Bmatrix}_k' \frac{\partial w_k}{\partial v} - \mathfrak{E}_k w_k, \\ (D_k'')' &= -\frac{\partial^2 w_k}{\partial v^2} + \begin{Bmatrix}22\\1\end{Bmatrix}_k' \frac{\partial w_k}{\partial u} + \begin{Bmatrix}22\\2\end{Bmatrix}_k' \frac{\partial w_k}{\partial v} - \mathfrak{G}_k w_k, \end{aligned}\right. \tag{69}$$

where the symbols $\begin{Bmatrix}rs\\t\end{Bmatrix}_k'$ are formed with respect to (53). When we put $k=0$ in these expressions, we obtain the expressions for the coefficients $(D)'$ and $(D'')'$ for N' by definition.

When the epressions (66) are substituted in (69), we deduce the relations

$$\frac{(D_k)'}{w_k}\,\frac{1-kU}{1-kc}=\frac{(D)'}{w}, \qquad \frac{(D_k'')'}{w_k}\,\frac{1+kV}{1-kc}=\frac{(D'')'}{w}.$$

From (49) and (54) it follows that we must have

$$(D_k)'=\sqrt{\frac{1+kV}{1-kU}}\,(D)', \qquad (D_k'')'=\sqrt{\frac{1-kU}{1+kV}}\,(D'')'.$$

Hence

(70) $$w_k=\frac{\sqrt{(1-kU)(1+kV)}}{1-kc}\,w.$$

In § 27 we saw that if $N(x)$ and $N_k(x_k)$ are applicable nets, and $N'(x')$ and $N_k'(x_k')$ are a pair of applicable nets parallel to N and N_k respectively, the F transforms, N_1 and $N_{k,1}$ of N and N_k determined by the nets N' and N_k' and the function $\theta'=\sum x_k'^2-\sum x'^2$ are applicable to one another. In order to apply this result to the present case we calculate the expression for θ'. From [§ 67] we have

$$\sum x_k'^2 = w_k^2+\frac{1}{\mathfrak{H}^2}\left[\mathfrak{G}_k\left(\frac{\partial w_k}{\partial u}\right)^2-2\mathfrak{F}_k\frac{\partial w_k}{\partial u}\frac{\partial w_k}{\partial v}+\mathfrak{E}_k\left(\frac{\partial w_k}{\partial v}\right)^2\right],$$

$$\sum x'^2= w^2+\frac{1}{\mathfrak{H}^2}\left[\mathfrak{G}\left(\frac{\partial w}{\partial u}\right)^2-2\mathfrak{F}\frac{\partial w}{\partial u}\frac{\partial w}{\partial v}+\mathfrak{E}\left(\frac{\partial w}{\partial v}\right)^2\right].$$

Substituting the values from the preceding equations, we find that

$$\theta'=\frac{k}{1-kc}\,\frac{w^2\sin 2\omega}{\mathfrak{H}^2}\Big[\mathfrak{E}\mathfrak{G}\,(U+V)\sin 2\alpha$$

$$-\sqrt{\mathfrak{E}}\,\mathfrak{G}\cot\frac{\varepsilon}{2}\sin(\alpha-\omega)\,U'+\mathfrak{E}\sqrt{\mathfrak{G}}\tan\frac{\varepsilon}{2}\sin(\alpha+\omega)\,V'\Big].$$

We note that k appears in this expression only in the factor $k/(1-kc)$, and consequently it does not appear in the equation $x_1=x-\frac{\theta}{\theta'}x'$, since θ also involves this factor. Hence as k

varies and consequently N_k, we find that all the transforms $N_{k,1}$ are applicable to N_1[44]).

58. Transformations Ω in point coordinates. Nets in relation O. In § 28 we saw that if $N(x)$ and $\overline{N}(\overline{x})$ are two nets corresponding with orthogonality of linear elements, that is are in *relation* O, they have the same point equation, say

$$\frac{\partial^2\theta}{\partial u\,\partial v}=\frac{\partial \log a}{\partial v}\frac{\partial\theta}{\partial u}+\frac{\partial\log b}{\partial u}\frac{\partial\theta}{\partial v}. \tag{71}$$

Moreover, if h and l are any solutions of equations (I, 13), the corresponding parallel nets $N'(x')$ and $\overline{N}'(\overline{x})$ are in relation O, and θ', given by

$$\theta'=\sum x'\,\overline{x}', \tag{72}$$

is a solution of the common point equation of N' and $\overline{N}'$ (cf. § 28). Furthermore, if θ is the solution of (71) corresponding to θ', then the nets $N_1(x_1)$ and $\overline{N}_1(\overline{x}_1)$ defined by

$$x_1=x-\frac{\theta}{\theta'}x',\qquad \overline{x}_1=\overline{x}-\frac{\theta}{\theta'}\overline{x}' \tag{73}$$

are in relation O and are respective F transforms of N and $\overline{N}$.

Suppose now that N and $\overline{N}$ are nets in 3-space. Then, as follows from [§ 157] they have equal tangential invariants; similarly N_1 and $\overline{N}_1$. It is our purpose to show that N and N_1 are in relation Ω, and likewise $\overline{N}$ and $\overline{N}_1$, and thus obtain the equations of transformations Ω in terms of the point coordinates.

If $\overline{N}(\overline{x})$ is any net with equal tangential invariants, and $N(x)$ is in relation O with $\overline{N}$, we have [cf. § 157]

$$\frac{\partial x}{\partial u}=\overline{z}_0\frac{\partial\overline{y}}{\partial u}-\overline{y}_0\frac{\partial\overline{z}}{\partial u},\qquad \frac{\partial x}{\partial v}=\overline{z}_0\frac{\partial\overline{y}}{\partial v}-\overline{y}_0\frac{\partial\overline{z}}{\partial v}, \tag{74}$$

and

$$\frac{\partial\overline{x}}{\partial u}=z_0\frac{\partial y}{\partial u}-y_0\frac{\partial z}{\partial u},\qquad \frac{\partial\overline{x}}{\partial v}=z_0\frac{\partial y}{\partial v}-y_0\frac{\partial z}{\partial v}, \tag{75}$$

---

44) Cf. Transactions, vol. 19 (1918), p. 179. The existence of transformations Ω of permanent nets for which $\mathfrak{E}=0$, $\mathfrak{G}\neq 0$ is established also; the restriction in the theorem of page 183 is not necessary, since the second of equations (61) should include the term $-V'/(1+\cos\sigma)V$.

where $\overline{x}_0, \overline{y}_0, \overline{z}_0$ and x_0, y_0, z_0 are the point coordinates of the surfaces $\overline{\Sigma}$ and Σ associate to $\overline{N}$ and N, and the asymptotic lines on $\overline{\Sigma}$ and Σ are parametric. From (74) and (75) we have also

$$(76) \qquad \sum \overline{x}_0 \frac{\partial x}{\partial u} = 0, \qquad \sum \overline{x}_0 \frac{\partial x}{\partial v} = 0,$$

$$(77) \qquad \sum x_0 \frac{\partial \overline{x}}{\partial u} = 0, \qquad \sum x_0 \frac{\partial \overline{x}}{\partial v} = 0.$$

Consequently $\overline{x}_0, \overline{y}_0, \overline{z}_0$ and x_0, y_0, z_0 are direction-parameters of the normals to N and $\overline{N}$ respectively. Furthermore, if the expressions for the derivatives of y and z as given by (74) are substituted in (75), we have in consequence of (77)

$$(78) \qquad x_0 \overline{x}_0 + y_0 \overline{y}_0 + z_0 \overline{z}_0 + 1 = 0.$$

Hence Σ and $\overline{\Sigma}$ are polar reciprocal with respect to the imaginary sphere[45])

$$(79) \qquad x^2 + y^2 + z^2 + 1 = 0.$$

If $\overline{N}'$ and N' are nets parallel to $\overline{N}$ and N by means of the same pair of solutions h and l of (I, 13), we have

$$(80) \qquad \frac{\partial x'}{\partial u} = \overline{z}_0 \frac{\partial \overline{y}'}{\partial u} - \overline{y}_0 \frac{\partial \overline{z}'}{\partial u}, \qquad \frac{\partial x'}{\partial v} = \overline{z}_0 \frac{\partial \overline{y}'}{\partial v} - \overline{y}_0 \frac{\partial \overline{z}'}{\partial v}.$$

For the F transforms N_1 and $\overline{N}_1$ defined by (73) we have

$$(81) \qquad \frac{\partial x_1}{\partial u} = \overline{z}_{01} \frac{\partial \overline{y}_1}{\partial u} - \overline{y}_{01} \frac{\partial \overline{z}_1}{\partial u}, \qquad \frac{\partial x_1}{\partial v} = \overline{z}_{01} \frac{\partial \overline{y}_1}{\partial v} - \overline{y}_{01} \frac{\partial \overline{z}_1}{\partial v},$$

$$(82) \qquad \frac{\partial \overline{x}_1}{\partial u} = z_{01} \frac{\partial y_1}{\partial u} - y_{01} \frac{\partial z_1}{\partial u}, \qquad \frac{\partial \overline{x}_1}{\partial v} = z_{01} \frac{\partial y_1}{\partial v} - y_{01} \frac{\partial z_1}{\partial v},$$

where $\overline{x}_{01}, \overline{y}_{01}, \overline{z}_{01}$ and x_{01}, y_{01}, z_{01} are the point coordinates of surfaces $\overline{\Sigma}_1$ and Σ_1 associate to $\overline{N}_1$ and N_1 with their asymptotic

45) Darboux, Leçons, vol. 4, p. 67; also [Ex. 15, p. 391].

lines parametric, and they are direction-parameters of the normals to N_1 and $\overline{N}_1$ respectively. Moreover, we have analogously to (78)

$$x_{01}\,\overline{x}_{01}+y_{01}\,\overline{y}_{01}+z_{01}\,\overline{z}_{01}+1=0. \tag{83}$$

From (81) we have

$$\frac{\partial x_1}{\partial u}\frac{\partial \overline{z}_1}{\partial v}-\frac{\partial x_1}{\partial v}\frac{\partial \overline{z}_1}{\partial u}=\overline{z}_{01}\left(\frac{\partial \overline{y}_1}{\partial u}\frac{\partial \overline{z}_1}{\partial v}-\frac{\partial \overline{y}_1}{\partial v}\frac{\partial \overline{z}_1}{\partial u}\right). \tag{84}$$

On differentiating (73) we obtain

$$\frac{\partial x_1}{\partial u}=\frac{1}{\theta'^2}\left(\theta-\frac{\theta'}{h}\right)\left(x'\frac{\partial \theta'}{\partial u}-\theta'\frac{\partial x'}{\partial u}\right),\quad \frac{\partial x_1}{\partial v}=\frac{1}{\theta'^2}\left(\theta-\frac{\theta'}{l}\right)\left(x'\frac{\partial \theta'}{\partial v}-\theta'\frac{\partial x'}{\partial v}\right)$$

$$\frac{\partial \overline{x}_1}{\partial u}=\frac{1}{\theta'^2}\left(\theta-\frac{\theta'}{h}\right)\left(\overline{x}'\frac{\partial \theta'}{\partial u}-\theta'\frac{\partial \overline{x}'}{\partial u}\right),\quad \frac{\partial \overline{x}_1'}{\partial v}=\frac{1}{\theta'^2}\left(\theta-\frac{\theta'}{l}\right)\left(\overline{x}'\frac{\partial \theta'}{\partial v}-\theta'\frac{\partial \overline{x}'}{\partial v}\right)$$

When these expressions and analogous ones in $\overline{y}_1$ and $\overline{z}_1$ are substituted in (84) and θ' is given the value (72), the resulting equation is reducible, by means of (80) and the fact that x_0, y_0, z_0 are direction-parameters of the normal to $\overline{N}'$, to the form

$$\overline{z}_{01}=\frac{x'\,y_0-y'\,x_0-z'}{\sum \overline{x}'\,x_0}. \tag{85}$$

Similarly we have

$$z_{01}=\frac{\overline{x}'\,\overline{y}_0-\overline{y}'\,\overline{x}_0-z'}{\sum x'\,\overline{x}_0}. \tag{86}$$

From (85) and (86) we have

$$x_0\,\overline{x}_{01}+y_0\,\overline{y}_{01}+z_0\,\overline{z}_{01}+1=0,\qquad \overline{x}_0\,x_{01}+\overline{y}_0\,y_{01}+\overline{z}_0\,z_{01}+1=0. \tag{87}$$

Consider now the surfaces Σ and Σ_1. The quantities $\overline{x}_0$, $\overline{y}_0$, $\overline{z}_0$ and $\overline{x}_{01}$, $\overline{y}_{01}$, $\overline{z}_{01}$, are direction-parameters of the normals to these respective surfaces. Moreover, from (78), (83) and (87) it follows that

$$\sum \overline{x}_0\,(x_{01}-x_0)=0,\qquad \sum \overline{x}_{01}\,(x_{01}-x_0)=0.$$

Consequently Σ and Σ_1 are the focal surfaces of the congruence of lines joining corresponding points on these surfaces, and it is

W congruence, since the asymptotic lines are parametric on Σ and Σ_1. Hence from the last theorem of § 53 it follows that N and N_1 are in relation Ω, and also $\overline{N}$ and $\overline{N}_1$.

When a net $\overline{N}$ with equal tangential invariants is known, the associate surface $\overline{\Sigma}$ can be found by quadratures [§ 78]. Then by equations (74) we obtain a net N, with equal tangential invariants, which is in relation O to $\overline{N}$. Each net $\overline{N}'$ parallel to $\overline{N}$ leads by a quadrature to an Ω transformation of $\overline{N}$ and N. Hence:

Each net parallel to a net N with equal tangential invariants determines an Ω transformation of N, and the determination of the point coordinates of the transform requires only quadratures[46]).

59. Transformations Ω and K of the focal nets of a W congruence. We have seen that the surface Σ of the preceding section is associate to the surface S on which N lies. Since this relation is reciprocal, there exists a surface $\tilde{S}$ in relation O to Σ; its coordinates, $\tilde{x}, \tilde{y}, \tilde{z}$, are given by quadratures of the form (analogous to (75))

$$\frac{\partial \tilde{x}}{\partial u} = z\frac{\partial y_0}{\partial u} - y\frac{\partial z_0}{\partial u}, \qquad \frac{\partial \tilde{x}}{\partial v} = z\frac{\partial y_0}{\partial v} - y\frac{\partial z_0}{\partial v}.$$

From these equations and (75) we see that $\tilde{S}$ can be so placed in space that

$$\tilde{x} = \overline{x} + z y_0 - y z_0. \tag{88}$$

From [§ 157] it follows that the asymptotic lines correspond on $\tilde{S}$ and $\overline{S}$ the surface on which $\overline{N}$ lies. Also since x_0, y_0, z_0 and x, y, z are direction-parameters of the normals to $\overline{S}$ and $\tilde{S}$ respectively, it follows from (88) that $\overline{S}$ and $\tilde{S}$ are the focal surfaces of a W congruence.

Since $\tilde{S}$ and Σ are in relation O, there can be found by means of equations analogous to (74), the coordinates $\tilde{x}_0, \tilde{y}_0, \tilde{z}_0$ of a surface $\tilde{\Sigma}$ associate to $\tilde{S}$; moreover, from [§ 156] it follows that the parametric curves on $\tilde{S}$ and $\tilde{\Sigma}$ form nets with equal point invariants. Furthermore, since $\tilde{\Sigma}$ and S bear to $\tilde{S}$ and Σ relations analogous to the relations of Σ and $\overline{\Sigma}$ to S and $\overline{S}$, it follows that $\tilde{\Sigma}$ and S are polar reciprocal with respect to (79).

---

[46]) Cf. the first theorem of § 53.

When the net $\bar{N}$ is subjected to a transformation Ω, in accordance with the preceding section, we get surfaces $\bar{S}_1$, S_1, Σ_1, $\tilde{S}_1$ and $\tilde{\Sigma}_1$ related to one another as in the preceding paragraph. Since S and $\tilde{\Sigma}$, and S_1 and $\tilde{\Sigma}_1$, are polar reciprocal with respect to (79), it follows that $\tilde{\Sigma}$ and $\tilde{\Sigma}_1$ are in the relation of a transformation K (V, Ex. 11). Moreover, $\tilde{S}$ and $\tilde{S}_1$ being associate to $\tilde{\Sigma}$ and $\tilde{\Sigma}_1$ respectively are also in relation K (II, Ex. 18). Furthermore, $\bar{S}_1$ and $\tilde{S}_1$ are the focal surfaces of a W congruence.

From [§ 172] it follows that if $\bar{S}$ and $\tilde{S}$ are the focal surfaces of any W congruence, it is possible to find by quadratures two surfaces S and Σ associate to one another and in relation O with $\bar{S}$ and $\tilde{S}$ respectively. If Σ is referred to its asymptotic lines, the parametric curves on $\bar{S}$ and $\tilde{S}$ form nets with equal tangential and point invariants respectively. Hence:

A W congruence admits of transformations into W congruences such that one pair of corresponding focal nets are in relation Ω and the other pair in relation K[47]).

60. Nets with equal point invariants and equal tangential invariants. In consequence of [(38) § 83] equations [(36) § 83] can be written in the form

$$\frac{\partial}{\partial v}\log D = \frac{\partial}{\partial v}\log a\alpha, \qquad \frac{\partial}{\partial u}\log D'' = \frac{\partial}{\partial u}\log b\beta.$$

Hence:

When a net has two of the following properties, it has the third also; equal point invariants, equal tangential invariants, isothermal-conjugate.

We consider such a net, and put

$$\begin{Bmatrix}12\\1\end{Bmatrix} = \frac{\partial\log\sqrt{\varrho}}{\partial v}, \qquad \begin{Bmatrix}12\\2\end{Bmatrix} = \frac{\partial\log\sqrt{\varrho}}{\partial u}, \qquad D = -D''.$$

From [(3) § 63] and [(13′) § 64] we have

$$\begin{Bmatrix}11\\1\end{Bmatrix} = \frac{\partial}{\partial u}\log\frac{H}{\sqrt{\varrho}}, \qquad \begin{Bmatrix}11\\2\end{Bmatrix} = \frac{\partial}{\partial v}\log\frac{D}{\sqrt{\varrho}},$$

$$\begin{Bmatrix}22\\1\end{Bmatrix} = \frac{\partial}{\partial u}\log\frac{D}{\sqrt{\varrho}}, \qquad \begin{Bmatrix}22\\2\end{Bmatrix} = \frac{\partial}{\partial v}\log\frac{H}{\sqrt{\varrho}}.$$

---

47) Cf. Demoulin, l. c., p. 276.

Consequently the point coordinates of the net satisfy the equations

$$
(89) \quad \begin{cases} \dfrac{\partial^2\theta}{\partial u^2}+\dfrac{\partial^2\theta}{\partial v^2}=\dfrac{\partial \log r}{\partial u}\dfrac{\partial\theta}{\partial u}+\dfrac{\partial \log r}{\partial v}\dfrac{\partial\theta}{\partial v}, \\ \dfrac{\partial^2\theta}{\partial u\,\partial v}=\dfrac{\partial \log \sqrt{\varrho}}{\partial v}\dfrac{\partial\theta}{\partial u}+\dfrac{\partial \log \sqrt{\varrho}}{\partial u}\dfrac{\partial\theta}{\partial v}, \end{cases}
$$

where

$$
r=\frac{HD}{\varrho}.
$$

From § 25 we have:

If $N(x)$ is a net with equal point and equal tangential invariants, a parallel net of the same kind is given by the quadratures

$$
\frac{\partial \bar{x}}{\partial u}=-\frac{1}{\varrho}\frac{\partial x}{\partial u}, \qquad \frac{\partial \bar{x}}{\partial v}=\frac{1}{\varrho}\frac{\partial x}{\partial v}.
$$

In order to establish transformations F of a net N of this type into nets of the same kind, we consider N expressed in terms of homogeneous coordinates, the point and tangential equations being

$$
(90) \quad \begin{cases} \dfrac{\partial^2\theta}{\partial u\,\partial v}+\dfrac{\partial \log \sqrt{\varrho}}{\partial v}\dfrac{\partial\theta}{\partial u}+\dfrac{\partial \log \sqrt{\varrho}}{\partial u}\dfrac{\partial\theta}{\partial v}+c\theta=0, \\ \dfrac{\partial^2\lambda}{\partial u\,\partial v}+\dfrac{\partial \log \sqrt{\varrho}}{\partial v}\dfrac{\partial\lambda}{\partial u}+\dfrac{\partial \log \sqrt{\varrho}}{\partial u}\dfrac{\partial\lambda}{\partial v}+\gamma\lambda=0. \end{cases}
$$

It is readily shown that the equations

$$
(91) \quad \begin{cases} \dfrac{\partial x_1}{\partial u}=\varrho\left(\dfrac{\partial x}{\partial u}\sum X_1 x-x\sum X_1\dfrac{\partial x}{\partial u}\right), \\ \dfrac{\partial x_1}{\partial v}=-\varrho\left(\dfrac{\partial x}{\partial v}\sum X_1 x-x\sum X_1\dfrac{\partial x}{\partial v}\right), \\ \dfrac{\partial X_1}{\partial u}=\bar{\varrho}\left(\dfrac{\partial X}{\partial u}\sum X x_1-X\sum x_1\dfrac{\partial X}{\partial u}\right), \\ \dfrac{\partial X_1}{\partial v}=-\bar{\varrho}\left(\dfrac{\partial X}{\partial v}\sum X x_1-X\sum x_1\dfrac{\partial X}{\partial v}\right) \end{cases}
$$

and similar equations in y_1, z_1, w_1, Y_1, Z_1 and W_1 form a completely integrable system. For each set of solutions the function $\sum x_1 X_1$ is constant. Consequently each set of solutions, for which

$$(92) \qquad \sum x_1 X_1 = 0,$$

defines a net N_1 for which these functions are the point and tangential coordinates. Furthermore, for a set of solutions the functions

$$(93) \qquad \theta = \sum X_1 x, \qquad \lambda = \sum X x_1$$

are solution of the respective equations (90), so that equations (91) are equivalent to (III, Ex. 25) and (36). Consequently N_1 is both a K and Ω transform of N, and therefore has equal point and equal tangential invariants. Hence, since (92) is bilinear we have:

A net with equal point and equal tangential invariants admits ∞^6 transformations K and Ω into nets of the same kind.

If N_1 and N_2 aré two of these transforms of N, from (III, 73, 75) it follows that for a net N_{12} to be a K transform of N_1 and N_2, we must have $\theta_{12} + \theta_{21} = 0$. In like manner for N_{12} to be an Ω transform we have from the equations preceding (21) that $\lambda_{12} + \lambda_{21} = 0$. Hence from (23) we have $\sum X_1 x_2 + \sum X_2 x_1 = 0$. It is readily shown that the left-hand member of this expression is constant. Only when it is zero is there a net N_{12} which is both a K and an Ω transform of N_1 and N_2, and then there are an infinity of such nets, since θ_{12} is determined only to within an additive constant, but θ_{21}, λ_{12} and λ_{21} are then completely determined.

Exercises.

1. If $x^{(1)}$, $x^{(2)}$, $x^{(3)}$ are the cartesian coordinates of a net N in 3-space and θ is any solution of the point equation of N, then $\frac{\partial x^{(1)}}{\partial u}$, $\frac{\partial x^{(2)}}{\partial u}$, $\frac{\partial x^{(3)}}{\partial u}$, $\frac{\partial \theta}{\partial u}$ are tangential coordinates of a net.

2. A necessary and sufficient condition that the curves $v = \text{const.}$ of a net be plane is that the minus first Laplace transform be a developable surface; the analytical condition is that the invariant H of the tangential equation of the net be equal to zero.

3. A necessary and sufficient condition that the curves of a net be plane is that the tangential coordinates can be taken in the form

$$X = U_1 + V_1, \qquad Y = U_2 + V_2, \qquad Z = U_3 + V_3, \qquad W = U_4 + V_4,$$

where the U's and V's are functions of u and v respectively.

4. When two nets N and N_1 in relation F are subjected to a polar reciprocal transformation, the resulting nets are in relation F; and the conjugate and harmonic congruences of the given relation F are transformed into the harmonic and conjugate congruences of the resulting relation F.

5. In a transformation F defined by (11) the functions $\frac{\partial}{\partial u}\left(\frac{X}{\lambda}\right), \ldots, \frac{\partial}{\partial u}\left(\frac{W}{\lambda}\right)$ and $\frac{\partial}{\partial v}\left(\frac{X}{\lambda}\right), \ldots, \frac{\partial}{\partial v}\left(\frac{W}{\lambda}\right)$ are tangential coordinates of the first and second focal surfaces of the conjugate congruence of the transformation.

6. A necessary and sufficient condition that the transformation defined by (11) be radial is that $\lambda = aX + bY + cZ + dW$, where a, b, c, d are constants.

7. When in (26) we take $w = aX + bY + cZ$, where a, b and c are constants, the conjugate congruence of the transformation consists of parallel lines.

8. Show that the functions $\overline{X}_1$ and $\overline{X}_2$ given by (15) are tangential coordinates of the focal surfaces of the harmonic congruence of the corresponding transformation F.

9. Each solution of the adjoint of the tangential equation of a net determines a congruence harmonic to the net (cf. Ex. 8). What is the dual of this theorem?

10. If the direction equation of a congruence G is the same as the tangential equation of a net N, the determination of nets harmonic to G and congruences harmonic to N are equivalent problems, namely the solution of the adjoint of the given equation.

11. When a polar reciprocal transformation is applied to two nets in relation Ω, the resulting nets are in relation K, and conversely.

12. A necessary and sufficient condition that the axis curves of a net N form a net is that N have equal tangential invariants (cf. IV, Ex. 20, 22).

13. If four nets N, N_1, N_2, N_{12} form a quatern under transformations Ω determined by w_1, w_2, w_{12} and w_{21}, the four nets parallel to them determined by w_1, $1/\sqrt{\rho\rho_1}\, w_1$, w_{21} and $1/\sqrt{\rho_2\,\rho_{12}}\, w_{21}$ form a quatern; likewise the four nets determined by w_2, $1/\sqrt{\rho\rho_2}\, w_2$, w_{12} and $1/\sqrt{\rho_1\,\rho_{12}}\, w_{12}$.

14. Let $N(x)$ be a net with equal tangential invariants and $\overline{N}(\overline{x})$ the net of the same kind in relation O to N, and $N'(x')$, $N''(x'')$ and $\overline{N}'(\overline{x}')$, $\overline{N}''(\overline{x}'')$ corresponding parallel nets to N and $\overline{N}$. If we put $\theta_1' = \Sigma x'\overline{x}'$, $\theta_2'' = \Sigma x''\overline{x}''$, then the nets $N_1(x_1)$ and $N_2(x_2)$, where

$$x_1 = x - \frac{\theta_1}{\theta_1'}x', \qquad x_2 = x - \frac{\theta_2}{\theta_2''}x''$$

are Ω transforms of N. If we draw through points of N_1 and N_2 lines with direction-parameters of the respective forms (cf. § 21)

$$x_1''' = x'' - \frac{\theta_1''}{\theta_1'}x', \qquad x_2'''' = x' - \frac{\theta_2'}{\theta_2''}x'',$$

where θ_1'' and θ_2' are solutions of the point equations of N'' and N' corresponding to θ_1 and θ_2, the point M_{12} of intersection of these corresponding lines generates a net N_{12}. Show that this net N_{12} will be an Ω transform of N_1 and N_2 if

$$\theta_1'' + \theta_2' = \Sigma x''\overline{x}' + \Sigma x'\overline{x}''.$$

15. Show that all the conditions of the preceding example are satisfied, if we replace θ_1'' and θ_2' by $\theta_1''+c$ and $\theta_2'-c$, where c is an arbitrary constant, and consequently there are ∞^1 nets N_{12} in relation Ω with N_1 and N_2; that corresponding points of these nets N_{12} lie on a conic through the corresponding points of N, N_1 and N_2; also that the tangents planes to these nets N_{12} at corresponding points form a pencil (cf. § 26 and II, Ex. 19).

16. Let N be a net with equal point invariants, N_1 and N_2 be K transforms of N, and N_{12} one of the K transforms of N_1 and N_2 in accordance with the theorem of § 26; show that the tangent planes to the ∞^1 nets N_{12} at corresponding points envelop a quadric cone (cf. Ex. 15).

17. Prove directly that the surfaces $\tilde{S}$ and $\tilde{S}_1$ of § 59 are in relation K.

18. Two nets N and $\overline{N}$ with equal tangential invariants which are in relation O determine twelve surfaces forming a closed system of Darboux [Ex. 19, p. 391]; similarly two nets N_1 and $\overline{N}_1$ which are Ω transforms of N and $\overline{N}$ determine a second system; find the relations between the two systems of surfaces other than those treated in § 59.

19. If S and $\overline{S}$ two surfaces in relation O are referred to their common nets, $N(x)$ and $\overline{N}(\overline{x})$, the equations of the form

$$\hat{x} = x + e\overline{x},$$

where e is an infinitesimal, define a surface $\hat{S}$ which is an infinitesimal deform of S, and the parametric curves form a net $\hat{N}$ [cf. § 158]. If $N'(x')$ and $\overline{N}'(\overline{x}')$ are corresponding parallel nets to N and $\overline{N}$ respectively, the equations of the form

$$\hat{x}' = x' + e\overline{x}'$$

define a net $\hat{N}'$ which is an infinitestimal deform of N'. Then equations of the form

$$\hat{x}_1 = \hat{x} - \frac{\theta}{\theta'}\hat{x}',$$

where $\theta' = \Sigma x'\overline{x}'$, define a net $\hat{N}_1$, which is an F transform of $\hat{N}$ and an infinitestimal deform of N_1 whose coordinates are given by (73).

20. When the spherical representation of a permanent net is such that $\mathfrak{E} \neq 0$, $\mathfrak{G} \neq 0$, the parameters can be chosen so that either (i) $\rho = a$, a constant; (ii) $\rho = v$; (iii) $\rho = u+v$. In these respective cases the coefficients of the spherical representation can be given the respective forms

$$\text{(i)} \qquad \mathfrak{E} = \mathfrak{G} = 1, \qquad \mathfrak{F} = \cos 2\omega;$$

$$\text{(ii)} \qquad \mathfrak{E} = \frac{1}{v}, \qquad \mathfrak{F} = -\frac{\partial\psi}{\partial u}, \qquad \mathfrak{G} = \frac{\psi}{v};$$

$$\text{(iii)} \qquad \mathfrak{E} = \frac{\partial\psi}{\partial u}(u+v)^{-1}, \qquad \mathfrak{F} = -\frac{\partial^2\psi}{\partial u\,\partial v}, \qquad \mathfrak{G} = \frac{\partial\psi}{\partial v}(u+v)^{-1}.$$

Determine the conditions which ω and ψ must satisfy in each case.

21. When the curves $v = \text{const.}$ of a permanent net are represented on the gaussian sphere by isotropic generators, the coefficients of (52) are reducible to the form

$$\mathfrak{E} = 0, \quad \mathfrak{F} = \frac{2}{(1+uv)^2}, \quad \mathfrak{G} = \frac{2V'}{Vv(1+uv)} + V_1,$$

where V and V_1 are functions of v alone; also the tangential coordinates of such a net are given by

$$X = \frac{a_1}{1+uv} + b_1, \quad Y = \frac{a_2}{1+uv} + b_2, \quad Z = \frac{a_3}{1+uv} + b_3,$$

$$W\sqrt{V} = 2\frac{v\varphi + u\psi}{1+uv} - \varphi' - \psi',$$

where φ and ψ are arbitrary functions of u and v respectively, and the a's and b's are functions of v alone subject to the conditions:

$$\sum_i a_i^2 = 0, \quad \sum_i a_i'^2 = \frac{4}{v^2}, \quad \sum_i a_i''^2 = \frac{4}{v^2}\left(V_1 - \frac{5}{4}\frac{V'^2}{V^2} + \frac{2V'}{vV} + \frac{V''}{V}\right),$$

$$b_i = \left(\frac{V'v}{4V} - \frac{1}{2}\right) a_i + \frac{v}{2} a_i' \qquad (i = 1, 2, 3),$$

the primes indicating differentiation.

Drach, Ann. de Toulouse, ser. 2, vol. 10 (1908), p. 135.

Chapter VI.

Orthogonal nets.

61. Nets O and p, O. Congruences I and p, I. A net $N(x)$, whose cartesian coordinates x satisfy an equation

$$(1)\qquad \frac{\partial^2\theta}{\partial u\,\partial v}=\frac{\partial\log a}{\partial v}\frac{\partial\theta}{\partial u}+\frac{\partial\log b}{\partial u}\frac{\partial\theta}{\partial v},$$

is called an *orthogonal net*, or for the sake of brevity an *O net*[48]), if

$$(2)\quad E=\sum\left(\frac{\partial x}{\partial u}\right)^2\neq 0,\qquad F=\sum\frac{\partial x}{\partial u}\frac{\partial x}{\partial v}=0,\qquad G=\sum\left(\frac{\partial x}{\partial v}\right)^2\neq 0.$$

The second of these conditions is equivalent to the requirement that ω, defined by

$$(3)\qquad 2\,\omega=\sum x^2$$

is a solution of (1). We say that a net N is p, O, if its point equation (1) admits $p-1$ solutions, $y_1,\ldots,y_{p-1}$ linearly independent of the x's, such that

$$(4)\quad \begin{cases}\sum\left(\frac{\partial x}{\partial u}\right)^2-\sum\left(\frac{\partial y}{\partial u}\right)^2\neq 0, & \sum\left(\frac{\partial x}{\partial v}\right)^2-\sum\left(\frac{\partial y}{\partial v}\right)^2\neq 0,\\ \sum\frac{\partial x}{\partial u}\frac{\partial x}{\partial v}-\sum\frac{\partial y}{\partial u}\frac{\partial y}{\partial v}=0. & \end{cases}$$

We call the y's the *complementary* functions[49]). This means that $\sum x^2-\sum y^2$ is a solution of (1). It is understood that none of

---

[48]) The results of §§ 61—65 are due to Guichard, Annales de L'École Norm. Sup., ser. 3, vol. 14 (1897), pp. 467—516; vol. 15 (1898), pp. 179—227.

[49]) Note that if each y be replaced by iy, where $i^2=-1$, a net p, O is the projection in n-space of an O net in $(n+p-1)$-space. It is this point of view that Guichard takes in considering these systems.

the y's are constant. Hence if we have a net so that the x's and $p-1$ functions y satisfy $\sum x^2 - \sum y^2 =$ const., we say that the net is p, O and not $p+1$, O.

We say that the equations

$$(5) \qquad y_i = \alpha_{i1}\overline{y}_1 + \ldots + \alpha_{ip-1}\overline{y}_{p-1}, \quad (i = 1 \ldots p-1),$$

define an orthogonal substitution, when the constants α_{ij} satisfy the conditions

$$(6) \qquad \sum_{i=1}^{p-1} \alpha_{ij}^2 = 1, \quad \sum_{i=1}^{p-1} \alpha_{ij}\,\alpha_{ik} = 0, \quad (j \neq k).$$

When such a substitution is effected upon the complementary functions y of a net p, O, we have $\sum \overline{y}^2 = \sum y^2$ and consequently the functions $\overline{y}$ serve equally well as complementary functions.

When there is a linear relation between the y's, such as

$$(7) \qquad a_1 y_1 + \ldots + a_{p-1}\, y_{p-1} = a,$$

where $\sum a_i^2 \neq 0$, that is, when the relation is *non-isotropic*, we can assume that $\sum a_i^2 = 1$, so that in the new variables $\overline{y}$, we may take $\overline{y}_{p-1} = a$ where a is a constant. Hence the net is $p-1$, O.

If, however, $\sum a_i^2 = 0$, that is, if the relation is *isotropic*, we can choose the orthogonal substitution so that (7) is reducible to

$$\overline{a}_{p-2}\,\overline{y}_{p-2} + \overline{a}_{p-1}\,\overline{y}_{p-1} = a,$$

where now $\overline{a}^2_{p-2} + \overline{a}^2_{p-1} = 0$. Hence

$$\overline{y}_{p-1} = \pm i\,\overline{y}_{p-2} + b,$$

where b is a constant. Since any complementary function may be replaced by itself with an additive constant, we have

$$y_1^2 + \ldots + y_{p-1}^2 = \overline{y}_1^2 + \ldots + \overline{y}_{p-3}^2.$$

Hence the net is $p-2$, O, and we have:

When for a net apparently p, O, there is an isotropic linear relation between the complementary functions, the net is in fact *p—2, O; when there is a non-isotropic linear relation, the net is p—1, O.*

We say that a congruence is I, when its direction-parameters X satisfy the conditions

$$(8)\qquad \begin{cases} \sum X^2 = 0, \\ \sum \left(\frac{\partial X}{\partial u}\right)^2 \neq 0, \quad \sum \left(\frac{\partial X}{\partial v}\right)^2 \neq 0. \end{cases}$$

Since the X's satisfy an equation of the form

$$(9)\qquad \frac{\partial^2 \theta}{\partial u\, \partial v} = \frac{\partial \log A}{\partial v}\frac{\partial \theta}{\partial u} + \frac{\partial \log B}{\partial u}\frac{\partial \theta}{\partial v} + C\theta,$$

it follows from the first of (8) that

$$(10)\qquad \sum \frac{\partial X}{\partial u}\frac{\partial X}{\partial v} = 0.$$

It is readily seen that these conditions are satisfied also when each X is replaced by λX, where λ is any function of u and v.

A congruence is p, I when there are $p—1$ functions Y satisfying (9) such that

$$(11)\qquad \begin{cases} \sum X^2 - \sum Y^2 = 0, \\ \sum \left(\frac{\partial X}{\partial u}\right)^2 - \sum \left(\frac{\partial Y}{\partial u}\right)^2 \neq 0, \quad \sum \left(\frac{\partial X}{\partial v}\right)^2 - \sum \left(\frac{\partial Y}{\partial v}\right)^2 \neq 0. \end{cases}$$

The functions Y are called the *complementary* functions of the congruence p, I. We have also

$$(12)\qquad \sum \frac{\partial X}{\partial u}\frac{\partial X}{\partial v} - \sum \frac{\partial Y}{\partial u}\frac{\partial Y}{\partial v} = 0.$$

When a congruence is 2, I, we may choose for the parameters the X's divided by the single complementary function. In this case we have

$$(13)\qquad \sum X^2 = 1, \qquad \sum \frac{\partial X}{\partial u}\frac{\partial X}{\partial v} = 0,$$

so that a congruence 2, I is the generalization of the normal congruence in 3-space.

62. Nets conjugate to congruences I and p, I. In § 5 we saw that if θ is a solution of (9), the functions x' defined by

$$X = \frac{x}{\theta} \tag{14}$$

are the cartesian coordinates of a net N' whose radii vectores from the origin are parallel to the lines of a congruence G of direction-parameters X.

If G is a congruence I, we have from (8)

$$\sum x'^2 = 0 \tag{15}$$

and

$$\begin{cases} \sum\left(\frac{\partial x'}{\partial u}\right)^2 = \frac{1}{\theta^2}\sum\left(\frac{\partial X}{\partial u}\right)^2 \neq 0, \quad \sum\left(\frac{\partial x'}{\partial v}\right)^2 \neq 0, \\ \sum \frac{\partial x'}{\partial u}\frac{\partial x'}{\partial v} = 0. \end{cases} \tag{16}$$

Hence N' is a net O. In consequence of the second theorem of § 5 and the last of (16) we have:

All nets conjugate to a congruence I *are* O.

If G is a congruence p, I, the $p-1$ functions y' defined by

$$y' = \frac{Y}{\theta} \tag{17}$$

are solutions of the point equation of N'. In consequence of (11) and (12) we have

$$\begin{cases} \sum\left(\frac{\partial x'}{\partial u}\right)^2 - \sum\left(\frac{\partial y'}{\partial u}\right)^2 \neq 0, \quad \sum\left(\frac{\partial x'}{\partial v}\right)^2 - \sum\left(\frac{\partial y'}{\partial v}\right)^2 \neq 0, \\ \sum \frac{\partial x'}{\partial u}\frac{\partial x'}{\partial v} - \sum \frac{\partial y'}{\partial u}\frac{\partial y'}{\partial v} = 0. \end{cases} \tag{18}$$

Hence in general N' is a net p, O. When, however,

$$\theta = a_1 Y_1 + \ldots + a_{p-1} Y_{p-1}, \qquad \left(\sum a_i^2 \neq 0\right) \tag{19}$$

there is a non-isotropic linear relation between the functions y', and N' is $p-1$, O (cf. § 61). When in (19),

$$\sum a_i^2 = 0, \tag{20}$$

there is an isotropic linear relation between the functions y', and N' is $p-2$, O.

We have shown that the nets conjugate to the given congruence are parallel to nets of the type (14), and are given by equations of the form (I, 12). By means of the same equations we obtain $p-1$ functions y from the functions y'. It is readily seen that these functions satisfy equations of the same form as (18). Hence the nets conjugate to the congruence are of the same type as the parallel nets N'. In accordance with the fifth theorem of § 5 there are ∞^1 of these nets parallel to each net N'. If we call them a *parallel family*, we have:

Of the nets conjugate to a congruence p, I, there are
∞^{p-3} parallel families of nets $p-2$, O,
∞^{p-2} parallel families of nets $p-1$, O,
the others are p, O.

In particular, we have:

Of the nets conjugate to a congruence 2, I there is one parallel family of nets O, and all the others are 2, O.

The nets O arise from the case when θ in (17) is equal to Y.

For a congruence 3, I, when θ is equal to $Y_1 + iY_2$ or $Y_1 - iY_2$ condition (20) is satisfied, and only in this case. Hence:

Of the nets conjugate to a congruence 3, I there are
two parallel families of nets O,
∞^1 parallel families of nets 2, O,
all the others are 3, O.

63. Orthogonal determinants. Since $F=0$ for an O net, it follows from (I, 3) that a and b in (1) may be chosen so that

$$a = \sqrt{E}, \qquad b = \sqrt{G}, \tag{21}$$

in which case the normal parameters ξ^i and η^i of the net, given by

$$\frac{\partial x}{\partial u} = \sqrt{E}\,\xi, \qquad \frac{\partial x}{\partial v} = \sqrt{G}\,\eta, \tag{22}$$

are the direction-cosines and are in the relations

$$\sum \xi^2 = \sum \eta^2 = 1, \qquad \sum \xi\eta = 0. \tag{23}$$

In this case (I, 6, 7) become

$$\frac{\partial \xi}{\partial v} = n\eta, \qquad \frac{\partial \eta}{\partial u} = m\xi, \tag{24}$$

and

$$n = \frac{1}{\sqrt{E}}\frac{\partial \sqrt{G}}{\partial u}, \qquad m = \frac{1}{\sqrt{G}}\frac{\partial \sqrt{E}}{\partial v}. \tag{25}$$

Consider now the orthogonal determinant

$$\Delta = \begin{vmatrix} X_1^1 & X_1^2 \ldots\ldots X_1^n \\ X_2^1 & X_2^2 \ldots\ldots X_2^n \\ \ldots\ldots & \ldots\ldots\ldots\ldots \\ X_{n-2}^1 & X_{n-2}^2 \ldots X_{n-2}^n \\ \xi^1 & \xi^2 \ldots\ldots \xi^n \\ \eta^1 & \eta^2 \ldots\ldots \eta^n \end{vmatrix}, \tag{26}$$

the X's being functions of u and v satisfying the conditions

$$\sum_{i=1}^{n} X_k^{i2} = 1, \quad \sum_{i=1}^{n} X_k^i X_j^i = 0, \quad \sum_{i=1}^{n} \xi^i X_k^i = 0, \quad \sum_{i=1}^{n} \eta^i X_k^i = 0. \tag{27}$$

Therefore we may look upon these functions as the direction-parameters of n mutually perpendicular lines. Since the first derivatives of the X's of any row are direction-parameters of some direction in the space, they are expressible as linear homogeneous functions of the other terms of the same column. It is our purpose to show that there is a set of X's such that the latter expressions take the simple form

$$\frac{\partial X_k}{\partial u} = a_k \xi, \qquad \frac{\partial X_k}{\partial v} = b_k \eta, \qquad (k = 1, 2, \ldots . n-2), \tag{28}$$

and

$$\frac{\partial \xi}{\partial u} = -\sum_k a_k X_k - m\eta, \qquad \frac{\partial \eta}{\partial v} = -\sum_k b_k X_k - n\xi, \tag{29}$$

the ξ, η and the X's in each equation having the same superscript, and a_k, b_k, m and n being the same for all values of the superscripts of ξ, η and the X's.

From (24), (28), and (29) we get

$$\begin{aligned}
\frac{\partial^2 \xi}{\partial u \partial v} &= \frac{\partial n}{\partial u}\eta + m n \xi \\
&= -\sum_k\left(\frac{\partial a_k}{\partial v}X_k + a_k b_k \eta - m b_k X_k\right) - \eta\frac{\partial m}{\partial v} + m n \xi, \\
\frac{\partial^2 \eta}{\partial u \partial v} &= -\sum_k\left(\frac{\partial b_k}{\partial u}X_k + a_k b_k \xi - n a_k X_k\right) - \xi\frac{\partial n}{\partial u} + m n \eta \\
&= \frac{\partial m}{\partial v}\xi + m n \eta, \\
\frac{\partial^2 X_k}{\partial u \partial v} &= \frac{\partial a_k}{\partial v}\xi + a_k n \eta = \frac{\partial b_k}{\partial u}\eta + b_k m \xi.
\end{aligned}$$

Since there are n equations of each of these types, obtained by letting the superscript i take values $1, 2, \ldots . n$, the following $2n-3$ relations must be satisfied:

$$(30) \qquad \left\{\begin{aligned}
&\frac{\partial a_k}{\partial v} = m b_k, \qquad \frac{\partial b_k}{\partial u} = n a_k, \\
&\frac{\partial m}{\partial v} + \frac{\partial n}{\partial u} + \sum_k a_k b_k = 0.
\end{aligned}\right.$$

In consequence of (25) the last of these is equivalent to

$$(31) \quad \frac{\partial}{\partial v}\left(\frac{1}{\sqrt{G}}\frac{\partial \sqrt{E}}{\partial v}\right) + \frac{\partial}{\partial u}\left(\frac{1}{\sqrt{E}}\frac{\partial \sqrt{G}}{\partial u}\right) + \sum_k a_k b_k = 0.$$

Whenever we have a set of functions satisfying these equations, the system (24), (28) and (29) is completely integrable. Moreover, from the form of the equations of the system it follows that each set of solutions satisfies the conditions

$$(32) \qquad \left\{\begin{aligned}
&\sum_k X_k^{i^2} + \xi^{i^2} + \eta^{i^2} = \text{const.}, \\
&\sum_k X_k^i X_k^j + \xi^i \xi^j + \eta^i \eta^j = \text{const.}
\end{aligned}\right.$$

Hence by a suitable choice of the constants of integration the functions will satisfy (27). It can be shown, as in the case of three dimensions [cf. § 65], that the most general solution can be obtained from a particular solution by effecting an orthogonal substitution with constant coefficients on the elements of the determinant Δ; thus

$$(33)\qquad X_k^{i'} = \sum_{j=1}^{n} \alpha_i^j X_k^j, \qquad \xi^{i'} = \sum_{j=1}^{n} \alpha_i^j \xi^j, \qquad \eta^{i'} = \sum_{j=1}^{n} \alpha_i^j \eta^j.$$

A determinant of the type (26) satisfying the conditions (24), (28), (29) and (30) is called *an orthogonal determinant in space of n dimensions.*

Suppose we have $2n$ functions ξ and η satisfying conditions of the form (23) and (24). We inquire whether there exists a corresponding orthogonal determinant Δ for which these functions are the elements of the last two rows.

By purely algebraic processes we can find $n(n-2)$ functions Y_j^i, $(i=1,\dots n;\ j=1,\dots n-2)$ such that

$$\begin{vmatrix} Y_1^1 & \dots\dots & Y_1^n \\ - & - & - \\ Y_{n-2}^1 & \dots & Y_{n-2}^n \\ \xi^1 & \dots\dots & \xi^n \\ \eta^1 & \dots\dots & \eta^n \end{vmatrix}$$

is the determinant of an orthogonal substitution. Since

$$\sum_{i=1}^{n} Y_j^i \xi^i = 0, \qquad \sum_{i=1}^{n} Y_j^i \eta^i = 0,$$

we have equations of the form

$$(34)\qquad \begin{cases} \dfrac{\partial Y_j^i}{\partial u} = \sum\limits_k P_{jk} Y_k^i + A_j \xi^i, \\ \dfrac{\partial Y_j^i}{\partial v} = \sum\limits_k Q_{jk} Y_k^i + B_j \eta^i, \\ \dfrac{\partial \xi^i}{\partial u} = -\sum A_k Y_k^i - m\eta^i, \qquad \dfrac{\partial \xi^i}{\partial v} = n\eta^i, \\ \dfrac{\partial \eta^i}{\partial u} = m\xi^i, \qquad \dfrac{\partial \eta^i}{\partial v} = -\sum B_k Y_k^i - n\xi^i, \end{cases}$$

where $i = 1, \ldots n$; $j, k = 1, \ldots n-2$ $(j \neq k)$. Expressing the condition of integrability of the first two equations, we find that the functions P, Q, A, B must satisfy the following equations:

$$(35)\qquad \begin{cases} \dfrac{\partial}{\partial v} P_{jl} - \dfrac{\partial}{\partial u} Q_{jl} = \sum\limits_k Q_{jk} \cdot P_{kl} - \sum\limits_k P_{jk} \cdot Q_{kl}, \\ \qquad\qquad \dfrac{\partial B_j}{\partial u} = \sum\limits_k P_{jk} B_k + A_j n, \\ \qquad\qquad \dfrac{\partial A_j}{\partial v} = \sum\limits_k Q_{jk} A_k + B_j m. \end{cases}$$

We are interested, however, in seeing whether there is a set of Y's for which the first two of (34) shall assume the form (28). Suppose we put

$$X_k^i = y_1^k Y_1^i + y_2^k Y_2^i + \ldots + y_{n-2}^k Y_{n-2}^i \quad \begin{pmatrix} i = 1, 2 \ldots n \\ k = 1, 2 \ldots n-2 \end{pmatrix},$$

where the y's are the elements of an orthogonal substitution of order $n-2$. These functions X_k^i serve with the ξ's and η's to make Δ (26) the determinant of an orthogonal substitution of order n. We have accordingly in the general case equations of the form (34). If, however, we wish the first two to be of the form (28), the functions y must satisfy the equations

$$(36)\qquad \frac{\partial y_l^k}{\partial u} + \sum_{j=1}^{n-2} y_j^k P_{jl} = 0, \qquad \frac{\partial y_l^k}{\partial v} + \sum_{j=1}^{n-2} y_j^k Q_{jl} = 0.$$

The conditions of integrability of these equations reduce to the first equation (35). But all of the latter are satisfied, and hence there exist solutions of (36). Hence we have the theorem:

When $2n$ *functions* ξ *and* η *are known satisfying* (23) *and* (24), *there exist functions* X_j^i *which with* ξ *and* η *form an orthogonal determinant* Δ.

From the form of (36) it follows that the functions y are determined to within an orthogonal substitution with constants coefficients. The effect of such a substitution on the y's is equivalent to an orthogonal substitution of the form

$$X'^i_k = \sum_{j=1}^{n-2} \alpha^j_k X^i_j$$

on the elements of the columns of the matrix of the first $n-2$ rows of Δ. Hence the last two rows of an orthogonal determinant Δ determine Δ to within such an orthogonal substitution with constant coefficients effected upon the matrix of the first $n-2$ rows of Δ.

When an O net is known, the functions ξ and η can be found at once, and the further problem of putting its determinant in the canonical form requires the solution of $2(n-2)$ completely integrable equations of the form (36). Guichard[50] calls this a *problem of the order* $n-2$. In particular for a net in 5-space this is equivalent to finding the direction-cosines of an O net in 3-space when the rotations of its trihedral are known. In [§ 65] we saw that this requires the solution of a Riccati equation.

64. Determination of O nets. We consider now the determination of the O nets corresponding to a given orthogonal determinant. Evidently the coordinates x of any net N are expressible in the form

$$x = \sum_{k=1}^{n-2} p_k X_k + q\xi + r\eta, \tag{37}$$

the superscripts of x, X, ξ, and η being the same, and p_k, q and r being functions of u and v independent of the superscript of x. We have now to find the conditions to be satisfied by p_k, q and r in order that (37) be the equation of the net.

By differentiation of (37) we find

$$\frac{\partial x}{\partial u} = \sum_{k=1}^{n-2}\left(\frac{\partial p_k}{\partial u} - a_k q\right)X_k + \xi\left(\sum_k a_k p_k + \frac{\partial q}{\partial u} + mr\right) + \eta\left(\frac{\partial r}{\partial u} - qm\right),$$

$$\frac{\partial x}{\partial v} = \sum_{k=1}^{n-2}\left(\frac{\partial p_k}{\partial v} - b_k r\right)X_k + \xi\left(\frac{\partial q}{\partial v} - rn\right) + \eta\left(\sum_k b_k p_k + \frac{\partial r}{\partial v} + nq\right).$$

Equating these expressions to those of (22), we see that we must have

---

50) L. c., p. 500.

$$(38)\qquad \begin{cases} \dfrac{\partial p_k}{\partial u} = a_k q, \quad \dfrac{\partial p_k}{\partial v} = b_k r, \\ \dfrac{\partial q}{\partial u} = -\sum_k a_k p_k - m r + \sqrt{E}, \quad \dfrac{\partial q}{\partial v} = n r, \\ \dfrac{\partial r}{\partial u} = m q, \quad \dfrac{\partial r}{\partial v} = -\sum_k b_k p_k - n q + \sqrt{G}, \end{cases}$$

where m and n are given by (25).

By differentiating these equations, we find that they form a completely integrable system, and consequently their solution involves n arbitrary constants.

We find also that a function p_k and the n functions X_k^i are solutions of the equation

$$(39)\qquad \frac{\partial^2 \theta_k}{\partial u \partial v} = \frac{\partial \log a_k}{\partial v}\frac{\partial \theta_k}{\partial u} + \frac{\partial \log b_k}{\partial u}\frac{\partial \theta_k}{\partial v}.$$

Suppose now that we have a solution of any one of these $n-2$ equations, say p_l. From the equations

$$\frac{\partial p_l}{\partial u} = a_l q, \quad \frac{\partial p_l}{\partial v} = b_l r$$

we find two functions q and r. Then from the other $2n-3$ equations of this type we find by quadratures the functions p_k. When these values are substituted in (37), we have an O net corresponding to the given orthogonal determinant. Hence:

The determination of the O nets corresponding to a given orthogonal determinant is equivalent to the integration of any one of the $n-2$ equations of Laplace (39).

We shall speak of p_k and X_k^i as the *tangential coordinates* of the O net defined by (37).

From (3) and (37) we have

$$(40)\qquad 2\omega = \sum p_k^2 + q^2 + r^2.$$

Making use of (38), we find

$$(41)\qquad \frac{\partial \omega}{\partial u} = \sqrt{E} q, \quad \frac{\partial \omega}{\partial v} = \sqrt{G} r.$$

As an immediate consequence of these equations we have the theorem:

A necessary and sufficient condition that an O net corresponding to a given orthogonal determinant be such that $\sum x^2$ is constant is that its coordinates be given by

$$x = \sum_{k=1}^{n-2} e_k X_k, \tag{42}$$

in which the e's are constant.

When we have a solution θ of the point equation (1) of an O net N, the functions q and r given by

$$\frac{\partial \theta}{\partial u} = \sqrt{E} q, \qquad \frac{\partial \theta}{\partial v} = \sqrt{G} r, \tag{43}$$

satisfy the fourth and fifth of equations (38). These functions and the functions $p_k (k = 1, \ldots, n-2)$ obtained by the quadratures

$$\frac{\partial p_k}{\partial u} = a_k q, \qquad \frac{\partial p_k}{\partial v} = b_k r, \tag{44}$$

determine an O net N', whose coordinates are of the form

$$x' = \sum p_k X_k + q\xi + r\eta, \tag{45}$$

and which corresponds to the same orthogonal determinant as N. Since the p's are determined only to within additive constants, there are ∞^{n-2} nets N' corresponding to a solution θ of (1).

From (41) and (43) it follows that when $\theta = \omega$, N' coincides with N. When θ is a constant, we have the case of the preceding theorem. Hence we have:

Each solution of the point equation of an O net N other than ω given by (3) leads by quadratures alone to ∞^{n-2} nets N' corresponding to the same orthogonal determinant as N.

By means of (40) and (41) we establish the converse theorem:

Each net parallel to an O net N gives by quadratures a solution of the point equation of N.

65. Congruences conjugate to O nets. From § 5 it follows that the direction-parameters of any congruence conjugate to an O net N can be chosen so that they are the cartesian coordinates of a net N' parallel to N, and therefore corresponding to the same orthogonal determinant. These nets N' are of three kinds.

1°. When the coordinates of N' are of the form (42) with the e's in the isotropic relation

$$\sum e_k^2 = 0, \tag{46}$$

the congruence is I. Evidently there are ∞^{n-4} such congruences.

2°. When in (42) the constants satisfy

$$\sum e_k^2 = 1, \tag{47}$$

the congruence is 2, I; there are ∞^{n-3} such congruences.

3°. For the others, if we put

$$X_i = x'^i, \qquad Y_1 = \frac{1}{2}(\sum x'^2 + 1), \qquad Y_2 = \frac{i}{2}(\sum x'^2 - 1),$$

we have

$$\sum X^2 = Y_1^2 + Y_2^2,$$

$$\sum \left(\frac{\partial X}{\partial u}\right)^2 - \left(\frac{\partial Y_1}{\partial u}\right)^2 - \left(\frac{\partial Y_2}{\partial u}\right)^2 = \sum \left(\frac{\partial x'}{\partial u}\right)^2 \neq 0,$$

$$\sum \left(\frac{\partial X}{\partial v}\right)^2 - \left(\frac{\partial Y_1}{\partial v}\right)^2 - \left(\frac{\partial Y_2}{\partial v}\right)^2 = \sum \left(\frac{\partial x'}{\partial v}\right)^2 \neq 0.$$

Hence all the other congruences are 3, I, and we have:

Of the congruences conjugate to an O net in n-space, ∞^{n-4} are I, ∞^{n-3} *are* 2, I, *and all the rest are* 3, I.

In view of the second theorem of § 64 and the above results we remark:

1°. In 3-space of the congruences conjugate to an O net, one is 2, I and the others are 3, I.

2°. In 4-space of the congruences conjugate to an O net, two are I, their parameters being $X_1 + iX_2$ and $X_1 - iX_2$; ∞^1 are 2, I and the others are 3, I.

66. Transformations F of an O net for which the conjugate congruence is normal to the net. A congruence of direction-parameters X is said to be *normal* to a net $N(x)$, if

$$\sum X \frac{\partial x}{\partial u} = 0, \quad \sum X \frac{\partial x}{\partial v} = 0. \tag{48}$$

When we take for the direction-parameters the cartesian coordinates x' of a suitably chosen net N' parallel to N, these equations of condition may be replaced by

$$\sum x' \frac{\partial x'}{\partial u} = 0, \quad \sum x' \frac{\partial x'}{\partial v} = 0,$$

from which follow

$$(49) \qquad \sum x'^2 = k, \quad \sum \frac{\partial x'}{\partial u}\frac{\partial x'}{\partial v} = 0, \quad \sum \frac{\partial x}{\partial u}\frac{\partial x}{\partial v} = 0,$$

where k is a constant. Hence the congruence is I or 2, I, according as k is zero or not, provided that

$$(50) \qquad \sum \left(\frac{\partial x}{\partial u}\right)^2 \neq 0, \quad \sum \left(\frac{\partial x}{\partial v}\right)^2 \neq 0,$$

which we assume to be the case. Furthermore from (49) we see that N and N' are O nets. Hence:

A congruence conjugate to a net for which (50) *holds can be normal to N only in case N is an O net; then the congruence is* I *or* 2, I.

Conversely:

A congruence I or 2, I *is normal to the O nets conjugate to it.*

If a congruence G conjugate to an O net N is normal to N, it follows from the second theorem of § 64 that the coordinates $\hat{x}$ of the parallel net $\hat{N}$ determining the congruence are of the form

$$(51) \qquad \hat{x} = \sum_{k=1}^{n-2} e_k X_k,$$

where the e's are constants. By differentiation we have in consequence of (22) and (28)

$$(52) \qquad \frac{\partial \hat{x}}{\partial u} = \hat{h}\frac{\partial x}{\partial u}, \quad \frac{\partial \hat{x}}{\partial v} = \hat{l}\frac{\partial x}{\partial v},$$

where

$$(53) \qquad \hat{h} = \sum_{k=1}^{n-2} \frac{e_k a_k}{\sqrt{E}}, \quad \hat{l} = \sum_{k=1}^{n-2} \frac{e_k b_k}{\sqrt{G}}.$$

An F transform $N_0(x_0)$ of N for which G is the conjugate congruence is given by (§ 15)

$$x_0 = x - \frac{\theta}{\hat{\theta}}\hat{x}, \tag{54}$$

where θ is a solution of the point equation of N, and

$$\frac{\partial \hat{\theta}}{\partial u} = \hat{h}\frac{\partial \theta}{\partial u}, \qquad \frac{\partial \hat{\theta}}{\partial v} = \hat{l}\frac{\partial \theta}{\partial v}. \tag{55}$$

If p_k are the solutions of (43) and (44) for this function θ, we find that these equations are satisfied by

$$\hat{\theta} = \sum_{k=1}^{n-2} e_k p_k. \tag{56}$$

We assume that it is this value of $\hat{\theta}$ which is used in (54) to determine N_0 (cf. § 17).

From (II, 9) we have

$$\frac{\partial x_0}{\partial u} = \frac{\tau}{\hat{\theta}^2}\left(\hat{x}\frac{\partial \theta}{\partial u} - \hat{\theta}\frac{\partial x}{\partial u}\right), \qquad \frac{\partial x_0}{\partial v} = \frac{\sigma}{\hat{\theta}^2}\left(\hat{x}\frac{\partial \theta}{\partial v} - \hat{\theta}\frac{\partial x}{\partial v}\right), \tag{57}$$

and consequently

$$\sum \frac{\partial x_0}{\partial u}\frac{\partial x_0}{\partial v} = \frac{\tau\sigma}{\hat{\theta}^4}\left(\sum \hat{x}^2 \frac{\partial \theta}{\partial u}\frac{\partial \theta}{\partial v} - \sum \hat{x}\frac{\partial x}{\partial u}\hat{\theta}\frac{\partial \theta}{\partial v} - \sum \hat{x}\frac{\partial x}{\partial v}\hat{\theta}\frac{\partial \theta}{\partial v}\right). \tag{58}$$

When the congruence is I, that is when (46) holds, then $\sum \frac{\partial x_0}{\partial u}\frac{\partial x_0}{\partial v} = 0$, whatever be θ. Hence all the F transforms are O nets (cf. § 62).

When G is 2, I, that is when (47) holds, we have from (58)

$$\sum \frac{\partial x_0}{\partial u}\frac{\partial x_0}{\partial v} - \frac{\partial \theta_0}{\partial u}\frac{\partial \theta_0}{\partial v} = 0, \tag{59}$$

where θ_0, given by

$$\theta_0 = -\frac{\theta}{\hat{\theta}}, \tag{60}$$

is the solution of the point equation of N_0 which determines N as an F transform of N_0 (§ 16). Since (59) is the condition that $\sum x_0^2 - \theta_0^2$ be a solution of the point equation of N_0, we have that N_0 is a net 2, O, θ_0 being the complementary function. Furthermore from (54) and (60) we have

$$\sum (x - x_0)^2 = \theta_0^2. \tag{61}$$

From (44), (56), (59) and (60) it follows that, when θ in (43) is constant, N_0 is an O net and is parallel to N (§ 16). Hence:

The F transforms of an O net for which the congruences of the transformations are normal to N are O nets and 2, O nets; when the transform is 2, O, the complementary function is equal to the distance between corresponding points on N and the transform.

When in particular $\theta = \omega$, we have from (52) $\sum x\hat{x} = \hat{\omega}$, where $\hat{\omega}$ is the corresponding solution of (55). Hence $\sum x_0^2 = \theta_0^2$, that is, the hyperspheres with centers on N_0 and radii given by θ_0 pass through the origin. Each of the ∞^{n-3} congruences normal to an O net is conjugate to a net of this kind[51]).

67. Transformations F of O nets into O nets. In § 65 we saw that in n-space the congruences conjugate to an O net are I, 2, I or 3, I. In the preceding section we discussed the transformations F of O nets for which the congruence of the transformation is I or 2, I. We consider now the case where the congruence is 3, I. We recall (§ 62) that in addition to N and its parallels there is one other family of parallel O nets conjugate to the congruence. We shall make a study of the transformation F of $N(x)$ into one of the nets of the second family, say $N_1(x_1)$.

We recall from § 15 that the coordinates of N_1 are given by

$$x_1 = x - \frac{\theta}{\theta'} x', \tag{62}$$

where

$$\frac{\partial x'}{\partial u} = h \frac{\partial x}{\partial u}, \qquad \frac{\partial x'}{\partial v} = l \frac{\partial x}{\partial v}, \tag{63}$$

---

[51]) Similar results follow when $\theta = \frac{1}{2} \Sigma (x - a)^2$, where the a's are constant. In this case the spheres pass through the point whose coordinates are the a's. We shall refer to this as the case where $\theta = \omega$.

and

$$\frac{\partial \theta'}{\partial u} = h\frac{\partial \theta}{\partial u}, \qquad \frac{\partial \theta'}{\partial v} = l\frac{\partial \theta}{\partial v}. \tag{64}$$

Also we have

$$\frac{\partial x_1}{\partial u} = \frac{\tau}{\theta'^2 h}\left(x'\frac{\partial \theta'}{\partial u} - \theta'\frac{\partial x'}{\partial u}\right), \qquad \frac{\partial x'}{\partial v} = \frac{\sigma}{\theta'^2 l}\left(x'\frac{\partial \theta'}{\partial v} - \theta'\frac{\partial x'}{\partial v}\right), \tag{65}$$

τ and σ having the values

$$\tau = h\theta - \theta', \qquad \sigma = l\theta - \theta'. \tag{66}$$

From (65) it follows that a necessary and sufficient condition that N_1 be an O net is that

$$\frac{\partial \theta'}{\partial u}\frac{\partial \theta'}{\partial v}\sum x'^2 - \theta'\frac{\partial \theta'}{\partial u}\sum x'\frac{\partial x'}{\partial v} - \theta'\frac{\partial \theta'}{\partial v}\sum x'\frac{\partial x'}{\partial u} = 0. \tag{67}$$

This equation is satisfied by

$$\theta' = \frac{1}{2}\sum x'^2. \tag{68}$$

The coordinates x' of the net N' parallel to N which are the direction-parameters of the congruence of the transformation are of the form

$$x' = \sum p_k X_k + q\xi + r\eta, \tag{69}$$

where p_k, q and r satisfy equations (38) with E and G replaced by E' and G', the first fundamental coefficients of N'. Hence equation (68) may be written

$$\theta' = \frac{1}{2}\sum x'^2 = \frac{1}{2}\left(\sum p_k^2 + q^2 + r^2\right). \tag{70}$$

The corresponding function θ of the transformation is given by the quadratures (64), which are reducible by means of (38) to

$$\frac{\partial \theta}{\partial u} = \sqrt{E}\,q, \qquad \frac{\partial \theta}{\partial v} = \sqrt{G}\,r. \tag{71}$$

From these equations and the results of § 64 it follows that θ is the solution of the point equation of N which determines N'. Hence θ is given by a quadrature and the additive arbitrary constant leads to a family of parallel nets N_1 (§ 16). Accordingly:

Each net N' parallel to a given O net determines ∞^1 parallel O nets each of which is an F transform of N; they are obtained by a quadrature.

Conversely, if θ is any solution of the point equation of N other than ω, and N' is any one of the ∞^{n-2} nets parallel to N determined by θ (§ 64), the function θ' defined by (70) satisfies the corresponding equation (64). Hence:

Each solution of the point equation of N other than ω leads to ∞^{n-2} O nets $N_1(x_1)$ which are F transforms of N; the coordinates x_1 are given by

$$x_1 = x - 2\frac{\theta x'}{\sum x'^2}, \tag{72}$$

where

$$x' = \sum_{k=1}^{n-2} p_k X_k + \frac{1}{\sqrt{E}}\frac{\partial\theta}{\partial u}\xi + \frac{1}{\sqrt{G}}\frac{\partial\theta}{\partial v}\eta, \tag{73}$$

the functions p_k being obtained by the quadratures

$$\frac{\partial p_k}{\partial u} = \frac{a_k}{\sqrt{E}}\frac{\partial\theta}{\partial u}, \qquad \frac{\partial p_k}{\partial v} = \frac{b_k}{\sqrt{G}}\frac{\partial\theta}{\partial v}. \tag{74}$$

Moreover, all of these nets $N_1(x_1)$ are harmonic to the congruence harmonic to N determined by θ.

68. Transformations R. The nets N_0 and N_1 defined by (54) and (62) respectively form with N a triad (§ 20). From (51), (69) and (56) we have

$$\sum x'\hat{x} = \sum e_k p_k = \hat{\theta}. \tag{75}$$

Consequently we obtain from (65) and (60)

$$\sum (x_1 - x_0)\frac{\partial x_1}{\partial u} = 0, \qquad \sum (x_1 - x_0)\frac{\partial x_1}{\partial v} = 0,$$

$$\sum (x_1 - x_0)^2 = \left(\frac{\theta}{\hat{\theta}}\right)^2 = \theta_0^2.$$

From these equations and (61) we remark that the hyperspheres with centers at points of N_0 and radii determined by θ_0 are tangent to N and N_1. Since there are ∞^{n-3} congruences 2, I conjugate and normal to N, there are ∞^{n-3} nets N_0 forming such a triad with N and N_1. Hence:

If N and N_1 are two O nets in the relation of a transformation F, for which the congruence is 3, I, *there are ∞^{n-3} two-parameter families of hyperspheres tangent to N and N_1; the locus of the centers of the hyperspheres of any family is a net N_0 which is* 2, *O, the complementary function being the radius of the hypersphere; the nets N, N_1 and N_0 form a triad under transformations F.*

In view of this result we call the transformation from N into N_1 a *generalized transformation of Ribaucour*[52]), or simply a *transformation R.* We call the corresponding net N_0 a *central net of the transformation.*

From (63), (64) and (68) we have

$$(76) \qquad \sum x' \frac{\partial x}{\partial u} = \frac{\partial \theta}{\partial u}, \qquad \sum x' \frac{\partial x}{\partial v} = \frac{\partial \theta}{\partial v}.$$

By means of these equations, (57) and (75) we find that

$$\sum x' \frac{\partial x_0}{\partial u} = 0, \qquad \sum x' \frac{\partial x_0}{\partial v} = 0.$$

Hence:

The tangent planes of N_0 are normal bisectors of the joins of corresponding points of N and N_1.

Also it follows from § 17 that:

Corresponding tangent planes to N, N_1 and N_0 meet in a line generating a congruence harmonic to each of these nets.

By means of N' we can obtain a transformation R of any net parallel to N (§ 67). From the above results we obtain the theorem:

When a transformation R of a net N is known, a transformation R of any net $\bar{N}$ parallel to N can be found by a quadrature; the transforms of N and $\bar{N}$ are parallel, as are also corresponding central nets of the transformations.

---

52) In his study of cyclic systems Ribaucour considered two-parameter families of spheres in 3-space upon the sheets of whose envelope the lines of curvature correspond. The relation between the two sheets has been called a *transformation of Ribaucour.*

When in particular $\bar{N}$ is N', the transform of $\bar{N}$ is the origin, as follows from (62). This is the case treated at the end of § 66.

From (II, 1) and (68) we have

$$x_1' = \frac{2x'}{\sum x'^2}.$$

Hence:

When N and N_1 are O nets in the relation of a transformation R, the nets N' and N_1' whose coordinates are direction-parameters of the congruence of the transformation may be obtained from one other by inversion.

In § 75 we shall show that only for certain types of O nets do there exist transformations F into non-parallel O nets which are not transformations R. Hence:

In general an inversion is the only radial transformation of an O net into an O net.

The function ω_1, where

$$2\omega_1 = \sum x_1^2, \tag{77}$$

is a solution of the point equation of N_1. We wish to show, furthermore, that ω_1 is the transform of ω by an equation analogous to (62), namely

$$\omega_1 = \omega - \frac{\theta}{\theta'}\omega', \tag{78}$$

where ω' is defined by

$$\frac{\partial \omega'}{\partial u} = h\frac{\partial \omega}{\partial u}, \qquad \frac{\partial \omega'}{\partial v} = l\frac{\partial \omega}{\partial v}. \tag{79}$$

When the expression (62) for x_1 is substituted in (78), the latter reduces to

$$\theta + \omega' - \sum xx' = 0. \tag{80}$$

By differentiating the left-hand member of this equation we find that it is constant. Hence the additive constant of ω' can be chosen so that (80), and consequently (78), is satisfied.

69. Transformations R in another form. From (65) and (68) we have

$$E_1 = \sum\left(\frac{\partial x_1}{\partial u}\right)^2 = \frac{\tau^2 E}{\theta'^2}, \qquad G_1 = \sum\left(\frac{\partial x_1}{\partial v}\right)^2 = \frac{\sigma^2 G}{\theta'^2}. \tag{81}$$

If we choose the algebraic signs of $\sqrt{E_1}$ and $\sqrt{G_1}$, so that

$$(82)\qquad \tau = \theta' \sqrt{\frac{E_1}{E}}, \qquad \sigma = \theta' \sqrt{\frac{G_1}{G}},$$

we have from (66)

$$(83)\qquad h = \frac{\theta'}{\theta}\left(1 + \sqrt{\frac{E_1}{E}}\right), \qquad l = \frac{\theta'}{\theta}\left(1 + \sqrt{\frac{G_1}{G}}\right).$$

If we define a function w by

$$(84)\qquad \theta' = \theta w,$$

equation (70) becomes

$$(85)\qquad \sum_{k=1}^{n-2} p_k^2 + q^2 + r^2 - 2\theta w = 0.$$

The equations (62) of a transformation R may be written

$$(86)\qquad x_1 = x - \frac{1}{w}\left(\sum_{k=1}^{n-2} p_k X_k + q\xi + r\eta\right),$$

where the functions involved satisfy (85) and

$$(87)\qquad \left\{\begin{aligned}
&\frac{\partial \theta}{\partial u} = \sqrt{E}\, q, \qquad \frac{\partial \theta}{\partial v} = \sqrt{G}\, r,\\
&\frac{\partial p_k}{\partial u} = a_k q, \qquad \frac{\partial p_k}{\partial v} = b_k r,\\
&\frac{\partial q}{\partial u} = -\sum_{k=1}^{n-2} a_k p_k - \frac{1}{\sqrt{G}} \frac{\partial \sqrt{E}}{\partial v} r + w(\sqrt{E} + \sqrt{E_1}),\\
&\frac{\partial q}{\partial v} = \frac{1}{\sqrt{E}} \frac{\partial \sqrt{G}}{\partial u} r, \qquad \frac{\partial r}{\partial u} = \frac{1}{\sqrt{G}} \frac{\partial \sqrt{E}}{\partial v} q,\\
&\frac{\partial r}{\partial v} = -\sum_{k=1}^{n-2} b_k p_k - \frac{1}{\sqrt{E}} \frac{\partial \sqrt{G}}{\partial u} q + w(\sqrt{G} + \sqrt{G_1}),\\
&\frac{\partial \log w}{\partial u} = \sqrt{E_1}\, \frac{q}{\theta}, \qquad \frac{\partial \log w}{\partial v} = \sqrt{G_1}\, \frac{r}{\theta}\ {}^{53)}.
\end{aligned}\right.$$

53) The expressions for $\frac{\partial \log w}{\partial u}$ and $\frac{\partial \log w}{\partial v}$ follow from (64), (71), (83) and (84), and those for $\frac{\partial q}{\partial u}$ and $\frac{\partial r}{\partial v}$ are obtained by differentiating (85).

The integrability conditions of this system of equations are satisfied provided that θ is a solution of the point equation of N and that

$$(88)\quad \begin{cases} \dfrac{\partial \sqrt{E_1}}{\partial v} = \sqrt{G_1}\left(\dfrac{1}{\sqrt{G}}\dfrac{\partial \sqrt{E}}{\partial v} - (\sqrt{E}+\sqrt{E_1})\dfrac{r}{\theta}\right), \\[2ex] \dfrac{\partial \sqrt{G_1}}{\partial v} = \sqrt{E_1}\left(\dfrac{1}{\sqrt{E}}\dfrac{\partial \sqrt{G}}{\partial u} - (\sqrt{G}+\sqrt{G_1})\dfrac{q}{\theta}\right), \end{cases}$$

as can be verified readily with the aid of (21), (30) and (31). Moreover, any set of functions satisfying (87) make the left-hand member of (85) constant, as can be shown by differentiation.

If we write

$$(89)\qquad \frac{\partial x_1}{\partial u} = \sqrt{E_1}\,\xi_1, \qquad \frac{\partial x_1}{\partial v} = \sqrt{G_1}\,\eta_1,$$

it follows from (65) and (82) that

$$(90)\qquad \xi_1 = \frac{q}{\theta'}x' - \xi, \qquad \eta_1 = \frac{r}{\theta'}x' - \eta.$$

If we define functions $X_{1,k}$ by

$$(91)\qquad X_{1,k} = \frac{p_k}{\theta'}x' - X_k \qquad (k = 1, \ldots n-2),$$

the functions ξ_1, η_1 and $X_{1,k}$ satisfy equations of the form (27). By differentiation we have

$$(92)\quad \begin{cases} \dfrac{\partial \xi_1}{\partial v} = n_1\,\eta_1, & \dfrac{\partial \eta_1}{\partial u} = m_1\,\xi_1, \\[2ex] \dfrac{\partial X_{1,k}}{\partial u} = a_{1,k}\,\xi_1, & \dfrac{\partial X_{1,k}}{\partial v} = b_{1,k}\,\eta_1, \end{cases}$$

where

$$(93)\quad \begin{cases} n_1 = n - \dfrac{q}{\theta}(\sqrt{G}+\sqrt{G_1}), & m_1 = m - \dfrac{r}{\theta}(\sqrt{E}+\sqrt{E_1}), \\[2ex] a_{1,k} = a_k - \dfrac{p_k}{\theta}(\sqrt{E}+\sqrt{E_1}), & b_{1,k} = b_k - \dfrac{p_k}{\theta}(\sqrt{G}+\sqrt{G_1}). \end{cases}$$

Hence (§ 63) the functions ξ_1, η_1, $X_{1,k}$ are the elements of the orthogonal determinant corresponding to N_1.

70. Inverse of a transformation *R*. Let p_k^{-1}, q^{-1}, r^{-1}, w^{-1} denote the functions determining the inverse transformation by means of which N is obtained from N_1, so that

$$x = x_1 - \frac{1}{w^{-1}}\left(\sum p_k^{-1} X_{1,k} + q^{-1}\xi_1 + r^{-1}\eta_1\right).$$

When this expression for $(x - x_1)$ is equated to that given by (86), and $X_{1,k}$, ξ_1 and η_1 are replaced by their above values it is readily found that

$$p_k^{-1} = \varrho p_k, \qquad q^{-1} = \varrho q, \qquad r^{-1} = \varrho r, \qquad w^{-1} = -\varrho w,$$

where ϱ is to be determined. When we require that these functions and θ^{-1} satisfy an equation analogous to (85), we find that $\theta^{-1} = -\varrho\theta$. Comparing this with (II, 19), we have $\varrho = 1/\theta' = 1/\theta w$. Hence

$$(94) \qquad \begin{cases} p_k^{-1} = \dfrac{p_k}{\theta w}, \qquad q^{-1} = \dfrac{q}{\theta w}, \\ r^{-1} = \dfrac{r}{\theta w}, \qquad w^{-1} = -\dfrac{1}{\theta}, \qquad \theta^{-1} = -\dfrac{1}{w}. \end{cases}$$

By means of (93) we show that these functions satisfy a system of equations of the form (87) for N_1.

From (51), (54), (56), (60) and (91) we find

$$(95) \qquad x_1 - x_0 = \theta_0 \sum e_k X_{1,k},$$

which shows that the parameters of the congruences conjugate to N_1 and N_0 and to N and N_0 are the same linear functions of the quantities $X_{1,k}$ and X_k respectively.

71. Transformations *R* in tangential coordinates. Let P_k, Q and R denote the tangential coordinates of an O-net $N(x)$. They satisfy (cf. § 64)

$$(96) \qquad \begin{cases} \dfrac{\partial P_k}{\partial u} = a_k Q, \qquad \dfrac{\partial P_k}{\partial v} = b_k R, \\ \dfrac{\partial \omega}{\partial u} = \sqrt{E}\,Q, \qquad \dfrac{\partial \omega}{\partial v} = \sqrt{G}\,R, \end{cases}$$

where ω is given by

$$2\omega = \sum P_k^2 + Q^2 + R^2. \tag{97}$$

Also we have

$$x = \sum P_k X_k + Q\xi + R\eta. \tag{98}$$

Equation (80) may be written

$$\omega' = \sum P_k p_k + Qq + Rr - \theta, \tag{99}$$

where p_k, q, r and θ determine a transformation R of N into an O-net $N_1(x_1)$, whose coordinates are of the form

$$x_1 = \sum P_{1,k} X_{1,k} + Q_1 \xi_1 + R_1 \eta_1, \tag{100}$$

the functions $P_{1,k}$, Q_1 and R_1 being the tangential coordinates of N_1.

In consequence of (86), (90) and (91) we have

$$P_{1,k} = \frac{\omega'}{\theta'} p_k - P_k, \quad Q_1 = \frac{\omega'}{\theta'} q - Q, \quad R_1 = \frac{\omega'}{\theta'} r - R. \tag{101}$$

These formulas and (91) define the given transformation R in terms of the tangential coordinates of N and N_1.

72. Theorem of permutability of transformations R. We apply the theorem of permutability of transformations F to the case of transformations R, and assume that N_1 and N_2 are two R transforms of N determined by functions θ_1 and θ_2 respectively, and nets $N'(x')$ and $N''(x'')$.

Now the analogues of (68) are

$$\sum x'^2 = 2\theta_1', \qquad \sum x''^2 = 2\theta_2''. \tag{102}$$

Making use of (II, 31), we obtain

$$\left\{\begin{aligned} \frac{\partial \theta_1}{\partial u} &= \sum x' \frac{\partial x}{\partial u}, & \frac{\partial \theta_1}{\partial v} &= \sum x' \frac{\partial x}{\partial v}, \\ \frac{\partial \theta_2}{\partial u} &= \sum x'' \frac{\partial x}{\partial u}, & \frac{\partial \theta_2}{\partial v} &= \sum x'' \frac{\partial x}{\partial v}. \end{aligned}\right. \tag{103}$$

By means of these results we establish by differentiation that $\sum x' x'' - \theta_1'' - \theta_2'$ is constant.

From the above and (II, 33) we have

$$\sum (x_1''')^2 = 2\,\theta_2'' - 2\frac{\theta_1''}{\theta_1'}\left(\sum x' x'' - \theta_1''\right). \tag{104}$$

The functions θ_1'' and θ_2' are determined to within additive constants. Hence there are ∞^1 cases for which

$$\sum x' x'' - \theta_1'' - \theta_2' = 0. \tag{105}$$

Then, as follows from (II, 38),

$$\theta_{12}''' = \frac{1}{2}\sum (x_1''')^2. \tag{106}$$

Hence, by § 67, N_{12} is an R transform of N_1.

As (105) is symmetrical in functions of the two transformations, N_{12} is an R transform of N_2 also. Consequently:

If N_1 and N_2 are R transforms of an O net N, there are ∞^1 O nets N_{12} which are R transforms of N_1 and N_2, and they can be found by quadratures[54]).

The transformations from N into N_1 and N_2 are given by equations of the form

$$x_i = x - \frac{1}{w_i}\left(\sum p_{i,k} X_k + q_i \xi + r_i \eta\right) \quad (i = 1, 2), \tag{107}$$

where the functions p, q and r are solutions of (87).

If we write the coordinates of $N_1'''(x_1''')$, which are the direction-parameters of the transformation of N_1 into a net N_{12}, in the form

$$x_1''' = \sum_k p_{12,k} X_{1,k} + q_{12}\xi_1 + r_{12}\eta_1, \tag{108}$$

[54]) This theorem is the generalization for n-space of the similar theorem for 3-space established by Bianchi by applying the Lie line-sphere transformation to the theorem of permutability of W congruences; cf. Rendiconti dei Lincei, ser. 5, vol. 13[1] (1904), p. 361.

it follows from (II, 33), (90) and (91) that

$$(109)\quad p_{12,k}=\frac{\theta_2'}{\theta_1'}p_{1,k}-p_{2,k},\qquad q_{12}=\frac{\theta_2'}{\theta_1'}q_1-q_2,\qquad r_{12}=\frac{\theta_2'}{\theta_1'}r_1-r_2.$$

These quantities satisfy the relation

$$\sum_k p_{12,k}^2+q_{12}^2+r_{12}^2=2\,\theta_{12}''',$$

and also because of (II, 37) the equations

$$\frac{\partial\theta_{12}}{\partial u}=\sqrt{E_1}\,q_{12},\qquad \frac{\partial\theta_{12}}{\partial v}=\sqrt{G_1}\,r_{12},$$

$$\frac{\partial p_{12,k}}{\partial u}=a_{1,k}\,q_{12},\qquad \frac{\partial p_{12,k}}{\partial v}=b_{1,k}\,r_{12}.$$

The tangential coordinates of N_{12} are given by the following formulas which are analogous to (91) and (101):

$$(110)\quad \left\{\begin{aligned} X_{12,k}&=\frac{p_{12,k}}{\theta_{12}'''}x_1'''-X_{1,k}, & P_{12,k}&=\frac{\omega_1'''}{\theta_{12}'''}p_{12,k}-P_{1,k},\\ Q_{12}&=\frac{\omega_1'''}{\theta_{12}'''}q_{12}-Q_1, & R_{12}&=\frac{\omega_1'''}{\theta_{12}'''}r_{12}-R_1,\end{aligned}\right.$$

where θ_{12}''' is given by (II, 38) and

$$(111)\quad \omega_1'''=\omega''-\frac{\theta_1''}{\theta_1'}\omega'.$$

When these expressions and those from (101) and (109) are substituted in

$$(112)\quad \left\{\begin{aligned} X_{12,k}&=X_k+\frac{(\theta_2'x''-\theta_2''x')p_{1,k}+(\theta_1''x'-\theta_1'x'')p_{2,k}}{\theta_1'\,\theta_{12}'''},\\ P_{12,k}&=P_k+\frac{\Omega_2 p_{1,k}+\Omega_1 p_{2,k}}{\theta_1'\,\theta_{12}'''},\qquad Q_{12}=Q+\frac{\Omega_2 q_1+\Omega_1 q_2}{\theta_1'\,\theta_{12}'''},\\ R_{12}&=R+\frac{\Omega_2 r_1+\Omega_1 r_2}{\theta_1'\,\theta_{12}'''},\end{aligned}\right.$$

where

$$(113)\quad \Omega_1=\theta_1''\,\omega'-\theta_1'\,\omega'',\qquad \Omega_2=\theta_2'\,\omega''-\theta_2''\,\omega',$$

we find that they are satisfied.

Since the first of (112) involves the direction-cosines of N, the coordinates of N' and N'', and solutions of the point equations of N' and N'', we have the theorem:

If N, N_1, N_2, N_{12} form a quatern under transformations R, $\overline{N}$ is any net parallel to N, and $\overline{N}_1$ and $\overline{N}_2$ are R transforms of $\overline{N}$ parallel to N_1 and N_2 respectively, lines drawn through points of $\overline{N}_1$ and $\overline{N}_2$ parallel to the joins of N_1 and N_2 respectively with N_{12} meet in points of a net $\overline{N}_{12}$ parallel to N_{12}.

73. Cyclic congruences. Let $N(x)$ be any net and $N_1(x_1)$ an F transform defined by (62). The tangent planes to N and N_1 meet in the lines of the congruence harmonic to N determined by θ; the coordinates y and z of the focal points F_1 and F_2 of the congruence are of the forms (II, 22)

$$(114) \qquad y = x - \frac{\theta}{\frac{\partial \theta}{\partial v}} \frac{\partial x}{\partial v}, \qquad z = x - \frac{\theta}{\frac{\partial \theta}{\partial u}} \frac{\partial x}{\partial u}.$$

If M and M_1 denote corresponding points of N and N_1, a necessary and sufficient condition that $F_1 M = F_1 M_1$ is that

$$\sum x'^2 \frac{\partial \theta'}{\partial v} - 2 \sum x' \frac{\partial x'}{\partial v} \cdot \theta' = 0.$$

Hence in order that $F_1 M = F_1 M_1$ and $F_2 M = F_2 M_1$, it is necessary and sufficient that

$$\theta' = c \sum x'^2, \qquad \text{or} \qquad \sum x'^2 = 0,$$

where c is a constant different from zero. In this case N' is an O net, and N and N_1 are O nets. Consequently (§§ 66, 67):

When N and N_1 are in relation F a necessary and sufficient condition that each of the focal points of the harmonic congruence of the transformation be equidistant from the corresponding points of N and N_1 is that N and N_1 be O nets in relation R, or conjugate to a congruence I.

We consider the case for transformations R. In consequence of (22) and (87) the expressions (114) are reducible to the forms

$$(115) \qquad y = x - R_2 \eta, \qquad z = x - R_1 \xi,$$

where

(116) $$R_1 = \frac{\theta}{q}, \qquad R_2 = \frac{\theta}{r}.$$

From these equations and the preceding theorem it follows that the hyperspheres, S_1 and S_2, with centers at the focal points and of radii R_1 and R_2 pass through corresponding points of N and of each of the ∞^{n-2} R transforms of N by means of θ (§ 67). Moreover, since

(117) $$\sum (y-z)^2 = R_1^2 + R_2^2,$$

S_1 and S_2 meet orthogonally. From the fifth theorem of § 10 and the second of § 67 it follows that the hyperspheres with centers at the focal points of any congruence harmonic to an O net N and passing through points of N meet orthogonally and pass through the ∞^{n-2} R transforms of N determined by the solution θ of the point equation of N which determines the harmonic congruence. We call them focal *hyperspheres* of the congruence. In 3-space S_1 and S_2 are spheres meeting in circles orthogonal to ∞^1 R transforms of N, that is in circles of a cyclic system. Conversely, in [§ 177] it was seen that the O nets orthogonal to the circles of a cyclic system are harmonic to the congruence of axes of the circles. Hence we say that for space of any order any congruence harmonic to an O net is a *cyclic congruence*.

From the last theorem of § 13 we have the theorem:

If the direction-parameters X of a cyclic congruence are solutions of the equation

(118) $$\frac{\partial^2 \theta}{\partial u \partial v} = \frac{\partial \log A}{\partial v}\frac{\partial \theta}{\partial u} + \frac{\partial \log B}{\partial u}\frac{\partial \theta}{\partial v} + C\theta,$$

then

(119) $$\sum X^2 = U^2 A^2 + V^2 B^2,$$

where U and V are functions of u and v alone respectively.

In § 116 we show that the condition (119) is characteristic of cyclic congruences.

If we put $X = y - z$, equation (117) is a special form of (119).

In fact, from (I, 54, 55) we have

$$(120)\qquad \frac{\partial y}{\partial u} = \frac{\partial \log R_2}{\partial u}(y-z), \qquad \frac{\partial z}{\partial v} = \frac{\partial \log R_1}{\partial v}(z-y).$$

If we express the condition that X satisfy (118), we have

$$(121)\qquad R_1 = AU, \qquad R_2 = BV,$$

where U and V are functions of u and v alone respectively.

74. Multiply cyclic congruences. Let N and N_1 be two O nets in relation F and let G denote the harmonic congruence of the transformation F. If N and N_1 are R transforms of one another, the focal hyperspheres with centers on the focal nets of G and passing through points of N also pass through the corresponding points of N_1. If, however, N_1 is not an R transform of N, then there are at least two pairs of focal hyperspheres associated with G. If we denote by $\overline{R}_1$ and $\overline{R}_2$ the radii of the focal hyperspheres passing through points of N_1, it follows from (121) that $\overline{R}_1 = U_1 R_1$ and $\overline{R}_2 = V_1 R_2$, where U_1 and V_1 are functions of u and v alone. From (117) it follows that $\overline{R}_1^2 + \overline{R}_2^2 = R_1^2 + R_2^2$. From these two conditions we find that the functions R must be of the forms

$$(122)\qquad R_1 = U\lambda, \quad R_2 = V\lambda; \quad \overline{R}_1 = \lambda\sqrt{U^2 - c}, \quad \overline{R}_2 = \pm\lambda\sqrt{V^2 + c},$$

where c is a constant and λ is to be determined.

From (114), (115) and (122) we have

$$(123)\qquad \frac{\partial \theta}{\partial u} = \frac{\sqrt{E}}{U}\frac{\theta}{\lambda}, \qquad \frac{\partial \theta}{\partial v} = \frac{\sqrt{G}}{V}\frac{\theta}{\lambda}.$$

Since θ must satisfy the point equation of N, namely

$$(124)\qquad \frac{\partial^2 \theta}{\partial u \partial v} = \frac{\partial \log\sqrt{E}}{\partial v}\frac{\partial \theta}{\partial u} + \frac{\partial \log\sqrt{G}}{\partial u}\frac{\partial \theta}{\partial v},$$

we must have

$$(125)\qquad \frac{\partial}{\partial u}\log\frac{\theta}{\lambda} = \frac{V}{U}\frac{1}{\sqrt{G}}\frac{\partial\sqrt{E}}{\partial v}, \qquad \frac{\partial}{\partial v}\log\frac{\theta}{\lambda} = \frac{U}{V}\frac{1}{\sqrt{E}}\frac{\partial\sqrt{G}}{\partial u}.$$

The condition of integrability of these equations is

$$\text{(126)} \qquad \frac{\partial}{\partial v}\left(\frac{V}{U}\frac{1}{\sqrt{G}}\frac{\partial\sqrt{E}}{\partial v}\right)=\frac{\partial}{\partial u}\left(\frac{U}{V}\frac{1}{\sqrt{E}}\frac{\partial\sqrt{G}}{\partial u}\right).$$

From this equation and (31) we have

$$\text{(127)} \qquad \begin{cases} (U^2+V^2)\dfrac{\partial}{\partial v}\left(\dfrac{1}{\sqrt{G}}\dfrac{\partial\sqrt{E}}{\partial v}\right) \\ = UU'\dfrac{1}{\sqrt{E}}\dfrac{\partial\sqrt{G}}{\partial u}-VV'\dfrac{1}{\sqrt{G}}\dfrac{\partial\sqrt{E}}{\partial v}-U^2\sum_k a_k b_k, \\ (U^2+V^2)\dfrac{\partial}{\partial u}\left(\dfrac{1}{\sqrt{E}}\dfrac{\partial\sqrt{G}}{\partial u}\right) \\ = -UU'\dfrac{1}{\sqrt{E}}\dfrac{\partial\sqrt{G}}{\partial u}+VV'\dfrac{1}{\sqrt{G}}\dfrac{\partial\sqrt{E}}{\partial v}-V^2\sum a_k b_k. \end{cases}$$

When a net N satisfies conditions (127), the function θ/λ is found from (125) by a quadrature and then θ from (123) by another quadrature. Since these conditions do not involve the constant c in (122), it follows that:

When a cyclic congruence admits more than one pair of focal hyperspheres cutting orthogonally it admits an infinity of pairs.

In this case we say that congruence is *multiply cyclic.*

The constant factor of integration of (125) can be taken equal to unity in all generality, but the additive constant in (123) gives a family of parallel multiply cyclic congruences. Hence:

When an O net N satisfies the conditions (127) *there is a unique family of parallel multiply cyclic congruences harmonic to it, which can be found by quadratures.*

75. Transformations F of O nets into O nets which are not transformations R. We return to the consideration of the O nets $N(x)$ and $N_1(x_1)$ harmonic to a multiply cyclic congruence, and such that the focal hyperspheres of radii $\overline{R}_1$ and $\overline{R}_2$ given by (122) pass through points of N_1. If we put

$$\text{(128)} \qquad E_1=\sum\left(\frac{\partial x_1}{\partial u}\right)^2, \qquad G_1=\sum\left(\frac{\partial x_1}{\partial v}\right)^2,$$

then from (115) and analogous equations for N_1 we have

$$(129)\quad x-\frac{R_2}{\sqrt{G}}\frac{\partial x}{\partial v}=x_1-\frac{\overline{R}_2}{\sqrt{G_1}}\frac{\partial x_1}{\partial v},\quad x-\frac{R_1}{\sqrt{E}}\frac{\partial x}{\partial u}=x_1-\frac{\overline{R}_1}{\sqrt{E_1}}\frac{\partial x_1}{\partial u}.$$

Substituting in these equations from (62), (122) and (65), we get

$$(130)\quad \sqrt{E_1}=-\frac{\tau}{\theta'}\frac{\sqrt{E}}{U}\sqrt{U^2-c},\quad \sqrt{G_1}=\mp\frac{\sigma}{\theta'}\frac{\sqrt{G}}{V}\sqrt{V^2+c}.$$

When these expressions and those given by (65) are substituted in (128), we get, in consequence of (63), (64) and (123),

$$(131)\quad \frac{\partial}{\partial u}\left(\frac{1}{\theta'}\sum x'^2\right)=ch\frac{\sqrt{E}}{U}\frac{\lambda}{\theta'},\quad \frac{\partial}{\partial v}\left(\frac{1}{\theta'}\sum x'^2\right)=-cl\frac{\sqrt{G}}{V}\frac{\lambda}{\theta}.$$

If we put

$$(132)\quad \frac{\partial \varrho}{\partial u}=\frac{\sqrt{E}}{U}\frac{\lambda}{\theta'},\quad \frac{\partial \varrho}{\partial v}=-\frac{\sqrt{G}}{V}\frac{\lambda}{\theta'},$$

we find that these equations are consistent, and that ϱ so defined is a solution of (124). Consequently ϱ', defined by

$$(133)\quad \frac{\partial \varrho'}{\partial u}=h\frac{\partial \varrho}{\partial u},\quad \frac{\partial \varrho'}{\partial v}=l\frac{\partial \varrho}{\partial v},$$

is a solution of the point equation of the net N'. Hence the integral of (131) is

$$(134)\quad \sum x'^2=c\,\theta'\varrho',$$

where ϱ' is determined only to within an additive constant.

From (129) and (62) we have

$$\frac{R_2}{\sqrt{G}}\frac{\partial x}{\partial v}-\frac{\theta}{\theta'}x'=\frac{\overline{R}_2}{\sqrt{G_1}}\frac{\partial x_1}{\partial v},\quad \frac{R_1}{\sqrt{E}}\frac{\partial x}{\partial u}-\frac{\theta}{\theta'}x'=\frac{\overline{R}_1}{\sqrt{E_1}}\frac{\partial x_1}{\partial u}.$$

Squaring these equations and summing for the x's, we have, in consequence of (122) and (134),

$$(135)\quad 2\sum x'\eta=\frac{c}{V}\left(\frac{\theta\varrho'}{\lambda}-\frac{\theta'}{\theta}\lambda\right),\quad 2\sum x'\xi=\frac{c}{U}\left(\frac{\theta\varrho'}{\lambda}+\frac{\theta'}{\theta}\lambda\right).$$

The coordinates x' of N' are expressible in the form (69), where the functions p_k, q, r are subject to the conditions (cf. 35):

$$(136)\quad \begin{cases} \dfrac{\partial p_k}{\partial u} = a_k q, \qquad \dfrac{\partial p_k}{\partial v} = b_k r, \\ \dfrac{\partial q}{\partial u} = -\sum_k a_k p_k - \dfrac{1}{\sqrt{G}} \dfrac{\partial \sqrt{E}}{\partial v} r + h\sqrt{E}, \quad \dfrac{\partial q}{\partial v} = \dfrac{1}{\sqrt{E}} \dfrac{\partial \sqrt{G}}{\partial u} r, \\ \dfrac{\partial r}{\partial u} = \dfrac{1}{\sqrt{G}} \dfrac{\partial \sqrt{E}}{\partial v} q, \quad \dfrac{\partial r}{\partial v} = -\sum_k b_k p_k - \dfrac{1}{\sqrt{E}} \dfrac{\partial \sqrt{G}}{\partial u} q + l\sqrt{G}. \end{cases}$$

From (135) and (69) we have

$$(137)\quad 2q = \frac{c}{U}\left(\frac{\theta\varrho'}{\lambda} + \frac{\theta'}{\theta}\lambda\right), \qquad 2r = \frac{c}{V}\left(\frac{\theta\varrho'}{\lambda} - \frac{\theta'}{\theta}\lambda\right).$$

Substituting these expressions in the last four of equations (136), we obtain

$$(138)\quad \begin{cases} h\sqrt{E}(U^2 - c) = U^2 \sum_k a_k p_k - UU'q + (U^2 + V^2)\dfrac{1}{\sqrt{G}} \dfrac{\partial \sqrt{E}}{\partial v} r, \\ l\sqrt{G}(V^2 + c) = V^2 \sum_k b_k p_k - VV'r + (U^2 + V^2)\dfrac{1}{\sqrt{E}} \dfrac{\partial \sqrt{G}}{\partial u} q. \end{cases}$$

In consequence of (30), (127) and (136) these expressions for h and l satisfy the equations

$$(139)\quad \frac{\partial h}{\partial v} = (l - h)\frac{\partial \log \sqrt{E}}{\partial v}, \qquad \frac{\partial l}{\partial u} = (h - l)\frac{\partial \log \sqrt{G}}{\partial u}.$$

Hence equations (123), (125), and the following in which q, r, h and l have the expressions (137) and (138) form a completely integrable system:

$$(140)\quad \begin{cases} \dfrac{\partial p_k}{\partial u} = a_k q, \qquad \dfrac{\partial p_k}{\partial v} = b_k r, \\ \dfrac{\partial \varrho'}{\partial u} = h\dfrac{\sqrt{E}}{U}\dfrac{\lambda}{\theta}, \qquad \dfrac{\partial \varrho'}{\partial v} = -l\dfrac{\sqrt{G}}{V}\dfrac{\lambda}{\theta}, \\ \dfrac{\partial \theta'}{\partial u} = h\dfrac{\sqrt{E}}{U}\dfrac{\theta}{\lambda}, \qquad \dfrac{\partial \theta'}{\partial v} = l\dfrac{\sqrt{G}}{V}\dfrac{\lambda}{\theta}. \end{cases}$$

In addition to c the complete integral of the system involves $n+1$ constants of integration, since for each set of solutions the left-hand member of

$$(141)\qquad \sum p_k^2 + q^2 + r^2 - c\theta'\varrho' = 0$$

is constant, and in order that (134) be satisfied, we must choose solutions satisfying (141). Therefore we have the theorem:

If an O net N satisfies the condition (127), *it admits* ∞^{n+2} *transformations F into O nets, which are not R transforms of N; the harmonic congruences of these transformations are multiply cyclic.*

76. Nets 2, O. Let $N(x)$ be a net 2, O in n-space, the complementary function being y. Then $x^{(1)}, \ldots, x^{(n)}, iy$ are the coordinates of an O net N in $n+1$ space. From § 65 it follows that there are ∞^{n-3} nets N' parallel to N for which

$$(142)\qquad \sum x'^2 = y'^2.$$

We say that such a net N' is a *special net* 2, O. Hence there are ∞^{n-3} special nets 2, O parallel to N. If N' is a special net, we effect the transformation F of N by means of the solution y of its equation and the conjugate congruence of direction-parameters x', so that the coordinates x_1 of the transform N_1 are of the form

$$(143)\qquad x_1 = x - \frac{y}{y'}x'.$$

In consequence of (142) we have

$$(144)\qquad \sum (x_1 - x)^2 = y^2.$$

Also in consequence of (142) and the equations

$$(145)\qquad \frac{\partial x'}{\partial u} = h\frac{\partial x}{\partial u},\quad \frac{\partial x'}{\partial v} = l\frac{\partial x}{\partial v},\quad \frac{\partial y'}{\partial u} = h\frac{\partial y}{\partial u},\quad \frac{\partial y'}{\partial v} = l\frac{\partial y}{\partial v},$$

we have from (143) by differentiation $\sum \frac{\partial x_1}{\partial u}\frac{\partial x_1}{\partial v} = 0$, that is N_1 is an O net.

Consider two of these transforms N_1 and N_2 by means of two parallel special nets $N'(x')$ and $N''(x'')$ satisfying (142) and $\sum x''^2 = y''^2$. In consequence of (145) and analogous equations we find that

$$\sum x' x'' - y' y'' = c, \tag{146}$$

where c is a constant. Since N_1 and N_2 are transforms of N by means of y, the nets N, N_1 and N_2 form a triad (§ 20), and N_2 is an F transform of N by means of $-y/y'$, and the corresponding solution $-y''/y'$ of the point equation of the net N_1''', parallel to N_1, whose coordinates are given by (cf. II, 33)

$$x_1''' = x'' - \frac{y''}{y'} x'. \tag{147}$$

In consequence of (146) and (142), we have

$$\sum (x_1''')^2 = -2c \frac{y''}{y'}.$$

Hence if $c = 0$, the conjugate congruence of the transformation from N_1 into N_2 is I. If $c \neq 0$, N_1 and N_2 are in relation R (§ 67). Hence in consequence of (144):

If N is a net 2, O in n-space, the complementary function being y, the net N admits ∞^{n-3} F transforms N_i which are O nets and the corresponding points of these nets lie on the hypersphere of radius y and center at the corresponding point of N; moreover, any two nets N_1 and N_2 are R transforms, unless the congruence of lines joining corresponding points of N_1 and N_2 is I.

When, in particular, N is a net 2, O in 3-space, it follows from the last remark of § 65 that there are two special nets N' parallel to N. Moreover, there are no congruences I conjugate to an O net in 3-space (§ 65). Hence:

If N is a non-special 2, O net in 3-space, the complementary function being y, on the envelope of the spheres of radius y and centers on N the parametric curves form O nets in relation R with one another and in relation F with N.

We return to the consideration of a net N in n-space which is 2, O, the complementary function being y. Let N' be a parallel net; then equations (145) hold. If θ and θ' are corresponding solutions of the point equations of N and N', the equations of the form (62) define an F transform N_1 of N, and the point equation of N_1 admits the solution

$$y_1 = y - \frac{\theta}{\theta'} y'.$$

From these equations we have

$$(148)\quad \sum x_1^2 - y_1^2 = \sum x^2 - y^2 - 2\frac{\theta}{\theta'}\left(\sum xx' - yy'\right) + \frac{\theta^2}{\theta'^2}\left(\sum x'^2 - y'^2\right).$$

Since $\sum x^2 - y^2$ is a solution of the point equation of N, the function σ' defined by

$$(149)\quad \frac{\partial \sigma'}{\partial u} = h\frac{\partial}{\partial u}\left(\sum x^2 - y^2\right), \qquad \frac{\partial \sigma'}{\partial v} = l\frac{\partial}{\partial v}\left(\sum x^2 - y^2\right)$$

is a solution of the point equation of N'. If N' is a special net, a solution of (149) is $\sigma' = 2\left(\sum xx' - yy'\right)$, and equation (148) becomes

$$(150)\quad \sum x_1^2 - y_1^2 = \sum x^2 - y^2 - \frac{\theta}{\theta'}\sigma'.$$

Consequently $\sum x_1^2 - y_1^2$ is the solution of the point equation of N_1 corresponding to the solution $\sum x^2 - y^2$ of the point equation of N whatever be θ.

If N' is not a special net, a solution of its point equation is

$$\theta' = \frac{1}{2}\left(\sum x'^2 - y'^2\right),$$

and the corresponding solution of the point equation of N is given by

$$\frac{\partial \theta}{\partial u} = \sum x' \frac{\partial x}{\partial u} - y' \frac{\partial y}{\partial u}, \qquad \frac{\partial \theta}{\partial v} = \sum x' \frac{\partial x}{\partial v} - y' \frac{\partial y}{\partial v}.$$

In this case a solution of (149) is

$$\sigma' = 2\left(\sum xx' - yy' - \theta\right).$$

By means of this function equation (148) is reducible to (150). Hence:

If N is a net 2, O and N' is a parallel net which is not special, an F transform N_1 of N which is 2, O can be found by a quadrature; if N' is special, each solution of the point equation of N determines an F transform which is 2, O.

Exercises.

1. A net N' parallel to a net N which is p, O is p, O, the complementary functions of N' being solutions of its point equation corresponding to the complementary functions of N.

2. Of the O nets corresponding to a given orthogonal determinant, those defined by

$$x = \sum_{k=1}^{n-2} e_k X_k, \qquad \sum_k e_k^2 = 0,$$

where the e's are constants, lie on the hypercone $\Sigma x^2 = 0$, and any such O net is so determined; for such a net

$$\sqrt{E} = \sum_k e_k a_k, \qquad \sqrt{G} = \sum_k e_k b_k.$$

3. If N is an O net on the hypercone $\Sigma x^2 = 0$, and G is any congruence conjugate to N, the developables of G meet the hypercone in a net which is an R transform of N; for this transformation

$$\theta = \Sigma e_k p_k, \qquad \omega' = 0.$$

4. If N_1 and N_2 are R transforms of a net N and all of these nets lie on the hypercone $\Sigma x^2 = 0$, so also do the nets N_{12} which are R transforms of N_1 and N_2, in accordance with § 72.

5. A congruence parallel to a cyclic congruence is cyclic, and for ∞^1 of the parallel cyclic congruences the circles of the cyclic system pass through a point (cf. § 13).

6. The equation of Laplace satisfied by the direction-parameters of a multiply cyclic congruence has equal invariants.

7. If N is an O net harmonic to a multiply cyclic congruence G, any net N' parallel to N possesses the same property, and the multiply cyclic congruence harmonic to N' is determined by the solution of the point equation of N' corresponding to the solution determining G.

8. Any congruence parallel to a multiply cyclic congruence is multiply cyclic.

9. If N is a net 2, O and N_1 is any O net conjugate to a congruence 2, I conjugate to N, the distance between corresponding points of N and N_1 is the complementary function of N.

10. In order that the first and minus first Laplace transforms of a net N with point equation (1) be O nets it is necessary that a and b can be chosen so that

$$\text{(i)} \qquad \sum\left(\frac{\partial x}{\partial u}\right)^2=\left(\frac{\partial b}{\partial u}\right)^2, \qquad \sum\left(\frac{\partial x}{\partial v}\right)^2=\left(\frac{\partial a}{\partial v}\right)^2.$$

From (I, 3) it follows that we must have

$$\text{(ii)} \quad \begin{cases} \left(\frac{\partial b}{\partial u}\right)^2\left(\frac{\partial a}{\partial v}\right)^2-\left(\sum\frac{\partial x}{\partial u}\frac{\partial x}{\partial v}\right)^2 = a\left(\frac{\partial b}{\partial u}\frac{\partial a}{\partial v}\frac{\partial^2 b}{\partial u\,\partial v}-\frac{\partial^2 a}{\partial u\,\partial v}\sum\frac{\partial x}{\partial u}\frac{\partial x}{\partial v}\right) \\ \qquad = b\left(\frac{\partial b}{\partial u}\frac{\partial a}{\partial v}\frac{\partial^2 a}{\partial u\,\partial v}-\frac{\partial^2 b}{\partial u\,\partial v}\sum\frac{\partial x}{\partial u}\frac{\partial x}{\partial v}\right). \end{cases}$$

The consistency of the equations (ii) necessitates the condition

$$\text{(iii)} \qquad \frac{\partial b}{\partial u}\frac{\partial a}{\partial v}\left(\frac{a}{b}-\frac{b}{a}\right)=a\frac{\partial^2 a}{\partial u\,\partial v}-b\frac{\partial^2 b}{\partial u\,\partial v}.$$

When this condition is satisfied, the equations

$$\text{(iv)} \qquad \frac{\partial \log\sigma}{\partial u}=\frac{1}{a}\frac{\partial b}{\partial u}, \qquad \frac{\partial \log\sigma}{\partial v}=\frac{1}{b}\frac{\partial a}{\partial v}$$

are consistent (Cf. II, Ex. 12) and (ii) may be replaced by

$$\text{(v)} \qquad \sum\frac{\partial x}{\partial u}\frac{\partial x}{\partial v}=ab\frac{\partial^2}{\partial u\,\partial v}\log\sigma.$$

When (i), (iii) and (v) are satisfied, the net N possesses the desired property. We call it a G net.

11. The point equation of a G net N admits the solutions

$$\theta_1=\Sigma x^2-a^2, \qquad \theta_2=\Sigma x^2-b^2.$$

The first Laplace transform of θ_1 is Σx_1^2 and the minus first Laplace transform of θ_2 is Σx_{-1}^2, where x_1 and x_{-1} are the coordinates of the first and minus first Laplace transforms of N.

12. Any net parallel to a G net is a G net. From (II, Ex. 12) and (iii) of Ex. 10 it follows that two of these parallel nets have point equations with equal invariants, and are associates of one another. If the point equation of one of them is written

$$\text{(i)} \qquad \frac{\partial^2\theta}{\partial u\,\partial v}=\frac{\partial\log\sigma}{\partial v}\frac{\partial\theta}{\partial u}+\frac{\partial\log\sigma}{\partial u}\frac{\partial\theta}{\partial v},$$

in place of (i) and (v) of Ex. 10, we have

(ii) $$\sum\left(\frac{\partial x}{\partial u}\right)^2 = \left(\frac{\partial \sigma}{\partial u}\right)^2, \quad \sum\left(\frac{\partial x}{\partial v}\right)^2 = \left(\frac{\partial \sigma}{\partial v}\right)^2, \quad \sum\frac{\partial x}{\partial u}\frac{\partial x}{\partial v} = \sigma^2\frac{\partial^2}{\partial u\,\partial v}\log\sigma.$$

A net G of this type we call a net G_0.

13. The point equation of a net G_0 admits the solution $\theta_0 = \Sigma x^2 - \sigma^2$. The first and minus first Laplace transforms of θ_0 are Σx_1^2 and Σx_{-1}^2.

14. Show that the radial transform of a net G_0 by means of the function $\theta_0 = \Sigma x^2 - \sigma^2$ is a net G_0.

15. If a G net N is subjected to a transformation F for which the direction-parameters of the conjugate congruence of the transformation are the coordinates x' of one of the nets G_0 parallel to N and the function θ' of the transformation is $\Sigma x'^2 - \sigma^2$, the transform is a G net, and its Laplace transforms are R transforms of the corresponding Laplace transforms of N.

Chapter VII.

Transformations of Ribaucour.

77. Orthogonal determinants and O nets in 3-space. In the case of 3-space an orthogonal determinant is of the form

$$(1) \qquad \Delta = \begin{vmatrix} X^1 \ldots\ldots X^3 \\ \xi^1 \ldots\ldots \xi^3 \\ \eta^1 \ldots\ldots \eta^3 \end{vmatrix}$$

Now

$$(2) \qquad \begin{cases} \dfrac{\partial X}{\partial u} = a\xi, & \dfrac{\partial X}{\partial v} = b\eta, \\[2ex] \dfrac{\partial \xi}{\partial u} = -aX - m\eta, & \dfrac{\partial \xi}{\partial v} = n\eta, \\[2ex] \dfrac{\partial \eta}{\partial u} = m\xi, & \dfrac{\partial \eta}{\partial v} = -bX - n\xi, \end{cases}$$

whereas it follows from [§ 65] that

$$(3) \qquad \begin{cases} a = -\dfrac{D}{\sqrt{E}} = -\dfrac{\sqrt{E}}{\varrho_1}, & b = -\dfrac{D''}{\sqrt{G}} = -\dfrac{\sqrt{G}}{\varrho_2}, \\[2ex] m = \dfrac{1}{\sqrt{G}} \dfrac{\partial \sqrt{E}}{\partial v}, & n = \dfrac{1}{\sqrt{E}} \dfrac{\partial \sqrt{G}}{\partial u}, \\[2ex] \dfrac{\partial a}{\partial v} = mb, & \dfrac{\partial b}{\partial u} = na, \end{cases}$$

where ϱ_1 and ϱ_2 are the radii of principal curvature of an O net corresponding to Δ.

When an orthogonal determinant is known, the coordinates of a corresponding net are of the form (cf. VI, 37)

(4) $$x = PX + Q\xi + R\eta,$$

where, as follows from (VI, 38), P, Q and R satisfy

(5) $$\begin{cases} \dfrac{\partial P}{\partial u} = -\dfrac{D}{\sqrt{E}} Q, \quad \dfrac{\partial P}{\partial v} = -\dfrac{D''}{\sqrt{G}} R, \\ \dfrac{\partial Q}{\partial u} = \dfrac{D}{\sqrt{E}} P - \dfrac{1}{\sqrt{G}} \dfrac{\partial \sqrt{E}}{\partial v} R + \sqrt{E}, \quad \dfrac{\partial Q}{\partial v} = \dfrac{1}{\sqrt{E}} \dfrac{\partial \sqrt{G}}{\partial u} R, \\ \dfrac{\partial R}{\partial u} = \dfrac{1}{\sqrt{G}} \dfrac{\partial \sqrt{E}}{\partial v} Q, \quad \dfrac{\partial R}{\partial v} = \dfrac{D''}{\sqrt{G}} P - \dfrac{1}{\sqrt{E}} \dfrac{\partial \sqrt{G}}{\partial u} Q + \sqrt{G}. \end{cases}$$

78. Transformations R in 3-space. In 3-space the equations of a transformation R of an O net $N(x)$ are of the form

(6) $$x_1 = x - \frac{1}{w}(pX + q\xi + r\eta),$$

where, as follows from (VI, 87, 88), the functions satisfy the equations

(7) $$\begin{cases} \dfrac{\partial \theta}{\partial u} = \sqrt{E}\, q, \quad \dfrac{\partial \theta}{\partial v} = \sqrt{G}\, r, \\ \dfrac{\partial p}{\partial u} = -\dfrac{\sqrt{E}}{\varrho_1} q, \quad \dfrac{\partial p}{\partial v} = -\dfrac{\sqrt{G}}{\varrho_2} r, \\ \dfrac{\partial q}{\partial u} = \dfrac{\sqrt{E}}{\varrho_1} p - \dfrac{1}{\sqrt{G}} \dfrac{\partial \sqrt{E}}{\partial v} r + w(\sqrt{E} + \sqrt{E_1}), \quad \dfrac{\partial q}{\partial v} = \dfrac{1}{\sqrt{E}} \dfrac{\partial \sqrt{G}}{\partial u} \\ \dfrac{\partial r}{\partial u} = \dfrac{1}{\sqrt{G}} \dfrac{\partial \sqrt{E}}{\partial v} q, \quad \dfrac{\partial r}{\partial v} = \dfrac{\sqrt{G}}{\varrho_2} p - \dfrac{1}{\sqrt{E}} \dfrac{\partial \sqrt{G}}{\partial u} q + w(\sqrt{G} + \sqrt{G_1} \\ \dfrac{\partial \log w}{\partial u} = \sqrt{E_1} \dfrac{q}{\theta}, \quad \dfrac{\partial \log w}{\partial v} = \sqrt{G_1} \dfrac{r}{\theta}, \\ \dfrac{\partial \sqrt{E_1}}{\partial v} = \sqrt{G_1} \left[\dfrac{1}{\sqrt{G}} \dfrac{\partial \sqrt{E}}{\partial v} - (\sqrt{E} + \sqrt{E_1}) \dfrac{r}{\theta} \right], \\ \dfrac{\partial \sqrt{G_1}}{\partial u} = \sqrt{E_1} \left[\dfrac{1}{\sqrt{E}} \dfrac{\partial \sqrt{G}}{\partial u} - (\sqrt{G} + \sqrt{G_1}) \dfrac{q}{\theta} \right], \end{cases}$$

and also from (VI, 85)

$$p^2+q^2+r^2-2w\theta=0. \tag{8}$$

From (VI, 93) we have that the principal radii of curvature of the net N_1, denoted by ϱ_{11} and ϱ_{12}, are given by

$$\frac{\sqrt{E_1}}{\varrho_{11}}=\frac{\sqrt{E}}{\varrho_1}+\frac{p}{\theta}(\sqrt{E_1}+\sqrt{E}), \quad \frac{\sqrt{G_1}}{\varrho_{12}}=\frac{\sqrt{G}}{\varrho_2}+\frac{p}{\theta}(\sqrt{G_1}+\sqrt{G}). \tag{9}$$

From (VI, 54, 56) we have that the coordinates x_0, y_0, z_0, of the central net and the radius R of the spheres, are given by

$$x_0=x-\frac{\theta}{p}X, \qquad R=\frac{\theta}{p}. \tag{10}$$

We recall from § 68 the following theorem:

When a transformation R of a net N is known, a transformation R of any parallel net $\overline{N}$ can be found by a quadrature; the transforms of N and $\overline{N}$ are parallel, as are also the central nets of the transformations.

The equations of the transformation of $\overline{N}$ are

$$\overline{x}_1=\overline{x}-\frac{1}{\overline{w}}(pX+q\xi+r\eta),$$

where $\overline{w}$ satisfies equations of the form (7). Since (8) must be satisfied, we have

$$\overline{\theta}\,\overline{w}=\theta w.$$

Also we have the theorem:

When N and N_1 are in relation R, the nets N' and N_1', whose coordinates are direction-parameters of the congruence of the transformation, may be obtained from one another by an inversion.

Conversely:

If two O nets N' and N_1' are related by an inversion each net N parallel to N' admits an R transform N_1 parallel to N_1' which can be found by quadratures.

From (VI, 91) we have that the direction-cosines of the normals to a net N and to an R transform N_1 are in the relation

$$(11)\qquad X_1 = -X + \frac{p}{\theta'}x'; \qquad \theta' = w\,\theta.$$

From (VI, 28, 74) we have

$$\frac{\partial x'}{\partial u} = \frac{\sqrt{E'}}{a}\frac{\partial X}{\partial u}, \qquad \frac{\partial x'}{\partial v} = \frac{\sqrt{G'}}{b}\frac{\partial X}{\partial v};$$
$$\frac{\partial \theta'}{\partial u} = \frac{\sqrt{E'}}{a}\frac{\partial p}{\partial u}, \qquad \frac{\partial \theta'}{\partial v} = \frac{\sqrt{G'}}{b}\frac{\partial p}{\partial v},$$

where E' and G' are the first fundamental coefficients of N'. Hence (11) is of the form (II, 2), and we have:

When N and N_1 are in relation R, their spherical representations are in relation F.

Conversely, we have the theorem:

If $N(x)$ is an orthogonal net on the unit sphere and $N'(x')$ is an O net with this spherical representation, the equations

$$(12)\qquad X_1 = -X + 2\frac{\sum x'X}{\sum x'^2}x'$$

define an orthogonal net $N_1(x_1)$ on the sphere such that N and N_1 are in relation F.

From (11) and (VI, 99, 101) it follows that the distance from a point of any O net N to the corresponding tangent plane to an R transform N_1 is given by

$$(13)\qquad \sum X_1(x_1 - x) = P_1 + P - \frac{p}{\theta'}\sum xx' = -\frac{p\,\theta}{\theta'}.$$

79. The cyclic system associated with a transformation *R*. If N and N_1 are two O nets in relation R, the circles orthogonal to N and N_1 at corresponding points have for axes the lines of the harmonic congruence G of the transformation, that is the harmonic congruence determined by the solution θ of the point equation of N (§ 73). In § 64 we saw that there are

∞^1 nets N' parallel to N determined by θ. By the last theorem § 67 each of these nets N' determines an R transform N_1 of N and all of these transforms are harmonic to G. Consequently the above circles are orthogonal to all of these nets N_1 and therefore form a cyclic system [§ 174]. Incidentally we have established the theorem:

If N is an O net and G any congruence harmonic to it, the circles with lines of G for axes and passing through corresponding points of N form a cyclic system.

We call the planes of the circles orthogonal to two nets N and N_1 in relation R the *circle-planes of the transformation.* From the second theorem of § 11 it follows that the circle-planes envelop a net $\overline{N}$. Since the circle-plane at a point M of N is determined by the normal to N at M and the line joining corresponding points of N and N_1 it follows that any point on the circle-plane has coordinates of the form

$$\overline{x} = x + jx' + kX, \tag{14}$$

and the direction-cosines of the plane are proportional to $r\xi - q\eta$. In order that the point $\overline{M}(\overline{x})$ be the point of contact of the plane with its envelope, the functions j and k must be such that

$$\sum(r\xi - q\eta)\frac{\partial \overline{x}}{\partial u} = 0, \qquad \sum(r\xi - q\eta)\frac{\partial \overline{x}}{\partial v} = 0.$$

By differentiation we find

$$\left\{\begin{aligned} \frac{\partial \overline{x}}{\partial u} &= \sqrt{E}\left(1 + jh - \frac{k}{\varrho_1}\right)\xi + x'\frac{\partial j}{\partial u} + X\frac{\partial k}{\partial u}, \\ \frac{\partial \overline{x}}{\partial v} &= \sqrt{G}\left(1 + jl - \frac{k}{\varrho_2}\right)\eta + x'\frac{\partial j}{\partial v} + X\frac{\partial k}{\partial v}. \end{aligned}\right. \tag{15}$$

Hence j and k are determined by

$$1 + jh - \frac{k}{\varrho_1} = 0, \qquad 1 + jl - \frac{k}{\varrho_2} = 0, \tag{16}$$

and we have

$$\frac{\partial \overline{x}}{\partial u} = x'\frac{\partial j}{\partial u} + X\frac{\partial k}{\partial u}, \qquad \frac{\partial \overline{x}}{\partial v} = x'\frac{\partial j}{\partial v} + X\frac{\partial k}{\partial v}. \tag{17}$$

If equations (16) are differentiated with respect to v and u respectively, we get

$$(18)\qquad h\frac{\partial j}{\partial v}-\frac{1}{\varrho_1}\frac{\partial k}{\partial v}=0, \qquad l\frac{\partial j}{\partial u}-\frac{1}{\varrho_2}\frac{\partial k}{\partial u}=0.$$

Making use of these relations, we find from (17) by differentiation

$$(19)\qquad \frac{\partial^2 \bar{x}}{\partial u\,\partial v}=x'\frac{\partial^2 j}{\partial u\,\partial v}+X\frac{\partial^2 k}{\partial u\,\partial v}.$$

Hence j and k are solutions of the point equation of $\bar{N}$. We shall show that $\bar{\omega}$, defined by

$$(20)\qquad \bar{\omega}=\theta' j+pk+\theta,$$

also is a solution. In fact, we find that

$$(21)\qquad \begin{cases} \dfrac{\partial \bar{\omega}}{\partial u}=\theta'\dfrac{\partial j}{\partial u}+p\dfrac{\partial k}{\partial u}, \qquad \dfrac{\partial \bar{\omega}}{\partial v}=\theta'\dfrac{\partial j}{\partial v}+p\dfrac{\partial k}{\partial v}, \\ \dfrac{\partial^2 \bar{\omega}}{\partial u\,\partial v}=\theta'\dfrac{\partial^2 j}{\partial u\,\partial v}+p\dfrac{\partial^2 k}{\partial u\,\partial v}. \end{cases}$$

Moreover, the linear element of $\bar{N}$ may be written

$$(22)\qquad d\bar{s}^2=dk^2+2\,dj\,d\bar{\omega}.$$

If we put

$$(23)\qquad j=m+in, \qquad 2\bar{\omega}=m-in,$$

equation (22) becomes

$$(24)\qquad d\bar{s}^2=dk^2+dm^2+dn^2.$$

Since k, m and n are solutions of the point equation of $\bar{N}$, they are the coordinates of a net applicable to $\bar{N}$.

This result is in accord with [§§ 141, 176] where it was shown that the planes of the circles of a cyclic system envelope a net corresponding to the developables of the congruence of axes. Moreover, it was shown that the applicable net is known intrinsically when the cyclic system is given, and conversely when the applicable net is known a cyclic system can be found directly. For the sake of brevity we say with Guichard that a net is C when it admits an applicable net.

We have just seen that $\bar{N}$ is a net C. It is harmonic both to the congruence normal to N and to the congruence G of the transformation from N into N_1 (§ 11). The coordinates of the focal points of first rank of these two congruences are of the respective forms $x + \varrho_1 X$ and $x - x'/h$ (I, 37). By means of the preceding formulas we prove the theorem:

The normal congruence and the congruence G are the harmonic congruences of $\bar{N}$ determined by the solutions $m + in$ and k of the point equation of $\bar{N}$.

Moreover from § 11 it follows that the derived net of $\bar{N}$ by means of $m + in$ and $k +$ const. is parallel to N.

Conversely, any net harmonic to a normal congruence G_0 is enveloped by the planes determined by G_0 and by any congruence conjugate to a net N normal to G_0. But in § 65 we saw that any other congruence conjugate to N is 3, I, and consequently leads to a transformation R of N. Hence the resulting net harmonic to G_0 is a net C. Since the determination of congruences conjugate to N is equivalent to finding nets parallel to N, we have:

The nets harmonic to a normal congruence are nets C; their determination is equivalent to finding nets parallel to a net orthogonal to the congruence: when such a parallel net is known, the corresponding harmonic net follows directly and the coordinates of the applicable net can be found by quadratures[55].

80. When the circle-planes of a transformation R pass through a point. Consider in particular the case for which the circle-planes pass through a point. From (17) it follows that j and k are constant. If the point is taken as the origin, we have from (14) that in all generality we may take

$$p = P - d, \qquad q = Q, \qquad r = R, \tag{25}$$

d being a constant.

---

[55]) In § 117 it will be shown that every net C is harmonic to ∞^1 families of parallel normal congruences.

From (VI, 96) and (7) it follows that $\theta = \omega - c$, where c is a constant.

From these results and (10) we have

$$\sum x_0^2 = \frac{\theta^2}{p^2} - 2d\frac{\theta}{p} + 2c.$$

Hence the spheres cut the fixed sphere with center at the origin and radius r_0 under the constant angle ε, where

$$r_0^2 = 2c, \qquad r_0 \cos\varepsilon = d.$$

Conversely, it can be shown that when the spheres of a transformation R meet under constant angle a fixed sphere with center at the origin, the functions of the transformation are of the form (25).

It is evident that any O net admits such transformations R. In consequence of (25) the coordinates of any point on the line of the congruence G of the transformation R are of the form $(1+\lambda)x' + d \cdot X$. When $\lambda = -1$, the point lies on the sphere of radius d with center at the origin and describes the spherical representation of N. These lines meet the same sphere again in the point of coordinates $d \cdot \left(X - \frac{p}{\theta'}x'\right)$, which describes the spherical representation of N_1 (cf. 11).

81. The circles K and congruence K. Let $N_1(x_1)$ and $N_2(x_2)$ be two R transforms of an O net $N(x)$, and write the equations of the transformations in the general forms

$$(26) \qquad \begin{cases} x_1 = x - \dfrac{\theta_1}{\theta_1'}x', & \theta_1' = \dfrac{1}{2}\sum x'^2 = \theta_1 w_1, \\[2ex] x_2 = x - \dfrac{\theta_2}{\theta_2''}x'', & \theta_2'' = \dfrac{1}{2}\sum x''^2 = \theta_2 w_2, \end{cases}$$

where $N'(x')$ and $N''(x'')$ are the nets parallel to N determining the conjugate congruences of the transformations[56]). If θ_1'' and θ_2' are solutions of the point equations of N'' and N' respectively corre-

[56]) Cf. Jonas, Sitz. Berl. Math. Gesell., vol. 14 (1915), p. 109.

sponding to the solution θ_1 and θ_2 of the point equation of N, and the additive constants are chosen so that

$$\theta_1'' + \theta_2' = \sum x' x'', \tag{27}$$

then as shown in § 72 the ∞^1 nets N_{12}, defined by (II, 46), namely

$$x_{12} = x + \frac{(\theta_1'' \theta_2 - \theta_2'' \theta_1) x' + (\theta_2' \theta_1 - \theta_1' \theta_2) x''}{\theta_1' \theta_2'' - \theta_1'' \theta_2'}, \tag{28}$$

are O nets in relations R with N_1 and N_2.

Consider the circle K through three corresponding points, M, M_1 and M_2 of N, N_1 and N_2. The coordinates of its center are of the form

$$x + \lambda x' + \mu x'', \tag{29}$$

where λ and μ are determined by the condition that the lines joining the center to the mid-points of the segments MM_1 and MM_2 are perpendicular to these segments. These conditions are reducible by means of (26) to

$$2\lambda\theta_1' + \mu \sum x' x'' + \theta_1 = 0, \qquad \lambda \sum x' x'' + 2\mu\theta_2'' + \theta_2 = 0. \tag{30}$$

In like manner the condition that the line joining the center to the mid-point of the line joining M_1 to the corresponding point of one of the nets N_{12} is perpendicular to this line is

$$\sum \left(x + \lambda x' + \mu x'' - x_1 + \frac{\theta_{12}}{\theta_{12}'''} \frac{x_1'''}{2} \right) x_1''' = 0.$$

By means of (II, 33, 36), (VI, 106), and (27) we find that this condition is satisfied when (30) hold, and consequently the corresponding points of each of the nets N_{12} lie on K. Hence:

If N, N_1, N_2, N_{12} are four O nets in the relation of a quatern under transformations R, four corresponding points M, M_1, M_2, M_{12} lie on a circle K; the four corresponding points on any four of the possible ∞^1 nets N_{12}, forming a quatern with N, N_1, N_2 are in constant cross-ratio[57]).

---

[57]) The last part of this theorem is due to Demoulin, Comptes Rendus, vol. 150 (1910), p. 156, and is left as an exercise.

If we put (§ 21)

$$\theta_c = \theta_1 + (c-1)\theta_2, \qquad x^{(c)} = x' + (c-1)x'', \tag{31}$$

then

$$\theta_c^{(c)} = \frac{1}{2}\sum x^{(c)2}, \qquad \sum x^{(c)} x'' = \theta_c'' + \theta_2^{(c)}. \tag{32}$$

Hence the transformation F determined by θ_c and the congruence of direction-parameters $x^{(c)}$ is a transformation R. Moreover, if N_c is the transform, each of the ∞^1 O nets N_{12} are R transforms of N_c, and consequently corresponding points of N, N_1, N_2, each of the ∞^1 nets N_c and each of the ∞^1 nets N_{12} lie on a circle K. Hence:

If θ_1 and θ_2 are solutions of the point equation of an O net N determining two R transforms, corresponding points of N and of the ∞^1 R transforms N_c of N by means of $\theta_1 + (c-1)\theta_2$ lie on a circle K, upon which lie also the corresponding points of the ∞^1 O nets N_{12} which are R transforms of all the nets N_c.

Let N_{c_1} and N_{c_2} be any two of these transforms of N, and let N_{01} and N_{02} be the central nets of the corresponding R transforms, both being conjugate to the congruence normal to N. From the third theorem of § 68 it follows that the tangent planes to N_{01} and N_{02} meet in the axis of the circle K, and consequently these axes form a congruence K harmonic to the nets N_{01} and N_{02}. Since the congruence K is determined by the circles K, we have that it is harmonic to the central net of the transformation R of N into any net N_c. Since N and any net N_{12} may be looked upon as R transforms of a net N_c, it follows that the central net of the transformation from N_c into any net N_{12} is harmonic to K.

From § 23 it follows that corresponding tangent planes to N, to all the nets N_c and to all the nets N_{12} meet in a point generating a net $\overline{N}$, the derived net of N determined by θ_1 and θ_2. Since the tangent plane of a central net passes through the intersection of the tangent planes to N and a transform N_c, a point of $\overline{N}$ is on the corresponding tangent plane of each central net of all the transformations R. Consequently the congruence K is conjugate to $\overline{N}$. Hence:

Corresponding tangent planes of N, the ∞^1 nets N_c and the ∞^1 nets N_{12} meet in a point generating a net $\overline{N}$ conjugate to the congruence K of the axes of the circles K through corresponding points of these nets[58]).

Since the congruence K is harmonic to the nets N_{01}, and N_{02}, and the tangents to the curves of these nets at corresponding points lie in the principal planes of N at the corresponding point, the focal points of K lie in these principal planes. In order to obtain the coordinates of these focal points, we remark (§ 78) that the coordinates of N_{01} and N_{02} are of the forms

$$x_{01} = x - \frac{\theta_1}{p_1} X, \qquad x_{02} = x - \frac{\theta_2}{p_2} X.$$

The point equation of N_{01} admits the solution $\theta_{01} = \theta_2 - \theta_1 p_2/p_1$, and from § 19 it follows that N_{02} is the F transform of N_{01}, by means of θ_{01}. Hence from (II, 22) and (7) we have for the coordinates of the focal nets $F_1(y_1)$, $F_2(y_2)$ of the congruence K, that is the intersections of the corresponding tangent planes to N_{01} and N_{02}, expressions of the forms

$$(33) \quad \begin{cases} y_1 = x_{01} - \dfrac{\theta_{01}}{\dfrac{\partial \theta_{01}}{\partial u}} \dfrac{\partial x_{01}}{\partial u} = x + \dfrac{(\theta_1 p_2 - \theta_2 p_1)\xi + (\theta_2 q_1 - \theta_1 q_2) X}{p_1 q_2 - p_2 q_1}, \\[2ex] y_2 = x_{01} - \dfrac{\theta_{01}}{\dfrac{\partial \theta_{01}}{\partial v}} \dfrac{\partial x_{01}}{\partial v} = x + \dfrac{(\theta_1 p_2 - \theta_2 p_1)\eta + (\theta_2 r_1 - \theta_1 r_2) X}{p_1 r_2 - p_2 r_1}. \end{cases}$$

From the preceding theorem it follows that the normals to all the nets N_c and to all the nets N_{12} at points of a circle K are tangent to the sphere S with center at the corresponding point on $\overline{N}$ and passing through K. Moreover, the normal to any net N_c meets the normal to any net N_{12}, in the center of the sphere tangent to N_c and N_{12}. Hence these normals lie on a hyperboloid of revolution to which S is tangent along K, unless all the normals lie in the plane of K. We consider the latter possibility.

---

58) Cf. Demoulin, l. c., p. 310.

If α, β, γ denote the direction-cosines of the congruence K, we have in consequence of (26) and (27)

$$(34) \qquad \alpha, \beta, \gamma = \frac{y'z''-y''z', \quad z'x''-z''x', \quad x'y''-x''y'}{[4\,\theta_1'\theta_2''-(\theta_1''+\theta_2')^2]^{\frac{1}{2}}}.$$

The direction-cosines of the normals to N_c and N_{12} are of the forms, by (11), (31) and (VI, 112),

$$X_c = \frac{p_1+(c-1)p_2}{\theta_c^{(c)}}(x'+(c-1)x'')-X,$$

$$X_{12} = X + \frac{(\theta_2'x''-\theta_2''x')p_1+(\theta_1''x'-\theta_1'x'')p_2}{\theta_1'\theta_2''-\theta_1''\theta_2'}.$$

In consequence of (VI, 69) we have

$$\sum X_c\alpha = -\sum X_{12}\alpha = \frac{q_1r_2-q_2r_1}{[4\,\theta_1'\theta_2''-(\theta_1''+\theta_2')^2]^{\frac{1}{2}}}.$$

Hence either all the normals lie in the plane of the circle K, or none do. In order that they do, we must have

$$(35) \qquad q_1r_2-q_2r_1=0.$$

From § 79 it follows that this is a necessary and sufficient condition that the circle-planes of the transformations of N into N_1 and N_2 coincide. If we replace (35) by $q_2=\lambda q_1$, $r_2=\lambda r_1$, from the sixth and seventh of (7) it follows that λ is a constant, which may be taken equal to unity. Then we have

$$(36) \qquad q_2=q_1, \qquad r_2=r_1, \qquad p_2=p_1+d, \qquad \theta_2=\theta_1+e,$$

where d and e are constants. When these expressions are substituted in (33), the latter become

$$x-\frac{e}{d}X+\left(p_1\frac{e}{d}-\theta_1\right)\frac{\xi}{q_1}, \qquad x-\frac{e}{d}X+\left(p_1\frac{e}{d}-\theta_1\right)\frac{\eta}{r_1}.$$

Hence the congruence K is harmonic to the O net of coordinates $x-eX/d$, that is K is a cyclic congruence (§ 79), and the net is orthogonal to the circles of the corresponding cyclic system. Accordingly we have the theorem of Demoulin[59]):

If N is any O net and N_1 and N_2 are two R transforms of N, the circles K determined by corresponding points of N, N_1 and N_2 are of two kinds; 1°, if the circle-planes of the two R transforms are coincident, the normals to the ∞^1 nets N_c and ∞^1 nets N_{12} lie in the planes of the circles K, and the congruence K is cyclic, the circles of the cyclic system being concentric with the circles K; 2°, if the circle-planes of the two transformations R are distinct, the normals to the nets N_c at points of a circle K form one set of generators of a hyperboloid of revolution, and the normals to the nets N_{12} the other family of generators[60]).

82. Transformations D_m of isothermic surfaces. From (VI, 81) it follows that a necessary and sufficient condition that the correspondence between the two surfaces of a transformation R be conformal is that $\tau^2=\sigma^2$. From (II, 8) and § 4 it is seen that τ and σ cannot be equal. Also from § 25 it follows that when $\tau+\sigma=0$ the transformation is K and the O nets N and N_1 have equal point invariants, that is they are isothermic. Hence we have the theorem of Cosserat[61]):

In order that the correspondence between two surfaces in relation R be conformal it is necessary and sufficient that both surfaces be isothermic.

We proceed to the consideration of these transformations and put

$$\sqrt{E}=\sqrt{G}=e^{\psi}, \tag{37}$$

where ψ is a function thus defined. Now the point equation of N is

$$\frac{\partial^2\theta}{\partial u\,\partial v}=\frac{\partial\psi}{\partial v}\frac{\partial\theta}{\partial u}+\frac{\partial\psi}{\partial u}\frac{\partial\theta}{\partial v}. \tag{38}$$

---

[59]) L. c.

[60]) Cf. § 108.

[61]) Annales de la Faculté des Sciences de Toulouse, vol. 8 (1894), p. E. 13.

Comparing this equation with (II, 79), we have

$$\frac{1}{\varrho} = m e^{-2\psi}, \tag{39}$$

where m is a constant.

From [§ 65] it follows that the Codazzi equations of N are

$$\frac{\partial}{\partial v}\left(\frac{1}{\varrho_1}\right) = \left(\frac{1}{\varrho_2} - \frac{1}{\varrho_1}\right)\frac{\partial \psi}{\partial v}, \qquad \frac{\partial}{\partial u}\left(\frac{1}{\varrho_2}\right) = \left(\frac{1}{\varrho_1} - \frac{1}{\varrho_2}\right)\frac{\partial \psi}{\partial u},$$

from which it follows that

$$\frac{\partial K_0}{\partial u} = -e^{-2\psi}\frac{\partial L}{\partial u}, \qquad \frac{\partial K_0}{\partial v} = e^{-2\psi}\frac{\partial L}{\partial v}, \tag{40}$$

where we have put

$$K_0 = \frac{1}{\varrho_1} + \frac{1}{\varrho_2}, \qquad L = e^{2\psi}\left(\frac{1}{\varrho_2} - \frac{1}{\varrho_1}\right). \tag{41}$$

Expressing the condition of integrability of (40), we find that L is a solution of (38).

The net conjugate to the congruence normal to N which is in relation K to N, that is the harmonic of N with respect to the centers of curvature of N, is given by

$$x + \frac{2}{K_0} X. \tag{42}$$

From this result, (40) and (II, 82) it follows that the functions θ and $\hat{\theta}$ of this transformation K are

$$\theta = \frac{L}{2m}, \qquad \frac{\hat{\theta}}{\theta} = -\frac{K_0}{2}. \tag{43}$$

We return to the consideration of transformations R of N and introduce the function ν by means of the equation

$$w = \frac{\theta'}{\theta} = m\nu. \tag{44}$$

We have from (II, 82)

$$\frac{\partial \nu}{\partial u} = e^{-2\psi}\frac{\partial \theta}{\partial u} = e^{-\psi} q, \qquad \frac{\partial \nu}{\partial v} = -e^{-\psi} r. \tag{45}$$

Comparing these equations and (7), we get

$$\sqrt{E_1} = -\sqrt{G_1} = \frac{\theta}{\nu} e^{-\psi}. \tag{46}$$

In terms of these functions equations (7) become

$$\left\{\begin{array}{l} \dfrac{\partial \theta}{\partial u} = e^{\psi} q, \qquad \dfrac{\partial \theta}{\partial v} = e^{\psi} r, \\ \dfrac{\partial p}{\partial u} = -\dfrac{e^{\psi}}{\varrho_1} q, \quad \dfrac{\partial p}{\partial v} = -\dfrac{e^{\psi}}{\varrho_2} r, \\ \dfrac{\partial q}{\partial u} = \dfrac{e^{\psi}}{\varrho_1} p - \dfrac{\partial \psi}{\partial v} r + m(e^{\psi}\nu + e^{-\psi}\theta), \qquad \dfrac{\partial q}{\partial v} = \dfrac{\partial \psi}{\partial u} r, \\ \dfrac{\partial r}{\partial u} = \dfrac{\partial \psi}{\partial v} q, \qquad \dfrac{\partial r}{\partial v} = \dfrac{e^{\psi}}{\varrho_2} p - \dfrac{\partial \psi}{\partial u} q + m(e^{\psi}\nu - e^{-\psi}\theta), \\ \dfrac{\partial \nu}{\partial u} = e^{-\psi} q, \qquad \dfrac{\partial \nu}{\partial v} = -e^{-\psi} r, \end{array}\right. \tag{47}$$

and (6) assumes the form

$$x_1 = x - \frac{1}{m\nu}(pX + q\xi + r\eta). \tag{48}$$

It is readily found that equations (47) form a completely integrable system, and that for any set of solutions the left-hand member of the following equation is constant:

$$p^2 + q^2 + r^2 - 2m\theta\nu = 0. \tag{49}$$

The complete integration of (47) involves five constants in addition to m. When these constants are chosen so that (49) is satisfied, three of these constants are essentially arbitrary. Hence we have the theorem of Darboux[62]):

[62]) Annales de L'École Norm. Sup., ser. 3, vol. 16 (1899), p. 503.

An isothermic net admits ∞^4 *transformations* R *into isothermic nets.*

These transformations have been called D_m by Bianchi[63]).

83. Theorem of permutability of transformations D_m. We consider two isothermic nets, N_1 and N_2, transforms of an isothermic net N by means of two sets of solutions, $\theta_i, \nu_i, p_i, q_i, r_i, m_i$ $(i = 1, 2)$ of equations (47) and (49), and apply the results of §§ 21, 72 to obtain a theorem of permutability of transformations D_m.

From (VI, 105) it follows that the additive constants of integration of θ_2' and θ_1'' must be chosen so that

$$p_1 p_2 + q_1 q_2 + r_1 r_2 = \theta_2' + \theta_1''. \tag{50}$$

Since in the two transformations of N we have taken $\varrho = e^{2\psi}/m_i$, equations (II, 92) become

$$\frac{\partial}{\partial u}\left(\theta_{12}\frac{\theta_1'}{\theta_1}\right) = -m_1 e^{-2\psi}\theta_1^2 \frac{\partial}{\partial u}\left(\frac{\theta_2}{\theta_1}\right),$$

$$\frac{\partial}{\partial v}\left(\theta_{12}\frac{\theta_1'}{\theta_1}\right) = m_1 e^{-2\psi}\theta_1^2 \frac{\partial}{\partial v}\left(\frac{\theta_2}{\theta_1}\right).$$

From these and analogous equations in θ_2, we find that the left-hand member of the following equation is constant; we consider in particular the case when

$$\theta_{21}\nu_2 + \theta_{12}\nu_1 = 0. \tag{51}$$

From this equation and (II, 36, 48) we have

$$m_1 \theta_{12}''' = m_2 \theta_{12}\left(m_1 \nu_2 - \frac{\theta_2'}{\theta_1}\right) = \frac{m_2 \nu_2}{\nu_1}\theta_{21}\left(\frac{\theta_2'}{\theta_1} - m_1 \nu_2\right), \tag{52}$$

from which follows, when θ_{21} and θ_{12}''' are replaced by their values (II, 38, 43),

$$m_1 m_2 (\nu_2 \theta_1 + \nu_1 \theta_2) = m_2 \theta_2' + m_1 \theta_1''. \tag{53}$$

---

[63]) Annali, ser. 3, vol. 11 (1905), pp. 93—158.

From (VI, 83) it follows that for any transformation R

$$(54)\quad \begin{cases} \dfrac{\partial \theta_2'}{\partial u} = m_1 \nu_1 (\sqrt{E}+\sqrt{E_1})\, q_2, & \dfrac{\partial \theta_2'}{\partial v} = m_1 \nu_1 (\sqrt{G}+\sqrt{G_1})\, r_2, \\ \dfrac{\partial \theta_1''}{\partial u} = m_2 \nu_2 (\sqrt{E}+\sqrt{E_2})\, q_1, & \dfrac{\partial \theta_1''}{\partial v} = m_2 \nu_2 (\sqrt{G}+\sqrt{G_2})\, r_1. \end{cases}$$

When equations (50) and (53) are solved for θ_2' and θ_1'', and the results are substituted in these equations, the latter are satisfied. Since θ_1'' and θ_2' are completely determined there is only one transform N_{12}, which is isothermic.

Making use of (54), we find

$$(55)\quad \frac{\partial}{\partial u}\left(\frac{\theta_{12}'''}{\theta_{12}}\right) = m_2 \frac{\nu_1}{\theta_1} e^{\phi}\left(\frac{\theta_2'}{\theta_1'} q_1 - q_2\right), \quad \frac{\partial}{\partial v}\left(\frac{\theta_{12}'''}{\theta_{12}}\right) = -m_2 \frac{\nu_1}{\theta_1} e^{\phi}\left(\frac{\theta_2'}{\theta_1'} r_1 - r_2\right).$$

In consequence of (VI, 109) the expressions for $\dfrac{\partial \nu_{12}}{\partial u}$ and $\dfrac{\partial \nu_{12}}{\partial v}$ analogous to the last two of (47) differ from the right-hand members of (55) only by the factor m_2. Consequently

$$(56)\quad \theta_{12}''' = m_2\, \theta_{12}\, \nu_{12},$$

and the transformation from N_1 into N_{12} is D_{m_2}. In like manner the transformation from N_2 into N_{12} is D_{m_1}.

By means of (51) and (52) the expressions (II, 46) for the coordinates of N_{12} are reducible to

$$(57)\quad x_{12} = x + \frac{m_2 \theta_2 x' - m_1 \theta_1 x''}{m_1 \theta_1 (\theta_1'' - m_2 \theta_2 \nu_1)}.$$

Making use of (50) and (53), we reduce this equation to

$$(58)\quad x_{12} = x + \frac{m_2 - m_1}{m_1 m_2} \, \frac{m_2 \theta_2 x' - m_1 \theta_1 x''}{p_1 p_2 + q_1 q_2 + r_1 r_2 - m_1 \theta_1 \nu_2 - m_2 \theta_2 \nu_1}.$$

From this it is seen that we must have $m_2 \neq m_1$. Hence we have the following theorem of Bianchi[64]:

[64]) L. c., p. 120.

If N is an isothermic O net, and N_1 and N_2 are two isothermic O nets obtained from N by transformations D_{m_1} and D_{m_2}, there can be found without quadrature an isothermic O net N_{12} such that N_{12} is a D_{m_2} transform of N_1 and D_{m_1} transform of N_2.

84. Special isothermic nets in 3-space. In § 81 it is shown that in order that two transformations R have the same circle-planes it is necessary that

$$(59)\quad \theta_2 = \theta_1 + j, \qquad p_2 = p_1 + k, \qquad q_2 = q_1, \qquad r_2 = r_1,$$

where j and k are constants. In § 119 we shall show that in the tangent planes of a deform of a quadric, meeting the circle at infinity in four distinct points, there are eight points which describe isothermic surfaces, any one of which is in the relation of a transformation R with three others, the corresponding cyclic systems admitting the tangent planes to the surface for circle-planes. We apply the preceding results to the determination of all isothermic surfaces admitting two transformations D_m for which the circle-planes are the same.

From the last of (47) it follows that $\nu_2 = \nu_1 + n$, where n is a constant. Moreover, since (49) must be satisfied by both transformations, we must have also

$$(60)\qquad p_1 k + \frac{k^2}{2} = m_2(\theta_1 + j)(\nu_1 + n) - \theta_1 \nu_1 m_1.$$

When this equation is differentiated with respect to u and v, the two resulting equations are equivalent, by means of (47), to

$$2(m_2 - m_1)\nu_1 + 2 m_2 n = -k K_0, \qquad 2(m_2 - m_1)\theta_1 + 2 m_2 j = k L,$$

where K_0 and L are defined by (41). These equations may be replaced by

$$(61)\qquad \theta_1 = L + e, \qquad \nu_1 = -K_0 + f,$$

where e and f are constants. From the last two of (47) we find that

$$(62)\qquad q_1 = -e^{\psi}\frac{\partial K_0}{\partial u}, \qquad r_1 = e^{\psi}\frac{\partial K_0}{\partial v}.$$

In consequence of (40) these functions satisfy (47), if we take

$$(63) \qquad p_1 = -\frac{1}{2} L K_0 + g,$$

where g is a constant. In order that (49) hold we must have

$$(64) \quad e^{2\psi}\left[\left(\frac{\partial K_0}{\partial u}\right)^2 + \left(\frac{\partial K_0}{\partial v}\right)^2\right] + \frac{1}{4} K_0^2 L^2 + A K_0 L + 2 B K_0 + 2 C L + D = 0,$$

where

$$(65) \quad A = 2m_1 - g, \qquad B = m_1 e, \qquad C = -m_1 f, \qquad D = g^2 - 2m_1 e f.$$

Eliminating e, f and g from these equations, we have that m_1 must satisfy

$$(66) \qquad (A - 2m)^2 m - Dm + 2BC = 0.$$

If then a net N satisfies the condition (64) where A, B, C, D are constants, there are in general three solutions m of (66). When these are substituted in (65), we have three sets of values of e, f and g and the corresponding functions (61), (62) and (63) determine transformations of N into three isothermic nets such that the circle-planes of the three transformations are the same. The foregoing results are due to Darboux[65]. Bianchi[66] also has considered these surfaces, and in order to put in evidence the essential constants appearing in (64), he refers to such a surface as a *special isothermic surface of class (A, B, C, D).*

85. Complementary transformations D_m of special isothermic nets. The three nets obtained from N by the transformations determined by the values (61), (62), (63) have been called the *complementary nets* by Bianchi. We shall show that they are special nets of class (A, $-B$, $-C$, D). In fact, in consequence of (9) and (46) we find that the functions $K_{0,1}$ and L_1 for one of these nets N_1, defined by equations analogous to (41), have the values

$$(67) \qquad K_{0,1} = \frac{-\nu_1 L + 2p_1}{\theta_1}, \qquad L_1 = -\frac{\theta_1 K_0 + 2p_1}{\nu_1}.$$

---

[65]) L. c., p. 507.

[66]) L. c., p. 130.

From these and the foregoing formulas we find

$$L_1 - e = -\frac{ef+2g}{\nu_1}, \qquad K_{0,1} + f = \frac{ef+2g}{\theta_1},$$

$$-\frac{1}{2} K_{0,1} L_1 + g = (ef+2g)\frac{p_1}{\nu_1 \theta_1}.$$

From these expressions and (VI, 94) it follows that N may be obtained from N_1 by a transformation D_{m_1} determined by the functions

$$\theta_1^{-1} = L_1 - e, \quad \nu_1^{-1} = -(K_{0,1}+f), \quad p_1^{-1} = -\frac{1}{2} K_{0,1} L_1 + g\text{[67]}.$$

Since the effect of changing the signs of e and f is to change the signs of B and C, but not to affect (66) we have that N_1 is a special net $(A, -B, -C, D)$.

Now we show, as Darboux has done[68]), that the circle-planes of a complementary transformation envelope a surface applicable to a general quadric. To this end we make use of the results of § 79. From (VI, 83) and the preceding formulas, we find that for the present case

$$h = m(\nu + \theta e^{-2\phi}), \qquad l = m(\nu - \theta e^{-2\phi}),$$

$$j = \frac{e-\theta}{m(\theta f - e\nu)}, \qquad k = \frac{2\theta}{\theta f - e\nu}, \qquad \overline{\omega} = \theta \frac{2g + ef - \nu e}{\theta f - e\nu}.$$

From (23) it follows that if we put

$$x = k, \qquad y + iz = j, \qquad y - iz = 2\overline{\omega},$$

the point (x, y, z) describes a surface Σ applicable to the envelope of the circle-planes. When the above values of j, k and $\overline{\omega}$ are substituted, and θ and ν are eliminated, we find that Σ is the quadric

$$(y - iz)[x + 2m(y+iz)] = 2gx^2 + 2ex + 2m(2g+ef)x(y+iz).$$

---

[67]) If $2g + ef = 0$, N_1 has constant mean curvature and the corresponding equation (64) is $\frac{1}{4} K_{0,1}^2 L_1^2 + A K_{0,1} L_1 - 2BK_{0,1} - 2CL_1 + D = 0$ which is satisfied because of (65).

[68]) L. c., p. 508.

86. Transformations D_m of special isothermic nets. Let N be a special isothermic net of class (A, B, C, D) and N_1 a complementary transform by means of the functions given by (61), (62) and (63). We shall show that it is possible to find solutions $\theta_2, \nu_2, p_2, q_2$ and r_2 of equations (47) such that the net N_2 is a special isothermic net. This is done by finding under what conditions a net N_{12}, arising from N_1 and N_2 in accordance with the theorem of permutability of § 83 is a complementary transform of N_2.

From (II, 43), (VI, 109) and (52) we have

$$\theta_{21} = \theta_1 - \frac{\theta_1''}{\theta_2''}\theta_2, \qquad p_{21} = \frac{\theta_1''}{\theta_2''}p_2 - p_1,$$

$$\nu_{21} = \frac{1}{m_1}\frac{\theta_{21}''''}{\theta_{21}} = \frac{1}{m_2}\left(m_2\nu_1 - \frac{\theta_1''}{\theta_2}\right).$$

Also from (50) and (53) we obtain

$$(m_2 - m_1)\theta_1'' = m_2(p_1p_2 + q_1q_2 + r_1r_2 - m_1\nu_2\theta_1 - m_1\nu_1\theta_2).$$

The analogues of (67) are

$$K_{0,2} = -\frac{\nu_2 L + 2p_2}{\theta_2}, \qquad L_2 = -\frac{\theta_2 K_0 + 2p_2}{\nu_2}.$$

The equations

$$(68)\quad \theta_{21} = -L_2 + e, \qquad \nu_{21} = K_{0,2} + f, \qquad p_{21} = \frac{1}{2}K_{0,2}L_2 - g,$$

are consistent with the above results, provided that

$$(69)\quad p_1p_2 + q_1q_2 + r_1r_2 - m_2(\nu_2\theta_1 + \nu_1\theta_2) + (m_2 - m_1)(\nu_2 e + \theta_2 f + 2p_2) = 0.$$

By differentiation we find that the left-hand member of this equation is constant for each set of solutions $\theta_2, \nu_2, p_2, q_2$ and r_2 of (47). Hence if the constants entering in the latter are chosen so that (69) is satisfied, the net N_{12} is a complementary transform of N_2. The latter is a special isothermic net of class $(A, -B, -C, D)$. Hence we have the theorem of Bianchi[69]):

Of the ∞^4 isothermic nets obtained from a special isothermic net of class (A, B, C, D) by transformations D_m, ∞^3 are nets of class $(A, -B, -C, D)$.

---

[69]) L. c., p. 141. We note that Bianchi showed that N_2 is of the same class as N. This is due to his choice of directions in the trihedron of N_2.

87. Transformations D_m of minimal surfaces. A minimal surface is isothermic, and the spherical representation of its lines of curvature is such that we may take [§ 109]

$$\frac{\sqrt{E}}{\varrho_1} = -\frac{\sqrt{G}}{\varrho_2} = -e^{-\psi}, \tag{70}$$

where $\sqrt{E} = \sqrt{G} = e^{\psi}$. From (9) and (46) it follows that the transform is minimal, if $\nu = p$, and only in this case. The equations of such a transformation are:

$$(71)\left\{\begin{aligned} &\frac{\partial \theta}{\partial u} = e^{\psi} q, \qquad \frac{\partial \theta}{\partial v} = e^{\psi} r, \\ &\frac{\partial p}{\partial u} = e^{-\psi} q, \qquad \frac{\partial p}{\partial v} = -e^{-\psi} r, \\ &\frac{\partial q}{\partial u} = -e^{-\psi} p - \frac{\partial \psi}{\partial v} r + m\,(c^{\psi} p + e^{-\psi}\theta), \qquad \frac{\partial q}{\partial v} = \frac{\partial \psi}{\partial u} r, \\ &\frac{\partial r}{\partial u} = \frac{\partial \psi}{\partial v} q, \qquad \frac{\partial r}{\partial v} = e^{-\psi} p - \frac{\partial \psi}{\partial u} q + m\,(e^{\psi} p - e^{-\psi}\theta). \end{aligned}\right.$$

These equations form a completely integrable system. Since $p^2 + q^2 + r^2 - 2mp\theta = 0$ must be satisfied, we have:

A minimal surface admits ∞^3 transformations D_m into minimal surfaces[70]).

From (56), (52) and (VI, 109) we have $\nu_{12} = -p_{12}$, and therefore:

If a minimal surface is transformed into minimal surfaces S_1 and S_2 by transformations D_{m_1} and D_{m_2}, there can be found without quadrature a minimal surface which is a D_{m_2} transform of S_1 and a D_{m_1} transform of S_2[71]).

88. Transformations E_m of O nets with isothermal spherical representation. Since the spherical representation of the O net on a minimal surface is isothermal, each transformation D_m of a minimal surface into a minimal surface leads by a quadrature to a transformation R of an O net with isothermal spherical representation into an O net of the same type, in accor-

---

70) Bianchi, Rendiconti dei Lincei, ser. 5, vol. 8^1 (1899), p. 151.

71) Cf. Bianchi, l. c.

dance with the first theorem of § 78. These transformations were studied by the author[72]) and later by Bianchi[73]), who called them *transformations* E_m. In this section we show that these transformations are the most general transformations R of O nets with isothermal spherical representation into nets of the same kind.

The tangential coordinates of N satisfy (V, 29) with $\varrho = e^{2\psi}$ and $\gamma = 0$. From (VI, 94) we have that the functions w and w^{-1} of § 52 are p and p/θ' respectively. Hence if a transformation R of N is to be a transformation Ω, that is if N_1 is to have isothermal spherical representation, its tangential equation must be of the form

$$\frac{\partial^2 \lambda_1}{\partial u\, \partial v} + \frac{\partial \psi_1}{\partial v}\frac{\partial \lambda_1}{\partial u} + \frac{\partial \psi_1}{\partial u}\frac{\partial \lambda_1}{\partial v} = 0.$$

From (V, 35) it follows that ψ_1 can be chosen so that

$$e^{-\psi_1} = \frac{m p^2}{\theta'} e^{\psi} = \frac{p^2}{\nu\theta} e^{\psi}, \tag{72}$$

if we take

$$\theta' = m\nu\theta. \tag{73}$$

If in accordance with (9) we put

$$\sqrt{E_1} + \sqrt{E} = \frac{p}{\nu} e^{\psi} + \frac{\theta}{p} e^{-\psi}, \quad \sqrt{G_1} + \sqrt{G} = \frac{p}{\nu} e^{\psi} - \frac{\theta}{p} e^{-\psi}, \tag{74}$$

we find that the last two of equations (7) are satisfied, and consequently the following system of equations is completely integrable:

$$(75)\quad \left\{ \begin{aligned} &\frac{\partial \theta}{\partial u} = \sqrt{E}\, q, \qquad \frac{\partial \theta}{\partial v} = \sqrt{G}\, r, \\ &\frac{\partial p}{\partial u} = e^{-\psi} q, \qquad \frac{\partial p}{\partial v} = -e^{-\psi} r, \\ &\frac{\partial q}{\partial u} = -e^{-\psi} p - \frac{\partial \psi}{\partial v} r + m\left(p e^{\psi} + \frac{\theta\nu}{p} e^{-\psi}\right), \qquad \frac{\partial q}{\partial v} = \frac{\partial \psi}{\partial u} r, \\ &\frac{\partial r}{\partial u} = \frac{\partial \psi}{\partial v} q, \qquad \frac{\partial r}{\partial v} = e^{-\psi} p - \frac{\partial \psi}{\partial u} q + m\left(p e^{\psi} - \frac{\theta\nu}{p} e^{-\psi}\right), \\ &\frac{\partial \nu}{\partial u} = \frac{q}{\theta}\left(p e^{\psi} + \frac{\theta\nu}{p} e^{-\psi} - \sqrt{E}\,\nu\right), \quad \frac{\partial \nu}{\partial v} = \frac{r}{\theta}\left(p e^{\psi} - \frac{\theta\nu}{p} e^{-\psi} - \sqrt{G}\,\nu\right). \end{aligned} \right.$$

72) Transactions Amer. Math. Soc., vol. 9 (1908), pp. 149—177.

73) Rendiconti dei Lincei, ser. 5, vol. 24 (1915), p. 371.

From these equations we have

$$(76) \qquad \frac{\partial}{\partial u}\left(\frac{\theta \nu}{p}\right) = e^{\psi} q, \qquad \frac{\partial}{\partial v}\left(\frac{\theta \nu}{p}\right) = e^{\psi} r,$$

and consequently $\theta\nu/p$ is a solution $\bar{\theta}$ of the point equation of the minimal surface $\bar{N}$ with the same spherical representation as N. In terms of this function the above expressions for the derivatives of q and r assume the same form as (71). Consequently the transformation of $\bar{N}$ by means of $p, q, r, \bar{\theta}$ is a D_m into a minimal surface. Hence we have the theorem:

When an O net N with isothermal spherical representation admits a transformation R into a net N_1 of the same kind, the minimal surface parallel to N is transformed into the minimal surface parallel to N_1 by a transformation D_m.

Conversely, if $\bar{N}$ and $\bar{N}_1$ are O nets on minimal surfaces in relation D_m, and N is a net parallel to $\bar{N}$, the set of functions p, q, r of this transformation and θ and ν, where $\theta\nu = \bar{\theta} p$ determine transformations E_m of N into ∞^1 nets N_1 parallel to $\bar{N}_1$. For θ is determined to within an additive arbitrary constant by the first two of (75) and then ν is fixed. Hence:

An O net with isothermal spherical representation admits ∞^2 transformations E_m, for each value of m, into ∞^1 parallel O nets of the same kind.

From these results and the fifth theorem of § 78 we have:

An isothermic net on a sphere admits ∞^3 transformations F into isothermic nets on the sphere.

Consider a quatern of minimal surfaces in accordance with the last theorem of § 87, and four nets N, N_1, N_2, N_{12} parallel to the O nets $\bar{N}, \bar{N}_1, \bar{N}_2, \bar{N}_{12}$ of the minimal surfaces in accordance with the last theorem of § 72.

From (56) it follows that

$$\bar{\theta}_{12}^{\prime\prime\prime} = -m_2 \bar{\theta}_{12} p_{12}, \qquad \bar{\theta}_{21}^{\prime\prime\prime\prime} = -m_1 \bar{\theta}_{21} p_{21},$$

where $\bar{\theta}_{12}$ and $\bar{\theta}_{21}$ determine the transformations from $\bar{N}_1$ and $\bar{N}_2$ into $\bar{N}_{12}$. From equations analogous to (76) and (49) we have

$$\theta_{12}\nu_{12} = -p_{12}\bar{\theta}_{12}, \qquad \theta_{21}\nu_{21} = -p_{21}\bar{\theta}_{21}.$$

Hence, since $\theta_{12}''' = \overline{\theta}_{12}'''$ and $\theta_{21}'''' = \overline{\theta}_{21}''''$,

$$\theta_{12}''' = m_2\,\theta_{12}\,\nu_{12}, \qquad \theta_{21}'''' = m_1\,\theta_{21}\,\nu_{21},$$

and consequently we have the theorem:

If N_1 and N_2 are obtained from an O net N with isothermal spherical representation by transformations E_{m_1} and E_{m_2}, there can be found without quadratures a net N_{12} of the same kind, such that N_{12} is an E_{m_2} transform of N_1 and an E_{m_1} transform of N_2.

89. Nets Ω. By definition an O net N is a *net* Ω if there exists a net N_0 with equal point invariants conjugate to the congruence G normal to N. Let N be a net Ω and let θ_0 be the solution of the point equation of N, namely

$$\frac{\partial^2\theta}{\partial u\,\partial v} = \frac{\partial \log\sqrt{E}}{\partial v}\frac{\partial\theta}{\partial u} + \frac{\partial\log\sqrt{G}}{\partial u}\frac{\partial\theta}{\partial v}, \tag{77}$$

by means of which $N_0(x_0)$ is obtained from N by a transformation F. The equations of the transformation are of the form

$$x_0 = x - \frac{\theta_0}{\hat{\theta}_0}X, \tag{78}$$

where $\hat{\theta}_0$ is defined by

$$\frac{\partial\hat{\theta}_0}{\partial u} = \hat{h}\frac{\partial\theta_0}{\partial u}, \qquad \frac{\partial\hat{\theta}_0}{\partial v} = \hat{l}\frac{\partial\theta_0}{\partial v}, \tag{79}$$

and

$$\hat{h} = -\frac{1}{\varrho_1}, \qquad \hat{l} = -\frac{1}{\varrho_2}, \tag{80}$$

since [§ 51]

$$\frac{\partial X}{\partial u} = -\frac{1}{\varrho_1}\frac{\partial x}{\partial u}, \qquad \frac{\partial X}{\partial v} = -\frac{1}{\varrho_2}\frac{\partial x}{\partial v}. \tag{81}$$

If the point equation of N_0 is written in the form

$$\frac{\partial^2\theta}{\partial u\,\partial v} = \frac{\partial}{\partial v}\log\sqrt{\varrho_0}\frac{\partial\theta}{\partial u} + \frac{\partial}{\partial u}\log\sqrt{\varrho_0}\frac{\partial\theta}{\partial v}, \tag{82}$$

we have from (77) and (II, 12)

$$(83)\qquad \sqrt{\varrho_0} = \frac{\tau_0\sqrt{E}}{\hat{\theta}_0}U = \frac{\sigma_0\sqrt{G}}{\hat{\theta}_0}V,$$

where U and V are functions of u and v respectively, and from (II, 8)

$$(84)\qquad \tau_0 = -\left(\frac{\theta_0}{\varrho_1}+\hat{\theta}_0\right), \qquad \sigma_0 = -\left(\frac{\theta_0}{\varrho_2}+\hat{\theta}_0\right).$$

When these expressions are substituted in (83), we obtain

$$(85)\qquad \hat{\theta}_0 = \theta_0\frac{\varrho_2 U\sqrt{E}-\varrho_1 V\sqrt{G}}{\varrho_1\varrho_2(V\sqrt{G}-U\sqrt{E})}, \qquad \sqrt{\varrho_0} = \frac{UV\sqrt{EG}(\varrho_1-\varrho_2)}{U\sqrt{E}\varrho_2-V\sqrt{G}\varrho_1}.$$

The Codazzi equations for N are [§ 65]

$$(86)\qquad \frac{\partial}{\partial v}\left(\frac{\sqrt{E}}{\varrho_1}\right) = \frac{1}{\varrho_2}\frac{\partial\sqrt{E}}{\partial v}, \qquad \frac{\partial}{\partial u}\left(\frac{\sqrt{G}}{\varrho_2}\right) = \frac{1}{\varrho_1}\frac{\partial\sqrt{G}}{\partial u}.$$

When we require that the function (85) satisfy (79), we find, in consequence of (86),

$$(87)\qquad \begin{cases} \dfrac{\partial\log\theta_0}{\partial u} = \dfrac{U\sqrt{E}}{V\sqrt{G}}\dfrac{\varrho_1\varrho_2}{\varrho_1-\varrho_2}\dfrac{\partial}{\partial u}\left(\dfrac{1}{\varrho_1}\right)+\dfrac{\partial}{\partial u}\log(U\sqrt{E}-V\sqrt{G}), \\[2ex] \dfrac{\partial\log\theta_0}{\partial v} = \dfrac{V\sqrt{G}}{U\sqrt{E}}\dfrac{\varrho_1\varrho_2}{\varrho_2-\varrho_1}\dfrac{\partial}{\partial v}\left(\dfrac{1}{\varrho_2}\right)+\dfrac{\partial}{\partial v}\log(U\sqrt{E}-V\sqrt{G}). \end{cases}$$

The condition of integrability of (87) is

$$(88)\qquad \frac{\partial}{\partial v}\left(\frac{U\sqrt{E}}{V\sqrt{G}}\frac{\varrho_1\varrho_2}{\varrho_1-\varrho_2}\frac{\partial}{\partial u}\left(\frac{1}{\varrho_1}\right)\right) = \frac{\partial}{\partial u}\left(\frac{V\sqrt{G}}{U\sqrt{E}}\frac{\varrho_1\varrho_2}{\varrho_2-\varrho_1}\frac{\partial}{\partial v}\left(\frac{1}{\varrho_2}\right)\right).$$

When this condition is satisfied, we find that θ_0 given by (87) satisfies (77), and consequently N is a net Ω. Hence we have the theorem of Demoulin[74]):

A necessary and sufficient condition that an O net be a net Ω is that (88) *be satisfied.*

In consequence of the second theorem of § 25 we have that when N is a net Ω, there is a second net N_ω with equal point invariants conjugate to the congruence G normal to N, and that the points of N_0 and N_ω on a line of G are harmonic to the focal points of G on this line. Since the coordinates of these focal points are of the forms, $x+\varrho_1 X$ and $x+\varrho_2 X$, we have from (78) and the analogous equations for N_ω, namely

$$x_\omega = x - \frac{\theta_\omega}{\hat{\theta}_\omega} X,$$

the equation

$$\hat{\theta}_\omega = -\theta_\omega \frac{\varrho_2 U\sqrt{E}+\varrho_1 V\sqrt{G}}{\varrho_1\varrho_2(U\sqrt{E}+V\sqrt{G})}. \tag{89}$$

The equations analogous to (87) are obtained from them by replacing V by $-V$. From these equations we have

$$\theta_\omega\theta_0 = U^2E - V^2G, \qquad \sqrt{\varrho_\omega} = \frac{UV\sqrt{EG}(\varrho_2-\varrho_1)}{U\sqrt{E}\varrho_2+V\sqrt{G}\varrho_1}. \tag{90}$$

Since N_0 and N_ω are conjugate to the normal congruence to N, they are nets 2, O, the respective complementary functions being $\theta_0/\hat{\theta}_0$ and $\theta_\omega/\hat{\theta}_\omega$ (§ 66). Conversely, if N_0 is a net 2, O with equal invariants, the two sheets of the envelope of spheres with centers on N_0 and radii given by the complementary function of N_0 are surfaces Ω in relation R.

The foregoing results may be stated as follows:

When a net N is a net Ω, the nets with equal invariants conjugate to the congruence normal to N can be found without quadratures; these nets are 2, O. Conversely, when a 2, O net N_0 with equal invariants is known, there can be found without quadratures two nets Ω, in relation R, whose normal congruences are conjugate to N_0.

---

[74]) Comptes Rendus, vol. 153 (1911), pp. 590, 705, 927.

From (II, 87) it follows that the net $N_0'(x_0')$, where

$$\frac{\partial x_0'}{\partial u} = -\frac{1}{\varrho_0}\frac{\partial x_0}{\partial u}, \qquad \frac{\partial x_0'}{\partial v} = \frac{1}{\varrho_0}\frac{\partial x_0}{\partial v},$$

has equal point invariants. From § 76 we have that N_0' is 2, O, the complementary function t' being given by a quadrature, and that the sheets of the envelope of the spheres with centers on N_0' and radius t' are parallel to the corresponding sheets of the envelope of the above congruence R of spheres with centers on N_0. Hence:

When a net Ω is known, a parallel net Ω can be found by quadratures.

90. Transformations R of nets Ω. Let N be a net Ω and N_1 an R transform of N by means of a set of solutions θ, p, q, r and w of equations (7) and (8). As in the preceding section, we denote by N_0 one of the nets with equal point invariants conjugate to the congruence normal to N; it is an F transform of N by means of θ_0 and $\hat{\theta}_0$. In accordance with the theorem of permutability of transformations F (§ 21) there exist ∞^2 nets N_{01}, which are F transforms of N_0 and N_1.

From (11) and § 21 it follows that if we take $\hat{\theta} = p$ we obtain ∞^1 nets N_{01} conjugate to the congruence normal to N_1, as the additive constant of θ_0' varies. We seek the conditions that one of these nets be a K transform of N_1 and thus has equal point invariants, in which case N_1 is a net Ω.

From (II, 43, 44) we have that the functions θ_{01} and θ_{01}'''' of the transformation from N_0 into a net N_{01} are given by

$$(91) \qquad \theta_{01} = \theta - \frac{\theta_0}{\hat{\theta}_0}p, \qquad \theta_{01}'''' = \theta' - \frac{\theta_0'}{\hat{\theta}_0}p,$$

and from (II, 53) and (80) we have

$$(92) \qquad h_{01} = -\frac{\frac{1}{\rho_1}\theta_0' + h\hat{\theta}_0}{\tau_0}, \qquad l_{01} = -\frac{\frac{1}{\rho_2}\theta_0' + l\hat{\theta}_0}{\sigma_0}$$

with

$$\frac{\partial \theta_{01}''''}{\partial u} = h_{01}\frac{\partial \theta_{01}}{\partial u}, \qquad \frac{\partial \theta_{01}''''}{\partial v} = l_{01}\frac{\partial \theta_{01}}{\partial v}. \tag{93}$$

A necessary and sufficient condition that N_{01} be a K transform of N_0 is that (II, 81)

$$h_{01} = \frac{m\,\theta_{01}}{\varrho_0} + \frac{\theta_{01}''''}{\theta_{01}}, \qquad l_{01} = -\frac{m\,\theta_{01}}{\varrho_0} + \frac{\theta_{01}''''}{\theta_{01}}, \tag{94}$$

where m is a constant.

From (II, 36, 38) we have that the functions θ_{10} and θ_{10}''' of the transformation from N_1 into N_{01} have the form

$$\theta_{10} = \theta_0 - \frac{\theta_0'}{m\nu}, \qquad \theta_{10}''' = \hat{\theta}_0 - \frac{p\,\theta_0'}{m\nu\,\theta}, \tag{95}$$

where $\theta' = m\nu\,\theta$.

When we equate the expressions (92) and (94) for h_{01} and l_{01}, the resulting equations are reducible by means of (VI, 83), (91) and (95)

$$\left\{\begin{aligned} U\sqrt{E_1} &= -U\sqrt{E}\,\frac{\theta_{10}}{\theta_0} - \frac{\theta_{01}}{\nu\sqrt{\varrho_0}} - \sqrt{\varrho_0}\,\frac{\theta}{\theta_0}\,\frac{\theta_{10}}{\theta_{01}}, \\ V\sqrt{G_1} &= -V\sqrt{G}\,\frac{\theta_{10}}{\theta_0} + \frac{\theta_{01}}{\nu\sqrt{\varrho_0}} - \sqrt{\varrho_0}\,\frac{\theta}{\theta_0}\,\frac{\theta_{10}}{\theta_{01}}. \end{aligned}\right. \tag{96}$$

From (91) we have by differentiation

$$\frac{\partial \theta_{01}}{\partial u} = -\frac{\sqrt{\varrho_0}}{U}\left(q - \frac{p}{\hat{\theta}_0}\,\frac{1}{\sqrt{E}}\,\frac{\partial \theta_0}{\partial u}\right),$$

$$\frac{\partial \theta_{01}}{\partial v} = -\frac{\sqrt{\varrho_0}}{V}\left(r - \frac{p}{\hat{\theta}_0}\,\frac{1}{\sqrt{G}}\,\frac{\partial \theta_0}{\partial v}\right).$$

By means of these equations and the last two of (97), which are obtained by differentiating (95), we find that the expressions (96) satisfy the last two of (7). Hence the following system of equations in which E_1 and G_1 have the form (96) is completely integrable:

$$
(97)\quad\left\{
\begin{aligned}
&\frac{\partial\theta}{\partial u}=\sqrt{E}q, \qquad \frac{\partial\theta}{\partial v}=\sqrt{G}r,\\
&\frac{\partial p}{\partial u}=-\frac{\sqrt{E}}{\varrho_1}q, \qquad \frac{\partial p}{\partial v}=-\frac{\sqrt{G}}{\varrho_2}r,\\
&\frac{\partial q}{\partial u}=\frac{\sqrt{E}}{\varrho_1}p-\frac{1}{\sqrt{G}}\frac{\partial\sqrt{E}}{\partial v}r+m\nu(\sqrt{E}+\sqrt{E_1}), \quad \frac{\partial q}{\partial v}=\frac{1}{\sqrt{E}}\frac{\partial\sqrt{G}}{\partial u}r,\\
&\frac{\partial r}{\partial u}=\frac{1}{\sqrt{G}}\frac{\partial\sqrt{E}}{\partial v}q, \quad \frac{\partial r}{\partial v}=\frac{\sqrt{G}}{\varrho_2}p-\frac{1}{\sqrt{E}}\frac{\partial\sqrt{G}}{\partial u}q+m\nu(\sqrt{G}+\sqrt{G_1}),\\
&\frac{\partial\nu}{\partial u}=\sqrt{E_1}\frac{\nu q}{\theta}, \qquad \frac{\partial\nu}{\partial v}=\sqrt{G_1}\frac{\nu r}{\theta},\\
&\frac{\partial\theta_{10}}{\partial u}=-\sqrt{E_1}\left[\frac{q}{\theta}(\theta_{10}-\theta_0)+\frac{1}{\sqrt{E}}\frac{\partial\theta_0}{\partial u}\right],\\
&\frac{\partial\theta_{10}}{\partial v}=-\sqrt{G_1}\left[\frac{r}{\theta}(\theta_{10}-\theta_0)+\frac{1}{\sqrt{G}}\frac{\partial\theta_0}{\partial v}\right].
\end{aligned}
\right.
$$

When we have a set of solutions θ, ν, p, q, r, θ_{10} satisfying the quadratic relation

$$
(98)\qquad p^2+q^2+r^2-2m\nu\theta=0,
$$

the R transform N_1 is a net Ω, and the coordinates of N_1 are given by equations of the form (48). The same functions multiplied by the same constant determine the same transformation. Hence in addition to m there are four significant constants of integration, and consequently:

A net Ω admits ∞^5 transformations R into nets Ω[75]).

From (II, 86) (91) and (95) we find that the function ϱ_{10} for N_{10} has the expression

$$
(99)\qquad \sqrt{\varrho_{10}}=\frac{\theta_{01}^2}{\sqrt{\varrho_0\theta_{01}''''}}=\frac{\theta_{01}^2\,\hat{\theta}_0}{\sqrt{\varrho_0\theta'\theta_{10}'''}}=\frac{\theta_{01}^2\,\hat{\theta}_0}{\sqrt{\varrho_0 m\nu\theta\theta_{10}'''}}.
$$

91. Theorem of permutability of the transformations of nets Ω.

Let N be a net Ω, and N_1 and N_2 two R transforms of N by means of functions θ_i, p_i, q_i, r_i, ν_i, θ_{io}, m_i $(i=1, 2)$, solutions

[75]) Cf., Transactions of the Amer. Math. Soc., vol. 16 (1915), pp. 275—310.

of (97) and (98). We wish to show that of the ∞^1 O nets N_{12}, which are R transforms of N_1 and N_2 in accordance with § 72, one is a net Ω.

Consider the nets N_{10} and N_{20} which are K transforms of N_0 by means of the pairs of functions θ_{01}, w_{01} and θ_{02}, w_{02}. From § 24 we have that there is a net N_{120} which is an F transform of each of the nets N_{12}, N_{10} and N_{20}, and the functions θ'_{10} and θ'_{20} of the respective transformations from N_{10} and N_{20} are given by

$$\theta_0\,\theta_{01}\,w_{01}\,\theta'_{01} = w_1(\theta_0\,\theta_{01}\,\theta_{12} + \theta_1\,\theta_{10}\,\theta_{02} - \theta_2\,\theta_{10}\,\theta_{01}),$$
$$\theta_0\,\theta_{02}\,w_{02}\,\theta'_{02} = w_2(\theta_0\,\theta_{02}\,\theta_{21} + \theta_2\,\theta_{20}\,\theta_{01} - \theta_1\,\theta_{20}\,\theta_{02}).$$

Moreover, from (II, 91) it follows that N_{120} will be a K transform of N_{10} and N_{20}, and consequently have equal point invariants, if

$$m_1\,\theta'_{02}w_{02} + m_2\,\theta'_{01}w_{01} = 0.$$

Substituting the above values in this equation, we reduce the resulting equation to

$$\text{(100)}\quad \left\{\begin{aligned} m_2\,\theta'_2 + m_1\,\theta''_1 = \frac{m_1 m_2}{\theta_0}\Big\{\nu_1\Big[\frac{\theta_1\,\theta_{10}\,\theta_{02}}{\theta_{01}} - \theta_2(\theta_{10}-\theta_0)\Big] \\ + \nu_2\Big[\frac{\theta_2\,\theta_{20}\,\theta_{01}}{\theta_{02}} - \theta_1(\theta_{20}-\theta_0)\Big]\Big\}. \end{aligned}\right.$$

If this equation is differentiated with respect to u and v, we find that the resulting equations are satisfied identically.

Since θ'_2 and θ''_1 are completely determined by (50) and (100), only one of the nets N_{12} is an Ω net. Hence we have the theorem:

If N_1 and N_2 are Ω nets which are R transforms of an Ω net N, there exists a unique Ω net N_{12} which is an R transform of N_1 and N_2; moreover, N_{12} can be found directly, as soon as the coordinates of N_1 and N_2 are known.

92. Surfaces of Guichard of the first kind. In order that the O net N on a surface S be defined by

$$\text{(101)}\quad \left\{\begin{aligned} &\sqrt{E} = e^{\xi}\sinh\alpha, & &\sqrt{G} = e^{\xi}\cosh\alpha, \\ &\frac{1}{\varrho_1} = e^{-\xi}(\coth\alpha + h), & &\frac{1}{\varrho_2} = e^{-\xi}(\tanh\alpha + h), \end{aligned}\right.$$

it is necessary and sufficient that h, ξ and α satisfy the equations

$$(102)\begin{cases} \dfrac{\partial h}{\partial u} = (\coth\alpha + h)\dfrac{\partial \xi}{\partial u}, \qquad \dfrac{\partial h}{\partial v} = (\tanh\alpha + h)\dfrac{\partial \xi}{\partial v}, \\ \dfrac{\partial^2 \xi}{\partial u \partial v} = \dfrac{\partial \xi}{\partial u}\dfrac{\partial \xi}{\partial v} + \coth\alpha \dfrac{\partial \xi}{\partial u}\dfrac{\partial \alpha}{\partial v} + \tanh\alpha \dfrac{\partial \xi}{\partial v}\dfrac{\partial \alpha}{\partial u}, \\ \dfrac{\partial^2 \alpha}{\partial u^2} + \dfrac{\partial^2 \alpha}{\partial v^2} + \coth\alpha \dfrac{\partial^2 \xi}{\partial u^2} + \tanh\alpha \dfrac{\partial^2 \xi}{\partial v^2} - \operatorname{csch}^2\alpha \dfrac{\partial \alpha}{\partial u}\dfrac{\partial \xi}{\partial u} \\ + \operatorname{sech}^2\alpha \dfrac{\partial \alpha}{\partial v}\dfrac{\partial \xi}{\partial v} + (\cosh\alpha + h\sinh\alpha)(\sinh\alpha + h\cosh\alpha) = 0, \end{cases}$$

as follows from the Codazzi equations (86) and the Gauss equation [§ 64]. These equations are satisfied also by $\bar{\xi}$, $\bar{\alpha}$, h, where

$$(103) \qquad e^{\bar{\xi}} = e^{-\xi}(1-h^2), \qquad e^{\bar{\alpha}} = e^{-\alpha}\frac{1-h}{1+h}.$$

An O net $\bar{N}$ parallel to N is defined by

$$(104)\begin{cases} \sqrt{\bar{E}} = e^{\bar{\xi}}\sinh\bar{\alpha}, \qquad \sqrt{\bar{G}} = -e^{\bar{\xi}}\cosh\bar{\alpha}, \\ \dfrac{1}{\bar{\varrho}_1} = e^{-\bar{\xi}}(\coth\bar{\alpha} + h), \qquad \dfrac{1}{\bar{\varrho}_2} = e^{-\bar{\xi}}(\tanh\bar{\alpha} + h). \end{cases}$$

By means of (101) and (104) we have

$$\varrho_1\bar{\varrho}_2 + \varrho_2\bar{\varrho}_1 = -2.$$

Following Calapso[76]) we call S a *surface of Guichard of the first kind*, and the parallel surface $\bar{S}$ its *associate* (cf. VII, Ex. 28).

When the expressions for $\sqrt{E}$, $\sqrt{G}$, ϱ_1 and ϱ_2 from (101) are substituted in (88), this condition is satisfied, if we take $U = V = 1$. Hence we have the theorem of Demoulin[77]):

The surfaces of Guichard of the first kind are surfaces Ω. From (87) and (85) we have

$$(105) \qquad \theta_0 = e^{\xi}, \qquad \hat{\theta}_0 = 1-h, \qquad \sqrt{\varrho_0} = \frac{e^{\xi+\alpha}}{h-1}.$$

---

[76]) Annali, ser. 3, vol. 11 (1905), p. 211.

[77]) L. c.

We apply the results of § 90 to establish transformations R of surfaces of Guichard of the first kind. Analogously to (105) we have

$$\theta_{10} = e^{\xi_1}, \qquad \theta_{10}''' = 1 - h_1.$$

From (95) it follows that

$$h_1 + \frac{p}{\theta} e^{\xi_1} = h + \frac{p}{\theta} e^{\xi} = t, \tag{106}$$

where t is thus defined. Now $\theta_{01} = \theta - e^{\xi} p/(1-h)$, and consequently (96) are reducible to

$$\left\{\begin{aligned} \sqrt{E_1} &= \frac{e^{\xi_1}\varphi}{1-t} + \frac{\theta}{\nu}(1-t)\, e^{-(\xi+\alpha)}, \\ \sqrt{G_1} &= \frac{e^{\xi_1}\psi}{1-t} - \frac{\theta}{\nu}(1-t)\, e^{-(\xi+\alpha)}, \end{aligned}\right. \tag{107}$$

where

$$\varphi = \cosh\alpha + t\sinh\alpha, \qquad \psi = \sinh\alpha + t\cosh\alpha.$$

Since $\varphi^2 - \psi^2 = 1 - t^2$, when we require that $G_1 - E_1 = e^{2\xi_1}$, we get

$$e^{\xi_1} = \frac{\theta}{\nu} e^{-\xi}(t^2 - 1). \tag{108}$$

If we put $\sqrt{\varrho_{10}} = e^{\xi_1 + \alpha_1}/m\,(h_1 - 1)$ in (99), we obtain

$$e^{\alpha_1} = e^{-\alpha}\frac{t-1}{t+1}. \tag{109}$$

Hence we find

$$\sqrt{E_1} = e^{\xi_1}\sinh\alpha_1, \qquad \sqrt{G_1} = -e^{\xi_1}\cosh\alpha_1.$$

Furthermore, equations (9) are satisfied by

$$\frac{\sqrt{E_1}}{\varrho_{11}} = -(\cosh\alpha_1 + h_1\sinh\alpha_1), \qquad \frac{\sqrt{G_1}}{\varrho_{12}} = \sinh\alpha_1 + h_1\cosh\alpha_1.$$

Hence the surface S_1 is a surface of Guichard of the first kind.
By means of (108) the expressions (107) are reducible to

$$\sqrt{E_1} = -\frac{\theta}{\nu} e^{-\xi} (\varphi t + \psi), \qquad \sqrt{G_1} = -\frac{\theta}{\nu} e^{-\xi} (\psi t + \varphi).$$

Consequently the functions determining a transformation R of a surface of Guichard of the first kind into surface of this type are solutions of the completely integrable system:

$$(110) \quad \begin{cases} \dfrac{\partial \theta}{\partial u} = e^{\xi} \sinh \alpha\, q, \qquad \dfrac{\partial \theta}{\partial v} = e^{\xi} \cosh \alpha\, r, \\ \dfrac{\partial p}{\partial u} = -(\cosh \alpha + h \sinh \alpha)\, q, \qquad \dfrac{\partial p}{\partial v} = -(\sinh \alpha + h \cosh \alpha)\, r, \\ \dfrac{\partial q}{\partial u} = (\cosh \alpha + h \sinh \alpha)\, p - \left(\tanh \alpha \dfrac{\partial \xi}{\partial v} + \dfrac{\partial \alpha}{\partial v}\right) \cdot r \\ \qquad + m[-\theta e^{-\xi} (\varphi t + \psi) + \nu e^{\xi} \sinh \alpha], \\ \dfrac{\partial q}{\partial v} = \left(\coth \alpha \dfrac{\partial \xi}{\partial u} + \dfrac{\partial \alpha}{\partial u}\right) r, \qquad \dfrac{\partial r}{\partial u} = \left(\tanh \alpha \dfrac{\partial \xi}{\partial v} + \dfrac{\partial \alpha}{\partial v}\right) q, \\ \dfrac{\partial r}{\partial v} = (\sinh \alpha + h \cosh \alpha)\, p - \left(\coth \alpha \dfrac{\partial \xi}{\partial u} + \dfrac{\partial \alpha}{\partial u}\right) \cdot q \\ \qquad + m[-\theta e^{-\xi} (\psi t + \varphi) + \nu e^{\xi} \cosh \alpha], \\ \dfrac{\partial \nu}{\partial u} = -e^{-\xi} (\varphi t + \psi)\, q, \qquad \dfrac{\partial \nu}{\partial v} = -e^{-\xi} (\psi t + \varphi)\, r. \end{cases}$$

The equations of the transformation are of the form (48) in these functions. Accordingly we have the theorem[78]:

A surface of Guichard of the first kind admits ∞^3 transformations R_m, for each value of $m \neq 0$, into surfaces of the same kind.

When S is transformed into S_1, the associate surface $\bar{S}$ is transformed into a surface $\bar{S}_1$, parallel to S_1, by means of the functions $p, q, r, \bar{\theta}$ and $\bar{\nu}$, where in consequence of (49) $\bar{\theta}\bar{\nu} = \theta \nu$. The equations in $\bar{\theta}$ are

$$\frac{\partial \bar{\theta}}{\partial u} = e^{\bar{\xi}} \sinh \bar{\alpha}\, q, \qquad \frac{\partial \bar{\theta}}{\partial v} = -e^{\bar{\xi}} \cosh \bar{\alpha}\, r,$$

---

[78]) Annali, ser. 3, vol. 22 (1914), p. 205; also Transactions of Amer. Math. Soc. vol. 17 (1916), p. 68.

It is readily found that

$$\bar{\theta} = \nu - \frac{p^2}{\theta}, \qquad \bar{\nu} = \frac{\nu\theta^2}{\nu\theta - p^2}.$$

The associate of S_1 is determined by equations analogous to (103), namely

$$e^{\bar{\xi}_1} = e^{-\xi_1}(1-h_1^2) = -\frac{\nu}{\theta}e^{\xi} + \frac{2pt}{\theta} + \frac{p^2}{\theta\nu}e^{-\xi}(1-t^2),$$

$$e^{\bar{\alpha}_1} = e^{-\alpha_1}\frac{1-h_1}{1+h_1} = e^{\alpha}\frac{t+1}{t-1}\,\frac{1-t+\frac{p}{\theta}e^{\xi_1}}{1+t-\frac{p}{\theta}e^{\xi_1}},$$

$$\bar{h}_1 = h_1.$$

If this associate is to be the R transform of $\bar{S}$ by means of $\bar{\theta}$, $\bar{\nu}$, p, q, r, then analogously to (106), (108) and (109) we must have

$$h_1 + \frac{p}{\bar{\theta}}e^{\bar{\xi}_1} = h + \frac{p}{\bar{\theta}}e^{\bar{\xi}} = \bar{t},$$

$$e^{\bar{\xi}_1} = \frac{\bar{\theta}}{\bar{\nu}}e^{-\bar{\xi}}(\bar{t}^2-1), \qquad e^{\bar{\alpha}_1} = e^{-\bar{\alpha}}\frac{\bar{t}-1}{\bar{t}+1}.$$

It is readily shown that these expressions are equivalent to the preceding. Hence:

When a surface of Guichard of the first kind is transformed into a surface of the same kind, the associate surfaces are in relation R[79]).

Exercises.

1. If N is a net 2, O the complementary function being y, the lines of curvature on the sheets of the envelope of the spheres of radius y and centers on N are represented on the unit sphere by the central projections on this sphere of the two special nets 2, O parallel to N; the coordinates of the spherical representations are x'/y' and x''/y''.

2. Corresponding tangent planes to two pairs of O nets in relation R whose central nets are parallel are parallel.

3. A necessary and sufficient condition that the spheres, tangent to a surface S and with centers at the mid-points of the segments of the normals to S

---

[79]) Annali, l. c. p. 209.

included between the centers of principal curvature of S, determine an R transform of S is that the lines of curvature of S have isothermic spherical representation (cf. § 6 and I, Ex. 8).

4. A necessary and sufficient condition that the spheres tangent to a surface S with centers at points harmonic to the points on S with respect to the centers of principal curvature determine an R transform of S is that S be an isothermic surface (cf. § 25).

Darboux, Annales Norm., ser. 3, vol. 16 (1899) p. 504.

5. Show that the first three theorems of § 81 are equally true for the transformations R of nets O in n-space.

6. For a system of circles K of the second kind (§ 81) the focal points of the congruence K are harmonic to the foci of the meridian sections of the hyperboloid of revolution whose generators are the normals to the nets N_c and N_{12}.

Demoulin, Comptes Rendus, vol. 150 (1910), p. 159.

7. If N is an isothermic O net, the point equation of N admits the solution $\theta_0 = e^{2\phi}\left(\frac{1}{\rho_1}-\frac{1}{\rho_2}\right)$, and the corresponding parallel O nets $N_0(x_0)$ are defined by equations of the form

$$x_0 = \left(\frac{1}{2}\theta_0 K_0 + c\right) X + e^{\phi}\left(\frac{\partial K_0}{\partial u}\xi - \frac{\partial K_0}{\partial v}\eta\right),$$

where c is an arbitrary constant and $K_0 = \frac{1}{\rho_1}+\frac{1}{\rho_2}$.

8. If N is an isothermic O net defined by (37), the Christoffel transform $\bar{N}$ [§ 159] is defined by

$$\sqrt{\bar{E}} = -\sqrt{\bar{G}} = e^{-\phi}, \qquad \bar{\rho}_1 = \rho_1 e^{-2\phi}, \qquad \bar{\rho}_2 = -\rho_2 e^{-2\phi}.$$

Show that if N_1 is a D_m transform of N, a D_m transform $\bar{N}_1$ of $\bar{N}$ is given by

$$\bar{p} = p, \quad \bar{q} = q, \quad \bar{r} = r, \quad \bar{\theta} = \nu, \quad \bar{\nu} = \theta, \quad \bar{m} = m,$$

and that $\bar{N}_1$ is the Christoffel transform of N_1. Also if M, M_1 and $\bar{M}$, $\bar{M}_1$ denote corresponding points on these nets, the product of the segments $M M_1$ and $\bar{M}\bar{M}_1$ is equal to $2/m$.

Bianchi, l. c., p. 105.

9. If M, M_1, M_2, M_{12} are corresponding points of four nets satisfying the theorem of permutability of transformations D_m (§ 83), the cross-ratio ($M M_{12}$, $M_1 M_2$) is equal to m_2/m_1.

Demoulin, l. c., p. 157.

10. Show that the O net of a minimal surface may be considered of class (0, 0, 0, 0) (§ 84) and obtain the results of § 87 from those of § 86.

Bianchi, l. c., p. 149.

11. From [§ 125] we have for a surface of mean curvature $K_0 = 1$,

$$\frac{1}{\rho_1} = e^{-\phi}\sinh\phi, \qquad \frac{1}{\rho_2} = e^{-\phi}\cosh\phi.$$

In this case from (47) it follows that $\theta - \nu + 2p = a$, where a is a constant. Show that when $a = 0$, the mean curvature of N_1 is -1.

12. Show that the O net of a surface of mean curvature $K_0 = 1$ may be considered a special isothermic net of class $(-\frac{1}{2}, 0, 0, \frac{1}{4})$, and apply the results of § 86 to obtain those of Ex. 11. Bianchi, l. c., p. 151.

13. The Christoffel transform of a special isothermic surface of class (A, B, C, D) is a special surface of class $(A, -C, -B, D)$. Bianchi, l. c., p. 131.

14. If from a special isothermic net N of class (A, B, C, D), we obtain two nets of N_1, N_2, of class $(A, -B, -C, D)$ by transformations D_{m_1} and D_{m_2}, the surface N_{12} is of class (A, B, C, D). Bianchi, l. c., p. 146.

15. Determine the special isothermic surfaces for which the circle-planes of the complementary transformations pass through a point.

16. Show that the nets N' of transformations D_m of isothermic nets and of transformations E_m of O nets with isothermal spherical representation have the property

$$E' - G' = 2m(x'^2 + y'^2 + z'^2).$$

Calapso, Annali, ser. 3, vol. 26 (1917), p. 168.

17. If N_1 is a D_m transform of an isothermic O net N, an isothermic O net $\overline{N}$ is defined by

$$\sqrt{\overline{E}} = \sqrt{\overline{G}} = \frac{e^{\psi}}{\theta}, \qquad \frac{1}{\overline{\rho}_1} = p + \frac{\theta}{\rho_1}, \qquad \frac{1}{\overline{\rho}_2} = p + \frac{\theta}{\rho_2}.$$

Bianchi, Annali, ser. 3, vol. 12 (1906) p. 22.

18. If N and N_1 are two O nets in relation E_m, the minimal surfaces Σ and Σ_1, whose asymptotic lines have the same spherical representation as the curves of N and N_1 respectively, can be so placed in space that they are the focal surfaces of a W congruence (§ 53).

19. When two O nets N and N_1 are in relation E_m, the spherical representation of these nets are isothermal orthogonal nets on the unit sphere in relation F, and these two nets are related conformally. The equations of the transformation are of the form

$$X_1 = -X + \frac{p}{m\theta\nu}(pX + q\xi + r\eta),$$

where θ, ν, p, q and r are solutions of (75).

20. A necessary and sufficient condition that the spherical representations of two O nets in relation R be conformal is that the transformation be E_m.

Annals, Ser. 2, vol. 17 (1915) p. 69.

21. If four nets N, N_1, N_2, N_{12}, form a quatern under transformations E_m, and N_3 is an E_{m_3} transform, then the nets N_3, N_{13}, N_{23}, N' of § 24 form a similar quatern. Transactions, vol. 9 (1908), p. 170.

22. If N is an O net with isothermal spherical representation, the point equation of N admits the solution $\theta_0 = E - G$, and the corresponding parallel O nets N_0 are defined by equations of the form

$$x_0 = [2e^{-\psi}(\sqrt{E} + \sqrt{G}) + c]X + \frac{1}{\sqrt{E}}\left(\frac{\partial E}{\partial u} - \frac{\partial G}{\partial u}\right)\xi + \frac{1}{\sqrt{G}}\left(\frac{\partial E}{\partial v} - \frac{\partial G}{\partial v}\right)\eta,$$

where c is a constant.

23. If in (88) we put $\sqrt{E}=\sqrt{G}$, $U=-V=1$, this condition is satisfied, that is isothermic surfaces are surfaces Ω. In this case

$$\theta_0 = e^{2\psi}\left(\frac{1}{\rho_2}-\frac{1}{\rho_1}\right), \qquad \hat{\theta}_0 = -\theta_0\frac{\rho_1+\rho_2}{2\rho_1\rho_2}.$$

In order that the transformations determined by (97) be D_m, we must have

$$e^{\psi}\theta_{10}\,\nu\sqrt{\rho_0}+\theta_0\theta_{01}=0.$$

24. Determine the character of the surfaces Ω which are R transforms of an isothermic surface other than D_m transforms.

25. If in (88) we put

$$\sqrt{E}=-\rho_1 e^{-\psi}, \qquad \sqrt{G}=\rho_2 e^{-\psi}, \qquad U=V=1,$$

the equation is satisfied in consequence of (86); that is a surface with isothermal representation of its lines of curvature is a surface Ω. In this case $2\theta_0=-\hat{\theta}_0(\rho_1+\rho_2)$; consequently the mid-point of the segment between centers of principal curvature of the surface describes a net N_0 with equal point invariants; also N_∞ is at infinity. When we express the condition $\sqrt{E_1}/\rho_{11}=\sqrt{G_1}/\rho_{12}$ we get

$$2e^{-\psi}\frac{\theta}{p}+(\sqrt{G}-\sqrt{E})\left(1-\frac{\theta_{10}}{\theta_0}\right)+2\frac{\theta_{01}}{\nu\sqrt{\rho_0}}=0.$$

By means of this relation the expressions (74) are obtainable from (96), and these transformations R_m are E_m.

26. Determine the character of the surfaces Ω which are R transforms of a surface with isothermal spherical representation of its lines of curvature other than the E_m transforms.

27. If S_1 and S_2 are surfaces of Guichard of the first kind obtained from such a surface S by transformation R_{m_1} and R_{m_2}, there can be found without quadratures a surface S_{12} of the same kind which is in relations R_{m_2} and R_{m_1} with S_1 and S_2. Annali, ser. 3, vol. 22 (1914), p. 212.

28. In order that the O net N on a surface S be defined by

$$\sqrt{E}=e^{\xi}\sin a,\quad \sqrt{G}=e^{\xi}\cos a,\quad \frac{1}{\rho_1}=e^{-\xi}(\cot a+h),\quad \frac{1}{\rho_2}=e^{-\xi}(-\tan a+h),$$

it is necessary and sufficient that h, ξ and a satisfy

$$\frac{\partial h}{\partial u}=(h+\cot a)\frac{\partial \xi}{\partial u}, \qquad \frac{\partial h}{\partial v}=(h-\tan a)\frac{\partial \xi}{\partial v},$$

$$\frac{\partial^2 \xi}{\partial u\,\partial v}=\frac{\partial \xi}{\partial u}\frac{\partial \xi}{\partial v}+\cot a\frac{\partial a}{\partial v}\frac{\partial \xi}{\partial u}-\tan a\frac{\partial a}{\partial u}\frac{\partial \xi}{\partial v},$$

$$\frac{\partial^2 a}{\partial u^2}-\frac{\partial^2 a}{\partial v^2}+\cot a\frac{\partial^2 \xi}{\partial u^2}+\tan a\frac{\partial^2 \xi}{\partial v^2}-\csc^2 a\frac{\partial a}{\partial u}\frac{\partial \xi}{\partial u}+\sec^2 a\frac{\partial a}{\partial v}\frac{\partial \xi}{\partial v}$$
$$-(\cos a+h\sin a)(\sin a-h\cos a)=0.$$

These equations are satisfied by $\bar{\xi}$, $\bar{\alpha}$ and h defined by

$$e^{\bar{\xi}} = e^{-\xi}(1+h^2),$$

$$\sin\bar{\alpha} = -\frac{1}{1+h^2}[\sin\alpha(1-h^2)-2h\cos\alpha],$$

$$\cos\bar{\alpha} = \frac{1}{1+h^2}[\cos\alpha(1-h^2)+2h\sin\alpha].$$

An O net $\bar{N}$ parallel to N is defined by

$$\sqrt{\bar{E}} = e^{\bar{\xi}}\sin\bar{\alpha}, \qquad \sqrt{\bar{G}} = -e^{\bar{\xi}}\cos\bar{\alpha},$$

$$\frac{1}{\bar{\rho}_1} = e^{-\bar{\xi}}(\cot\bar{\alpha}+h), \qquad \frac{1}{\bar{\rho}_2} = e^{-\bar{\xi}}(-\tan\bar{\alpha}+h)$$

and $\rho_1\bar{\rho}_2+\rho_2\bar{\rho}_1 = -2$. The surface S is called a *surface of Guichard of the second kind,* and $\bar{S}$ its *associate.* Calapso, Annali, ser. 3, vol. 11 (1905), p. 216.

29. Show that a surface of Guichard of the second kind is a surface Ω and determine the transformations R of such a surface into surfaces of the same kind.

Annali, ser. 3, vol. 22 (1914), p. 205.

30. A necessary and sufficient condition that a surface of Guichard of the first kind be a spherical surface [§ 115] is that $e^{\xi} = a$, $h = 0$, where a is a constant; then $\rho_1 = a\tanh\alpha$, $\rho_2 = a\coth\alpha$. In this case the associate surface is homothetic to the given one.

31. If S is a spherical surface (cf. Ex. 30), equations (106), (108) and (110) are consistent when $\nu = (a^2p^2-\theta^2)/\theta a^2$. Thus a spherical surface admits ∞^2 transformations R_m, for each value of $m \neq 0$, into spherical surfaces.

Annali, l. c. p. 230.

32. For the circle-plane of a transformation R_m of a spherical surface (Ex. 31), the functions j, k and $\bar{\omega}$ of § 79 have the values $j = a^2/2m\theta$, $k = -pa^2/\theta$, $\bar{\omega} = (\theta^2-p^2a^2)/2\theta$. Consequently the planes of these circles envelope a surface applicable to the quadric of revolution $x^2+2m(y^2+z^2) = a^2$.

Annali, l. c. p. 235.

33. If S is a surface of Guichard of the first kind and S_1 is an R_m transform of the same kind, a surface of Guichard of the first kind is defined by

$$\sqrt{\bar{E}} = \frac{e^{\xi}}{\theta}\sinh\alpha, \qquad \sqrt{\bar{G}} = \frac{e^{\xi}}{\theta}\cosh\alpha,$$

$$\frac{1}{\bar{\rho}_1} = \theta e^{-\xi}(1-2m)\left(\coth\alpha+h+e^{\xi}\frac{p}{\theta}\right),$$

$$\frac{1}{\bar{\rho}_2} = \theta e^{-\xi}(1-2m)\left(-\tanh\alpha+h+e^{\xi}\frac{p}{\theta}\right).$$

Calapso, Annali, ser. 3, vol. 29 (1920), p. 84.

Chapter VIII.

Circles and spheres.

93. Coordinates of a sphere. The equation of a sphere in 3-space can be written in the form

$$(1)\qquad \begin{aligned} 2\alpha_1 y_1 + 2\alpha_2 y_2 + 2\alpha_3 y_3 + i\alpha_4 (y_1^2 + y_2^2 + y_3^2 + 1) \\ + \alpha_5 (y_1^2 + y_2^2 + y_3^2 - 1) = 0, \end{aligned}$$

where $\alpha_1, \ldots, \alpha_5$ are constants, and y_1, y_2, y_3 are current coordinates. We call the five constants α the *coordinates of the sphere.* If x_1, x_2, x_3 are the coordinates of the center of the sphere and R its radius, we have

$$(2)\left\{\begin{array}{l} \alpha_1 = hx_1, \qquad \alpha_2 = hx_2, \qquad \alpha_3 = hx_3, \\ \alpha_4 = \frac{ih}{2}(x_1^2 + x_2^2 + x_3^2 - R^2 + 1), \quad \alpha_5 = \frac{h}{2}(x_1^2 + x_2^2 + x_3^2 - R^2 - 1), \end{array}\right.$$

where h is a factor of proportionality. These equations can be written also thus

$$(3)\left\{\begin{array}{l} x_1 = -\frac{\alpha_1}{\alpha_5 + i\alpha_4}, \qquad x_2 = -\frac{\alpha_2}{\alpha_5 + i\alpha_4}, \qquad x_3 = -\frac{\alpha_3}{\alpha_5 + i\alpha_4}, \\ x_1^2 + x_2^2 + x_3^2 - R^2 = -\frac{\alpha_5 - i\alpha_4}{\alpha_5 + i\alpha_4}, \qquad h = -(\alpha_5 + i\alpha_4). \end{array}\right.$$

An exception arises when

$$(4)\qquad \alpha_5 + i\alpha_4 = 0,$$

which is a necessary and sufficient condition that (1) defines a plane.

From (3) we have

$$(5)\qquad R = \frac{\sqrt{\sum \alpha^2}}{\alpha_5 + i\alpha_4},$$

where we assume the sign of the radical chosen so that R is positive for a real sphere. It follows that a necessary and sufficient condition that a sphere defined by (1) be a point-, or *null-sphere*, is

$$\alpha_1^2+\alpha_2^2+\alpha_3^2+\alpha_4^2+\alpha_5^2=0. \tag{6}$$

By definition the *power of a point with respect to a sphere* is the product of the distances to any two points of the sphere collinear with it, that is the square of the tangent to the sphere when the point is outside. Hence the left-hand member of (1) divided by $i\alpha_4+\alpha_5$ is the power of the point (y_1, y_2, y_3) with respect to the sphere (1).

Consider the sphere (1) and another of center (x_1^1, x_2^1, x_3^1) and radius R' defined by

$$\begin{cases} 2\alpha_1^1 y_1+2\alpha_2^1 y_2+2\alpha_3^1 y_3+i\alpha_4^1(y_1^2+y_2^2+y_3^2+1) \\ \qquad +\alpha_5^1(y_1^2+y_2^2+y_3^2-1)=0. \end{cases} \tag{7}$$

The angle under which they cut is given by

$$\cos\theta=\frac{R^2+R'^2-\sum_{i=1}^{3}(x_i-x_i')^2}{2RR'}. \tag{8}$$

With the aid of (3) and (5) one shows that this is expressible in terms of the coordinates α and α' of the two spheres in the form

$$\cos\theta=\frac{\sum_{i=1}^{5}\alpha_i\alpha_i'}{(\sum\alpha_i^2\cdot\sum\alpha_i'^2)^{\frac{1}{2}}}. \tag{9}$$

In certain discussions it is advantageous to introduce a sixth coordinate α_6 defined by

$$i\alpha_6=R(\alpha_5+i\alpha_4). \tag{10}$$

Comparing this equation with (5), we note that

$$\alpha_1^2+\ldots+\alpha_6^2=0. \tag{11}$$

Now equation (9) becomes

$$\text{(12)} \qquad \cos\theta = -\frac{\sum_{i=1}^{5}\alpha_i\alpha_i'}{\alpha_6\alpha_6'}.$$

94. Pentaspherical coordinates of a point. When the sphere (1) is not a null-sphere, its coordinates α may be chosen so that $\sum\alpha^2 = 1$. These coordinates α are direction-cosines of a line in 5-space and from (9) it follows that the angle between two spheres in 3-space is equal to the angle between two lines in 5-space whose direction-cosines are the corresponding α's and α''s. Accordingly we can choose a set of five mutually orthogonal spheres in 3-space whose coordinates α_{ij} satisfy the conditions

$$\text{(13)} \qquad \sum_{i=1}^{5}\alpha_{ij}^2 = 1, \qquad \sum_{i=1}^{5}\alpha_{ij}\alpha_{ik} = 0 \begin{pmatrix} j, k = 1 \ldots, 5 \\ j \neq k \end{pmatrix}.$$

With this choice we consider the functions

$$\text{(14)} \qquad 2\lambda z_j = 2\sum_{i=1}^{3}\alpha_{ij}y_i + i\alpha_{4j}(y_1^2+y_2^2+y_3^2+1) + \alpha_{5j}(y_1^2+y_2^2+y_3^2-1).$$

The right-hand member is the power of the point (y_1, y_2, y_3) with respect to the sphere S_j, divided by its radius $R_j = 1/(\alpha_{5j}+i\alpha_{4j})$. When

$$\text{(15)} \qquad i\alpha_{4j} + \alpha_{5j} = 0,$$

the sphere S_j is a plane and λz_j is the distance from the point (y_1, y_2, y_3) to the plane.

The quantities $z_j (j = 1, \ldots .\ 5)$ are called the *pentaspherical coordinates* of the point, λ being a parameter. In consequence of (13) we have the fundamental relation

$$\text{(16)} \qquad \sum_{j=1}^{5} z_j^2 = 0.$$

From equations (14) we have

$$\text{(17)} \qquad \begin{cases} y_1 = \lambda\sum_{j=1}^{5}\alpha_{1j}z_j, \qquad y_2 = \lambda\sum_{j=1}^{5}\alpha_{2j}z_j, \qquad y_3 = \lambda\sum_{j=1}^{5}\alpha_{3j}z_j, \\ 1 + \lambda\sum_{j=1}^{5}(\alpha_{5j}+i\alpha_{4j})z_j = 0, \qquad y_1^2+y_2^2+y_3^2 = \lambda\sum_{j=1}^{5}(\alpha_{5j}-i\alpha_{4j})z_j. \end{cases}$$

Hence when five quantities satisfying (16) are given, they are the pentaspherical coordinates of a point, whose cartesian coordinates are given by (17)[80]).

As an immediate consequence of these results, we have:

The equation of a general sphere is of the form

$$\alpha_1 z_1 + \alpha_2 z_2 + \ldots + \alpha_5 z_5 = 0, \tag{18}$$

where z_i are the pentaspherical coordinates of a point on the sphere, and the α's are constants.

If z_j and z'_j are the pentaspherical coordinates of two points M and M', whose respective cartesian coordinates are y_i and y'_i, the distance between them is given by

$$\overline{MM'}^2 = \sum_{i=1}^{3} (y_i - y'_i)^2 = -2\lambda\lambda' \sum_{j=1}^{5} z_j z'_j = \lambda\lambda' \sum_{j=1}^{5} (z_j - z'_j)^2, \tag{19}$$

in consequence of (17), where, because of (5) and (14)

$$1 + \lambda \sum_{j=1}^{5} \frac{z_j}{R_j} = 0, \qquad 1 + \lambda' \sum_{j=1}^{5} \frac{z'_j}{R_j} = 0,$$

R_j being the radius of the sphere of coordinates α_j.

If M' approaches M along a curve, the linear element is given by

$$ds^2 = \frac{\sum_{j=1}^{5} (dz_j)^2}{\left(\sum_{j=1}^{5} \frac{z_j}{R_j}\right)^2} = \frac{\sum_{j=1}^{5} (dz_j)^2}{\left[\sum_{j=1}^{5} z_j (\alpha_{5j} + i\alpha_{4j})\right]^2}. \tag{20}$$

When in (17) we take $\alpha_{ii} = 1$ $(i = 1, \ldots 5)$, $\alpha_{ij} = 0$ $(i \neq j)$, these equations reduce to

$$\begin{cases} y_1 = \lambda z_1, \quad y_2 = \lambda z_2, \quad y_3 = \lambda z_3, \\ 1 + \lambda(z_5 + i z_4) = 0, \quad y_1^2 + y_2^2 + y_3^2 = \lambda(z_5 - i z_4). \end{cases} \tag{21}$$

---

[80]) An exception is afforded by $z_j = \alpha_{5j} + i\alpha_{4j}$ in which case the point is at infinity (cf. VIII, Ex. 1).

From (4) it follows that the fundamental spheres of coordinates $\alpha_{i1}, \alpha_{i2}, \alpha_{i3}$ are planes. In this case we say that the z's are *special pentaspherical coordinates.* For this case equation (20) reduces to

(22) $$ds^2 = \frac{\sum (dz_j)^2}{(z_5 + iz_4)^2}.$$

95. Pentaspherical coordinates of an O net. If y_1, y_2, y_3 are the cartesian coordinates of a point on a surface referred to its lines of curvature, the functions λz_j satisfy the point equation of the surface, as follows from (14); and consequently, if λ involves u and v, the z's satisfy an equation of the form

(23) $$\frac{\partial^2 \theta}{\partial u \partial v} = \frac{\partial \log a}{\partial v}\frac{\partial \theta}{\partial u} + \frac{\partial \log b}{\partial u}\frac{\partial \theta}{\partial v} + c\theta.$$

Conversely, if we have five solutions of this equation satisfying (16), say z_j, and an independent solution $1/\lambda$, then the functions z'_j, where $z_j\lambda = z'_j$, satisfy an equation of this form with $c = 0$, and consequently $y_1, y_2, y_3, y_1^2 + y_2^2 + y_3^2$, 1, given by (17) or (21), are solutions of the latter equation. Hence:

If five particular solutions of an equation of the form (23) *satisfy the relation*

(24) $$z_1^2 + z_2^2 + \ldots + z_5^2 = 0,$$

they are the pentaspherical coordinates of a surface referred to its lines of curvature.

If the invariants of (23) are equal, the O net is isothermic. In this case the equation is reducible to the Moutard form

(25) $$\frac{\partial^2 \theta}{\partial u \partial v} = M\theta.$$

Hence:

If an equation of the Moutard form admits five particular solutions z_j satisfying the relations $\sum z_j^2 = 0$, the quantities are the pentaspherical coordinates of an isothermic net.

96. Congruences of spheres. When the quantities α in (1) are functions of two parameters u_1 and v_1, we say that (1) defines a *congruence of spheres.* When the α's are independent, we can find by differentiation alone an equation of the form

$$D\frac{\partial^2\theta}{\partial u_1^2}+2E\frac{\partial^2\theta}{\partial u_1\,\partial v_1}+F\frac{\partial^2\theta}{\partial v_1^2}+G\frac{\partial\theta}{\partial u_1}+H\frac{\partial\theta}{\partial v_1}+K\theta=0,$$

of which the five functions α are solutions. If we take as independent variables u and v, defined by

$$u=\varphi(u_1, v_1), \qquad v=\psi(u_1, v_1)$$

such that φ and ψ satisfy the differential equation

$$D\left(\frac{\partial\varphi}{\partial u_1}\right)^2+2E\frac{\partial\varphi}{\partial u_1}\frac{\partial\varphi}{\partial v_1}+F\left(\frac{\partial\varphi}{\partial v_1}\right)^2=0,$$

the above equation is transformed into the Laplace form

$$\frac{\partial^2\theta}{\partial u\,\partial v}=\frac{\partial\log A}{\partial v}\frac{\partial\theta}{\partial u}+\frac{\partial\log B}{\partial u}\frac{\partial\theta}{\partial v}+C\theta. \tag{26}$$

The determination of u and v requires the integration of the differential equation

$$F\,du_1^2-2E\,du_1\,dv_1+D\,dv_1^2=0. \tag{27}$$

The curves on the envelope of the spheres uniquely defined by this equation are called the *principal curves.*

We assume hereafter that the parameters of a congruence of spheres are such that the spherical coordinates α satisfy an equation of the Laplace form (26). Then the principal curves on the envelope are parametric. The equation of the congruence is of the form

$$\sum_{i=1}^{5}\alpha_i z_i=0. \tag{28}$$

We consider the congruence of spheres defined by (28). As u varies a sphere touches a tubular envelope along the circle C_{-1}, given by

$$\sum\alpha_i z_i=0, \qquad \sum\frac{\partial\alpha_i}{\partial u}z_i=0, \tag{29}$$

and as v varies, along the circle C_1 given by

$$(30) \qquad \sum \alpha_i z_i = 0, \qquad \sum \frac{\partial \alpha_i}{\partial v} z_i = 0.$$

The intersections A_1 and A_2 of these circles are the points of tangency of the sphere (28) with the envelope of the congruence of spheres, that is, the points defined by

$$(31) \quad \sum \alpha_i z_i = 0, \qquad \sum \frac{\partial \alpha_i}{\partial u} z_i = 0, \qquad \sum \frac{\partial \alpha_i}{\partial v} z_i = 0.$$

The circles (29) and (30) are called the *focal circles* of the first and second rank respectively of the congruence of spheres.

Differentiating the first two of (31) with respect to v and making use of the third, we get

$$\sum \alpha_i \frac{\partial z_i}{\partial v} = 0, \qquad \sum \frac{\partial \alpha_i}{\partial u} \frac{\partial z_i}{\partial v} = 0.$$

Hence as v varies the points A_1 and A_2 begin to move along the circle C_{-1}. Similarly as u varies, these points begin to move along C_1. But as u and v vary, the points A_1 and A_2 trace out the principal curves on the envelope of the sphere of coordinates α. Hence we have the theorem of Darboux[81]):

On the envelope of a congruence of spheres, when a displacement is made along one of the principal curves, the four points of contact of two infinitely near spheres with the envelope lie on a circle which is a focal circle of the congruence.

We have also from the above that the line $A_1 A_2$ and the line $A_1' A_2'$, joining nearby points, meet in the plane of C_{-1} or C_1 as v or u varies. Hence these planes are the focal planes of the congruence of lines $A_1 A_2$. Accordingly in view of the preceding theorem we have the theorem of Ribaucour:

The chords of contact of the spheres of a congruence with its envelope generate a congruence whose focal planes are the planes of the circles of contact $u =$ const., $v =$ const., and the developables of the congruence are parametric.

---

[81]) Leçons, 2nd ed., vol. 2, p. 335.

97. Derived congruences of spheres. Since the five functions α satisfy equation (26), they are the direction-parameters of a congruence G of lines in 5-space. Conversely, the direction-parameters of such a congruence determine a congruence of spheres in 3-space. From (I, 60) it follows that the direction-parameters of the congruence G_1 and G_{-1} of tangents to the curves of parameter v on the first focal surface of G and of parameter u on the second focal surface may be given the respective forms

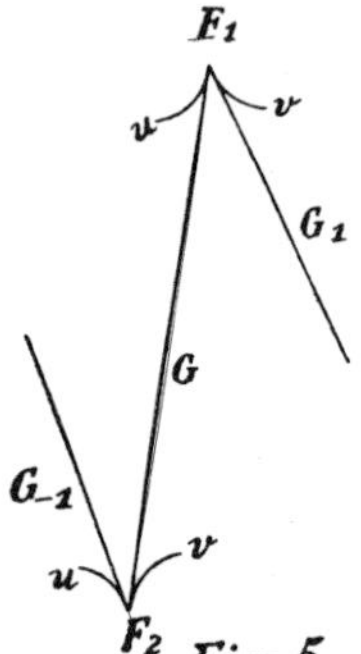

Fig. 5

$$\alpha_i \frac{\partial}{\partial v} \log \frac{\alpha_i}{A}, \qquad \alpha_i \frac{\partial}{\partial u} \log \frac{\alpha_i}{B}. \tag{32}$$

These congruences G_1 and G_{-1} in 5-space correspond to the congruences of spheres in 3-space with the respective equations

$$\sum \alpha_i \frac{\partial}{\partial v} \log \frac{\alpha_i}{A} \cdot z_i = 0, \qquad \sum \alpha_i \frac{\partial}{\partial u} \log \frac{\alpha_i}{B} \cdot z_i = 0. \tag{33}$$

Hence we speak of these congruences of spheres as the *first and minus first derived congruences* of the congruence defined by (28).

Evidently the circles (29) are the intersections of corresponding spheres of the given congruence and its minus first derived congruence, and similarly the circles (30) of spheres of the given congruence and its first derived congruence.

Consider now the congruence of spheres defined by the first of (33). As u varies, a sphere describes a tubular surface, to which the sphere is tangent along the circle defined by (33) and

$$\sum \frac{\partial}{\partial u} \left(\alpha_i \frac{\partial}{\partial v} \log \frac{\alpha_i}{A} \right) \cdot z_i = 0,$$

which is readily seen to be the circle (30). In like manner for the congruence of spheres defined by the second of (33) as v varies a sphere describes a tubular surface to which the sphere is tangent along the circle (29).

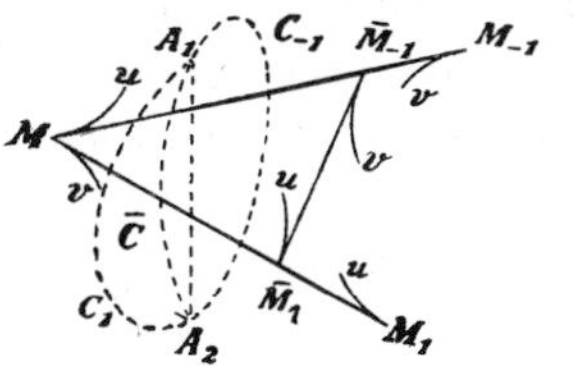

Fig. 6

From (3) it follows that $\alpha_1, \alpha_2, \alpha_3, -(\alpha_5 + i\alpha_4)$ are homogeneous coordinates of the center M of the sphere. Since they satisfy equation (26), M describes a net N. When we compare (32) with (III, 2) we remark that the centers M_1 and M_{-1} of these spheres describe nets which are the first and minus first Laplace transforms of N. Since the lines MM_{-1} and MM_1 are necessarily the axes of the circles (29) and (30) respectively, we have the theorem:

If G is a congruence of spheres, and G_{-1} and G_1 its minus first and first derived congruences, as u or v varies a sphere describes a tubular surface tangent to the sphere along a circle which is the intersection of the sphere and the corresponding sphere of the minus first or first derived congruence respectively. The centers M, M_{-1} and M_1 of corresponding spheres describe nets in 3-space forming a Laplace sequence, and the joins MM_{-1} and MM_1 are the axes of the circles of intersection.

Consider further the circle (29). We saw in § 96 that its plane is the focal plane of the congruence $A_1 A_2$ tangent to the second focal surface of this congruence. Hence on the envelope of the plane the parametric curves form a net $\overline{N}$. This circle lies also on the corresponding sphere given by the second of (33). If B_1 and B_2 are the points where this sphere touches its envelope, this plane is a focal plane of the congruence of lines $B_1 B_2$ and $\overline{N}$ is the first focal net of the congruence. Hence:

The planes of the focal circles of either rank of a congruence of spheres envelope a net whose tangents are the chords of contact of the spheres and the corresponding derived congruence of spheres with their envelopes.

98. Congruences of circles. By definition the circles of intersection of corresponding spheres of two congruences of spheres determined by the congruences of tangents to a net in 5-space form a *congruence of circles*, for which the spheres are the *focal spheres*. The centers of the spheres are the focal points of the congruence of axes of the circles (§ 97). Moreover, as we have just seen, the planes of the circles envelop a net, whose tangents meet the circles in the points where the focal spheres touch their envelopes. Equations (29) define a congruence of circles, as do also equations (30). Moreover, any congruence of circles may be so defined.

When for the congruences of circles C_{-1} as defined by (29) the parameter v varies, the circles $C_{-1}(u, v)$ and $C_{-1}(u, v+dv)$ meet in the points, A_1 and A_2, where the sphere of parameter α touches its envelope; they are defined by (31). When the parameter u varies, the circles $C_{-1}(u, v)$ and $C_{-1}(u+du, v)$ meet in the points, A_1', A_2', of intersection of the spheres of coordinates

$$\alpha_i, \quad \frac{\partial \alpha_i}{\partial u}, \quad \frac{\partial^2 \alpha_i}{\partial u^2}. \tag{34}$$

Hence as u or v varies the circle C_{-1} meets the infinitely near circle in two points.

Consider, conversely, a two parameter family of circles such that as either parameter, u or v, varies, two infinitely near circles meet in two points. Hence as u or v varies the axes of the circles generate developables. Let F_1 and F_2 be the focal points of this congruence. The spheres S_1 with centers F_1 and containing the circles of the system envelope, as u varies, a tubular surface tangent along the circles. If the equation of the spheres S_1 is $\sum \beta_i z_i = 0$, the circles are defined by this equation and $\sum \frac{\partial \beta_i}{\partial u} z_i = 0$.

In like manner, the spheres S_2 with centers F_2 and passing through the circles envelop, as v varies, a tubular surface to which they are tangent along the circles. Thus the circles are defined also by

$$\sum \alpha_i z_i = 0, \qquad \sum \frac{\partial \alpha_i}{\partial v} z_i = 0,$$

where the first equation defines the spheres S_2.

Since the circles are the same in both cases, we must have

$$\frac{\partial \beta_i}{\partial u} = l\alpha_i + m\beta_i, \qquad \frac{\partial \alpha_i}{\partial v} = n\alpha_i + r\beta_i.$$

But from § 2 it follows that the α's and β's are direction-parameters of a net in 5-space. Combining this result with the second theorem of the preceding section, we have:

A congruence of circles is characterized by the property that as u or v varies a circle meets the infinitely near circle in two points, which are the points of intersection of the circle and the tangents to the net enveloped by the plane of the circle.

We call these points the *focal points* of the congruence of circles.

99. Congruences of spheres and circles in cartesian coordinates. From (3) it follows that the cartesian coordinates x_1, x_2, x_3 of the center of the sphere, and also the function

$$2\theta = x_1^2 + x_2^2 + x_3^2 - R^2 \tag{35}$$

are solutions of the equation

$$\frac{\partial^2 \theta}{\partial u \partial v} = \frac{\partial \log a}{\partial v} \frac{\partial \theta}{\partial u} + \frac{\partial \log b}{\partial u} \frac{\partial \theta}{\partial v}, \tag{36}$$

where as follows from (3) and (26)

$$a = \frac{A}{h}, \qquad b = \frac{B}{h}. \tag{37}$$

Conversely, if x_1, x_2, x_3 and θ are four solutions of an equation (36), it follows that the quantities α defined by (2) are solutions of an equation of the form (26). Hence:

If θ is a solution of the point equation of a net N, the spheres with centers on N and radii given by

$$R^2 = x_1^2 + x_2^2 + x_3^2 - 2\theta \tag{38}$$

form a congruence upon whose envelope the parametric curves are the principal curves.

As a corollary we have:

The points of an O net in 3-space form a congruence of null spheres.

When the equation of a congruence of spheres is written in the form

$$\sum (y - x)^2 - R^2 = 0, \tag{39}$$

the y's being current coordinates, the equations of the focal circles C_{-1} and C_1 of the congruence are given by (39) and the respective equations

$$(40)\quad \sum(y-x)\frac{\partial x}{\partial u}+R\frac{\partial R}{\partial u}=0, \qquad \sum(y-x)\frac{\partial x}{\partial v}+R\frac{\partial R}{\partial v}=0,$$

which shows that the axes of the circles are tangent to the curves of the net of centers. Since equations (39) and (40) are equivalent to (31), we have:

Equations (40) *define the focal planes of the congruence of lines joining corresponding points on the envelope of the spheres* (39), *the developables being parametric.*

By means of (38) equations (40) may be written

$$(41)\qquad \sum y\frac{\partial x}{\partial u}-\frac{\partial \theta}{\partial u}=0, \qquad \sum y\frac{\partial x}{\partial v}-\frac{\partial \theta}{\partial v}=0.$$

If we write

$$\theta_{-1}=\theta-\frac{b}{\frac{\partial b}{\partial u}}\frac{\partial \theta}{\partial u}, \qquad \theta_1=\theta-\frac{a}{\frac{\partial a}{\partial v}}\frac{\partial \theta}{\partial v},$$

in consequence of (I, 48), the preceding equations are equivalent to

$$\sum y\frac{\partial x_{-1}}{\partial v}-\frac{\partial \theta_{-1}}{\partial v}=0, \qquad \sum y\frac{\partial x_1}{\partial u}-\frac{\partial \theta_1}{\partial u}=0.$$

Hence:

If θ is a solution of the point equation of a net N, the spheres with centers on the minus first and first Laplace transforms of N and with radii given by the respective equations

$$R_{-1}^2=\sum x_{-1}^2-2\theta_{-1}, \qquad R_1^2=\sum x_1^2-2\theta_1$$

meet the spheres with centers on N and radius given by (38) *in congruences of circles.*

When the central net $N(x)$ of a congruence of spheres is an O net, the congruence of lines joining the corresponding points of contact on the envelopes of the spheres is normal, since the focal planes are perpendicular. A surface $\overline{N}$ normal to the congruence is given by equations of the form [§ 67]

$$\overline{x} = WX + \frac{\partial W}{\partial u}\frac{1}{\mathfrak{E}}\frac{\partial X}{\partial u} + \frac{\partial W}{\partial v}\frac{1}{\mathfrak{G}}\frac{\partial X}{\partial v},$$

where the X's are the direction-cosines of the congruence and also of the normal to the given net N. The function W is to be determined by the condition that the point of $\overline{N}$ lies on the line whose equations are (40). Making use of (41), we find that this condition reduces to

$$(42) \qquad -\varrho_1 \frac{\partial W}{\partial u} = \frac{\partial \theta}{\partial u}, \qquad -\varrho_2 \frac{\partial W}{\partial v} = \frac{\partial \theta}{\partial v},$$

where ϱ_1 and ϱ_2 are the principal radii of curvature of N. Hence W is found by a quadrature.

Conversely, if a net $\overline{N}$ parallel to N is known, we find by the quadrature (42) the radius of the corresponding sphere. Hence we have the following theorem of Ribaucour[82]):

If S and $\overline{S}$ are two surfaces with the same spherical representation of their lines of curvature, the normals of either are the chords of contact with their envelope of a family of spheres having their centers on the other surface; the radii of the spheres are found by a quadrature.

100. Congruences R of spheres. We are in a position now to establish the theorem:

If the principal curves form a net on each of the sheets of the envelope of a congruence of spheres, they are O nets in relation R, provided that the radii of the spheres are not constant.

If the quantities y in (39) are the coordinates of the point of contact of the spheres with one sheet of the envelope, we have

$$(43) \qquad \sum (y-x)\frac{\partial y}{\partial u} = 0, \qquad \sum (y-x)\frac{\partial y}{\partial v} = 0.$$

If equation (41) be differentiated with respect to v and u, respectively we obtain

$$\sum \frac{\partial y}{\partial v}\frac{\partial x}{\partial u} = 0, \qquad \sum \frac{\partial y}{\partial u}\frac{\partial x}{\partial v} = 0.$$

[82]) Comptes Rendus, vol. 67 (1868), p. 1334.

Differentiating the first of (43) with respect to v or the second with respect to u, we get

$$\sum(y-x)\frac{\partial^2 y}{\partial u\,\partial v}+\sum\frac{\partial y}{\partial u}\frac{\partial y}{\partial v}=0.$$

Hence if the y's are to satisfy an equation of the form (36), we must have $\sum\frac{\partial y}{\partial u}\frac{\partial y}{\partial v}=0$, which is the condition that the net $\overline{N}(y)$ be an O net. In consequence of this result the central net is 2, O, and by the last theorem of § 66 and the second theorem of § 76, the theorem is established.

By definition a congruence of spheres is a *congruence* R if the central net N_0 is 2, O and the complementary function of N_0 is the radius of a representative sphere.

From § 68 we have:

The spheres of a transformation R form a congruence R.

When two congruences R of spheres have parallel central nets we say that the *congruences of spheres are parallel.* Hence from the last theorem of § 76 we have:

If G and G' are parallel congruences R of spheres and the spheres G' do not pass through a point, there can be found by a quadrature a congruence R of spheres G_1 such that the central nets of G and G_1 are in relation F.

In this sense the congruences G and G_1 are *in relation F.*

The spheres with centers on any surface S and passing through a point form a congruence R, the central net 2, O on S being determined by the equation of the lines of curvature of the envelope of the spheres; it is the net on S determined by the function $\sqrt{x^2+y^2+z^2}$ (§ 3). In like manner the spheres with centers on a surface S and tangent to a plane π, or a fixed sphere, form a congruence R, the central 2, O net on S corresponding to the lines of curvature on the other sheet of the envelope.

The spheres tangent to two fixed spheres form a congruence R with centers on a central quadric of revolution, whose foci are the centers of the fixed spheres. When one of the fixed spheres is replaced by a plane, the surface of centers is a paraboloid of revolution.

If the centers of the fixed spheres are the points $(a, 0, 0)$ and $(-a, 0, 0)$ and the radii are r_1 and r_2, we have

$$(x-a)^2+y^2+z^2=(R+\varepsilon_1 r_1)^2, \quad (x+a)^2+y^2+z^2=(R+\varepsilon_2 r_2)^2,$$

where $\varepsilon_1 = \pm 1$ and $\varepsilon_2 = \pm 1$. From these equations it follows that

$$x^2+y^2+z^2-R^2=bx+c, \qquad R=dx+e,$$

where b, c, d and e are constants. Hence these two functions are solutions of the point equation of any net on the quadric. Similar results hold for a paraboloid of revolution. Consequently:

On a quadric of revolution any net is 2, *O*.

Conversely, if every net on a surface S is 2, O, the functions $x^2+y^2+z^2-R^2$ and R must be linear functions of the coordinates. Consequently:

If every net on a surface is 2, *O, the surface is a quadric of revolution.*

101. Plücker line coordinates. If x_1, x_2, x_3, x_4 and y_1, y_2, y_3, y_4 are the homogeneous point coordinates of two points P and Q, the numbers $p_{12}, p_{13}, p_{14}, p_{23}, p_{34}, p_{42}$ defined by

$$p_{ij}=\begin{vmatrix} x_i & x_j \\ y_i & y_j \end{vmatrix} \quad (i, j = 1, 2, 3, 4, i \neq j) \tag{44}$$

are called the *Plücker coordinates* of the line PQ. Evidently the ratios only of these coordinates are so determined. Since these ratios are unaltered, if x_1, x_2, x_3, x_4, are replaced by $\lambda x_1+\mu y_1$, ..., $\lambda x_4+\mu y_4$, any two points of the line determine the same set of line coordinates. The six coordinates satisfy the equation

$$p_{12}\,p_{34}+p_{13}\,p_{42}+p_{14}\,p_{23}=0, \tag{45}$$

as may be seen by expanding in terms of two-rowed minors the identity

$$\begin{vmatrix} x_1 & x_2 & x_3 & x_4 \\ y_1 & y_2 & y_3 & y_4 \\ x_1 & x_2 & x_3 & x_4 \\ y_1 & y_2 & y_3 & y_4 \end{vmatrix}=0.$$

Conversely, if we have any six numbers p_{ij} satisfying (45), we can find two points, $(x_1, x_2, x_3, 0)$ and $(y_1, 0, y_3, y_4)$ satisfying (44), and consequently there is a line with these coordinates.

Consider two lines p and p' meeting in the point (x_i) and determined by $Q(y_i)$ and $Q'(y'_i)$. Since

$$\begin{vmatrix} x_1 & x_2 & x_3 & x_4 \\ y_1 & y_2 & y_3 & y_4 \\ x_1 & x_2 & x_3 & x_4 \\ y'_1 & y'_2 & y'_3 & y'_4 \end{vmatrix} = 0,$$

we have

$$(46) \qquad p_{12}p'_{34} + p_{13}p'_{42} + p_{14}p'_{23} + p_{34}p'_{12} + p_{42}p'_{13} + p_{23}p'_{14} = 0,$$

where $p'_{ij} = (x_i y'_j - x_j y'_i)$. Conversely, if two sets of line coordinates satisfy this condition, any two points on one line are coplanar with two points on the other. The line coordinates of the line joining P and the point $(\lambda y_i + \mu y'_i)$ are of the form $\lambda p_{ij} + \mu p'_{ij}$. Hence:

A flat pencil of lines consists of the lines whose coordinates are $\lambda p_{ij} + \mu p'_{ij}$, *if* p *and* p' *are lines of the pencil.*

Consider the lines of space whose coordinates satisfy a linear relation

$$(47) \qquad a_{34}p_{12} + a_{42}p_{13} + a_{23}p_{14} + a_{12}p_{34} + a_{13}p_{42} + a_{14}p_{23} = 0,$$

where the a's are constants. If (b_1, b_2, b_3, b_4) is any point of space, the coordinates (x_1, x_2, x_3, x_4) of any point of the lines through the given point for which (47) holds, satisfy a linear equation whose coefficients involve the a's and the b's. Hence all the lines through the given point lie in a plane. Consequently the lines satisfying (47) form a *linear complex*. The plane in which all the lines of the complex through a point lie is called the *null-plane* of the point.

When the a's in (47) satisfy (45), they are the coordinates of a line which all the lines of the complex meet. In this case the complex is called special.

102. The Lie line-sphere transformation. Consider the relation between two 3-spaces r and R whose cartesian coordinates x_i and X_i are in the relations

$$\text{(48)} \qquad \begin{cases} (X_1+iX_2)+X_3x_1+x_3=0, \\ (X_1-iX_2)\,x_1-x_2-X_3=0 \end{cases}$$ [83].

To each point of either space corresponds a line of the other. If (x_i) and (x_i') are two points of a line of r corresponding to a point (X_i) of R, we find that equations (48) and similar equations in x_i' are consistent, provided that

$$\text{(49)} \qquad p_{12}-p_{34}=0;$$

here $p_{ij}=x_i x_j'-x_j x_i'$ and $x_4=x_4'=1$. Hence to the points of R correspond lines of the linear complex (49), which is called *the complex of the transformation.* If we have any line of the complex and substitute the coordinates of any two of its points in (48), we find the corresponding point in R.

In like manner the coordinates X_i and X_i' of two points in R whose line corresponds to a point in r, satisfy the condition

$$\sum (X_i-X_i')^2=0,$$

that is to a point in r corresponds a minimal line in R.

To the points of a line a of the complex (49) correspond minimal lines in R passing through the point A which corresponds to a. Also to the points of a minimal line M in R correspond the lines of the complex through the point of r corresponding to M. Moreover, since the transformation is continuous, to the tangents of a minimal curve in R correspond the points in r of a curve whose tangents are lines of the complex (49).

A general line in r is defined by

$$\text{(50)} \qquad \begin{cases} x_1 p_{34}+x_3 p_{41}+p_{13}=0, \\ x_2 p_{34}+x_3 p_{42}+p_{23}=0. \end{cases}$$

---

[83]) Lie, Geometrie der Berührungstransformationen, p. 453 et seq.

Eliminating the x's from these equations and (48), we get

$$(51)\qquad 2\alpha_1 X_1 + 2\alpha_2 X_2 + 2\alpha_3 X_3 + i\alpha_4 (X_1^2 + X_2^2 + X_3^2 + 1) + \alpha_5 (X_1^2 + X_2^2 + X_3^2 - 1) = 0,$$

where

$$(52)\quad \begin{cases} p_{12} = \alpha_3 + i\alpha_6, & p_{13} = \alpha_1 + i\alpha_2, & p_{14} = \alpha_5 + i\alpha_4, \\ p_{34} = \alpha_3 - i\alpha_6, & p_{42} = \alpha_1 - i\alpha_2, & p_{23} = \alpha_5 - i\alpha_4. \end{cases}$$

Since the p's satisfy (45), the α's satisfy (11), and consequently:

To a general line in r correspond a sphere in R.

From these results and (10) it follows that to a line of complex (49) of the transformation corresponds a null-sphere in R.

From (46) and (52) it follows that to two intersecting lines of coordinates p_{ij} and p'_{ij} correspond two spheres S and S' whose coordinates α and α' satisfy the condition

$$(53)\qquad \alpha_1 \alpha'_1 + \alpha_2 \alpha'_2 + \dots + \alpha_6 \alpha'_6 = 0,$$

that is, as follows from (12), the spheres are tangent.

From (52) it follows that the line of coordinates p'_{ij}, given by

$$(54)\qquad \begin{cases} p'_{12} = \alpha_3 - i\alpha_6, & p'_{13} = p_{13}, & p'_{14} = p_{14}, \\ p'_{34} = \alpha_3 + i\alpha_6, & p'_{42} = p_{42}, & p'_{23} = p_{23}, \end{cases}$$

corresponds to the sphere (51). The equations of this line are

$$(55)\qquad \begin{cases} x_1 p_{12} + x_3 p_{41} + p_{13} = 0, \\ x_2 p_{12} + x_3 p_{42} + p_{23} = 0. \end{cases}$$

The lines of the complex (49) meeting the line (50) form a congruence. The line coordinates $\bar{p}_{ij}$ of a line of this congruence satisfy (49) and

$$p_{34}\bar{p}_{12} + p_{42}\bar{p}_{13} + p_{23}\bar{p}_{14} + p_{12}\bar{p}_{34} + p_{13}\bar{p}_{42} + p_{14}\bar{p}_{23} = 0.$$

It is readily seen that all of these lines meet the line (55). Hence the lines (50) and (55) are the directrices of the congruence. We refer to two such lines as *conjugate* with respect to the complex (49). Hence:

To a sphere in R corresponds two lines in r conjugate with respect to the complex of the transformation.

From the foregoing discussion it follows that to the points on the conjugate lines correspond the minimal lines of the sphere and to the lines of the complex meeting the conjugate lines correspond the points of the sphere.

Consider two intersecting lines in r of coordinates p_{ij} and p'_{ij}, not of the complex (49), and the two tangent spheres corresponding to them. The homogeneous point coordinates of the centers, C and C', of the spheres are $(\alpha_1, \alpha_2, \alpha_3, -\alpha_5 - i\alpha_4)$ and $(\alpha'_1, \alpha'_2, \alpha'_3, -\alpha'_5 - i\alpha'_4)$, and the point of tangency of the spheres is the intersection of the line CC' with either sphere. To a line of coordinates $\lambda p_{ij} + \mu p'_{ij}$ corresponds a sphere of coordinates $\lambda\alpha_i + \mu\alpha'_i$. Hence:

To a flat pencil of lines in r corresponds a pencil of spheres tangent to one another at the same point; moreover, the centers of the spheres form a linear pencil of points projective with the given pencil of lines.

From (4) it follows that the sphere of the pencil which is the tangent plane to all the spheres of the pencil is determined by $\lambda/\mu = -(\alpha'_5 + i\alpha'_4)/(\alpha_5 + i\alpha_4)$.

Suppose that this is the sphere of coordinates α. From (52) and (54) it follows that to a plane in R corresponds in r two lines of the special complex $p_{14} = 0$ conjugate with respect to the complex (49). All the lines of this special complex meet the line l at infinity in the plane $x_1 = 0$, that is the line $x_1 = 0$, $x_4 = 0$; this line is in the complex (49). Hence:

To a plane in R corresponds in r two lines of the special complex $p_{14} = 0$ conjugate with respect to the complex of the transformation, and to the points of these lines the two pencils of minimal lines in the given plane.

Let g and g' be the conjugate lines corresponding to a sphere S. A line a of the complex (49) meeting g and g' corresponds to a point A of S, and to the minimal generators of S through A correspond the points m and m' where a meets g and g'. Since g and g' are conjugate with respect to the complex, all the lines of the complex through m' meet g: that is, m' and g determine the null-plane of m'. In like manner m and g' determine the null-plane of m.

If S_1 is a sphere tangent to S at A, the conjugate lines g_1 and g_1' corresponding to S_1 pass through m and m' respectively. Hence:

To all the spheres tangent to S at A correspond a pencil of lines through m lying in the null-plane of m' and a pencil of lines through m' lying in the null-plane of m.

103. The Lie transformations of surfaces. A point and a plane through it constitute a *surface element* of which the point is the *center*. We consider the surface elements consisting of the points of a surface Σ in R and the corresponding tangent planes. By the Lie transformation the minimal curves of Σ correspond to two one parameter families of curves c and c' in r admitting lines of the complex (49) for tangents; these curves lie on two surfaces σ and σ'. To a point A of Σ corresponds a line a of the complex tangent to a curve c and to a curve c' at points m and m' corresponding to the respective minimal tangents to Σ at A. Hence σ and σ' are focal surfaces of a congruence of lines of the complex. Two nearby tangents to c determine a plane tangent to σ', that is the null-plane of m in the tangent plane to σ' at m'. In like manner the null-plane at m' is the tangent plane to σ at m. The spheres tangent to Σ at A correspond to two pencils of lines with centers at m and m', as shown in the preceding section. Hence to the surface elements of Σ correspond two sets of surface elements whose centers are the points of σ and σ', and whose planes are the tangent planes to σ and σ' at corresponding points. Therefore:

When a Lie transformation is applied to a surface Σ in R, the two corresponding surfaces σ and σ' in r are the focal surfaces of a congruence of lines of the complex of the transformation; corresponding directions in the tangent planes to σ and σ' correspond to spheres tangent to Σ; and the surface elements of Σ correspond to the surface elements of σ and σ'.

Thus the correspondence is a contact transformation.

As a point m moves along a curve γ on σ, the tangent planes intersect in directions conjugate to γ. Hence only in case γ is an asymtotic line do nearby surface elements have a corresponding direction in common. Two nearby surface elements of Σ are tangent to the same sphere only in case the center of the element moves along a line of curvature of Σ. Consequently we have the following important property of the Lie transformation:

The spheres with centers at the centers of principal curvature of Σ correspond to the tangents to the asymptotic lines on σ and σ'; the lines of curvature of Σ correspond to the asymptotic lines on σ and σ', which are the focal surfaces of a W congruence consisting of lines of the complex of the transformation.

Since the tangents to σ at a point m are projective with the centers of the spheres tangent to Σ (102), we have:

The centers of spheres corresponding to conjugate directions at m are harmonic with respect to the centers of principal curvature of Σ.

104. Congruences R of spheres. W congruences of lines. From § 100 it follows that a necessary and sufficient condition that a congruence of spheres be R is that the radius R be a solution of (36), which from (10) is equivalent to the condition that α_6 be a solution of (26). Hence:

A necessary and sufficient condition that a congruence of spheres be R is that the six coordinates of the congruence satisfying (11) *be solutions of the same equation of Laplace.*

If α_i and α'_i $(i = 1, \ldots . 6)$ are the coordinates of two congruences R of spheres tangent to the same surface, we have

$$\sum \alpha^2 = 0, \qquad \sum \alpha'^2 = 0, \qquad \sum \alpha \alpha' = 0.$$

Hence the quantities α_i and α'_i are homogeneous coordinates of two nets, $N(\alpha)$ and $N'(\alpha')$, in 5-space lying on the hyperquadric $\sum x^2 = 0$, and in relation F for which the lines of the congruence of the transformation are generators of the hyperquadric (cf. III, Ex. 23).

As an immediate consequence of the results of the preceding section we have the theorem:

If two surfaces Σ and Σ_1 are in relation R, and σ, σ' and σ_1, σ'_1 are the transforms of Σ and Σ_1 respectively by a Lie line-sphere transformation, the surfaces σ and σ_1 are the focal surfaces of a W congruence and likewise σ' and σ'_1; moreover, σ and σ' are focal surfaces of a W congruence consisting of lines of the complex of the transformation and likewise σ_1 and σ'_1.

Conversely if σ and σ_1 are the focal surfaces of a W congruence, and Σ and Σ_1 are transforms of σ and σ_1 by a Lie transformation then Σ and Σ_1 are in relation R. Hence we have the following theorem of Darboux[84]) as a consequence of the preceding theorems:

A necessary and sufficient condition that a congruence be a W congruence is that the Plücker coordinates of the lines be solutions of an equation of Laplace.

Since a W congruence is transformed into a W-congruence by a projective transformation, we have:

A net $N(x)$ in 5-space lying on a quadratic variety of four dimensions whose equation is

$$\sum a_{ij} x^{(i)} x^{(j)} = 0 \tag{56}$$

represents a W congruence.

From the results of § 38 we have:

Each transform F of a net representing a W congruence leads directly to a net representing another W congruence.

Consider in particular a surface σ upon which there lies an R net N (§ 45), that is a net for which the tangents to the curves of the net in each system form W congruences. When a Lie transformation is applied to σ, to the tangents to either family of curves of N correspond spheres tangent to Σ with centers describing nets 2, O conjugate to the congruence of normals to Σ. Moreover, corresponding points of these central nets, C and C', are harmonic to the centers of principal curvature of Σ and the nets have equal invariants (§ 25), that is Σ is a surface Ω (§ 89). Conversely, if a Lie transformation is applied to a surface Ω, there result two nets R. Consequently we have the theorem of Demoulin[85]):

A net R is transformed into an O net Ω by a Lie transformation and conversely.

Since the nets C and C' are in the relation of a transformation K (§ 25), the coordinates α_i and α'_i $(i = 1, \ldots. 6)$, of the spheres with centers on C and C' tangent to Σ satisfy equations of Laplace with equal invariants. Conversely, if the coordinates α_i of a sphere are solutions of such an equation, the central net C has equal invariants, and consequently (§ 89) the sheets of the envelope are surfaces Ω. Hence:

---

[84]) Leçons, 2nd ed., vol. 2, p. 358.

[85]) Comptes Rendus, vol. 153 (1911), p. 590.

When the Laplace equation of a congruence R of spheres has equal invariants, the sheets of the envelope are surfaces Ω, and conversely.

As a corollary we have:

A necessary and sufficient condition the a net be R is that the Plücker line coordinates of the tangents to either family of curves of the net are solutions of a Laplace equation with equal invariants.

105. Harmonic congruences of spheres and circles. Suppose we have a congruence of circles C_1, whose axes are tangent to the curves $u =$ const. of a net N, the circles being determined by a solution θ of the point equation of N, as discussed in § 99.

Any net $\overline{N}$ conjugate to this congruence of axes is defined by equations of the form

$$\overline{x} = x - \frac{\theta_1}{\frac{\partial \theta_1}{\partial v}} \frac{\partial x}{\partial v}, \tag{57}$$

where θ_1 is another solution of the point equation (36) of N (§ 8). Evidently $\overline{\theta}$ given by $\overline{\theta} = \theta - \theta_1 \frac{\partial \theta}{\partial v} \Big/ \frac{\partial \theta_1}{\partial v}$ is a solution of the point equation of $\overline{N}$. Hence the spheres $\overline{S}$ with centers on points of $\overline{N}$ and radii determined by

$$\sum \overline{x}^2 - \overline{R}^2 = 2\,\overline{\theta}$$

form a congruence. It is readily found that the circles C_1 lie on the corresponding spheres of this congruence.

We say that a congruence of spheres and a congruence of circles are *harmonic*, when the centers of the spheres describe a net conjugate to the axes of the circles, and the latter lie on the corresponding spheres[86]):

We may state the preceding results as follows:

If a congruence of circles is determined by a solution θ of the point equation of the net N whose curves $u =$ const. are tangent to the axes of the circles, and θ_1 is the solution determining a net $\overline{N}$ conjugate to the axes, the congruence of spheres harmonic to the circles and with centers on $\overline{N}$ is determined by

$$\overline{\theta} = \theta - \frac{\theta_1}{\frac{\partial \theta_1}{\partial v}} \frac{\partial \theta}{\partial v}. \tag{58}$$

---

[86]) Cf. Guichard, Annales L'École Norm. Sup., ser. 3, vol. 20 (1903), p. 197.

Consider the converse problem when the spheres are given with centers on a net $\overline{N}$ and radii determined by a solution $\overline{\theta}$ of its point equation. A congruence G conjugate to $\overline{N}$ is obtained by drawing through points of $\overline{N}$ lines parallel to the lines joining the origin to points of a parallel net $\overline{N}'$ whose coordinates $\overline{x}'$ are given by

$$\frac{\partial \overline{x}'}{\partial u} = h \frac{\partial \overline{x}}{\partial u}, \qquad \frac{\partial \overline{x}'}{\partial v} = l \frac{\partial \overline{x}}{\partial v}. \tag{59}$$

A function $\overline{\theta}'$ is given by the quadratures

$$\frac{\partial \overline{\theta}'}{\partial u} = h \frac{\partial \overline{\theta}}{\partial u}, \qquad \frac{\partial \overline{\theta}'}{\partial v} = l \frac{\partial \overline{\theta}}{\partial v}. \tag{60}$$

From (I, 37) we have that the focal point generating a net N whose curves $u =$ const. are tangent to the congruence G is given by equations of the form

$$x = \overline{x} - \frac{1}{l} \overline{x}'. \tag{61}$$

Moreover, $1/l$ is the solution of the point equation of N determining $\overline{N}$ as a Levy transform of N (§ 8), that is the function θ_1 referred to in the above theorem. Hence it is readily seen that the function

$$\theta = \overline{\theta} - \frac{1}{l} \overline{\theta}' \tag{62}$$

enables us to express $\overline{\theta}$ in the form (58). Consequently the spheres with centers on the net N and radii determined by θ meet the corresponding spheres of the given congruence in circles harmonic to the latter. Accordingly we have:

The determination of congruences of circles harmonic to a congruence of spheres is the problem of finding congruences conjugate to the net of centers of the spheres and a quadrature.

Since $\overline{\theta}'$ is determined by (60) to within an additive constant, there are ∞^1 congruences of circles harmonic to the given congruence of spheres such that corresponding circles have the same axis.

This result may be obtained in another manner which brings to light the role of transformations F in this theory. Let $\overline{N}_1(\overline{x}_1)$

be an F transform of $\bar{N}$ by means of a solution $\hat{\theta}$ of the point equation of $\bar{N}$, the congruence G of the transformation having parameters $\bar{x}'$. Thus

$$\bar{x}_1 = \bar{x} - \frac{\hat{\theta}}{\hat{\theta}'}\bar{x}'.$$

From (II, 7) we have

$$\frac{\partial \bar{x}_1'}{\partial u} = h_1 \frac{\partial \bar{x}_1}{\partial u}, \qquad \frac{\partial \bar{x}_1'}{\partial v} = l_1 \frac{\partial \bar{x}_1}{\partial v},$$

where

$$h_1 = \frac{h}{\hat{\theta}' - h\hat{\theta}}, \qquad l_1 = \frac{l}{\hat{\theta}' - l\hat{\theta}}.$$

Consequently from (61) we have

$$x = \bar{x}_1 - \frac{1}{l_1}\bar{x}_1'.$$

We call the functions

$$\bar{\theta}_1 = \bar{\theta} - \frac{\hat{\theta}}{\hat{\theta}'}\bar{\theta}', \qquad \frac{\bar{\theta}'}{\hat{\theta}'},$$

the solutions of the point equations of $\bar{N}_1$ and $\bar{N}_1'$ corresponding to the solution $\bar{\theta}$ of the point equation of $\bar{N}$. We find from (62) that

$$\theta = \bar{\theta}_1 - \frac{1}{l_1}\frac{\bar{\theta}'}{\hat{\theta}'}.$$

Consequently we have:

If $\bar{N}$ and $\bar{N}_1$ are F transforms of one another, and $\bar{\theta}$ and $\bar{\theta}_1$ are corresponding solutions of the point equations of $\bar{N}$ and $\bar{N}_1$ respectively, the congruences of spheres S and S_1 with centers on $\bar{N}$ and $\bar{N}_1$ and radii determined by $\bar{\theta}$ and $\bar{\theta}_1$ respectively, intersect in a congruence of circles having the lines of the congruence of the transformation F for axes.

When, in particular, $\hat{\theta} = \bar{\theta}$, the function $\bar{\theta}_1 = 0$, and the spheres S_1 pass through the origin. Hence:

If the central net $\bar{N}$ of a congruence of spheres S whose radii are determined by a solution $\bar{\theta}$ of the point equation of $\bar{N}$ is subjected to a transformation F determined by $\bar{\theta}$, the spheres S_1 with centers on the transform $\bar{N}_1$ and passing through the origin meet *the spheres S in a congruence of circles harmonic to S; moreover, the ∞^1 congruences of circles harmonic to the spheres S and with the same axes are obtained in this way by varying the additive constant of integration in $\overline{\theta}'$.*

From this result and (38) it follows that the circles are the intersections of the spheres

$$\sum x_0^2 - 2\sum x_0 \overline{x} + 2\overline{\theta} = 0, \qquad \sum x_0^2 - 2\sum x_0 \overline{x}_1 = 0,$$

where

$$\overline{x}_1 = \overline{x} - \frac{\overline{\theta}}{\overline{\theta}'}\,\overline{x}', \tag{63}$$

and the x_0's are current coordinates. Moreover, in consequence of (63) the equation of the planes of the circles is

$$\sum x_0 \overline{x}' - \overline{\theta}' = 0. \tag{64}$$

Consequently the coordinates x_0 of the net N_0 enveloped by these planes are found by solving (64) and

$$\sum x_0 \frac{\partial \overline{x}}{\partial u} - \frac{\partial \overline{\theta}}{\partial u} = 0, \qquad \sum x_0 \frac{\partial \overline{x}}{\partial v} - \frac{\partial \overline{\theta}}{\theta v} = 0, \tag{65}$$

in consequence of (59) and (60). From (41) it follows that (65) are the equations of the chord of contact of the spheres S with their envelope. Consequently N_0 is conjugate to the congruence of these chords of contact and we have the theorem of Guichard[87]:

The congruence of lines joining the points of contact of a congruence of spheres with their envelope is conjugate to the net enveloped by the planes of any congruence of circles harmonic to the spheres.

The quantities $\overline{x}'$ and $\overline{\theta}'$ are tangential coordinates of N_0. The tangential coordinates of the net N_{10} enveloped by the planes of any other congruence of circles harmonic to the spheres are given by

$$\left\{\begin{aligned} \frac{\partial \overline{x}''}{\partial u} &= \frac{h'}{h}\frac{\partial \overline{x}'}{\partial u}, & \frac{\partial \overline{x}''}{\partial v} &= \frac{l'}{l}\frac{\partial \overline{x}'}{\partial v}, \\ \frac{\partial \overline{\theta}''}{\partial u} &= \frac{h'}{h}\frac{\partial \overline{\theta}'}{\partial u}, & \frac{\partial \overline{\theta}''}{\partial v} &= \frac{l'}{l}\frac{\partial \overline{\theta}'}{\partial v}, \end{aligned}\right. \tag{66}$$

[87]) L. c., p. 197.

in consequence of (59) and similar equations defining the other congruence of circles. But from these equations it follows that N_0 and N_{10} are in relation F or are parallel. Hence:

When two congruences of circles are harmonic to the same congruence of spheres, the nets enveloped by the planes of the circles are in relation F or are parallel.

Conversely since the tangential coordinates of any two nets in relation F can be chosen so that they satisfy equations of the form (66), it follows that the tangential coordinates of any other net conjugate to the lines joining corresponding points of N_0 and N_{10} satisfy equations of the form (66). Hence:

If S is a sphere describing a congruence and G is the congruence of lines joining the points of contact of S with its envelope, the tangent planes of any net conjugate to G meet the spheres S in a congruence of circles harmonic to the spheres[88]).

106. Representation in 5-space. When we interpret the results of § 105 in terms of nets and congruences in 5-space, we find that a net representing the congruence of circles is harmonic to a congruence representing the congruence of spheres. We shall establish this result.

From (2), (32), (37) and (38) it follows that the parameters of the spheres giving rise to the circles C_1 are of the form

$$\alpha_i' = h x_i \, (i=1,2,3), \qquad \alpha_4' = ih\left(\theta + \frac{1}{2}\right), \qquad \alpha_5' = h\left(\theta - \frac{1}{2}\right);$$

$$\beta_i' = h\left(\frac{\partial x_i}{\partial v} - \frac{\partial \log a}{\partial v} x_i\right) \, (i=1,2,3),$$

$$\beta_4' = ih\left(\frac{\partial \theta}{\partial v} - \left(\theta + \frac{1}{2}\right)\frac{\partial \log a}{\partial v}\right), \quad \beta_5' = h\left(\frac{\partial \theta}{\partial v} - \left(\theta - \frac{1}{2}\right)\frac{\partial \log a}{\partial v}\right).$$

Since the functions α' and β' are the direction-parameters of the tangents to a net, they are solutions of a system of equations of the form (I, 4). Any other solution θ_1 of (36) gives two other solutions of this system, namely

$$p' = h\theta_1, \qquad q' = h\left(\frac{\partial \theta_1}{\partial v} - \frac{\partial \log a}{\partial v}\theta_1\right).$$

88) Cf. Guichard, l. c. p. 197.

We make use of this fact to obtain the parameters of the congruence in 5-space representing the congruence of spheres S harmonic to the circles C_1 in § 105. In fact, from (57) and (58) it follows that the parameters $\overline{\alpha}$ of the congruence are given by

$$\overline{\alpha}_i = \overline{h}\overline{x}_i = \frac{\overline{h}}{h^2 \frac{\partial \theta_1}{\partial v}} (\alpha_i' q' - \beta_i' p') \qquad (i = 1, 2, 3),$$

$$\overline{\alpha}_4 = i\overline{h}\left(\overline{\theta} + \frac{1}{2}\right) = \frac{\overline{h}}{h^2 \frac{\partial \theta_1}{\partial v}} (\alpha_4' q' - \beta_4' p'),$$

$$\overline{\alpha}_5 = \overline{h}\left(\overline{\theta} - \frac{1}{2}\right) = \frac{\overline{h}}{h^2 \frac{\partial \theta_1}{\partial v}} (\alpha_5' q' - \beta_5' p').$$

Hence (§ 13) the congruence and net in 5-space corresponding to the congruences of spheres and circles are harmonic.

In order to prove conversely that congruences of circles and spheres represented by a net and a congruence harmonic to it in 5-space are harmonic to one another, we take the direction-parameters, α and β, of the net in the normal form, so that

$$\frac{\partial \alpha}{\partial v} = n\beta, \qquad \frac{\partial \beta}{\partial u} = m\alpha. \tag{67}$$

The parameters of any harmonic net are of the form

$$\overline{\alpha} = \alpha q - \beta p, \tag{68}$$

where p and q are a pair of solutions of (67). From these expressions it follows that the spheres S of coordinates $\overline{\alpha}$ pass through the circles of intersection of the corresponding spheres of coordinates α and β. Hence their net of centers is conjugate to the congruence of the axes of these circles, since the curves of the net and the developables of the congruence are parametric.

From (68) we have by differentiation

$$\frac{\partial \overline{\alpha}}{\partial u} = q \frac{\partial \alpha}{\partial u} - \frac{\partial p}{\partial u} \beta, \qquad \frac{\partial \overline{\alpha}}{\partial v} = \frac{\partial q}{\partial v} \alpha - p \frac{\partial \beta}{\partial v}. \tag{69}$$

When u varies the characteristics of the spheres S are circles, Γ_1, the intersection of the spheres of coordinates $\bar{\alpha}$ and $\frac{\partial \bar{\alpha}}{\partial u}$, which in consequence of (67), (68) and (69) pass through the corresponding points, A_1 and A_2, where the spheres of coordinates α touch their envelope. Similarly, when v varies the characteristics of S are circles Γ_2 passing through the corresponding points B_1 and B_2, where the spheres of coordinates β touch their envelope. We have seen that the lines $A_1 A_2$ and $B_1 B_2$ are the tangents to the parametric net $\bar{N}$ on the envelope of the circle C_1 (§ 97). Moreover, we know that the lines of intersection of the planes of the circles Γ_1 and Γ_2, that is the joins of points of contact of the spheres S with their envelope, form a congruence with the developables parametric. Hence we have the fifth theorem of § 105.

107. Conjugate congruences of spheres and circles. We return to the consideration of the congruence of spheres S whose centers describe a net N and whose radius is determined by a solution θ of (36), the point equation of N. By means of a solution θ_1 of (36) we determine Levy transforms $\bar{N}_{-1}$ and $\bar{N}_1$ of N, such that $M\bar{M}_{-1}$ and $M\bar{M}_1$ are tangent to the curves of parameter u and v respectively of N. By means of the functions

$$(70) \qquad \bar{\theta}_{-1} = \theta - \frac{\theta_1}{\frac{\partial \theta_1}{\partial u}} \frac{\partial \theta}{\partial u}, \qquad \bar{\theta}_1 = \theta - \frac{\theta_1}{\frac{\partial \theta_1}{\partial v}} \frac{\partial \theta}{\partial v}$$

we determine spheres $\bar{S}_{-1}$ and $\bar{S}_1$ with centers on $\bar{N}_{-1}$ and $\bar{N}_1$ respectively. The spheres S meet the spheres $\bar{S}_{-1}$ and $\bar{S}_1$ in congruences of circles C_{-1} and C_1 respectively, harmonic to $\bar{S}_{-1}$ and $\bar{S}_1$. Moreover, corresponding circles C_{-1} and C_1 meet in the points A_1 and A_2 where S touches its envelope (cf. fig. 6).

Since the nets $\bar{N}_{-1}$ and $\bar{N}_1$ are Laplace transforms of one another, the same is true of the functions $\bar{\theta}_{-1}$ and $\bar{\theta}_1$ (I, Ex. 11). Consequently by the fourth theorem of § 99 the circles $\bar{C}$ of intersection of the spheres $\bar{S}_{-1}$ and $\bar{S}_1$ form a congruence. Since the spheres $\bar{S}_{-1}$ and $\bar{S}_1$ pass through A_1 and A_2, so also does their intersection $\bar{C}$.

From § 97 it follows that the points of contact, B_{-1}, B'_{-1} and B_1, B'_1 respectively, of the spheres $\bar{S}_{-1}$ and $\bar{S}_1$ with their

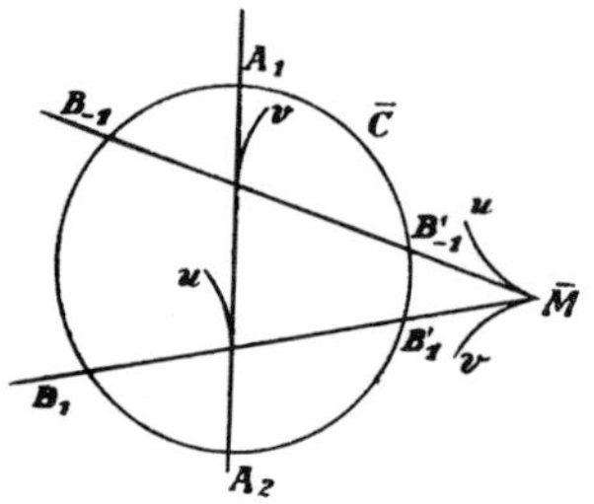

Fig. 7

envelopes lie on $\bar{C}$, and that the lines $B_{-1}B'_{-1}$ and $B_1B'_1$ are the tangents to the net $\bar{N}$ enveloped by the planes of $\bar{C}$. Since $\bar{S}_{-1}$ is harmonic to C_{-1}, it follows from § 105 that the line $B_{-1}B'_{-1}$ passes through the net enveloped by the plane of C_{-1}, that is the second focal net of A_1A_2. Similarly the line $B_1B'_1$ passes through the first focal net of A_1A_2 (cf. fig. 7). Consequently the congruence A_1A_2 is harmonic to $\bar{N}$. Hence[89]):

If A_1 and A_2 are the points of contact with its envelope of a congruences of spheres S with centers at points of a net N and G is any congruence harmonic to N, the circles with the lines of G for axes and passing through the corresponding points A_1 and A_2 form a congruence. Moreover, the congruence A_1A_2 is harmonic to the net enveloped by the planes of the circles.

Consider now the representation in 5-space. To the spheres S corresponds a congruence G, to C_1 and C_{-1} the focal nets F_1 and F_2 of G, to $\bar{S}_1$ and $\bar{S}_{-1}$ congruences harmonic to F_1 and F_2, which are tangents to a net P representing the congruence of circles $\bar{C}$. Hence the net P is conjugate to G.

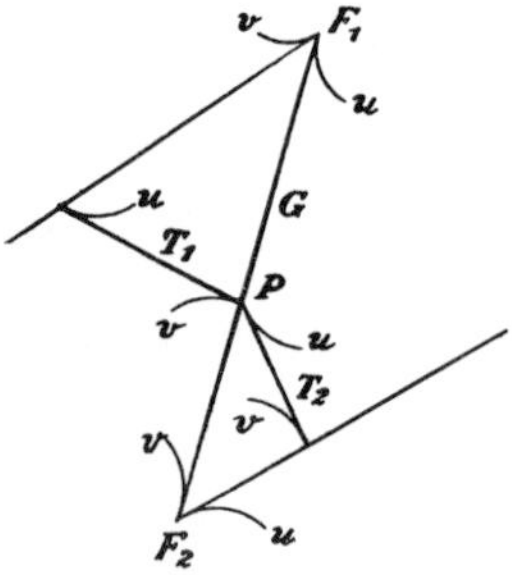

Fig. 8

Conversely, if we have a congruence G and a conjugate net P in 5-space, to G there corresponds in 3-space a congruence of spheres S with centers at points of a net N. It touches its envelope at the points, A_1 and A_2, of intersection of C_1 and C_{-1}, the characteristics of S when v and u vary respectively. Since the tangents T_1 and T_2 to the curves of parameter v and u of P are harmonic to the focal nets F_1 and F_2 of G, they generate congruences represented in 3-space by congruences of spheres harmonic to the circles C_1 and C_{-1} respectively, the centers of the spheres being on nets $\bar{N}_1$ and $\bar{N}_{-1}$ conjugate to the tangents to

[89]) Cf. Guichard, l. c., p. 198.

the curves of parameter v *and* u respectively of N. However, since T_1 and T_2 are tangents to the net P, the two congruences of spheres with centers on $\overline{N}_1$ and $\overline{N}_{-1}$ meet in a congruence of circles, and corresponding points of $\overline{N}_1$ and $\overline{N}_{-1}$ are the foci of the axes of the circles (§ 97). Hence (§ 10) the congruence of axes is harmonic to N. In view of these results we say, with Guichard, that congruences of spheres and circles related as in the preceding theorem are *conjugate* to one another[90]).

In order to obtain a congruence of circles conjugate to a congruence of spheres, we note that the coordinates of $\overline{N}_1$ are of the form (57) where θ_1 is a solution of the point equation of N, the net of centers of the spheres. The function $\overline{\theta}_1$ determining the radius of $\overline{S}_1$ is given by (70). Hence the circles are defined by the equations

$$(71)\quad \sum(y^2-2y\overline{x}_1)+2\overline{\theta}_1=0, \qquad \sum y\frac{\partial \overline{x}_1}{\partial u}-\frac{\partial \overline{\theta}_1}{\partial u}=0,$$

where the y's are current coordinates.

Conversely, if we have a congruence of circles, any net harmonic to the axes of the circles is given by equations of the form (61) and the radius of the spheres of the conjugate congruence is determined by (62). The converse may be stated in geometrical form, if we observe that it follows from the representation in 5-space that there is a reciprocal correspondence between the congruence harmonic to $\overline{N}$ and the nets harmonic to the congruence of axes of the circles. In view of this fact and the preceding results we have:

If G is a congruence harmonic to the net $\overline{N}$ enveloped by the planes of the circles of a congruence, and A_1 and A_2 are the points of meeting of a line of G and the corresponding circle of the congruence, the plane determined by the mid-point of the segment $A_1 A_2$ and the axis of the circle envelopes a net N; the spheres with centers on N and passing through A_1 and A_2 form a congruence conjugate to the given congruence of circles[91]).

108. Congruences of circles K determined by transformations R. In § 81 we found that if N_1 and N_2 are R trans-

---

[90]) L. c., p. 197.

[91]) Cf. Guichard, l. c., p. 198.

forms of an O net N, there can be found by quadratures alone a set of ∞^1 nets N_c, of which N_1 is a member, which are R transforms of a family of ∞^1 nets N_{12}, of which N is a member; corresponding points of these ∞^2 nets lie on a circle K; the tangent planes to the nets at points of K pass through a point M_d which describes a net N_d conjugate to the congruence K of the axes of the circles K, this congruence being harmonic to the central nets of the transformation of N into N_c; the normals to the nets N_{12} and N_c at points of K are tangent to the sphere S with center at M_d and passing through K. We wish to show that the circles K form a congruence of circles and the spheres S a congruence of spheres harmonic to the former.

Since $\omega = \frac{1}{2}\sum x^2$ is a solution of the point equation of N, the function (cf. § 81 and VI, 96)

$$\omega_{01} = \omega - \frac{\theta_1}{p_1} P$$

is a solution of the point equation of N_{01}, and consequently

$$\omega_{y_1} = \omega_{01} - \frac{\theta_{01}}{\frac{\partial \theta_{01}}{\partial u}} \frac{\partial \omega_{01}}{\partial u} = \omega + \frac{(\theta_1 p_2 - \theta_2 p_1) Q + (\theta_2 q_1 - \theta_1 q_2) P}{p_1 q_2 - p_2 q_1},$$

$$\omega_{y_2} = \omega_{01} - \frac{\theta_{01}}{\frac{\partial \theta_{01}}{\partial v}} \frac{\partial \omega_{01}}{\partial v} = \omega + \frac{(\theta_1 p_2 - \theta_2 p_1) R + (\theta_2 r_1 - \theta_1 r_2) P}{p_1 r_2 - p_2 r_1},$$

are solutions of the point equations of the focal nets F_1 and F_2 of the congruence K, and either is a Laplace transform of the other.

From (VII, 33) it follows that the radii of the spheres with centers on F_1 and F_2 and passing through the corresponding circles K are given by

$$R^2_{y_1} = \frac{(\theta_1 p_2 - \theta_2 p_1)^2 + (\theta_2 q_1 - \theta_1 q_2)^2}{(p_1 q_2 - p_2 q_1)^2},$$

$$R^2_{y_2} = \frac{(\theta_1 p_2 - \theta_2 p_1)^2 + (\theta_2 r_1 - \theta_1 r_2)^2}{(p_1 r_2 - p_2 r_1)^2}.$$

From these equations and (VII, 33) we find that

$$\sum y_1^2 - R_{y_1}^2 = 2\,\omega_{y_1}, \qquad \sum y_2^2 - R_{y_2}^2 = 2\,\omega_{y_2}.$$

Hence (§ 99) the circles K form a congruence, and the spheres S form a congruence harmonic to these circles (§ 105).

From the second theorem of § 11 it follows that the lines joining the focal points of the same rank of corresponding lines of the congruences of the transformations R of N into two nets of the class N_c meet in a point $\overline{M}$ which describes the net $\overline{N}$ enveloped by the planes of the circles K. If A_1 and A_2 are the points of contact of the sphere S with its envelope, the lines $A_1\,A_2$ form a congruence $\overline{G}$ which is conjugate to the net $\overline{N}$ (§ 105).

Since normals to a pair of nets N and N_1 are tangent to the corresponding sphere S, the circles orthogonal to N and N_1 form a cyclic system (§ 79) and lie on the spheres S. In § 113 it is shown that a cyclic system is a congruence, and consequently this cyclic system is harmonic to the sphere. From the results of § 105 it follows that the axes of these circles form a congruence conjugate to N_d.

109. Orthogonal congruences of spheres and circles. Consider the congruence of spheres $\overline{S}$ with centers on $\overline{N}(\overline{x})$ and radii determined by a solution $\overline{\theta}$ of the point equation of $\overline{N}$, and also the harmonic circles whose planes are defined by (64). The spheres S with centers on the net N enveloped by these planes and with radii determined by a solution φ of the point equation of N are orthogonal to the corresponding spheres $\overline{S}$, when, and only when,

$$\varphi = \sum \overline{x}\,x - \overline{\theta}. \tag{72}$$

In consequence of (65) we have

$$\frac{\partial \varphi}{\partial u} = \sum \overline{x}\,\frac{\partial x}{\partial u}, \qquad \frac{\partial \varphi}{\partial v} = \sum \overline{x}\,\frac{\partial x}{\partial v}. \tag{73}$$

Because of these equations it follows that the spheres $\overline{S}$ are orthogonal also to the first and minus first derived spheres of S (§ 99). Moreover, equations (73), being of the form (41), show that the line joining the points where S touches its envelope passes through the corresponding point of $\overline{N}$ and hence is the axis of the circle.

Conversely, let φ be any solution of the point equation of N, and let S denote the spheres with centers on N, and radii determined by φ. Let $\overline{N}(\overline{x})$ be any net conjugate to the line joining the points of contact of S with its envelope, then equations (73) hold. By differentiating them with respect to v and u respectively, we get

$$\sum \frac{\partial \overline{x}}{\partial v} \frac{\partial x}{\partial u} = 0, \qquad \sum \frac{\partial \overline{x}}{\partial u} \frac{\partial x}{\partial v} = 0.$$

In consequence of these equations $\overline{\theta}$ given by (72) is a solution of the point equation of $\overline{N}$, and therefore the spheres $\overline{S}$ with centers on $\overline{N}$ and radii determined by $\overline{\theta}$ meet S and the two derived congruences of spheres orthogonally. We say that the congruence of spheres S are *orthogonal* to the congruence of circles in which the spheres $\overline{S}$ are cut by the tangent planes of N.

By definition the *poles of a circle* are the two points on its axis, equidistant from the plane of the circle, which are the centers of the null spheres passing through the circle; any sphere with center in the plane of a circle and orthogonal to a sphere through the circle passes through the poles of the circle[92]). For the present case the points of contact of S with its envelope are the poles of the circles, since the spheres $\overline{S}$ are orthogonal to S and its derived spheres. Hence:

The circles in the tangent planes of the surface of centers of a congruence of spheres which have for poles the points of contact of the spheres with their envelope form a congruence of circles whose focal parameters are the same as for the congruence of spheres.

Also:

If C describes a congruence of circles, the spheres with centers on the net enveloped by the plane of C and passing through the poles of C form a congruence orthogonal to the congruence of circles[93]).

We have seen that the spheres S orthogonal to a congruence of circles C are orthogonal to any congruence of spheres $\overline{S}$ har-

[92]) Note that when the circles are real the poles are imaginary and vice-versa.

[93]) Cf. Guichard, l. c., p. 195.

monic to C, as are also the first and minus first derived spheres S_1 and S_{-1} of S. Hence if the equation of S is $\sum \gamma z = 0$, and the equations of C are $\sum \alpha z = 0$, $\sum \beta z = 0$, where the α's and β's satisfy (67), it follows from (68) that

$$\sum \gamma \alpha = 0, \qquad \sum \gamma \beta = 0, \qquad \sum \frac{\partial \gamma}{\partial u} \alpha = 0,$$
$$\sum \frac{\partial \gamma}{\partial u} \beta = 0, \qquad \sum \frac{\partial \gamma}{\partial v} \alpha = 0, \qquad \sum \frac{\partial \gamma}{\partial v} \beta = 0.$$

Consequently the spheres S, S_1 and S_{-1} are represented in 5-space by a congruence and its first and minus first derived congruences whose lines are perpendicular to the tangents to the net representing C. Conversely, if we have such a configuration in 5-space, the corresponding spheres S, S_1, S_{-1}, in 3-space are orthogonal to the congruences of spheres harmonic to the circles C represented by the net. Consequently the points of contact of S with its envelope are the poles of C. Since the centers of the spheres lie in the planes of C, and these planes are the tangent planes of the central net of S, the spheres are orthogonal to the circles. Hence:

A necessary and sufficient condition that a congruence of spheres and a congruence of circles be orthogonal is that the congruence of spheres and its first and minus first derived congruences be represented in 5-space by congruences of lines perpendicular to the tangents to the curves of the net representing the congruence of circles.

110. Transformations F of congruences of circles. Consider the congruence $\bar{S}$ of spheres and the circles C harmonic to them, as defined in the preceding section, and in addition a second congruence of circles C_1 harmonic to $\bar{S}$. Let $N_1(x_1)$ be the net enveloped by the planes of these circles and φ_1 be the solution of the point equation of N_1 determining the congruence of spheres with centers on N_1 and orthogonal to $\bar{S}$. Then

$$\varphi_1 = \sum \bar{x} x_1 - \bar{\theta}, \tag{74}$$

and

$$\frac{\partial \varphi_1}{\partial u} = \sum \bar{x} \frac{\partial x_1}{\partial u}, \qquad \frac{\partial \varphi_1}{\partial v} = \sum \bar{x} \frac{\partial x_1}{\partial v}. \tag{75}$$

From the fifth theorem of § 105 it follows that N_1 is an F transform of N, or is parallel to N, the nets N and N_1 being conjugate to the congruence G of lines joining the points where $\overline{S}$ touches its envelope. Consider first the case where N and N_1 are not parallel, then

$$x_1 = x - \frac{\theta}{\theta'} x', \tag{76}$$

where θ is a solution of the point equation of N, the direction-parameters x' of G and θ' being in the relations

$$\frac{\partial x'}{\partial u} = h \frac{\partial x}{\partial u}, \qquad \frac{\partial x'}{\partial v} = l \frac{\partial x}{\partial v}, \qquad \frac{\partial \theta'}{\partial u} = h \frac{\partial \theta}{\partial u}, \qquad \frac{\partial \theta'}{\partial v} = l \frac{\partial \theta}{\partial v}. \tag{77}$$

Since G is normal to the tangent plane to $\overline{N}$, we have

$$\sum x' \frac{\partial \overline{x}}{\partial u} = 0, \qquad \sum x' \frac{\partial \overline{x}}{\partial v} = 0, \tag{78}$$

and consequently φ' defined by

$$\varphi' = \sum x' \overline{x} \tag{79}$$

satisfies the equations

$$\frac{\partial \varphi'}{\partial u} = h \frac{\partial \varphi}{\partial u}, \qquad \frac{\partial \varphi'}{\partial v} = l \frac{\partial \varphi}{\partial v}. \tag{80}$$

From (72), (74), (76) and (79) we have

$$\varphi_1 = \varphi - \frac{\theta}{\theta'} \varphi', \tag{81}$$

that is φ_1 is the transform of φ.

Conversely, let N and N_1 be two nets in relation F, and φ and φ_1 be corresponding solutions of their point equations in the relation (81). Let C and C_1 be congruences of circles in the planes of N and N_1 determined by the functions φ and φ_1 respectively. The equations of the axes of these circles are

$$(82) \qquad \sum y \frac{\partial x}{\partial u} - \frac{\partial \varphi}{\partial u} = 0, \qquad \sum y \frac{\partial x}{\partial v} - \frac{\partial \varphi}{\partial v} = 0,$$

and

$$(83) \qquad \sum y \frac{\partial x_1}{\partial u} - \frac{\partial \varphi_1}{\partial u} = 0, \qquad \sum y \frac{\partial x_1}{\partial v} - \frac{\partial \varphi_1}{\partial v} = 0.$$

These two lines are found to intersect in consequence of (76) and (81). If we denote by $\bar{x}$ the coordinates of the point of intersection $\bar{M}$, we find that they satisfy (82) and (79).

From (79) and (80) equations (78) follow. In view of this result and the fact that x' and φ' are solutions of the point equation of N', equation (79) is the tangential equation of a net, and therefore $\bar{M}$ describes a net conjugate to both axes.

From the preceding section it follows that the spheres $\bar{S}$ with centers $\bar{M}$ and radius determined by $\bar{\theta}$ given by (72) are harmonic to the circles C. But by means of (76), (79) and (81) we find that (74) is a consequence of (72). Hence the spheres $\bar{S}$ are likewise harmonic to C_1.

We say that the circles C and C_1 whose planes envelope nets in relation F and which are determined by solutions of the point equations of these nets in the relation (81) are *F transforms of one another*, or simply *in relation F*. Hence:

Two congruences of circles which are F transforms of one another are harmonic to a congruence of spheres, and two congruences of circles harmonic to a congruence of spheres are F transforms of one another unless the corresponding circles lie in parallel planes.

Incidentally we have:

When two congruences of circles are in relation F, corresponding circles meet in the two points where each circle cuts the corresponding line of the harmonic congruence of the transformation F of the nets enveloped by the planes of the circles.

If N, N_1, N_2 and N_{12} are four nets of a quatern in relations F (§ 21) and the planes of congruences of circles C, C_1 and C_2 envelope the respective nets N, N_1 and N_2 and are determined by functions φ, φ_1 and φ_2 respectively, where

$$\varphi_1 = \varphi - \frac{\theta_1}{\theta_1'} \varphi', \qquad \varphi_2 = \varphi - \frac{\theta_2}{\theta_2''} \varphi'',$$

the function φ_{12}, defined by

$$\theta_1 \theta_{12}''' \varphi_{12} = \frac{\theta_2''}{\theta_2}(\theta_2 \theta_{21} \varphi_1 + \theta_1 \theta_{12} \varphi_2 - \theta_{12} \theta_{21} \varphi), \tag{84}$$

is the corresponding solution of the point equation of N_{12}, whose coordinates are given by (II, 49). Hence the circles C_{12} whose planes envelope N_{12} and which are determined by φ_{12} are F transforms of C_1 and C_2.

We shall give another geometric interpretation of transformations F of congruences of circles. Take two congruences of circles conjugate to the same congruence of spheres. Since their axes are harmonic to the net of centers of the spheres, the intersections of corresponding axes form a net, and consequently the spheres with centers at points of this net and containing the circles form a congruence of spheres harmonic to the two congruences of circles. Hence:

Two congruences of circles conjugate to a congruence of spheres are in the relation of a transformation F.

As a corollary we have:

The nets enveloped by the planes of the circles of two congruences of circles conjugate to a congruence of spheres are in the relation of a transformation F.

In consequence of the last theorem of § 107 and the second of § 110 we have:

Two congruences of circles in the relation of a transformation F are conjugate to a unique congruence of spheres.

From the foregoing theorems follows the theorem:

Any two congruences of circles harmonic to a congruence of spheres are conjugate to a congruence of spheres, and conversely.

Since two congruences of circles in relation F are conjugate to a congruence of spheres, it follows from that the nets in 5-space representing the congruences of circles are conjugate to the congruence of lines representing the spheres. Hence:

The nets in 5-space representing congruences of circles in relation F are F transforms of one another; and any two nets in 5-space in relation F correspond to congruences of circles in relation F.

The theorem preceding this one is a consequence of the latter and the fact that two nets in relation F are harmonic to a congruence.

111. Parallel transformations of congruences of circles. We consider the exceptional case where the corresponding planes of two congruences of circles harmonic to a congruence of spheres are parallel. Now

$$(85)\qquad \frac{\partial x_1}{\partial u} = h\frac{\partial x}{\partial u}, \qquad \frac{\partial x_1}{\partial v} = l\frac{\partial \varphi}{\partial v},$$

and consequently (75) is satisfied by

$$(86)\qquad \frac{\partial \varphi_1}{\partial u} = h\frac{\partial \varphi}{\partial u}, \qquad \frac{\partial \varphi_1}{\partial v} = l\frac{\partial \varphi}{\partial v}.$$

Suppose, conversely, that we have two congruences of circles, C and C_1, whose planes envelope parallel nets $N(x)$ and $N_1(x_1)$, and the circles are determined by corresponding functions φ and φ_1, that is in the relation (86), we say they are *parallel transforms* of one another.

We consider the point $\overline{M}$ of coordinates $\overline{x}$ defined by (73) and

$$(87)\qquad \sum \overline{x}\,(x_1 - x) = \varphi_1 - \varphi.$$

By differentiating this equation and making use of (73), (85) and (86), we find

$$\sum \frac{\partial \overline{x}}{\partial u}(x_1 - x) = 0, \qquad \sum \frac{\partial \overline{x}}{\partial v}(x_1 - x) = 0.$$

Since $x_1 - x$ and $\varphi_1 - \varphi$ satisfy an equation of the Laplace type, they are the tangential coordinates of a net, the locus of $\overline{M}$. From § 109 and (87) it follows that the spheres of center $\overline{M}$ and radius determined by $\overline{\theta}$ given by (72) are harmonic to the circles C and C_1. Hence:

Two congruences of circles which are parallel transforms of one another are harmonic to a sphere; and congruences of circles harmonic to a sphere such that corresponding planes are parallel, are parallel transforms of one another.

112. Congruences of spheres with applicable central nets. Let $N(x)$ and $\overline{N}(\overline{x})$ be two applicable nets in 3-space. Since they have the same point equation, the function

$$2\,\theta_0 = \sum x^2 - \sum \bar{x}^2 \tag{88}$$

is a solution of this equation. If θ is a solution of this equation, the spheres $\bar{S}$ with centers on $\bar{N}$ and radii given by

$$R^2 = \sum \bar{x}^2 - 2\,\theta \tag{89}$$

form a congruence. Since this may be written

$$R^2 = \sum x^2 - 2\,(\theta + \theta_0) \tag{90}$$

the spheres S of radius R and centers on N also form a congruence. Moreover, corresponding spheres of these two congruences touch their envelopes at the same points when N and $\bar{N}$ are applied to one another. This result follows from the following theorem of Beltrami which is a consequence of the last theorem of [§ 164]:

When the surface of centers of a two parameter family of spheres is deformed, the points of contact of the spheres with their envelope (which itself changes in the deformations) are fixed points with respect to the spheres.

When $\theta = 0$ in (89), the spheres $\bar{S}$ pass through the origin. The envelope of these spheres is the origin O and the locus of the point O' symmetric to O with respect to the tangent planes to $\bar{N}$. In accordance with the above theorem, when $\bar{N}$ is applied to N, the loci of O and O' are the sheets of the envelope of the spheres. Since O and O' are the points of contact, we have by § 109 that the null spheres with centers at O and O' meet the tangent planes to N in a congruence of circles orthogonal to the spheres S. Moreover, as $\bar{N}$ may be displaced in space the null sphere at the origin may be replaced by any fixed null sphere. Hence:

If N and $\bar{N}$ are applicable nets, the circles, in which the tangent planes of $\bar{N}$ are met by a fixed null sphere, become a congruence of circles when $\bar{N}$ is applied to N.

113. Generation of cyclic systems. It is our purpose now to show that the congruences of circles referred to in the last theorem are cyclic systems (§ 79) and that all cyclic systems can be obtained in this manner.

Suppose we have a surface S referred to a general moving trihedral. From [§ 69, (51)] it follows that if (x_0, y_0, z_0) is a point fixed in space, it is necessary and sufficient that

$$\frac{\partial x_0}{\partial u} + \xi + q z_0 - r y_0 = 0, \qquad \frac{\partial x_0}{\partial v} + \xi_1 + q_1 z_0 - r_1 y_0 = 0,$$

$$\frac{\partial y_0}{\partial u} + \eta + r x_0 - p z_0 = 0, \qquad \frac{\partial y_0}{\partial v} + \eta_1 + r_1 x_0 - p_1 z_0 = 0,$$

$$\frac{\partial z_0}{\partial u} + p y_0 - q x_0 = 0, \qquad \frac{\partial z_0}{\partial v} + p_1 y_0 - q_1 x_0 = 0.$$

If we put

$$A = \frac{\partial x_0}{\partial u} + \xi - r y_0, \qquad A_1 = \frac{\partial x_0}{\partial v} + \xi_1 - r_1 y_0,$$

$$B = \frac{\partial y_0}{\partial u} + \eta + r x_0, \qquad B_1 = \frac{\partial y_0}{\partial v} + \eta_1 + r_1 x_0,$$

the first four of the above equations may be written

$$(91) \quad q z_0 = -A, \qquad q_1 z_0 = -A_1, \qquad p z_0 = B, \qquad p_1 z_0 = B_1,$$

and the last two

$$z_0 \frac{\partial z_0}{\partial u} = -(x_0 A + y_0 B), \qquad z_0 \frac{\partial z_0}{\partial v} = -(x_0 A_1 + y_0 B_1).$$

It follows from (91) that

$$(p q_1 - p_1 q) z_0^2 - (A B_1 - A_1 B) = 0.$$

Comparing these results with equations [§ 174, (12), (13)], we have that the circles of radius $i z_0$ and center (x_0, y_0) lying in the plane $z = 0$ of the moving trihedral form a cyclic system. Evidently these are the circles in which these planes are met by the fixed null sphere

$$\sum (x - x_0)^2 = 0.$$

Conversely suppose we have any cyclic system consisting of circles, of center (x_0, y_0) and radius R, lying in the plane $z = 0$; then x_0, y_0, R must satisfy [§ 174, (12), (13)]. Since these equations involve only the first fundamental coefficients of S, an infinity of cyclic systems is obtained by the deformation of the envelope of the planes of the circles. As the values of p, q, p_1, q_1 given by (91) satisfy [§ 69, (48)] one of the deforms of S is determined by these values. The point whose coordinates with respect to its moving trihedral are $x_0, y_0, -iR$ is fixed in space and consequently we have the theorem of Darboux[94]):

A general cyclic system of circles situated in the tangent planes to a surface S is obtained by taking a deform of S, say $\bar{S}$, constructing the circles $\bar{C}$ of intersection of the tangent planes of $\bar{S}$ by a fixed null sphere and then taking the positions of $\bar{C}$ when $\bar{S}$ is deformed into S.

If the center of the fixed null sphere is (a_1, a_2, a_3), 2θ in (89) is $2\sum a\bar{x} - \sum a^2$, and consequently we have:

If $N(x)$ and $\bar{N}(\bar{x})$ are applicable nets, the circles in the tangent planes of $N(x)$ determined by the solution $\sum x^2 - \sum(\bar{x}-a)^2$ of its point equation form a cyclic system.

In other words we have:

If $N(x)$ and $\bar{N}(\bar{x})$ are applicable nets, the circles in the tangent planes of N which have for poles the points of contact with their envelope of spheres with centers on N and radii given by

$$R^2 = \sum(\bar{x} - a)^2$$

form a cyclic system.

114. Transformations F of cyclic systems. In § 110 we established transformations F of congruences of circles. Now we wish to show that certain of these transformations transform a cyclic system into cyclic systems[95]).

Let $N(x)$ be the net enveloped by the planes of the cyclic system C, $\bar{N}(\bar{x})$ the applicable net and φ given by

$$(92) \qquad 2\varphi = \sum x^2 - \sum \bar{x}^2$$

the function determining the cyclic system, the point equation of N and $\bar{N}$ being (36).

---

[94]) Leçons, vol. 3, p. 354.

[95]) Proc. Nat. Acad. Sci., vol. 5 (1919), p. 555.

In § 27 we showed that if h and l is any pair of solutions of the system

$$(93) \qquad \frac{\partial h}{\partial v} = (l-h)\frac{\partial \log a}{\partial v}, \qquad \frac{\partial l}{\partial u} = (h-l)\frac{\partial \log b}{\partial u},$$

the nets $N'(x')$ and $\overline{N}'(\overline{x}')$, whose coordinates are given by

$$(94) \quad \frac{\partial x'}{\partial u} = h\frac{\partial x}{\partial u}, \qquad \frac{\partial x'}{\partial v} = l\frac{\partial x}{\partial v}; \qquad \frac{\partial \overline{x}'}{\partial u} = h\frac{\partial \overline{x}}{\partial u}, \qquad \frac{\partial \overline{x}'}{\partial v} = l\frac{\partial \overline{x}}{\partial v},$$

are applicable, and parallel to N and $\overline{N}$ respectively. Also, if θ' is the solution of the point equations of N' and $\overline{N}'$ defined by

$$(95) \qquad \theta' = \sum x'^2 - \sum \overline{x}'^2,$$

and θ is given by

$$(96) \qquad \frac{\partial \theta'}{\partial u} = h\frac{\partial \theta}{\partial u}, \qquad \frac{\partial \theta'}{\partial v} = l\frac{\partial \theta}{\partial v},$$

the nets $N_1(x_1)$ and $\overline{N}_1(\overline{x}_1)$, whose coordinates are defined by

$$(97) \qquad x_1 = x - \frac{\theta}{\theta'}x', \qquad \overline{x}_1 = \overline{x} - \frac{\theta}{\theta'}\overline{x}',$$

are applicable, and are F transforms of N and $\overline{N}$ respectively.

The circles C_1 lying in the tangent planes of N_1 and determined by the function φ_1, given by (81), form a congruence which is an F transform of C (§ 110). These circles form a cyclic system, if

$$2\varphi_1 = \sum x_1^2 - \sum \overline{x}_1^2.$$

Substituting the values from (81) and (97), we find

$$\varphi' = \sum x x' - \sum \overline{x}\,\overline{x}' - \frac{\theta}{2}.$$

As this function satisfies (80), we have:

If $N(x)$ and $\overline{N}(\overline{x})$ are applicable nets and $N'(x')$ and $\overline{N}'(\overline{x}')$ are applicable nets parallel to them, and N_1 is the F transform of

N by means of N' and the corresponding functions θ and $\theta' = \sum x'^2 - \sum \bar{x}'^2$, the circles in the tangent planes of N_1 determined by φ_1, where

$$(98) \qquad 2\varphi_1 = \sum x^2 - \sum \bar{x}^2 - 2\frac{\theta}{\theta'}\left(\sum x x' - \sum \bar{x}\bar{x}' - \frac{\theta}{2}\right),$$

form a cyclic system which is an F transform of the cyclic system of circles in the planes of N determined by $2\varphi = \sum x^2 - \sum \bar{x}^2$.

We remark that similar results hold for the cyclic systems of circles in the tangent planes of $\bar{N}$ and $\bar{N}_1$ determined by $\bar{\varphi} = -\varphi$ and $\bar{\varphi}_1 = -\varphi_1$ respectively.

We shall show that these transformations admit a theorem of permutability. To this end we take two nets $N'(x')$ and $N''(x'')$ parallel to N and the nets $\bar{N}'$ and $\bar{N}''$ parallel to $\bar{N}$ and applicable to N' and N'' respectively. By means of these we determine two F transforms, N_1 and N_2, of N, and $\bar{N}_1$ and $\bar{N}_2$ of $\bar{N}$ such that N_1 and $\bar{N}_1$ are applicable, and also N_2 and $\bar{N}_2$. If we choose the additive constants in the functions θ_1'' and θ_2' so that (cf. II, 97)

$$\theta_1'' + \theta_2' - 2\left(\sum x' x'' - \sum \bar{x}'\bar{x}''\right) = 0,$$

there are ∞^1 pairs of applicable nets N_{12} and $\bar{N}_{12}$ such that N, N_1, N_2, N_{12} and $\bar{N}$, $\bar{N}_1$, $\bar{N}_2$, $\bar{N}_{12}$ are quaterns under transformations F.

In accordance with the preceding theorem, we set up a cyclic system in the planes of N_1 with circles determined by φ_1 given by (98), and a cyclic system in the planes of N_2 with circles determined by

$$\varphi_2 = \varphi - \frac{\theta_2}{\theta_2''}\left(\sum x x'' - \sum \bar{x}\bar{x}'' - \frac{\theta_2}{2}\right).$$

Since φ_1 and φ_2 are transforms of φ by (81) and an analogous equation, it follows that a solution φ_{12} of the point equation of N_{12} is given by (84).

In order that φ_{12} shall define a cyclic system for N_{12}, we must have, in accordance with (98),

$$\varphi_{12} = \varphi_1 - \frac{\theta_{12}}{\theta_{12}'''}\left(\sum x_1 x_1''' - \sum \bar{x}_1 \bar{x}_1''' - \frac{\theta_{12}}{2}\right).$$

It is readily found that this condition is satisfied identically. Hence:

If C_1 and C_2 are two cyclic systems which are F transforms of a cyclic system C, there can be found by quadratures ∞^1 cyclic system C_{12} which are F transforms of C_1 and C_2.

115. Cyclic systems in 3-space and nets O in 5-space. From the theorem of [§ 177] it follows that the spheres focal to a cyclic system are orthogonal. Consequently a cyclic system is represented in 5-space by an O net (§ 98). We consider the converse problem, taking an O net N in 5-space corresponding to the determinant

$$(99) \qquad \Delta = \begin{vmatrix} X_1^1 & X_1^2 \ldots\ldots X_1^5 \\ X_2^1 & \ldots\ldots\ldots\ldots \\ X_3^1 & \ldots\ldots\ldots\ldots \\ \xi^1 & \ldots\ldots\ldots\ldots \\ \eta^1 & \ldots\ldots\ldots\ldots \end{vmatrix}$$

We recall that

$$(100) \qquad \begin{cases} \dfrac{\partial \xi}{\partial v} = n\eta, & \dfrac{\partial \eta}{\partial u} = m\xi, \\ \dfrac{\partial X_k}{\partial u} = a_k \xi, & \dfrac{\partial X_k}{\partial v} = b_k \eta \qquad (k = 1, 2, 3), \\ \dfrac{\partial a_k}{\partial v} = m b_k, & \dfrac{\partial b_k}{\partial u} = n a_k. \end{cases}$$

Let Σ_1 and Σ_2 denote the spheres of coordinates ξ and η respectively. If α are the coordinates of the congruence of spheres S orthogonal to the circles C represented by N, we have

$$(101) \qquad \sum \alpha\xi = 0, \qquad \sum \alpha\eta = 0.$$

Since the two derived spheres of S must also be orthogonal to Σ_1 and Σ_2, we must have also (§ 97)

$$(102) \quad \sum \frac{\partial \alpha}{\partial u}\xi = 0, \quad \sum \frac{\partial \alpha}{\partial v}\xi = 0, \quad \sum \frac{\partial \alpha}{\partial u}\eta = 0, \quad \sum \frac{\partial \alpha}{\partial v}\eta = 0.$$

In order that (101) be satisfied, we must have

$$(103) \qquad \alpha = \sum_{k=1}^{3} \bar{x}_k X_k,$$

where $\bar{x}_1, \bar{x}_2, \bar{x}_3$ are determined by (102). Making use of (100), we find that they must satisfy

$$(104) \qquad \sum \bar{x}_k a_k = 0, \qquad \sum \bar{x}_k b_k = 0,$$

and consequently they are determined to within a factor, say t. Now

$$(105) \qquad \begin{gathered} \frac{\partial \alpha}{\partial u} = \sum \frac{\partial \bar{x}_k}{\partial u} X_k \qquad \frac{\partial \alpha}{\partial v} = \sum \frac{\partial \bar{x}_k}{\partial v} X_k, \\ \sum \frac{\partial \bar{x}_k}{\partial v} a_k = 0, \qquad \sum \frac{\partial \bar{x}_k}{\partial u} b_k = 0. \end{gathered}$$

From these equations it is readily shown that the $\bar{x}$'s satisfy the same Laplace equation as the α's. If we choose the factor t so that $\alpha_1, \alpha_2, \alpha_3$ are the coordinates x_1, x_2, x_3 of the net N of centers of S, this equation assumes the form (36), and consequently $\bar{x}_1, \bar{x}_2, \bar{x}_3$ are the coordinates of a net $\bar{N}$. Moreover, from (5), (104) and (105) we have

$$R^2 = \sum \alpha^2 = \sum \bar{x}_k^2, \qquad \sum d\alpha^2 = \sum dx^2 = \sum d\bar{x}^2.$$

Hence N and $\bar{N}$ are applicable, and the conditions of the second theorem of § 113 are satisfied, so that we have:

A necessary and sufficient condition that a congruence of circles be a cyclic system is that it be represented in 5-space by an O net.

From this result and the last theorem of § 110 we have:

The problem of transformations F of cyclic systems is the same as of transformations F of O nets into O nets in 5-space.

The centers of the spheres Σ_1 and Σ_2 are the focal points of the congruence G of axes of the cyclic system. Their homogeneous coordinates are

$$\xi^1, \xi^2, \xi^3, -(\xi^5 + i\xi^4); \qquad \eta^1, \eta^2, \eta^3, -(\eta^5 + i\eta^4).$$

Since the homogeneous coordinates of the net $\hat{N}_k$ of the centers of the sphere S_k of coordinates X_k are

$$X_k^1, X_k^2, X_k^3, -(X_k^5 + iX_k^4),$$

it follows from (100) and § 33 that the nets $\hat{N}_k$ are harmonic to G.

Moreover, the cartesian coordinates $\hat{x}$ of $\hat{N}_k$ satisfy an equation of the form (36), where

$$a = \frac{a_k}{X_k^5 + iX_k^4}, \qquad b = \frac{b_k}{X_k^5 + iX_k^4}.$$

As $R_k = 1/(X_k^5 + iX_k^4)$ and $(X_k^5 - iX_k^4)/(X_k^5 + iX_k^4)$ are solutions, so also is $\sum \hat{x}_k^2 - R_k^2$. Hence the nets $\hat{N}_k$ are $2, O$.

The equation of the sphere S_1 is

$$\sum X_1 z = 0.$$

The pentaspherical coordinates z and z_1 of the points where it touches its envelope are common solutions of this equation, and

(106) $$\sum \xi z = 0, \qquad \sum \eta z = 0.$$

Since they must satisfy $\sum z^2 = 0$ also, we have that they may be taken as

(107) $$z = X_2 + iX_3, \qquad z_1 = X_2 - iX_3.$$

These points lie on the circle of intersection of the spheres Σ_1 and Σ_2, namely (106), and since their pentaspherical coordinates satisfy an equation of the Laplace type (26), the points describe O nets N and N_1 (§ 95). As in the case of $\hat{N}_k$, these nets are harmonic to the congruence G, and consequently the net is orthogonal to the circles. Similar results follow for the spheres S_2 and S_3, which proves again that the circles of intersection of the spheres Σ_1 and Σ_2 form a cyclic system.

In the same manner it is shown that if a_1, a_2, a_3 are any constants satisfying the isotropic relation $\sum a^2 = 0$, the quantities $\sum a_k X_k$ are pentaspherical coordinates of an O net orthogonal to the circles. Hence:

The last two rows of an orthogonal determinant of the fifth order determine a cyclic system; any isotropic linear functions of the terms of the first three rows are pentaspherical coordinates of an O net orthogonal to the cyclic system.

116. Cyclic congruences. In § 73 we found that a necessary condition that a congruence be cyclic is that the direction-parameters satisfy the relation

$$\sum X^2 = A^2 U^2 + B^2 V^2, \tag{108}$$

where U and V are functions of u and v alone respectively, and A and B are the functions which appear in the direction-equation of the congruence (26). Guichard[96]) has shown that this condition is also sufficient for space of any order. We adapt his proof to the case of 3-space.

In § 30 we saw that the homogeneous coordinates z^i and y^i, of the foci of a congruence can be chosen so that

$$\frac{\partial z}{\partial u} = m y, \qquad \frac{\partial y}{\partial v} = n z, \tag{109}$$

in which case the direction-parameters

$$X^i = \frac{y^i}{y^4} - \frac{z^i}{z^4} \quad (i = 1, 2, 3)$$

satisfy an equation (26) with

$$A = \frac{1}{y^4}, \qquad B = \frac{1}{z^4}.$$

Since A and B are determined to within respective factors U and V, functions of u and v alone, the condition (108) may be written

$$\sum X^2 = \frac{1}{y^{2}_{4}} + \frac{1}{z^{2}_{4}}. \tag{110}$$

If we define functions ξ and η by the equations

$$\xi^i = y^i, \qquad \eta^i = z^i \; (i = 1, 2, 3),$$
$$-(\xi^5 + i\xi^4) = y^4, \qquad -(\eta^5 + i\eta^4) = z^4,$$
$$\sum_{i=1}^{5} \xi^2 = 1, \qquad \sum_{i=1}^{5} \eta^2 = 1,$$

96) Annales L'École Norm. Sup., ser. 3, vol. 15 (1898), p. 203.

the condition (110) reduces to

$$\sum_{i=1}^{5} \xi\eta = 0.$$

Moreover, from (109) it follows that the functions ξ and η satisfy the equations (100). Hence the ξ's and η's are the elements of the last two rows of a determinant Δ of the fifth order. In consequence of the preceding section, we have that the congruence is harmonic to O nets. Hence:

A necessary and sufficient condition that the direction-parameters of a congruence in 3-space be cyclic, that is harmonic to a net O, is that its parameters satisfy a condition of the form (108).

Exercises.

1. Show that $z_i = \frac{1}{R_i}$ are the pentaspherical coordinates of any point of the plane at infinity not on the circle at infinity; and that a point on the circle of infinity has an infinite set of coordinates of the form $z_i = z_i' + h/R_i$, where h is any constant and $\Sigma z_i'^2 = 0$, $\Sigma z_i'/R_i = 0$.

Darboux, Leçons, 2nd ed., vol. 1, p. 270.

2. When two spheres are orthogonal, the center of either is the pole of their radical plane with respect to the other; consequently any one of the five spheres of § 94 is conjugate with respect to the tetrahedron whose vertices are the centers of the other four spheres. Darboux, Principes de Géom. Anal. p. 384.

3. If a sphere S of center (a, b, c) and radius R is subjected to an inversion with respect to the sphere S_0 of center $(0, 0, 0)$ and radius k, the center (a', b', c') and radius R' of the transform S' are given by

$$\frac{a'}{a} = \frac{b'}{b} = \frac{c'}{c} = \frac{R'}{R} = \frac{k^2}{a^2 + b^2 + c^2 - R^2}.$$

When S is orthogonal to S_0, S' coincides with S. Darboux, l. c., p. 386.

4. When in Ex. 3 we replace S by S_0, we have $R' = -R$. Consequently the pentaspherical coordinates z_k of a point P and its inverse P' with respect to the fundamental sphere S_k differ in sign, but the other four coordinates of P and P' are respectively equal. Hence five successive inversions with respect to the five fundamental spheres transform a point into itself. Darboux, l. c., p. 387.

5. From (19) it follows that the equation in pentaspherical coordinates z of a sphere of radius ρ and center of pentaspherical coordinates z_i' is

$$2\sum_i z_i z_i' + \rho^2 \sum_i \frac{z_i}{R_i} \sum_i \frac{z_i'}{R_i} = 0.$$

Hence the pentaspherical coordinates of the center and the radius of the sphere $\Sigma a_i z_i = 0$ are given by

$$z_i' = a_i - \frac{1}{2R_i}\frac{\Sigma a_i^2}{\sum \frac{a_i}{R_i}}, \qquad \rho = \frac{\sqrt{\Sigma a_i^2}}{\sum \frac{a_i}{R_i}}.$$

Darboux, l. c., p. 390.

6. If in (20) we replace dz_j by $dz_j + k\delta z_j$ and equate the coefficients of k on both sides of the equation, we get

$$ds\,\delta s \cos(ds, \delta s) = \frac{\Sigma dz_j \cdot \delta z_j}{\left(\sum \frac{z_j}{R_j}\right)^2}$$

for the angle between two displacements. Darboux, l. c., p. 389.

7. A homogeneous equation $\varphi(z_1, \ldots. z_5) = 0$ defines a surface. For a displacement on the surface $\sum \frac{\partial \varphi}{\partial z_i} dz_i = 0$. If we put $\delta z_i = \lambda \frac{\partial \varphi}{\partial z_i}$, we have $\Sigma z_i \delta z_i = \lambda \Sigma z_i \frac{\partial \varphi}{\partial z_i} = 0$, since φ is homogeneous. From Ex. 6 it follows that the displacement δz_i is normal to the surface. Darboux, l. c., p. 403.

8. If $\varphi(z_1, \ldots. z_5) = 0$ and $\psi(z_1, \ldots. z_5) = 0$ define two surfaces, the angle θ between their tangent planes at any point is given by (cf. Exs. 6, 7)

$$\cos\theta = \frac{\sum_i \frac{\partial \varphi}{\partial z_i}\frac{\partial \psi}{\partial z_i}}{\sqrt{\sum\left(\frac{\partial \varphi}{\partial z_i}\right)^2 \cdot \sum\left(\frac{\partial \psi}{\partial z_i}\right)^2}}.$$

Darboux, l. c., p. 404.

9. The equation

$$2(u-v)\frac{\partial^2 \theta}{\partial u \partial v} + \frac{\partial \theta}{\partial u} + \frac{\partial \theta}{\partial v} = 0$$

admits the solutions $\theta = A\sqrt{(u-a)(v-a)}$, where A and a are arbitrary constants. If we put $f(w) = \Sigma_i (w - a_i)$ where $a_i (i = 1, \ldots 5)$ are constants, the five functions

$$z_i = \sqrt{\frac{(a_i - u)(a_i - v)(a_i - h)}{f'(a_i)}} \quad (i = 1, \ldots 5)$$

satisfy (24) and for each value of the constant h are the pentaspherical coordinates of a surface referred to its lines of curvature. The equation of this one parameter family of surfaces is

$$\text{(i)} \qquad \sum \frac{z_i^2}{a_i - h} = 0,$$

which, in consequence of (21), is expressible in cartesian coordinates as follows:

$$\text{(ii)} \quad \frac{y_1^2}{a_1 - h} + \frac{y_2^2}{a_2 - h} + \frac{y_3^2}{a_3 - h} - \frac{(y_1^2 + y_2^2 + y_3^2 + 1)^2}{4(a_4 - h)} + \frac{(y_1^2 + y_2^2 + y_3^2 - 1)^2}{4(a_5 - h)} = 0.$$

These surfaces of the fourth degree admitting the circle at infinity as a double line are called *cyclides*. Darboux, Leçons, 2nd ed., vol. 1, p. 258.

10. Show that

$$(h-h')\sum\frac{z_i^2}{(a_i-h)(a_i-h')}=\sum\frac{z_i^2}{a_i-h}-\sum\frac{z_i^2}{a_i-h'},$$

and consequently two cyclides meet orthogonally along their line of intersection. Show that three cyclides of the family (ii) Ex. 9 pass through a point, and that this equation defines a triply orthogonal system of surfaces.

Darboux, Principes de Géom. Anal., p. 478.

11. A cyclide defined by (i) Ex. 9 is transformed into itself by an inversion with respect to any of the five coordinate spheres (Ex. 4). Darboux, l. c., p. 421.

12. Show that transformations R of an O net defined in pentaspherical coordinates is the same problem as finding congruences conjugate to a net in 5-space on the hypercone (24) (cf. VI, Ex. 3).

13. A necessary and sufficient condition that the spheres of a congruence be orthogonal to a fixed sphere or pass through a point is that θ in (38) be a linear function of the x's. Show that in the former case either sheet of the envelope is obtainable from the other by an inversion with respect to the fixed sphere.

14. If the spheres S of a congruence cut a fixed sphere Σ under constant angle, different from 0 and π, by the addition of a constant to the radius of each sphere S the new spheres S_1 are orthogonal to a fixed sphere Σ_1 concentric with Σ. Hence the sheets of the envelope of the spheres S being parallel to the sheets of the envelope of the spheres S_1 are in relation R.

Darboux, Leçons, 2nd ed., vol. 1, p. 310.

15. When the equations (50) of a line in r are written in the form $x=rz+\rho$, $y=sz+\sigma$, the equation of the corresponding sphere in R is

$$\left(X-\frac{\rho+s}{2r}\right)^2+\left(Y-i\frac{s-\rho}{2r}\right)^2+\left(Z-\frac{\eta-1}{2r}\right)^2=\left(\frac{\eta+1}{2r}\right)^2,$$

where $\eta=s\rho-r\sigma$. Lie, l. c.

16. To the points in R correspond in r the lines defined by the Pfaffian equation

$$x\,dy-y\,dx+dz=0.$$

Lie, l. c.

17. The surface elements of a surface σ (§ 103) are defined by x, y, z, p, q. From Ex. 16 it follows that the null-plane of the point (x, y, z) is $yx'-xy'+z-z'=0$, where x', y', z' are current coordinates. Since this is the tangent plane to σ', the corresponding surface element of the latter is defined by

$$x'=-q,\qquad y'=p,\qquad z'=z-xp-yq,\qquad p'=y,\qquad q'=-x.$$

Lie, l. c., p. 467.

18. The lines through $m(x, y, z)$ of σ lying in the tangent plane are defined by

$$(x'-x)=r(z'-z),\qquad y'-y=s(z'-z),$$

where x', y', z' are current coordinates, and r and s are such that $pr+qs=1$. To these lines correspond the spheres

$$r(X^2+Y^2+Z^2)-(s+x-rz)X-i(s-x+rz)Y+(1-sx+ry)Z+y-sz=0. \quad \text{(i)}$$

Lie, l. c.

19. The tangent plane to Σ is defined by (i) Ex. 18 when $r=0$, $qs=1$, that is

$$(xq+1)X-i(xq-1)Y+(x-q)Z+z-qy=0.$$

This plane is tangent to each of the spheres (i) at the point (X, Y, Z), where

$$X+iY=-z+x\frac{px+qy}{q+x}, \qquad X-iY=\frac{y-p}{q+x}, \qquad Z=-\frac{px+qy}{q+x};$$

and the other functions, P, Q, of the surface elements of Σ are

$$P=\frac{xq+1}{q-x}, \qquad Q=-i\frac{xq-1}{q-x}.$$

These five equations determine the surface element of Σ corresponding to a surface element of σ. Lie, l. c.

20. Show that when the equations of Ex. 19 are applied to the surface σ' we get the same result as for σ. Lie, l. c.

21. Let a line d generate a congruence G, its focal points being A and B; and let d_1 and d_{-1} be the corresponding lines of the first and minus first derived congruences of G. When this configuration is subjected to a Lie transformation, spheres S, S_1 and S_{-1} correspond to d, d_1 and d_{-1}; the spheres S and S_1 are tangent at a point M_1 of one sheet Σ_1 of the envelope of the spheres S, and S and S_{-1} at a point M_{-1} of the other sheet Σ_{-1}; moreover, the centers C and C_1 of S and S_1 are harmonic to the centers of principal curvature of Σ_1 at M_1 and the centers C and C_{-1} are harmonic to the centers of principal curvature of Σ_{-1} at M_{-1}. Demoulin, Comptes Rendus, vol. 153 (1911), p. 590.

22. If in the preceding exercise the lines d belong to the linear complex of the transformation, the spheres S are points M, the two surfaces Σ_1 and Σ_{-1} coincide and are the locus Σ of these points; the spheres S_1 and S_{-1} coincide, are tangent to Σ and their centers are harmonic to points of Σ with respect to the centers of principal curvature of Σ; and the lines d_1 and d_{-1} are conjugate with respect to the complex. Demoulin, l. c.

23. To a surface with isothermal spherical representation of its lines of curvature corresponds by a Lie transformation a surface upon which there is an R net for which the tangents to all the curves is one family meet a fixed line (cf. VII, Ex. 25). Demoulin, l. c.

24. To an isothermic surface corresponds by a Lie transformation a surface upon which there is an R net for which the tangents to all the curves in one family are lines of the complex of the transformation. Demoulin, l. c.

25. When a congruence in 5-space is I, the corresponding congruence of spheres in 3-space is formed by point-spheres, whose centers describe a surface upon which the parametric net N consists of its lines of curvature. The orthogonal congruence of circles consists of circle points with centers on N and in the tangent plane of N. Guichard, l. c., p. 199.

26. The spheres of a transformation R in 3-space are represented in 5-space by a congruence 2, I, such that if the parameters of the congruence are given by (2) with $h=1$, the complementary function is R. Conversely any congruence 2, I of spheres gives a transformation of Ribaucour of the sheets of its envelope.

27. A necessary and sufficient condition that on an envelope of spheres the lines of curvature in both systems be spherical is that the six coordinates of the sphere be of the form $a_i = U_i + V_i$, where U_i and V_i are functions of u and v respectively subject to the condition $\Sigma(U_i+V_i)^2 = 0$.

Darboux, Leçons, 2nd ed., vol. 2, p. 357.

28. A necessary and sufficient condition that on an envelope of spheres the lines of curvature in one system be spherical is that the six coordinates a_i of the spheres satisfy an equation of Laplace for which one of the invariants is equal to zero. Darboux, l. c.

29. When the envelope S of the planes of a congruence of circles is referred to a moving trihedral, and the coordinates of the center are (a, b) and the radius is R, the coordinates of the poles of the circles are (a, b, iR) and $(a, b, -iR)$. The radii of the spheres with centers on S orthogonal to the circles are given by $\sqrt{a^2+b^2-R^2}$. In this case equations (40) assume the form [§ 174, (14)].

30. By means of the preceding exercise and [§ 175, 20] show that a necessary and sufficient condition that the circles form a cyclic system is that the focal points of the congruence of lines joining corresponding points on the envelope of spheres are harmonic with respect to the points of contact.

Ribaucour, Journ. de Math., ser. 4, vol. 7 (1891), p. 260.

31. From the preceding exercise and § 82 it follows that a necessary and sufficient condition that the circles orthogonal to the spheres of a transformation R form a cyclic system is that it be a transformation D_m of isothermal O nets.

32. If N and N_1 are two O nets in relation R, the circles orthogonal to N and N_1 form a cyclic system (§ 79); the poles P_0 and P_0' of the circles have coordinates of the form

$$x_0 = x - \theta\,\frac{\xi + i\eta}{q + ir}, \qquad x_0' = x - \theta\,\frac{\xi - i\eta}{q - ir};$$

the points P_0 and P_0' describe the sheets of the envelope of the spheres through P_0 and P_0' with centers on the net $\overline{N}(\overline{x})$ enveloped by the plane of the circles (cf. § 79); the radius of the spheres is given by

$$R^2 = 2j(j\theta' + kp + \theta) + k^2 = 2j\overline{\omega} + k^2;$$

also

$$\Sigma\overline{x}^2 - R^2 = \Sigma x^2 + 2j\omega' + 2Pk,$$

where ω' is given by (VI, 80). Show that the right-hand member of this equation is a solution of the point equation of $\overline{N}$. Show also that P_0 and P_0' are harmonic with respect to the focal points of the congruence of axes of the circles.

33. A necessary and sufficient condition that the poles P_0 and P'_0 of Ex. 32 describe O nets in relation R is that the point equation of $\overline{N}$ admit as solution $R = \sqrt{2j\overline{\omega} + k^2}$. This condition is reducible to

$$\text{(i)} \qquad \theta^2 + p\theta(\rho_1 + \rho_2) + \rho_1\rho_2[\theta(h+l) - q^2 - r^2] = 0.$$

Show that the two sheets of the envelope are conformally represented upon one another and the transformation R is D_m.

34. If S and S_1 are two surfaces of Guichard of the first kind in the relation of a transformation R_m (§ 92), the condition (i) of Ex. 33 is satisfied when $m = \frac{1}{2}$. The same is true for the associate surfaces $\overline{S}$ and $\overline{S}_1$. The points P_0 and $\overline{P}_0$ describe isothermic nets N_0 and $\overline{N}_0$ which are Christoffel transforms of one another; likewise P'_0 and $\overline{P}'_0$; and the product of the segments $P_0 P'_0$ and $\overline{P}_0 \overline{P}'_0$ is equal to 4. The nets N_0 and N'_0 are in relation $D_{\frac{1}{2}}$ and likewise $\overline{N}_0$ and $\overline{N}'_0$. Calapso, Annali, ser. 3, vol. 24 (1915), p. 25.

35. If two applicable nets N and $\overline{N}$ are O, the cyclic congruences determined by the method of § 112 are normal, and parallel to congruences of normals to a spherical surface [cf. § 178].

36. The problem of finding cyclic systems whose planes envelope a sphere is equivalent to the determination of surfaces S applicable to the sphere. If x_1, x_2, x_3 are the coordinates of a surface applicable to a sphere of radius a, the circles in the tangent planes of the sphere determined by $2\varphi = a^2 - \Sigma x_i^2$ form such a cyclic system.

37. Let S be a surface applicable to a sphere S_0, and x_i $(i = 1, 2, 3)$ the coordinates of S; then $x_1, x_2, x_3, \Sigma x_i^2$ are the tangential coordinates of a surface whose lines of curvature correspond to the lines of curvature of S.

Ribaucour, l. c., p. 55.

38. Consider a G_0 net N in 3-space as defined by (VI, Ex. 12), and take the congruence of spheres of radius σ with centers on N. Show that corresponding points of the Laplace transforms of N lie on the corresponding sphere; that the developables of the congruence G of lines joining corresponding points of contact of the sphere with its envelope are parametric and the focal planes of G are tangent to the sphere at corresponding points of the Laplace transforms, N_1 and N_{-1} of N; that the focal point of the first rank of G is the center of the osculating sphere of the curve $v = \text{const.}$ of N_1 and the center of normal curvature of the curve $u = \text{const.}$ of N_{-1}, and similarly for the focal point of second rank; and that the curves $u = \text{const.}$ of N_{-1} and $v = \text{const.}$ of N_1 have common osculating circles at corresponding points.

Stetson, Annals, vol. 19 (1917), p. 123.

39. If the curves of two nets N_1 and N_2 correspond and the osculating planes of the curves $v = \text{const.}$ of N_1 osculate the curves $u = \text{const.}$ of N_2 at corresponding points, then N_1 and N_2 are O nets, and N_1 is the first Laplace transform and N_2 the minus first transform of a net N, which is a net G_0.

Stetson, Annals, vol 19 (1917), p. 123.

Chapter IX.

Rolling surfaces.

117. Congruences harmonic to nets C. Let $N(x)$ be a net C in 3-space and $\overline{N}(\overline{x})$ the applicable net. If θ is a solution of their common point equation, the congruences G and $\overline{G}$ harmonic to these respective nets and determined by θ have direction-parameters of the form

$$X_i = \frac{\partial x_i}{\partial u}\frac{\partial \theta}{\partial v} - \frac{\partial x_i}{\partial v}\frac{\partial \theta}{\partial u}, \qquad \overline{X}_i = \frac{\partial \overline{x}_i}{\partial u}\frac{\partial \theta}{\partial v} - \frac{\partial \overline{x}_i}{\partial v}\frac{\partial \theta}{\partial u}.$$

These functions satisfy the same direction-equation and are in the relation

$$\sum X_i^2 = \sum \overline{X}_i^2,$$

since N and $\overline{N}$ are applicable.

If $\theta = \overline{x}_3$, then $\overline{X}_3 = 0$; if $\theta = \overline{x}_1 + i\overline{x}_2$, then $\overline{X}_1^2 + \overline{X}_2^2 = 0$. In the latter case G is 2, I, that is a normal congruence. The intersections of corresponding lines of G and of the harmonic congruence G' determined by $\theta = \overline{x}_3$ generate a net N_d conjugate to G and G', being a derived net of N (§ 11). From (I, Ex. 15) it follows that N_d is parallel to the net of coordinates

$$\frac{X_i}{\dfrac{\partial \overline{x}_3}{\partial u}\dfrac{\partial \theta}{\partial v} - \dfrac{\partial \overline{x}_3}{\partial v}\dfrac{\partial \theta}{\partial u}} = \frac{X_i}{\overline{X}_3}$$

and the complementary function y', defined by (VI, 17) is equal to 1. Hence this net and consequently N_d, is an O net. Therefore the ∞^1 O nets normal to G are determined by the congruences harmonic to N for which $\theta = \overline{x}_3 + \text{const}$. Then by applying an orthogonal substitution to the $\overline{x}$'s, or what is the same thing displacing $\overline{N}$ in space, we have:

If $N(x)$ *is a net C and* $\overline{N}(\overline{x})$ *the applicable net, of the congruences harmonic to N:*

∞^1 *families of parallel congruences are* 2, I;
∞^2 *families are* 3, I *and the others are* 4, I;

in the first and second cases $\theta = \sum a\overline{x} + d$ *with* $\sum a^2 = 0$ *and* $\sum a^2 \neq 0$ *respectively. The O nets normal to a congruence* 2, I *are generated by its points of intersection with the parallel harmonic congruences determined by* $\theta = \sum b\overline{x} + e$, *where* $\sum ab = 0$, $\sum a_0 b = 0$, a_0 *being the conjugate imaginary of* a.

If now we consider the congruence $\overline{G}$ harmonic to $\overline{N}$ determined by $\theta = \overline{x}_1 + i\overline{x}_2$, we find that the lines of this congruence lie in the plane $x_1 + ix_2 = 0$. Moreover the points of these lines corresponding to the points on the congruence G' which generate the O nets normal to G are the intersections of these lines in the plane $x_1 + ix_2 = 0$ and the planes $x_3 =$ const. In the general case when $\theta = \sum a\overline{x} + d$, with $\sum a^2 = 0$, the lines of the congruence $\overline{G}$ lie in the isotropic plane $\sum ax + d = 0$, and the points corresponding to the points on G describing the O nets are the intersections of these lines and the ∞^1 isotropic lines lying in this plane.

118. Rolling surfaces. Let S and $\overline{S}$ be two applicable surfaces, and M and $\overline{M}$ corresponding points. Imagine S held fixed and $\overline{S}$ moved in space so that $\overline{M}$ comes into coincidence with M, and the tangent planes at $\overline{M}$ and M come into coincidence, and likewise corresponding linear elements arising from $\overline{M}$ and M. For each pair of points M and $\overline{M}$ we have a different position of $\overline{S}$. Consequently $\overline{S}$ assumes ∞^2 different positions, unless S and $\overline{S}$ are ruled surfaces with generators in correspondence [cf. 142], in which case there are ∞^1 different positions. In this particular case the two surfaces do not have a net in common; it will be assumed that this case is excluded in what follows, unless mention is made of it. As $\overline{S}$ undergoes this rigid motion of two parameters it is said to *roll* on S. The common tangent plane at the point of coincidence of S and $\overline{S}$ is called the *plane of contact*.

The results of the last paragraph of the preceding section may be stated as follows[97]:

---

[97]) Darboux, Annales L'École Norm. Sup., ser. 3, vol. 16 (1899), p. 467.

When a surface $\bar{S}$ *rolls over an applicable surface* S, *a plane* π *invariably fixed to* $\bar{S}$, *cuts the plane of contact of* S *and* $\bar{S}$ *in a line* d *which generates a congruence, which is harmonic to the net common to* S *and* $\bar{S}$. *When* π *is isotropic, the congruence of lines* d *is normal to a family of surfaces whose lines of curvature correspond to the net common to* S *and* $\bar{S}$; *moreover, every isotropic line in* π *meets* d *in the point which describes one of these normal surfaces.*

Any line fixed to $\bar{S}$ may be looked upon as the intersection of two planes fixed to $\bar{S}$. Since furthermore, there is a unique isotropic plane through an isotropic line, we have:

When a surface $\bar{S}$ *rolls over an applicable surface* S, *a line* l *invariably fixed to* $\bar{S}$ *meets the plane of contact in a point which generates a derived net of the net common to* S *and* $\bar{S}$; *if* l *is an isotropic line this derived net is an* O *net, the normals to which are the positions of the intersections of the tangent planes to* $\bar{S}$ *and the unique isotropic plane through* l; *all derived* O *nets are so determined.*

As a corollary we have:

If two parallel isotropic lines are invariably bound to a surface $\bar{S}$ *as it rolls over* S, *the two* O *nets generated by the points of meeting of these lines and the plane of contact have the same spherical representation.*

We may now restate the first theorem of § 113 as follows:

If a surface $\bar{S}$ *rolls over an applicable surface* S *and* Q *is a point invariably fixed to* $\bar{S}$, *the isotropic lines through* Q *(null sphere) meet the plane of contact in points* P, *on a circle* C, *which generate the* O *nets orthogonal to the cyclic system of the circles* C.

Also:

If S *and* $\bar{S}$ *are applicable surfaces and lines* l *are drawn through a fixed point normal to the tangent planes to* $\bar{S}$, *as* $\bar{S}$ *rolls over* S *the lines* l *generate a cyclic congruence whose developables correspond to the net common to* S *and* $\bar{S}$.

If $N(x)$ and $N_1(x_1)$ are nets in relation F by means of a net $N'(x')$ and corresponding solutions θ and θ' of the point equations of N and N' respectively, and $\varphi, \varphi', \varphi_1$ and ψ, ψ', ψ_1 are sets of corresponding solutions of the point equations of N, N' and N_1 so that

$$x_1 = x - \frac{\theta}{\theta'} x', \qquad \varphi_1 = \varphi - \frac{\theta}{\theta'} \varphi', \qquad \psi_1 = \psi - \frac{\theta}{\theta'} \psi',$$

the derived nets of N and N_1 by means of the respective pairs of functions φ, ψ and φ_1, ψ_1 are in relation F (II, Ex. 6). Suppose now that N, N' and N_1 are nets C, and that the applicable nets are $\overline{N}$, $\overline{N}'$ and $\overline{N}_1$ so that

$$\overline{x}_1 = \overline{x} - \frac{\theta}{\theta'}\overline{x}',$$

the functions θ and θ' being chosen in accordance with § 27. If we take

$$\varphi = a_1\overline{x} + b_1\overline{y} + c_1\overline{z} + d_1, \qquad \varphi' = a_1\overline{x}' + b_1\overline{y}' + c_1\overline{z}',$$
$$\psi = a_2\overline{x} + b_2\overline{y} + c_2\overline{z} + d_2, \qquad \psi' = a_2\overline{x}' + b_2\overline{y}' + c_2\overline{z}',$$

where $a_1\ b_1, \ldots . d_2$ are arbitrary constants, then

$$\varphi_1 = a_1\overline{x}_1 + b_1\overline{y}_1 + c_1\overline{z}_1 + d_1, \qquad \psi_1 = a_2\overline{x}_1 + b_2\overline{y}_1 + c_2\overline{z}_1 + d_2.$$

In this case the derived nets of N and N_1 are the loci of the points of meeting of the line

$$a_1x + b_1y + c_1z + d_1 = 0, \qquad a_2x + b_2y + c_2z + d_2 = 0$$

with the respective planes of contact as $\overline{N}$ rolls over N and $\overline{N}_1$ over N_1. Hence:

If N and $\overline{N}$ are applicable nets, and N_1 and $\overline{N}_1$ are F transforms of N and $\overline{N}$ respectively, by means of $\theta' = \sum x'^2 - \sum \overline{x}'^2$, such that they are applicable, and l is a line invariably bound to $\overline{N}$ and $\overline{N}_1$, as $\overline{N}_1$ rolls on N_1 the point where l meets the plane of contact of N_1 and $\overline{N}_1$ generates a net which is an F transform of the net generated by the point where l meets the plane of contact when $\overline{N}$ rolls on N.

If the line l is isotropic, the two nets thus found are O nets in the relation R. Hence:

If N and $\overline{N}$ are applicable nets and N_1 and $\overline{N}_1$ are F transforms by means of $\theta' = \sum x'^2 - \sum \overline{x}'^2$, the cyclic systems in which a point sphere invariably bound to $\overline{N}$ and $\overline{N}_1$ meets the common tangent planes as $\overline{N}$ rolls on N and as $\overline{N}_1$ rolls on N_1 are in relation F; moreover, the two surfaces orthogonal to these cyclic systems determined by each generator of the null sphere are in relation R.

119. Special isothermic surfaces. We apply these results to the case where $\bar{S}$ is a quadric Q which meets the circle at infinity in four distinct points P_i. Through each of these points pass two isotropic generators, d_i, d_i'. The twelve points of intersection of lines d_i and d_k', where $i \neq k$, are the umbilical points of Q. If m_i and m_i' are the points where d_i and d_i' meet the plane of contact of Q and S, and Σ_i and Σ_i' denote the loci of m_i and m_i' as Q rolls over S, on the eight surfaces Σ_i and Σ_i' the lines of curvature correspond to the nets $\bar{N}$ and N common to Q and S. Two surfaces Σ_i and Σ_k $(k \neq i)$ are normal to the circles of intersection of the planes of contact with the point sphere having its center at the umbilical point of intersection P_{ik} of d_i and d_k'. Two surfaces Σ_i and Σ_i' have the same spherical representation of their lines of curvature, by the third theorem of § 118. The O nets on Σ_i and Σ_i' are conjugate to the congruence of the lines of intersection of the plane of contact and the plane of the lines d_i and d_i'. Likewise, the O nets on Σ_i and Σ_k' are conjugate to the congruence of lines of intersection of the plane of contact and the plane of the lines d_i and d_k', that is the tangent plane to Q at P_{ik}. The congruence of lines $m_i m_i'$ is harmonic to the net N on S, and its focal points divide harmonically the segment $m_i m_i'$, since the points m_i and m_i lie on the generators of Q. Similar results hold for the congruence of lines $m_i m_k'$. Hence Σ_i and Σ_i' are isothermic surfaces in the relation of a Christoffel transformation [§ 159]. Moreover Σ_i and Σ_k' are in the relation of a transformation K (§ 25) which is a transformation D_m since the nets are O nets. Hence we have the theorem of Darboux[98]):

When a quadric Q which meets the circle at infinity in four distinct points rolls on an applicable surface S, the eight surfaces generated by the points of intersection of the isotropic generators and the plane of contact are isothermic, their lines of curvature corresponding to the net common to Q and S; two of these surfaces determined by generators through a point at infinity are Christoffel transforms of one another; two determined by generators through an umbilical point are in the relation of a transformation D_m.

In § 84 we considered these isothermic surfaces from another

[98]) L. c., p. 492.

point of view and found that they are the type called *special* by Bianchi.

120. Rolling of a surface applicable to a surface of revolution. Let $\overline{S}$ be a surface of revolution defined by

$$\overline{x} = r\cos v, \qquad \overline{y} = r\sin v, \qquad \overline{z} = \varphi(r).$$

Its linear element is

$$ds^2 = (1+\varphi'^2)\,dr^2 + r^2\,dv^2. \tag{1}$$

Let S be a surface applicable to $\overline{S}$. If we put

$$du = \sqrt{1+\varphi'^2}\,dr, \qquad U = r, \tag{2}$$

the linear element assumes the form

$$ds^2 = du^2 + U^2\,dv^2.$$

The tangents to the deforms of the meridians of $\overline{S}$, that is the curves $v =$ const. form a normal congruence G for which the other focal surface, S_1, called the *complementary surface* to S, is given by equations of the form [cf. § 76]

$$x_1 = x - \frac{U}{U'}\frac{\partial x}{\partial u}. \tag{3}$$

We recall from [§ 124] that this surface S_1 is applicable to a surface of revolution, whose linear element is

$$ds_1^2 = U^2\left(\frac{1}{U'}\right)'^2 du^2 + \frac{1}{U'^2}\,dw^2, \tag{4}$$

that the normal congruence G is a W congruence and that any normal W congruence may be obtained in this manner.

When we apply equations (3) to $\overline{S}$, we obtain

$$\overline{x}_1 = \overline{y}_1 = 0, \qquad \overline{z}_1 = \varphi - r\varphi',$$

which is the point of intersection of the tangent to the meridian at a given point and the axis of revolution of $\overline{S}$. Hence:

When a surface of revolution $\bar{S}$ rolls on an applicable surface S, the point in which the axis of $\bar{S}$ meets the plane of contact generates the complementary surface S_1 of S, and the line joining this point to the corresponding point of S generates a normal W congruence of which S and S_1 are the focal surfaces; moreover, any normal W congruence may be generated in this manner.

If we put

$$r_1 = k\sqrt{1+\varphi'^2}, \qquad w = kv_1, \tag{5}$$

where k is any constant, by means of (2) equation (4) is reducible to

$$ds_1^2 = \frac{r^2}{k^2}\,dr_1^2 + r_1^2\,dv_1^2. \tag{6}$$

If $\bar{S}$ is the quadric of revolution

$$\frac{z^2}{a} + \frac{r^2}{b} = 1, \tag{7}$$

we have

$$1+\varphi'^2 = \frac{(a-b)\,r^2 + b^2}{b\,(b-r^2)}. \tag{8}$$

Substituting this expression in the first of (5), solving for r^2 and putting $k^2 = b^2/(b-a)$, we have

$$\frac{r^2}{k^2} = \frac{(a-b)\,r_1^2 + b^2}{b\,(b-r_1^2)}.$$

Hence (6) assumes the same form as (1) for the expression (8), that is S_1 is applicable to $\bar{S}$.

Similarly, if $\bar{S}$ is the paraboloid of revolution

$$2z = mr^2, \tag{9}$$

we have $1+\varphi'^2 = 1 + m^2 r^2$ and by taking $k^2 = -1/m^2$, we find that S_1 is applicable to $\bar{S}$. Hence:

When a non-developable quadric of revolution $\bar{S}$ rolls on an applicable surface S, the point in which the axis of $\bar{S}$ meets the *common tangent plane generates the complementary surface* S_1 *of* S, *and* S_1 *is applicable to* $\bar{S}$.

As a consequence of the results of § 100 we have the theorem:

When a non-developable quadric of revolution $\bar{S}$ *rolls on an applicable surface* S, *the spheres with centers on* $\bar{S}$ *passing through either focus are tangent to two surfaces in relation* R.

121. The fundamental theorems of Guichard. Let S be a surface applicable to the quadric of revolution $\bar{S}$ which is defined by (7). Denote by A and A' the extremities of the axis of revolution of $\bar{S}$, and let S be in contact with $\bar{S}$ at a point M. Denote by d, d_1 and d', d_1' the isotropic generators of $\bar{S}$ through A and A' respectively. These lines meet the common tangent plane π in the respective points a, a_1, a', a_1'. The lines $a a_1'$ and $a' a_1$ are the generators of $\bar{S}$ through M. The lines $a a'$ and $a_1 a_1'$ are the intersections with the plane π of the isotropic planes through AA' and the pairs of parallel generators d, d' and d_1, d_1'.

From the theorems of § 118 it follows that as $\bar{S}$ rolls on S, the lines $a a'$ and $a_1 a_1'$ generate normal congruences, and the points a, a' and a_1, a_1' generate O nets normal to these congruences. Moreover, these congruences are harmonic to the net N common to S and $\bar{S}$. Since the lines $a a_1'$ and $a' a_1$ are the generators of $\bar{S}$ and therefore form a harmonic pencil with the tangents to any net at M it follows that the focal points of the lines $a a'$ and $a_1 a_1'$ divide harmonically the segments $a a'$ and $a_1 a_1'$ both of which are of the constant length AA'. It can be shown by the methods of [§ 73], that the surfaces generated by a, a', a_1, a_1', have constant mean curvature $\pm \frac{2}{AA'}$.

The lines $a a'$ and $a_1 a_1'$ meet in the point M' in which the axis of $\bar{S}$ meets the common tangent plane. Hence M' describes a derived net N' of N, and as shown in the preceding section N' lies on a surface applicable to $\bar{S}$.

From the fourth theorem of § 118 it follows that a and a_1 describe two of the O nets orthogonal to the cyclic system of circles in which the null sphere at A meets the common tangent plane. Hence these O nets are in relation R, and the net N' is the central net. Similarly a' and a_1' describe O nets in relation R with the same central net.

Hence we have the theorem[99]):

When a central quadric of revolution $\bar{S}$ rolls on an applicable surface S, the points a, a_1 and a', a_1' in which the isotropic generators through the extremities, A, A', of the axis of $\bar{S}$ meet the common tangent plane, generate surfaces of constant mean curvature, such that (a) and (a_1), and (a') and (a_1'), are pairs in relation R; and (a) and (a'), and (a_1) and (a_1'), are pairs of parallel surfaces.

From the theorem of Bonnet [§ 73] it follows that the mean points of the segments $a\,a'$ and $a_1\,a_1'$ generate surfaces of constant total curvature in relation R.

Since the tangent planes to S and its complementary surface S_1 are normal to one another, when $\bar{S}$ rolls on S, the tangent planes π_1 to S_1 pass through the axis of $\bar{S}$, an infinity of them corresponding to one plane. When S_1 is applied to $\bar{S}$ the planes π_1 become tangent to $\bar{S}$ and the lines which coincided with the axis of $\bar{S}$ when S was applied to $\bar{S}$ become a family of generators of $\bar{S}$, since an infinity of the planes π_1 pass through each line. The isotropic planes through the axis become the isotropic tangent planes to $\bar{S}$ which have the property of passing through the foci of $\bar{S}$. Consequently when S_1 is applied to $\bar{S}$ either the lines $a\,a_1'$ (or $a'\,a_1$) coincide with the axis of $\bar{S}$ and a and a_1' (or a' and a_1) become the foci of $\bar{S}$. Accordingly as $\bar{S}$ rolls on S_1 the surfaces generated by a, a_1 and by $a'\,a_1'$ are the sheets of the envelope of spheres with centers on $\bar{S}$ and passing through one and the other focus of $\bar{S}$ respectively. Since a and a_1 are symmetric with respect to the common tangent plane, we have the above results in the following form as given by Guichard[100]):

If $\bar{S}$ is a central quadric of revolution whose axis is of length $2a$, F_1 and F_2 its foci, and φ_1 and φ_2 the symmetric points of F_1 and F_2 with respect to the tangent planes of $\bar{S}$, then as $\bar{S}$ rolls over an applicable surface the points F_1, F_2, φ_1, φ_2 describe surfaces of constant mean curvature $\pm 1/a$.

When $\bar{S}$ is the paraboloid (9), two of the points a' and a_1' are at infinity, and consequently the points a and a_1 bisect the focal segments of the normal congruences generated by the lines in which

---

99) Darboux, l. c., p. 477.

100) Comptes Rendus, vol. 128 (1899), p. 232; cf. also Darboux, l. c., p. 477.

the isotropic planes through the axis of $\bar{S}$ and the isotropic generators through the vertex of $\bar{S}$ meet the common tangent planes of S and $\bar{S}$. Hence:

When a paraboloid of revolution $\bar{S}$ rolls on an applicable surface S, the points in which the two isotropic generators through the vertex meet the common tangent plane generate two minimal surfaces in relation R, and the central net of the transformation R is described by the point in which the axis of $\bar{S}$ meets the common tangent planes.

In § 120 we showed that this central net lies on a surface also applicable to $\bar{S}$. By reasoning similar to that for a central quadric of revolution, we obtain the theorem of Guichard[101]):

When a paraboloid of revolution rolls on a surface applicable to the paraboloid, the focus and the point symmetric to it with respect to the common tangent plane generate minimal surfaces.

In § 127 we give analytical proofs of these theorems of Guichard.

122. Deformable transformations R of the first type. Let S_0 be the surface of centers of a congruence of spheres of radius $\underline{R}$. Corresponding points on the sheets, S and S_1, of the envelope are symmetric with respect to the tangent plane to S_0 at the corresponding point M. Let S_0 be referred to a moving trihedral whose plane $y=0$ is the plane $M M_0 M_1$, and let the parametric lines on S_0 be chosen so that the x and y axes are tangent to the curves $v=$ const. and $u=$ const. respectively. If σ denotes the angle which the line $M M_0$ makes with the plane $z=0$, the coordinates of M are $R\cos\sigma$, 0, $R\sin\sigma$.

The displacements of a point P of coordinates $t\cos\sigma$, 0, $t\sin\sigma$ are given by [§ 69]

$$(10)\quad \left\{\begin{aligned} \delta x &= d(t\cos\sigma)+\xi\,du+(q\,du+q_1\,dv)\,t\sin\sigma,\\ \delta y &= \eta_1\,dv+(r\,du+r_1\,dv)\,t\cos\sigma-(p\,du+p_1\,dv)\,t\sin\sigma,\\ \delta z &= d(t\sin\sigma)-(q\,du+q_1\,dv)\,t\cos\sigma. \end{aligned}\right.$$

When we replace t by R and require that

$$\cos\sigma\,\delta x+\sin\sigma\,\delta z=0$$

---

101) L. c.

for all displacements of M_0, we find

$$(11)\qquad \frac{\partial R}{\partial u}+\xi\cos\sigma=0, \qquad \frac{\partial R}{\partial v}=0.$$

In order that M describe a line of curvature on S, it is necessary that there be a point P such that

$$\frac{\delta x}{\cos\sigma}=\frac{\delta y}{0}=\frac{\delta z}{\sin\sigma}.$$

These conditions are equivalent to

$$(12)\quad \begin{cases} \eta_1\,dv+[(r\,du+r_1\,dv)\cos\sigma-(p\,du+p_1\,dv)\sin\sigma]\,t=0, \\ \xi\sin\sigma\,du+[q\,du+q_1\,dv-d\sigma]\,t=0. \end{cases}$$

Eliminating t from these equations, we obtain as the equation of the lines of curvature on S

$$(13)\quad \begin{cases} \xi\sin\sigma\,(p\sin\sigma-r\cos\sigma)\,du^2+\eta_1\left(q_1-\dfrac{\partial\sigma}{\partial v}\right)dv^2 \\ \qquad +\left[\eta_1\left(q-\dfrac{\partial\sigma}{\partial u}\right)+\xi\sin\sigma\,(p_1\sin\sigma-r_1\cos\sigma)\right]du\,dv=0. \end{cases}$$

The equation of the lines of curvature on S_1 is obtained from (13) by replacing σ by $-\sigma$. In order that the lines of curvature on S and S_1 correspond, that is that the congruence of spheres be of radius R, it is necessary and sufficient that

$$(14)\qquad \frac{r\cos\sigma}{p\sin\sigma}=\frac{\dfrac{\partial\sigma}{\partial v}}{q_1}=\frac{\eta_1\dfrac{\partial\sigma}{\partial u}+\xi\sin\sigma\cos\sigma\,r_1}{\eta_1\,q+\xi p_1\sin^2\sigma}.$$

We recall that, in accordance with the theorem of Beltrami (§ 112), if S_0 is deformed, the spheres touch their envelope at the same points of the spheres as for S_0. We investigate under what conditions a congruence R of spheres remains a congruence R in all deformations of the central surface S_0. Evidently σ remains unaltered, as do also the functions ξ, η_1, r, r_1, since they depend only on the linear element of S_0 [§ 72]. However, the functions p, q, p_1, q_1 vary in the deformation. Consequently if equations (14) are to hold for all deformations, we must have [cf. § 72, (75)]

$$(15)\quad r = -\frac{1}{\eta_1}\frac{\partial \xi}{\partial v} = 0, \quad \frac{\partial \sigma}{\partial v} = 0, \quad \eta_1 \frac{\partial \sigma}{\partial u} + \sin\sigma\cos\sigma \frac{\partial \eta_1}{\partial u} = 0.$$

Hence σ must be a function of u alone. Then from the last of (15) it follows that the parameter v can be chosen so that η_1 is a function of u alone. Moreover, from the first of (15) we find that ξ is a function of u alone. Hence S_0 is applicable to a surface of revolution. If we take the linear element of S_0 in the form

$$(16)\qquad ds_0^2 = U^2\,du^2 + u^2\,dv^2,$$

from the last of (15) we obtain

$$(17)\qquad \tan\sigma = \frac{c}{u},$$

where c is a constant. Then from (11) we have

$$(18)\qquad R = -\int \frac{U u\,du}{\sqrt{u^2+c^2}} + \text{const.}$$

Hence we have the theorem of Bianchi[102]):

In order that a congruence R of spheres remain a congruence R in all deformations of the central surface S_0, it is necessary and sufficient that S_0 be applicable to a surface of revolution and that the radius of the spheres be given by (18).

123. Deformable transformations R of the second type. In this section we determine every congruence R of spheres whose central net N_0 admits an applicable net $\overline{N}_0$ which is 2, O and consequently is the central net of another congruence R of spheres[103]). To this end we make use of the equations of a transformation R as given in § 78.

[102]) Lezioni, vol. 2, p. 117.

[103]) Cf. Trans. Amer. Math. Soc. vol. 17 (1916), pp. 437—458; also, Calapso, Annali, vol. 26 (1917), pp. 151—190.

From (VII, 7) we have

$$(19)\qquad \frac{\partial}{\partial u}\left(\frac{\theta}{p}\right)=\frac{q}{p}L_1,\qquad \frac{\partial}{\partial v}\left(\frac{\theta}{p}\right)=\frac{r}{p}L_2,$$

where

$$(20)\qquad L_1=\sqrt{E}\left(1+\frac{1}{\varrho_1}\frac{\theta}{p}\right),\qquad L_2=\sqrt{G}\left(1+\frac{1}{\varrho_2}\frac{\theta}{p}\right).$$

Since the radius of the spheres of the transformation is θ/p, and this radius must be the same for the spheres of centers on $\overline{N}_0$ applicable to N_0, by the theorem of Beltrami (§ 112), we must have for the functions $\overline{\theta}$ and $\overline{p}$ of the corresponding transformation

$$(21)\qquad \overline{\theta}=\varrho\,\theta,\qquad \overline{p}=\varrho p,$$

where ϱ is a factor of proportionality to be determined.

From (VII, 10) we find that the first fundamental coefficients E_0, F_0, G_0 of N_0 are

$$(22)\qquad E_0=L_1^2\left[1+\left(\frac{q}{p}\right)^2\right],\qquad F_0=L_1L_2\frac{qr}{p^2},\qquad G_0=L_2^2\left[1+\left(\frac{r}{p}\right)^2\right].$$

If we denote by $\overline{S}$ and $\overline{S}_1$ the sheets of the envelope of spheres of radius $\overline{\theta}/\overline{p}$ with centers on $\overline{N}_0$ and by $\overline{q}$, $\overline{r}$, $\overline{w}$ the functions of the R transformation from $\overline{S}$ into $\overline{S}_1$, the latter functions must satisfy equations of the form (VII, 7). From (19), (20) and the analogous equations for the transformation of $\overline{S}$, we get

$$(23)\qquad \begin{cases} \sqrt{E}\,q\varrho\left(1+\dfrac{1}{\varrho_1}\dfrac{\theta}{p}\right)=\sqrt{\overline{E}}\,\overline{q}\left(1+\dfrac{1}{\overline{\varrho}_1}\dfrac{\theta}{p}\right),\\[2ex] \sqrt{G}\,r\varrho\left(1+\dfrac{1}{\varrho_2}\dfrac{\theta}{p}\right)=\sqrt{\overline{G}}\,\overline{r}\left(1+\dfrac{1}{\overline{\varrho}_2}\dfrac{\theta}{p}\right). \end{cases}$$

From these equations and the ones obtained by expressing the equality of the first fundamental coefficients of S_0 and $\overline{S}_0$ as given by equations of the form (22), we have

$$(24)\qquad \overline{q}=\varrho q,\qquad \overline{r}=\varrho\,r,\qquad \overline{w}=\varrho w,$$

by making a suitable choice of signs of $\sqrt{\bar{E}}$ and $\sqrt{\bar{G}}$, and requiring that the quadratic relation (VII, 8) be satisfied also by the functions $\bar{p}$, $\bar{q}$, $\bar{r}$ and $\bar{w}$.

When the above expressions for $\bar{q}$ and $\bar{r}$ are substituted in the equations analogous to (VII, 7), we obtain

$$(25)\quad \frac{\partial \log \varrho}{\partial u} = \frac{q}{\theta}(\sqrt{\bar{E}}-\sqrt{E}), \qquad \frac{\partial \log \varrho}{\partial v} = \frac{r}{\theta}(\sqrt{\bar{G}}-\sqrt{G}),$$

$$(26)\quad \begin{cases} \dfrac{1}{\sqrt{\bar{G}}}\dfrac{\partial \sqrt{\bar{E}}}{\partial v} - \dfrac{1}{\sqrt{G}}\dfrac{\partial \sqrt{E}}{\partial v} = \dfrac{r}{\theta}(\sqrt{\bar{E}}-\sqrt{E}), \\[2ex] \dfrac{1}{\sqrt{\bar{E}}}\dfrac{\partial \sqrt{\bar{G}}}{\partial u} - \dfrac{1}{\sqrt{E}}\dfrac{\partial \sqrt{G}}{\partial u} = \dfrac{q}{\theta}(\sqrt{\bar{G}}-\sqrt{G}), \end{cases}$$

$$(27)\quad \sqrt{\bar{E}_1}-\sqrt{E_1} = \sqrt{\bar{E}}-\sqrt{E}, \quad \sqrt{\bar{G}_1}-\sqrt{G_1} = \sqrt{\bar{G}}-\sqrt{G},$$

$$(28)\quad \begin{cases} 2\sqrt{\bar{E}\bar{G}} + \sqrt{\bar{E}}(\sqrt{G_1}-\sqrt{G}) + \sqrt{\bar{G}}(\sqrt{E_1}-\sqrt{E}) \\ \qquad -\sqrt{E_1}\sqrt{G}-\sqrt{G_1}\sqrt{E} = 0. \end{cases}$$

The Gauss and Codazzi equations for S are [§ 65]

$$(29)\quad \begin{cases} \dfrac{\partial}{\partial v}\left(\dfrac{1}{\sqrt{G}}\dfrac{\partial \sqrt{E}}{\partial v}\right) + \dfrac{\partial}{\partial u}\left(\dfrac{1}{\sqrt{E}}\dfrac{\partial \sqrt{G}}{\partial u}\right) + \dfrac{\sqrt{EG}}{\varrho_1 \varrho_2} = 0, \\[2ex] \dfrac{\partial}{\partial v}\left(\dfrac{\sqrt{E}}{\varrho_1}\right) = \dfrac{1}{\varrho_2}\dfrac{\partial \sqrt{E}}{\partial v}, \qquad \dfrac{\partial}{\partial u}\left(\dfrac{\sqrt{G}}{\varrho_2}\right) = \dfrac{1}{\varrho_1}\dfrac{\partial \sqrt{G}}{\partial u}. \end{cases}$$

Similar equations for $\bar{S}$ are satisfied by the functions $\bar{E}$, $\bar{G}$, $\bar{\varrho}_1$ and and $\bar{\varrho}_2$ given by (23) and (26), provided (28) is satisfied. Hence if (23), (26) and (28) hold, the conditions of the problem are satisfied.

The central nets N_0 and $\bar{N}_0$ of the two transformations R are 2, O, the complementary function being the radius R of the spheres for each net. In § 27 it was shown that any net $\bar{N}_0'$ parallel to $\bar{N}_0$ is applicable to a net N_0' determined by a quadrature, which is parallel to N_0. From (VI, Ex. 1) it follows that N_0' and $\bar{N}_0'$ are nets 2, O, and that they have the same complementary function R' which is obtained by a quadrature. Moreover, from § 76 it follows that two of the nets $\overline{N}_0'$ parallel to $\overline{N}_0$ are special, that is $\sum \overline{x}_0'^2 = R'^2$. Hence if the central nets N_0 and $\overline{N}_0$ of two transformations R are applicable, there exist two transformations R whose central nets N_0' and $\overline{N}_0'$ are parallel to N_0 and $\overline{N}_0$, such that the spheres of the transformation with centers on $\overline{N}_0'$ pass through the origin. We apply the preceding formulas to this case.

If in (27) we put $\sqrt{\overline{E}_1'} = \sqrt{\overline{G}_1'} = 0$, we get

$$\sqrt{\overline{E}'} = \sqrt{E'} - \sqrt{E_1'}, \qquad \sqrt{\overline{G}'} = \sqrt{G'} - \sqrt{G_1'}. \tag{30}$$

Now equation (28) reduces to

$$\sqrt{E_1'}\sqrt{G'} + \sqrt{G_1'}\sqrt{E'} = 0,$$

that is N' and N_1' are conformal. But as shown in § 82 this is possible only in case N' and N_1' are isothermic nets in the relation of a transformation D_m. If we make use of the results of § 82 and put

$$\sqrt{E'} = \sqrt{G'} = e^{\psi}, \qquad \sqrt{E_1'} = -\sqrt{G_1'} = \frac{\theta'}{\nu'} e^{-\psi}, \tag{31}$$

in (30) we find that (26) is satisfied. Hence we have the theorem of Bianchi[104]):

The central net N_0' of a transformation D_m of an isothermic net N' into an isothermic net N_1' admits an applicable net $\overline{N}_0'$ such that as N_0' rolls on $\overline{N}_0'$ the spheres of the transformation pass through a fixed point O.

This result may be looked on as follows: When $\overline{N}_0'$ rolls on N_0', the point O invariably fixed to $\overline{N}_0'$ generates the surface S_1'. In the terminology of Bianchi[105]) S_1' is a *surface of rolling,* being generated by a point fixed to one surface as the latter rolls over an applicable surface. From the foregoing results we have also the converse theorem[106]):

---

104) Rendiconti dei Lincei, ser. 5, vol. 24 (1915), p. 303.

105) Rendiconti dei Lincei, ser. 5, vol. 23¹ (1914), p. 4.

106) Rendiconti dei Lincei, ser. 5, vol. 24 (1915), p. 349.

Transformations D_m are the only transformations R for which one of the two sheets of the envelope of the spheres is a surface of rolling as the central net rolls on its applicable net.

In § 78 we saw if N_0 is any net parallel to N_0' and R is the complementary function, the sheets of the envelope of the spheres of centers on N_0 and radius R are parallel to the isothermic nets N' and N_1'. Hence we have the theorem:

A necessary and sufficient condition that an O net N admits an R transform N_1 such that the central net of the transformation is applicable to a net is that N have the same spherical representation as an isothermic net.

From (VII, 3) it follows that the functions $\frac{1}{\sqrt{G}}\frac{\partial\sqrt{E}}{\partial v}$ and $\frac{1}{\sqrt{E}}\frac{\partial\sqrt{G}}{\partial u}$ have the same values for all parallel O nets. Consequently we must have

$$\frac{1}{\sqrt{G}}\frac{\partial\sqrt{E}}{\partial v}=\frac{\partial\psi}{\partial v}, \qquad \frac{1}{\sqrt{E}}\frac{\partial\sqrt{G}}{\partial u}=\frac{\partial\psi}{\partial u}. \tag{32}$$

From (31) it follows that

$$\begin{cases} \dfrac{1}{\sqrt{G_1}}\dfrac{\partial\sqrt{E_1}}{\partial v}=-\dfrac{\partial}{\partial v}\log\left(\dfrac{\theta'}{\nu'}e^{-\psi}\right), \\ \dfrac{1}{\sqrt{E_1}}\dfrac{\partial\sqrt{G_1}}{\partial u}=-\dfrac{\partial}{\partial u}\log\left(\dfrac{\theta'}{\nu'}e^{-\psi}\right). \end{cases} \tag{33}$$

We remark that p, q, r of the R transformation of N into N_1 and N' into N_1' are the same (§ 78). Hence if in (VII, 8) we put $w=m\nu$, where m is a constant, it follows from this equation and (VII, 49) written $p^2+q^2+r^2=2m\theta'\nu'$ that

$$\theta\nu=\theta'\nu'. \tag{34}$$

Consequently from (33), (VII, 47) and the last two of equations (VII, 7) we get

$$\sqrt{E_1}+\sqrt{E}=e^{\psi}\frac{\theta}{\theta'}+e^{-\psi}\frac{\theta'}{\nu}, \qquad \sqrt{G_1}+\sqrt{G}=e^{\psi}\frac{\theta}{\theta'}-e^{-\psi}\frac{\theta'}{\nu}. \tag{35}$$

The equations of the R transformation from N into N_1 are

$$x_1 = x - \frac{1}{m\nu}(pX + q\xi + r\eta),$$

where the functions satisfy the system

$$(36)\quad \begin{cases} \dfrac{\partial \theta}{\partial u} = \sqrt{E}\,q, & \dfrac{\partial \theta}{\partial v} = \sqrt{G}\,r, \\ \dfrac{\partial \theta'}{\partial u} = e^{\psi} q; & \dfrac{\partial \theta'}{\partial v} = e^{\psi} r, \\ \dfrac{\partial p}{\partial u} = -\dfrac{\sqrt{E}}{\varrho_1} q, & \dfrac{\partial p}{\partial v} = -\dfrac{\sqrt{G}}{\varrho_2} r, \\ \dfrac{\partial q}{\partial u} = \dfrac{\sqrt{E}}{\varrho_1} p - \dfrac{\partial \psi}{\partial v} r + m\left(e^{\psi}\dfrac{\theta}{\theta'}\nu + e^{-\psi}\theta'\right), & \dfrac{\partial q}{\partial v} = \dfrac{\partial \psi}{\partial u} r, \\ \dfrac{\partial r}{\partial u} = \dfrac{\partial \psi}{\partial v} q, \quad \dfrac{\partial r}{\partial v} = \dfrac{\sqrt{G}}{\varrho_2} - \dfrac{\partial \psi}{\partial u} q + m\left(e^{\psi}\dfrac{\theta}{\theta'}\nu - e^{-\psi}\theta'\right), & \\ \dfrac{\partial \nu}{\partial u} = \dfrac{q}{\theta}\left[\nu\left(e^{\psi}\dfrac{\theta}{\theta'} - \sqrt{E}\right) + e^{-\psi}\theta'\right], & \\ \dfrac{\partial \nu}{\partial v} = \dfrac{r}{\theta}\left[\nu\left(e^{\psi}\dfrac{\theta}{\theta'} - \sqrt{G}\right) - e^{-\psi}\theta'\right]. & \end{cases}$$

Hence:

Any O net having the same spherical reprensentation as an isothermic net admits ∞^5 R transformations for which the central net N_0 is applicable to a net $\overline{N}_0$ which is 2, O.

For the case of N' and $\overline{N}'$ equations (25) can be integrated with the result $\varrho = 1/\nu'$. Since p, q, r are the same for the transformation from N' into N_1' and N into N_1, it follows that ϱ has this value in general. Hence the transformation functions from $\overline{N}'$ into $\overline{N}_1'$ are

$$(37)\quad \overline{p} = \frac{p}{\nu'}, \qquad \overline{q} = \frac{q}{\nu'}, \qquad \overline{r} = \frac{r}{\nu'}, \qquad \overline{\theta}' = \frac{\theta'}{\nu'}, \qquad \overline{\nu}' = 1,$$

and for $\overline{N}$ into $\overline{N}_1$

$$(38)\quad \overline{p},\ \overline{q},\ \overline{r},\ \overline{\theta} = \frac{\theta}{\nu'}, \qquad \overline{\nu} = \frac{\nu}{\nu'}.$$

From (30), (31) and (23) we find

$$(39)\quad \begin{cases} \sqrt{\overline{E}'} = e^{\psi} - \dfrac{\theta'}{\nu'} e^{-\psi}, & \sqrt{\overline{G}'} = e^{\psi} + \dfrac{\theta'}{\nu'} e^{-\psi}, \\ \dfrac{\sqrt{\overline{E}'}}{\overline{\varrho}_1'} = \dfrac{e^{\psi}}{\varrho_1'} + \dfrac{p}{\nu'} e^{-\psi}, & \dfrac{\sqrt{\overline{G}'}}{\overline{\varrho}_2'} = \dfrac{e^{\psi}}{\varrho_2'} - \dfrac{p}{\nu'} e^{-\psi}, \end{cases}$$

where ϱ_1', ϱ_2' and $\overline{\varrho}_1'$, $\overline{\varrho}_2'$ are the principal radii of the isothermic net N' and the net $\overline{N}'$ respectively.

Since the left-hand members of (26) are the same for N', $\overline{N}'$ and N, $\overline{N}$, we have from this equation, (39) and (34)

$$(40)\quad \begin{cases} \sqrt{\overline{E}} = \sqrt{E} - \dfrac{\theta'}{\nu} e^{-\psi}, & \sqrt{\overline{G}} = \sqrt{G} + \dfrac{\theta'}{\nu} e^{-\psi}, \\ \dfrac{\sqrt{\overline{E}}}{\overline{\varrho}_1} = \dfrac{\sqrt{E}}{\varrho_1} + \dfrac{p}{\theta}\dfrac{\theta'}{\nu} e^{-\psi}, & \dfrac{\sqrt{\overline{G}}}{\overline{\varrho}_2} = \dfrac{\sqrt{G}}{\varrho_2} - \dfrac{p}{\theta}\dfrac{\theta'}{\nu} e^{-\psi}. \end{cases}$$

Also from (27), (35) and (VII, 9)

$$(41)\quad \begin{cases} \sqrt{\overline{E}_1} = \dfrac{\theta}{\theta'} e^{\psi} - \sqrt{\overline{E}}, & \sqrt{\overline{G}_1} = \dfrac{\theta}{\theta'} e^{\psi} - \sqrt{\overline{G}}, \\ \dfrac{\sqrt{\overline{E}_1}}{\overline{\varrho}_{11}} = \dfrac{\sqrt{E}}{\varrho_1} + e^{\psi}\dfrac{p}{\theta'}, & \dfrac{\sqrt{\overline{G}_1}}{\overline{\varrho}_{12}} = \dfrac{\sqrt{G}}{\varrho_2} + e^{\psi}\dfrac{p}{\theta'}. \end{cases}$$

Since the nets $\overline{N}'$ and $\overline{N}$ are defined intrinsically, the determination of the cartesian coordinates of these nets requires the solution of a Riccati equation.

124. Deformable transformations of the second type of minimal surfaces. We apply the results of the preceding section to the case when the transformation D_m is the one considered in § 87 which transforms the O net N' of a minimal surface into the O net N_1' of a minimal surface. Then $\nu' = p$ and from (39) and (VII, 70) we have

$$\frac{\sqrt{\overline{E}'}}{\overline{\varrho}_1'} = \frac{\sqrt{\overline{G}'}}{\overline{\varrho}_2'} = 0,$$

that is $\overline{N}'$ is a plane net. We have seen in the preceding section that $\overline{N}_1'$ is a point net. Hence the spheres of the transformation pass through a point and are tangent to a plane; consequently the central net lies on a paraboloid of revolution. In order to obtain the equation of the paraboloid, we find the distance from the point $\overline{N}_1'$ to the plane $\overline{N}'$. From (VII, 48) and the condition $\nu' = p$ we find that this distance is $1/m$. Hence the equation of the paraboloid is $mr^2 = 2z$. Therefore we have the theorem:

The surface of centers of a transformation D_m of a minimal surface into a minimal surface is applicable to the paraboloid of revolution $m(x^2+y^2) = 2z$[107]).

125. Deformable transformations E_m. From § 88 and (32) it is seen that a transformation E_m of a surface with isothermal representation of its lines of curvature into a surface of the same kind is a deformable transformation R of the second type. We apply the results of § 88 to this case.

Comparing equations (VII, 76) and (36), we find that the function θ' in (36) is given by

$$\theta' = \frac{\theta \nu}{p}. \tag{42}$$

From (40) it follows that $\sqrt{\overline{E}}/\overline{\varrho}_1 = \sqrt{\overline{G}}/\overline{\varrho}_2 = 0$, that is $\overline{N}$ is a planar net. This result may be stated as follows: As $\overline{S}_0$ rolls over S_0, a plane invariably fixed to $\overline{S}_0$ has S for its envelope. Bianchi[108]) calls S an *envelope of rolling* in this case. Hence we have the theorem of Bianchi[109]):

A surface S with isothermal representation of its lines of curvature is an envelope of rolling, when the central net N_0 of any E_m transformation of S rolls on its applicable net.

We shall prove the converse theorem[110]):

Transformations E_m are the only transformations R for which the given surface is an envelope of rolling as the central net N_0 rolls on its applicable net.

[107]) Cf. Bianchi, Memoire dei Lincei, ser. 5, vol. 12 (1918), p. 532.

[108]) Rendiconti dei Lincei, ser. 5, vol. 23¹ (1914), p. 3.

[109]) Rendiconti dei Lincei, ser. 5, vol. 24 (1915), p. 367.

[110]) Annals of Mathematics, ser. 2, vol. 17 (1915), p. 64.

If $\overline{S}$ is to be a plane, we must have from (40)

$$\frac{\sqrt{E}}{\varrho_1} + \frac{\sqrt{G}}{\varrho_2} = 0, \qquad \frac{\sqrt{E}}{\varrho_1} = -\frac{p}{\theta} \cdot \frac{\theta'}{\nu} e^{-\psi}.$$

From the first it follows that the spherical representation of S is isothermal. Replacing the first by (VII, 70), we have from the second that (42) must hold, and consequently the transformation is E_m[111]).

126. Transformations F of deformable transformations R of the second type. Consider a deformable congruence R of spheres of the second type G, and denote by G' the parallel deformable congruence R which gives a transformation D_m (§ 123). Let N_0 denote the central net of G and $\overline{N}_0$ of the deform $\overline{G}$; likewise N_0' and $\overline{N}_0'$. Then, as we have seen

$$\sum \overline{x}_0'^2 = R'^2. \tag{43}$$

From § 76 it follows that if we take the F transform of N_0 by means of $\theta' = \frac{1}{2}(\sum x_0'^2 - R'^2)$, the coordinates x_0' being the direction-parameters of the conjugate congruence of the transformation, we get a net N_{10} which is 2, O, the complementary function being

$$R_1 = R - \frac{\theta}{\theta'} R'.$$

Moreover, in consequence of (43) we have

$$\theta' = \frac{1}{2}(\sum x_0'^2 - \sum \overline{x}_0'^2).$$

Hence from § 27 it follows that the F transform of $\overline{N}_0$ by means of θ', the coordinates $\overline{x}_0'$ being the direction-parameters of the conjugate congruence of the transformation, is applicable to N_{10}. Then $\sum x_{10}^2 - \sum \overline{x}_{10}^2$ is a solution of the common point equation

---

[111]) Similar results follow, if we require that $\overline{S}_1$ be a plane.

of N_{10} and $\overline{N}_{10}$. Since $\sum x_{10}^2 - R_1^2$ is a solution of this equation (§ 76), so also is $\sum \overline{x}_{10}^2 - R_1^2$, and consequently $\overline{N}_{10}$ is $2, O$. Hence:

When a deformable congruence R of spheres of the second type is known, another congruence of the same type can be found by quadratures[112]).

127. Converses of the theorems of Guichard. In this section we determine under what conditions the two sheets of the envelope of a congruence of spheres have the same constant mean curvature for all deformations of the central surface S_0. We consider first the case when the sheets are minimal surfaces.

If ϱ_1 and ϱ_2 denote the principal radii of curvature of S, then

$$\varrho_1 = R - t_1, \qquad \varrho_2 = R - t_2,$$

where t_1 and t_2 are the roots of the equation obtained by eliminating du and dv from (12). In consequence of (15) this equation is reducible to

$$(44) \quad \begin{cases} t^2\left[(pq_1 - p_1 q)\sin\sigma + r_1\cos\sigma\left(q - \dfrac{\partial\sigma}{\partial u}\right) + p_1\sin\sigma\dfrac{\partial\sigma}{\partial u}\right] \\ \quad + t\left[\eta_1\left(q - 2\dfrac{\partial\sigma}{\partial u}\right) - \xi\sin^2\sigma\, p_1\right] + \xi\eta_1\sin\sigma = 0. \end{cases}$$

If S is to be a minimal surface, we must have $2R = t_1 + t_2$, that is

$$2\mathrm{R} = \frac{\xi\sin^2\sigma\, p_1 - \eta_1\left(q - 2\dfrac{\partial\sigma}{\partial u}\right)}{(pq_1 - p_1 q)\sin\sigma + r_1\cos\sigma\left(q - \dfrac{\partial\sigma}{\partial u}\right) + p_1\sin\sigma\dfrac{\partial\sigma}{\partial u}}.$$

If S_1 also is to be minimal, this equation must be satisfied also when σ is replaced by $-\sigma$. This gives the two equations

$$(45) \quad \begin{cases} \left[(pq_1 - p_1 q)\sin\sigma - r_1\cos\sigma\dfrac{\partial\sigma}{\partial u}\right] R = \eta_1\dfrac{\partial\sigma}{\partial u}, \\ (2Rr_1\cos\sigma + \eta_1)\, q + \left(2R\sin\sigma\dfrac{\partial\sigma}{\partial u} - \xi\sin^2\sigma\right) p_1 = 0. \end{cases}$$

112) Rendiconti dei Lincei, ser. 5, vol. 30² (1921).

The first of these equations involves only functions which do not vary as S_0 is deformed. In order that the second hold for all deformations of S_0, we must have

$$(46) \qquad 2Rr_1\cos\sigma + \eta_1 = 0, \qquad 2R\frac{\partial\sigma}{\partial u} - \xi\sin\sigma = 0.$$

Eliminating R, we get the third of (15).

From (16) we have $\eta_1 = u$, $r_1 = 1/U$. In consequence of (17) the first of (46) becomes $2R = -U\sqrt{c^2+u^2}$. When we substitute this expression in (11), we obtain $U = c_1\sqrt{c^2+u^2}$, where c_1 is an arbitrary constant. Hence by a suitable choice of the parameters the linear element of S_0 is reducible to the form

$$(47) \qquad ds_0^2 = (1+m^2u^2)\,du^2 + u^2dv^2.$$

This is the linear element of the paraboloid of revolution Q, defined by (9). Also we find

$$(48) \qquad R = \frac{1}{2m}(1+m^2u^2).$$

These expressions satisfy the first of (45) and thus all the conditions of the problem are satisfied. Moreover, it can be shown that R equals the distance from a point of Q to its focus on the axis of revolution. Hence we have the theorem[113]):

The spheres with centers on a paraboloid of revolution and passing through the focus constitute the only congruences R of spheres the sheets of whose envelope are minimal surfaces in all deformations of the central surface.

We consider next the case when the two sheets have the same constant mean curvature $1/a$ for all deformations of S_0. In this case

$$R^2 - 2aR + (a-R)(t_1+t_2) + t_1t_2 = 0.$$

Substituting the expressions for t_1+t_2 and t_1t_2 from (44) and requiring that this condition hold for both S and S_1, we get

113) Cf. Bianchi, Memoire dei Lincei, ser. 5, vol. 12 (1918), p. 479.

$$(49)\left\{\begin{aligned}&(R^2-2aR)\left[(pq_1-p_1q)\sin\sigma-r_1\cos\sigma\frac{\partial\sigma}{\partial u}\right]\\&\qquad\qquad+2(a-R)\eta_1\frac{\partial\sigma}{\partial u}+\xi\eta_1\sin\sigma=0,\\&[(R^2-2aR)r_1\cos\sigma-(a-R)\eta_1]q\\&\qquad+\left[(R^2-2aR)\frac{\partial\sigma}{\partial u}+(a-R)\xi\sin\sigma\right]p_1\sin\sigma=0.\end{aligned}\right.$$

Since these equations must be true for all deformations of S_0, the coefficients of q and p_1 in the second must be equal to zero. In consequence of the third of (15) this is equivalent to the single condition

$$(50)\qquad (R^2-2aR)\cos\sigma+Uu(R-a)=0.$$

On differentiating this equation with respect to u and making use of (11) and (15), we obtain

$$(51)\qquad (R-a)(U\cos^2\sigma-uU')+uU^2\cos\sigma=0.$$

Eliminating R from (50) and (51) and substituting for $\cos\sigma$ its expression from (17), we find

$$(52)\qquad U'^2-uU'\left(\frac{2U}{u^2+c^2}+\frac{U^3}{a^2}\right)+\frac{U^2u^2}{(u^2+c^2)^2}=0.$$

When (50) and (52) are satisfied, so also is the first of (49).

The general integral of (52) is

$$U=a\sqrt{\frac{u^2+c^2}{(l-c^2)(u^2+l)}},$$

where l is an arbitrary constant. Hence the linear element of S_0 is

$$(53)\qquad ds_0^2=\frac{a^2(u^2+c^2)}{(l-c^2)(u^2+l)}du^2+u^2dv^2.$$

This is the linear element also of the quadric Q of revolution of the conic

$$(54)\qquad \frac{x^2}{a^2}-\frac{y^2}{l}=1,$$

about the x-axis, provided that

$$c^2 = \frac{l^2}{a^2 + l}. \tag{55}$$

Hence to each choice of l there corresponds a value of c.

Equation (51) reduces to

$$R - a + \sqrt{\frac{a^2 + l}{l}} \sqrt{u^2 + l} = 0.$$

Furthermore since a^2 enters only in (52), we have that a in (50) and (51) may be replaced by $-a$. Accordingly we have also

$$R + a + \sqrt{\frac{a^2 + l}{l}} \sqrt{u^2 + l} = 0.$$

Hence the spheres with centers on the quadric Q may pass through either of the foci on the x-axis, and we have the theorem[114]):

The spheres with centers on a central quadric of revolution and passing through either focus on the axis of revolution constitute the only congruences R of spheres the sheets of whose envelope have the same constant mean curvature for all deformations of the central surface.

128. Theorems of Ribaucour and Bianchi. In accordance with the theorem of Beltrami (§ 112) the tangent planes to either sheet of the envelope of a congruence of spheres envelop a surface for all deformations of the surface of centers, if these planes are understood to be carried along in the deformation. We seek the general solution of the problem: To determine all cases for which the surface elements of a surface S_1 associated with a surface S continue to be the surface elements of a surface in any deformation of S[115]).

Let S be referred to any system of parametric lines. Between the coordinates, x, y, z, of S and x_1, y_1, z_1, of S_1 we have relations of the form

---

114) Cf. Bianchi, l. c., p. 481.

115) Cf. Bianchi, Rendiconti dei Lincei, ser. 5, vol. 24 (1915), p. 3.

(56) $$x_1 = x + l\frac{\partial x}{\partial u} + m\frac{\partial x}{\partial v} + nX,$$

where l, m and n are the same for y_1 and z_1. Differentiating this equation and making use of [§ 64, (7), (8)], we obtain

(57) $$\left\{\begin{aligned} \frac{\partial x_1}{\partial u} &= \left(L + n\frac{FD' - GD}{H^2}\right)\frac{\partial x}{\partial u} \\ &+ \left(M + n\frac{FD - ED'}{H^2}\right)\frac{\partial x}{\partial v} + \left(\frac{\partial n}{\partial u} + Dl + D'm\right)X, \\ \frac{\partial x_1}{\partial v} &= \left(P + n\frac{FD'' - GD'}{H^2}\right)\frac{\partial x}{\partial u} \\ &+ \left(Q + n\frac{FD' - ED''}{H^2}\right)\frac{\partial x}{\partial v} + \left(\frac{\partial n}{\partial v} + D'l + D''m\right)X, \end{aligned}\right.$$

where

(58) $$\left\{\begin{aligned} L &= \frac{\partial l}{\partial u} + \begin{Bmatrix} 11 \\ 1 \end{Bmatrix} l + \begin{Bmatrix} 12 \\ 1 \end{Bmatrix} m + 1, & P &= \frac{\partial l}{\partial v} + \begin{Bmatrix} 12 \\ 1 \end{Bmatrix} l + \begin{Bmatrix} 22 \\ 1 \end{Bmatrix} m, \\ M &= \frac{\partial m}{\partial u} + \begin{Bmatrix} 11 \\ 2 \end{Bmatrix} l + \begin{Bmatrix} 12 \\ 2 \end{Bmatrix} m, & Q &= \frac{\partial m}{\partial v} + \begin{Bmatrix} 12 \\ 2 \end{Bmatrix} l + \begin{Bmatrix} 22 \\ 2 \end{Bmatrix} m + 1, \end{aligned}\right.$$

the Christoffel symbols being formed with respect to the linear element of S.

If X_1, Y_1 and Z_1 denote the direction-cosines of the normal to S_1, we have

(59) $$X_1 = \lambda\frac{\partial x}{\partial u} + \mu\frac{\partial x}{\partial v} + \nu X,$$

and similar equations for Y_1 and Z_1, where λ, μ, ν must be such that

$$\sum \frac{\partial x_1}{\partial u} X_1 = 0, \qquad \sum \frac{\partial x_1}{\partial v} X_1 = 0.$$

Substituting from the above equations, we get

(60) $$\left\{\begin{aligned} (n\lambda - \nu l)\,D + (n\mu - \nu m)\,D' &= \lambda\,(EL + FM) + \mu(FL + GM) + \nu\,\frac{\partial n}{\partial u}, \\ (n\lambda - \nu l)\,D' + (n\mu - \nu m)\,D'' &= \lambda\,(EP + FQ) + \mu\,(FP + GQ) + \nu\,\frac{\partial n}{\partial v}. \end{aligned}\right.$$

If S is deformed in any manner carrying the surface-elements of S_1 invaribly bound to it, for a deform $\overline{S}$ of S we have

$$(61)\quad \left\{\begin{aligned} \overline{x}_1 &= \overline{x} + l\frac{\partial \overline{x}}{\partial u} + m\frac{\partial \overline{x}}{\partial v} + n\overline{X}, \\ \overline{X}_1 &= \quad\lambda\frac{\partial \overline{x}}{\partial u} + \mu\frac{\partial \overline{x}}{\partial v} + \nu\overline{X}, \end{aligned}\right.$$

where $l, m, n, \lambda, \mu, \nu$ are unaltered by the deformation. This fact is of prime importance.

The right-hand members of (60) involve only quantities unaltered by the deformation. Consequently we must have

$$(62)\qquad n\lambda = \nu l, \qquad n\mu = \nu m.$$

There are two cases to be considered,

I°. When $\nu \neq 0$, then

$$x_1 = x + \frac{n}{\nu} X_1,$$

which expresses the fact that S_1 is a sheet of the envelope of spheres with centers on S, that is the theorem of Beltrami.

2°. When $\nu = 0$, then $n = 0$. In this case the points of S_1 lie in the corresponding tangent planes to S, and since $\sum XX_1 = 0$, corresponding tangent planes to S and S_1 are perpendicular. The existence of this case was established by Ribaucour[116]). Hence we have the theorem of Bianchi[117]):

A necessary and sufficient condition that ∞^2 surface-elements invaribly associated with a surface S continue to be the surface-elements of a surface in all deformations of S is that they are the elements of a sheet of the envelope of a congruence of spheres with centers on S, or of a surface S_1 such that corresponding tangent planes to S and S_1 are perpendicular and points of S_1 lie in the corresponding tangent planes to S.

We remark that if equations (62) hold for one deformation of S, they hold for every deformation.

---

116) Journ. de Math., ser. 4, vol. 7 (1891), p. 92.

117) L. c., p. 4.

129. The surface generated by a point in the tangent plane to a surface $\overline{S}$ as $\overline{S}$ rolls on an applicable surface S. The formulas of the preceding section can be used to find the surface generated by a point P associated with $\overline{S}$ as $\overline{S}$ rolls on an applicable surface S. When in particular P lies in the tangent plane to $\overline{S}$, we have $n = 0$. We consider this case.

If we put

$$(63) \quad \begin{cases} \Omega_1 = L^2E + 2LMF + M^2G, \qquad \Omega_2 = LPE + (LQ + MP)F + MQG, \\ \qquad \Omega_3 = P^2E + 2PQF + Q^2G, \end{cases}$$

the first fundamental coefficients of S_1 are found from (57) to be

$$(64) \quad \begin{cases} E_1 = \Omega_1 + (lD + mD')^2, \quad F_1 = \Omega_2 + (lD + mD')(lD' + mD''), \\ \qquad G_1 = \Omega_3 + (lD' + mD'')^2. \end{cases}$$

Also the coefficients of $\overline{S}_1$ are

$$(65) \quad \begin{cases} \overline{E}_1 = \Omega_1 + (l\overline{D} + m\overline{D}')^2, \quad \overline{F}_1 = \Omega_2 + (l\overline{D} + m\overline{D}')(l\overline{D}' + m\overline{D}''), \\ \qquad \overline{G}_1 = \Omega_3 + (l\overline{D}' + m\overline{D}'')^2, \end{cases}$$

where $\overline{D}, \overline{D}', \overline{D}''$ are the second fundamental coefficients of $\overline{S}$.

Since the functions $\Omega_1, \Omega_2, \Omega_3$ are the same for both surfaces, we have from (64) and (65)

$$(66) \quad \begin{cases} ds_1^2 - d\overline{s}_1^2 = [(lD + mD')\,du + (lD' + mD'')\,dv]^2 \\ \qquad - [(l\overline{D} + m\overline{D}')\,du + (l\overline{D}' + m\overline{D}'')\,dv]^2. \end{cases}$$

As an application of this result we consider the case when $\overline{S}$ is a ruled surface and S is not ruled, and we take for the curves $v = \text{const.}$ the generators of $\overline{S}$, that is $\overline{D} = 0$. We take the point P determined by the condition that it lies on a generator of $\overline{S}$ and is such that as $\overline{S}$ rolls on S it describes a line of length zero on $\overline{S}$. Then we have $m = 0$, $d\overline{s}_1 = 0$. Since $DD'' - D'^2 = -\overline{D}'^2$, we have from (66)

$$(67) \qquad ds_1^2 = l^2 D(D\,du^2 + 2D'\,du\,dv + D''\,dv^2).$$

Hence we have the theorem of Darboux[118]):

[118]) Annales de l'École Norm. Sup., ser. 3, vol. 16 (1899), p. 497.

When a ruled surface $\bar{S}$ rolls on a non-ruled applicable surface S, the points where the different lines of length zero of $\bar{S}$ meet the generators of $\bar{S}$ describe surfaces which are conformably represented on one another; and their lines of length zero correspond to the asymptotic lines on S.

The surfaces described by the points a, a_1, a', a_1' in § 121 are examples of this theorem.

130. Kinematically conjugate directions on rolling surfaces. If on a surface $\bar{S}$ we take a curve C of the family determined by an equation of the form $dv = M du$, and at each point of C draw the tangents to the curves of another family determined by an equation $\delta v = N \delta u$, the coordinates of this ruled surface $\bar{R}$ are given by (61), when we put $l = t\delta u$, $m = t\delta v$, $n = 0$, t being the parameter of a point on the line. As $\bar{S}$ rolls on an applicable surface S, along C, these lines generate a ruled surface R tangent to S. From (66) it follows that a necessary and sufficient condition that R and $\bar{R}$ be applicable is that

$$(68)\quad (D+\bar{D})\,du\,\delta u + (D'+\bar{D}')(du\,\delta v + dv\,\delta u) + (D''+\bar{D}'')\,dv\,\delta v = 0,$$

or

$$(69)\quad (D-\bar{D})\,du\,\delta u + (D'-\bar{D}')(du\,\delta v + dv\,\delta u) + (D''-\bar{D}'')\,dv\,\delta v = 0.$$

If we desire the condition to be satisfied for all deformations of $\bar{S}$ and in particular when S and $\bar{S}$ are congruent, we must take (69). In fact (68) is obtained from (69), if $\bar{S}$ is replaced by its symmetric with respect to the origin.

Equation (69) coordinates with every family of curves on $\bar{S}$ a second family, and the relation is involutoric. Beltrami[119]) has called two such families *kinematically conjugate*. The preceding results may be stated as follows:

If S and $\bar{S}$ are applicable surfaces, and C and $\bar{C}$ are any two corresponding curves, the ruled surfaces, R and $\bar{R}$, consisting of the tangents to S and $\bar{S}$ in directions kinematically conjugate to C and $\bar{C}$ are applicable.

As $\bar{S}$ rolls on S and $\bar{C}$ rolls on C, coincident lines of R and $\bar{R}$ form the instantaneous axis of rotation of the rolling. Hence:

---

[119]) Giornale di Battagline, vol. 10 (1872), p. 103.

When a surface $\bar{S}$ rolls on an applicable surface S, the instantaneous axis of rotation lies in the plane of contact and its direction is kinematically conjugate to the direction of motion of the instantaneous center.

Since the common conjugate system of curves on S and $\bar{S}$ satisfies the equations

$$D\,du\,\delta u + D'(du\,\delta v + dv\,\delta u) + D''\,dv\,\delta v = 0,$$
$$\bar{D}\,du\,\delta u + \bar{D}'(du\,\delta v + dv\,\delta u) + \bar{D}''\,dv\,\delta v = 0,$$

we have the theorem:

The common conjugate system on two applicable surfaces is kinematically conjugate.

When $\bar{S}$ rolls along a curve of either family of the common conjugate system, the surfaces R and $\bar{R}$ are developables whose edges of regression correspond, since the points of these edges are Laplace transforms of points of C and $\bar{C}$.

The equation

$$(70)\qquad (D-\bar{D})\,du^2 + 2(D'-\bar{D}')\,du\,dv + (D''-\bar{D}'')\,dv^2 = 0$$

defines two families of curves on S and $\bar{S}$ which are *kinematically auto-conjugate,* that is as $\bar{S}$ rolls on S along one of these curves the instantaneous axis is tangent to the curve itself. In this case also the surfaces R and $\bar{R}$ are developable. Since S and $\bar{S}$ are applicable, the curves C and $\bar{C}$ have the same geodesic curvature, at corresponding points. Also as follows from (70) and [§ 49] their normal curvatures are equal, and consequently their first curvatures.

As an example of the foregoing we consider two applicable surfaces S and $\bar{S}$, and assume that the curves $u=$ const. are the asymptotic lines on $\bar{S}$. Then

$$\bar{D}'^2 = D'^2 - DD''.$$

In consequence of this relation we have that the equation of the asymptotic lines on S may be written

$$[(D'-\bar{D}')\,du + D''dv]\,[(D'+\bar{D}')\,du + D''dv] = 0.$$

From this equation it follows that the curves kinematically conjugate to $u=$ const. on $\bar{S}$ correspond to one family of asymptotic lines on S. Bianchi has called them *virtual asymptotic* lines on $\bar{S}$. Moreover, the other family of virtual asymptotic lines on $\bar{S}$ satisfy (68). Hence we have the theorem[120]):

If S and $\bar{S}$ are applicable surfaces, the ruled surface $\bar{R}$ consisting of the tangents to the asymptotic lines in one family where they meet a virtual asymptotic line of $\bar{S}$ is applicable to the ruled surface R of tangents to the corresponding virtual asymptotic lines of S where they are met by its corresponding asymptotic line.

If $\bar{S}$ is a ruled surface, we may take it for $\bar{R}$, and then R consists of the tangents to the corresponding virtual asymptotic lines on S, which are geodesics. Hence as a corollary of the above we have the theorem of Chieffi[121]):

If S is applicable to a ruled surface $\bar{R}$, the ruled surface consisting of tangents to the geodesic virtual asymptotic lines of S at points of meeting of any asymptotic line a of S is applicable to S with a rigid in the applicability.

131. Congruences of rolling. When a non-ruled surface $\bar{S}$ rolls on an applicable surface S, a line l invaribly fixed to $\bar{S}$ generates a congruence G called by Bianchi[122]) a *congruence of rolling*. In order to find the focal points of G, we note that there are two instantaneous axes of rotation in the plane of contact π at a point M for which l and a nearby position l' meet, namely the direction l_1 joining M and the point P_1 in which l meets π, and the direction l_2 normal to the plane through l perpendicular to π. When l_1 is the axis of rotation, the point P_1 generates one of the focal surfaces. When l_2 is the axis, the lines l and l'' meet in the foot P_2 of the common perpendicular of l and l_2, that is the foot of the perpendicular from M to l; and thus P_2 generates the second focal surface of G. The plane of the lines l and l'' is the tangent plane to the locus of P_1 and is perpendicular to π. The plane of l and l' is the tangent plane to the locus of P_2 and is normal to the line MP_2. Hence we have the theorem of Bianchi[123]):

For any congruence of rolling one focal surface is generated

---

[120]) Cf. Bianchi, Memoire dei Lincei, ser. 5, vol. 12 (1918), p. 445.

[121]) Giornale di Battagline, vol. 43 (1905), p. 9.

[122]) Rendiconti dei Lincei, ser. 5, vol. 24 (1915), p. 15.

[123]) L. c. These results have been established by him by analytical processes in the Rendiconti di Palermo, vol. 39 (1915), p. 187.

by the point P_1 *in which* l *meets the plane of contact* π, *and the other by the foot* P_2 *of the perpendicular from the point of contact* M *to* l; *the tangent planes to these respective surfaces are the plane through* l *normal to* π *and the plane through* P_2 *perpendicular to* MP_2.

From the above treatment it is seen that the focal surfaces of G are generated by the same surface-elements attached to $\bar{S}$ whatever be the surface S on which $\bar{S}$ rolls.

From the results of § 130 and the above considerations we have that the developables of a congruence of rolling correspond to the curves kinematically conjugate to the curves on S whose tangents are the lines l_1 and l_2 for a point of contact. The latter are the curves corresponding to the curves in which $\bar{S}$ is met by the pencil of planes through l and by the parallel pencil of planes normal to l. Bianchi has called them the *meridian profiles* and the *curves of level* respectively. Hence:

For a congruence of rolling the developables correspond to the curves on S *kinematically conjugate to the deforms of the meridian profiles and the curves of level on* $\bar{S}$.

Since a right conoid is the only surface posessing a family of meridian profiles which are also curves of level, we have the theorem of Bianchi:

The congruences of rolling with coincident developables are those, and only those, generated by the axis of a right conoid as it rolls on an applicable surface.

From the preceding considerations it is evident that the developables of a congruence of rolling are real. We remark also that the focal surfaces of a congruence of rolling afford examples of the theorems of Beltrami and Ribaucour (§ 128).

Exercises.

1. Show that the theorem of Bonnet [§ 73] may be interpreted as follows: When a sphere rolls on an applicable surface, its center describes a surface of constant mean curvature.

2. When a quadric $\bar{S}$ tangent to the circle at infinity at a single point P rolls on an applicable surface S, the two isotropic generators of $\bar{S}$ through P meet the common tangent plane in two points, a and a', which describe two parallel surfaces of constant mean curvature $\pm 1/aa'$.

Darboux, Annales L'École Norm. Sup., ser. 3, vol. 16 (1899), p. 468.

3. If S and $\bar{S}$ are applicable surfaces and the spheres with centers on $\bar{S}$ and passing through the origin become tangent to the plane $z=0$ as $\bar{S}$ rolls on S, it is necessary that

$$\bar{x}^2+\bar{y}^2+\bar{z}^2=z^2.$$

If we put [cf. § 47]

$$\bar{x}=z\frac{\alpha+\beta}{\alpha\beta+1},\qquad \bar{y}=iz\frac{\beta-\alpha}{\alpha\beta+1},\qquad \bar{z}=z\frac{\alpha\beta-1}{\alpha\beta+1},$$

$$x+iy=\omega\qquad x-iy=\omega_0,$$

then since S and $\bar{S}$ are applicable

$$\frac{4z^2\,d\alpha\,d\beta}{(\alpha\beta+1)^2}=d\omega\,d\omega_0.$$

Hence the projection of $\bar{S}$ on the unit sphere and of S on the plane $z=0$ are conformal. The general solution is given by

$$\omega=f(\alpha),\qquad \omega_0=f_0(\beta),\qquad z=\frac{1}{2}(1+\alpha\beta)\sqrt{f'(\alpha)f'_0(\beta)},$$

where f is arbitrary and f_0 is the conjugate function.

Calo, Annali, ser. 3, vol. 4 (1900), pp. 123—130.

4. If S and $\bar{S}$ are applicable surfaces and the spheres with centers on $\bar{S}$ and passing through the origin become tangents to a sphere of radius a with center at the origin as $\bar{S}$ rolls on S, is is necessary that $\bar{x}^2+\bar{y}^2+\bar{z}^2=R^2$, $x^2+y^2+z^2=(R\pm a)^2$.

If we put

$$\bar{x}=R\frac{\bar{\alpha}+\bar{\beta}}{\bar{\alpha}\bar{\beta}+1},\qquad \bar{y}=iR\frac{\bar{\beta}-\bar{\alpha}}{\bar{\alpha}\bar{\beta}+1},\qquad \bar{z}=R\frac{\bar{\alpha}\bar{\beta}-1}{\bar{\alpha}\bar{\beta}+1},$$

$$x=(R\pm a)\frac{\alpha+\beta}{\alpha\beta+1},\qquad y=i(R\pm a)\frac{\beta-\alpha}{\alpha\beta+1},\qquad z=(R\pm a)\frac{\alpha\beta-1}{\alpha\beta+1},$$

since S and $\bar{S}$ are applicable, we have

$$\text{(i)}\qquad \frac{R^2\,d\bar{\alpha}\,d\bar{\beta}}{(1+\bar{\alpha}\bar{\beta})^2}=(R\pm a)^2\frac{d\alpha\,d\beta}{(1+\alpha\beta)^2}.$$

Hence the projections of S and $\bar{S}$ on the unit sphere are conformal. The general solution is given by $\alpha=f(\bar{\alpha})$, $\beta=f_0(\bar{\beta})$, where f is an arbitrary function and f_0 is the conjugate function. Then R can be found directly from (*i*).

Calo, l. c.

5. When the Christoffel transform (cf. VII, Ex. 8) of N' in § 123 is taken as N, the corresponding net $\bar{N}$ is a point, and consequently the central net of this transformation is the other special net 2, O parallel to $\bar{N}'_0$.

6. Show by means of (VII, 3) that a necessary and sufficient condition that an O net have the same spherical representation as an isothermic O net is that

$$\frac{\partial}{\partial u}\left(\frac{1}{\sqrt{G}}\frac{\partial\sqrt{E}}{\partial v}\right)=\frac{\partial}{\partial v}\left(\frac{1}{\sqrt{E}}\frac{\partial\sqrt{G}}{\partial u}\right).$$

Trans. Amer. Math. Soc., vol. 17 (1916), p. 447.

7. A necessary and sufficient condition that an O net on the unit sphere be the spherical representation of an isothermic net is

$$\frac{\partial}{\partial u}\left(\frac{1}{\sqrt{\mathfrak{G}}}\frac{\partial\sqrt{\mathfrak{E}}}{\partial v}\right) = \frac{\partial}{\partial v}\left(\frac{1}{\sqrt{\mathfrak{E}}}\frac{\partial\sqrt{\mathfrak{G}}}{\partial u}\right).$$

8. Show that the net $\overline{N}'$ of § 123 is parallel to two isothermic nets $(\overline{N})'$ and $(\overline{N})''$ for which

$$\sqrt{(\overline{E})'} = -\sqrt{(\overline{G})'} = \frac{e^{-\psi}}{\nu}, \qquad \sqrt{(\overline{E})''} = \sqrt{(\overline{G})''} = e^{\psi}\nu;$$

that a transformation D of $(\overline{N})'$ is determined by the functions $\overline{p}, \overline{q}, \overline{r}$ of (37) and $(\overline{\theta})' = -1/\nu'$, $(\overline{\nu})' = \theta'$, $(\overline{m})' = -m$; and that the resulting transform is the net obtained from the given transformation of N' referred to in (VII, Ex. 17).

9. Show that there exists an O net, with the same spherical representation as an isothermic net, for which the tangential coordinate P is equal to $\mathfrak{E}-\mathfrak{G}$.

Calapso, Annali, ser. 3, vol. 26 (1917), p. 171.

10. If we have an O net N of the kind in Ex. 9 and put

$$\sqrt{\mathfrak{E}} = \frac{\sqrt{E}}{\rho_1} = \sqrt{P}\cosh\varphi, \qquad \sqrt{\mathfrak{G}} = \frac{\sqrt{G}}{\rho_2} = \sqrt{P}\sinh\varphi,$$

from (VII, 3, 5) we have

$$\frac{\partial\varphi}{\partial u} - \frac{\partial\psi}{\partial u} = \frac{1}{2}\frac{Q}{\sqrt{P}}\sinh\varphi, \qquad \frac{\partial\varphi}{\partial v} - \frac{\partial\psi}{\partial v} - = \frac{1}{2}\frac{R}{\sqrt{P}}\cosh\varphi.$$

From (VII, 9) and (35) we have for an R transform of this O net

$$\frac{E_1}{\rho_{11}^2} - \frac{G_1}{\rho_{12}^2} = P + 2\sqrt{P}\,\frac{p}{\theta}\left(e^{\psi-\varphi}\frac{\theta}{\theta'} + e^{-\psi+\varphi}\frac{\theta'}{\nu}\right) + 4\,\frac{p^2}{\nu\theta}.$$

In order that this expression be equal to P_1, namely (VI, 101)

$$P_1 = P - \frac{p}{m\nu\theta}(Pp + Qq + Rr - \theta),$$

we must have

$$Pp + Qq + Rr - \theta + 2\sqrt{P}m\nu\left(e^{\psi-\varphi}\frac{\theta}{\theta'} + e^{-\psi+\varphi}\frac{\theta'}{\nu}\right) + 4\,mp = 0.$$

The left-hand member is found by differentiation to be a constant. Hence there are ∞^4 transformations R of N into nets of the same kind.

Calapso, l. c., p. 152.

11. If N' and N'' are isothermic O nets in the relation of Christoffel (cf. VII, Ex. 8), the mid-point of the join of corresponding points on N' and N'' describes an O net N parallel to N' and N'' for which $\sqrt{E} = \cosh\psi$, $\sqrt{G} = \sinh\psi$. When these expressions are substituted in (36), the function $2\theta - \theta' - \nu\theta/\theta'$ is constant. Show that there are ∞^4 transformations R for which this constant is equal to zero, and that for each of these transformations $E_1 - G_1 = 1$; also that N_1 is the locus of the mid-point of the joins of corresponding points of N_1' and N_1'.

Calapso, Annali, ser. 3, vol. 26 (1917), p. 152.

12. A necessary and sufficient condition that the parametric curves of two applicable surfaces S and $\overline{S}'$ be kinematically conjugate is that $D' = \overline{D}'$.

13. A necessary and sufficient condition that the kinematically auto-conjugate curves for two applicable surfaces, $S, \overline{S}$, reduce to a single family is that S and $\overline{S}$ be ruled surfaces applicable with generators corresponding.

Bianchi, Memoirie dei Lincei, ser. 5, vol. 12 (1918), p. 441.

14. When two applicable surfaces are referred to their kinematically auto-conjugate-system, $D = \overline{D}$, $D' = -\overline{D}'$, $D'' = \overline{D}''$, and $\frac{\partial}{\partial u}\left\{ {12 \atop 1} \right\} = \frac{\partial}{\partial v}\left\{ {12 \atop 2} \right\}$, the Christoffel symbols being formed with respect to their linear element.

Bianchi, l. c., p. 445.

15. Given two quadratic differential forms

$$a_{11}\,du^2 + 2\,a_{12}\,du\,dv + a_{22}\,dv^2, \qquad b_{11}\,du^2 + 2\,b_{12}\,du\,dv + b_{22}\,dv^2. \tag{1}$$

When the Jacobian of these forms is equated to zero, the resulting equation, namely

$$\begin{vmatrix} a_{11}\,du + a_{12}\,dv, & a_{12}\,du + a_{22}\,dv \\ b_{11}\,du + b_{12}\,dv, & b_{12}\,du + b_{22}\,dv \end{vmatrix} = 0,$$

defines two functions $\overline{u} = \varphi(u, v)$, $\overline{v} = \psi(u, v)$ in terms of which the forms (1) become

$$\overline{a}_{11}\,d\overline{u}^2 + \overline{a}_{22}\,d\overline{v}^2, \qquad \overline{b}_{11}\,d\overline{u}^2 + \overline{b}_{22}\,d\overline{v}^2.$$

Bianchi, Lezioni, vol. 1, p. 82

16. If S and $\overline{S}$ are applicable surfaces, the curves defined by equating to zero the Jacobian of the forms

$$E\,du^2 + 2\,F\,du\,dv + G\,dv^2,$$

$$(D - \overline{D})\,du^2 + 2\,(D' - \overline{D}')\,du\,dv + (D'' - \overline{D}'')\,dv^2$$

form an orthogonal kinematically conjugate system. Bianchi, Lezioni, vol. 2, p. 38.

17. On two applicable surfaces of constant mean curvature $\pm 1/a$ whose lines of curvature correspond and for which ρ_1 and ρ_2 are the radii of principal curvature of one surface and $-\rho_2$, $-\rho_1$ of the other [cf. § 125], every orthogonal system is kinematically conjugate; moreover, this is the only case where every orthogonal system is kinematically conjugate. Bianchi, l. c., p. 39.

18. The lines of curvature on a surface of rolling described by a point O fixed with respect to a rolling surface $\overline{S}$ correspond to that kinematically conjugate system on $\overline{S}$ which projects into an orthogonal system on a sphere with center at O, the projection being from O as center.

Bianchi, Memorie dei Lincei, ser. 5, vol. 12 (1918), p. 448.

19. The lines of curvature on an envelope of rolling described by a plane π fixed with respect to a rolling surface $\overline{S}$ correspond to that kinematically conjugate system on $\overline{S}$ which projects orthogonally into an orthogonal system on π.

Bianchi, l. c., p. 448.

20. When a surface $\bar{S}$ rolls over an applicable surface S, any two parallel lines fixed with respect to $\bar{S}$ generate congruences for which one family of developables correspond, namely, those corresponding to the curves kinematically conjugate to the transforms of the curves of level of S.

Bianchi, Rendiconti dei Lincei, ser. 5, vol. 24 (1915), p. 16.

21. When a surface of revolution $\bar{S}$ rolls on an applicable surface S, the axis of $\bar{S}$ generates a normal congruence, since the focal planes are perpendicular. One of the focal surfaces is the complementary surface S_1 of S corresponding to the deforms of the meridians of S.

Bianchi, Rendiconti di Palermo, vol. 39 (1915), p. 205.

22. For the surface $\bar{S}$ defined by

$$\bar{x} = r\cos\theta, \qquad \bar{y} = r\sin\theta, \qquad \bar{z} = c\log r + f(\theta),$$

where f is an arbitrary function, the distance cut off on the z-axis by the perpendicular from any point P of the surface to the axis and the tangent plane at P is equal to c. Hence when $\bar{S}$ rolls on an applicable surface, the axis generates a congruence of rolling for which the focal distance is constant.

Bianchi, l. c., p. 207.

23. When the surface $\bar{S}$ defined by

$$\bar{x} = r\cos\theta, \qquad \bar{y} = r\sin\theta, \qquad \bar{z} = c\log r + m\theta$$

rolls on an applicable surface S, the z-axis generates a congruence G of rolling for which the distance between the focal points is c and the angle between the focal planes is $\sin^{-1} c/\sqrt{c^2+m^2}$. Hence G is a pseudospherical congruence whose focal surfaces have the same gaussian curvature $-1/(c^2+m^2)$ [cf. § 171].

Bianchi, l. c., p. 208.

Chapter X.

Surfaces applicable to a quadric.

132. Transformations F of nets on a quadric. Consider a net N on the general quadric Q, whose equation is

$$ex^2+fy^2+gz^2+2ayz+2bzx+2cxy+2rx+2sy+2tz+w=0.$$

Since the coordinates are solutions of an equation of the form (II, 6), we have on differentiating (1) with respect to u and v

$$(2)\quad \begin{cases} e\dfrac{\partial x}{\partial u}\dfrac{\partial x}{\partial v}+f\dfrac{\partial y}{\partial u}\dfrac{\partial y}{\partial v}+g\dfrac{\partial z}{\partial u}\dfrac{\partial z}{\partial v}+a\left(\dfrac{\partial y}{\partial u}\dfrac{\partial z}{\partial v}+\dfrac{\partial y}{\partial v}\dfrac{\partial z}{\partial u}\right) \\ \quad +b\left(\dfrac{\partial z}{\partial u}\dfrac{\partial x}{\partial v}+\dfrac{\partial z}{\partial v}\dfrac{\partial x}{\partial u}\right)+c\left(\dfrac{\partial x}{\partial u}\dfrac{\partial y}{\partial v}+\dfrac{\partial x}{\partial v}\dfrac{\partial y}{\partial u}\right)=0. \end{cases}$$

Any net $N'(x')$ parallel to N is given by equations of the form (II, 3). Consequently we have an equation of the form (2) in which x, y, z, are replaced by x', y', z'. From this it follows that the function

$$(3)\qquad \theta'=ex'^2+fy'^2+gz'^2+2(ay'z'+bz'x'+cx'y')$$

is a solution of the point of equation of N'[124]. It is readily found that θ' and θ, given by

$$(4)\quad \begin{cases} \theta=2\,[exx'+fyy'+gzz'+a(yz'+y'z)+b(zx'+z'x) \\ \qquad +c(xy'+x'y)+rx'+sy'+tz'] \end{cases}$$

satisfy the equations

$$(5)\qquad \frac{\partial\theta'}{\partial u}=h\frac{\partial\theta}{\partial u},\qquad \frac{\partial\theta'}{\partial v}=l\frac{\partial\theta}{\partial v}.$$

---

[124]) The function $\theta'\neq 0$, since N' cannot lie on a cone.

When these values are substituted in (II, 2), it is found that the F transform $N_1(x_1)$ lies on Q. It has been shown in § 5 that any congruence conjugate to a net N can be obtained by drawing through points of N lines whose direction-parameters are the coordinates of some net parallel to N. Hence we have the theorem of Ribaucour:

Any congruence conjugate to a net on a quadric meets the quadric again in a net to which it is conjugate.

We apply the results of § 21 to the particular case when N is on the quadric Q, and also N_1 and N_2, that is when θ_1 and θ_2 are of the form (4). In order that θ_{12} and θ_{12}''' be of the form (3) and (4) with $x'\ y'\ z'$; $x\ y\ z$ replaced by $x_1''',\ y_1''',\ z_1'''$; $x_1,\ y_1,\ z_1$ respectively, we must have

$$(6)\qquad \begin{cases} \theta_1'' + \theta_2' - 2\,[e x' x'' + f y' y'' + g z' z'' + a(y' z'' + y'' z') \\ \qquad + b(z' x'' + z'' x') + c(x' y'' + x'' y')] = 0. \end{cases}$$

By differentiation it is found that the left-hand member of this equation is constant, and consequently the additive constants in θ_1'' and θ_2' can be chosen in ∞^1 ways so that (6) shall hold. Hence:

If N_1 and N_2 are F transforms of N and all three nets lie on Q(1), there are ∞^1 other nets N_{12} on Q which are F transforms of N_1 and N_2; they can be found by a quadrature.

133. Permanent nets on a quadric. Let Q be a quadric referred to its asymptotic lines, and write its linear element in the form

$$(7)\qquad ds_0^2 = E_0\,d\alpha^2 + 2F_0\,d\alpha\,d\beta + G_0\,d\beta^2,$$

and its second quadratic form

$$(8)\qquad \Phi = 2D_0'\,d\alpha\,d\beta.$$

If $\bar{S}$ is an applicable surface, its linear element is (7) and its second quadratic form is

$$(9)\qquad \bar{\Phi} = \bar{D}_0\,d\alpha^2 + 2\bar{D}_0'\,d\alpha\,d\beta + \bar{D}_0''\,d\beta^2.$$

Since the asymptotic lines on Q are straight lines, we must have [§ 85]

(10)
$$\left\{ {11 \atop 2} \right\}_0 = \left\{ {22 \atop 1} \right\}_0 = 0,$$

the Christoffel symbols $\left\{ {rs \atop t} \right\}_0$ being formed with respect to (7).

If we put

(11)
$$H_0 = \sqrt{E_0 G_0 - F_0^2}, \qquad \sigma^2 = \frac{D_0'}{H_0} = \sqrt{-K},$$

from [§§ 63, 77] we have

(12)
$$\begin{cases} \left\{ {12 \atop 1} \right\}_0 = -\dfrac{\partial \log \sigma}{\partial \beta}, & \left\{ {12 \atop 2} \right\}_0 = -\dfrac{\partial \log \sigma}{\partial \alpha}, \\ \left\{ {11 \atop 1} \right\}_0 = \dfrac{\partial}{\partial \alpha} \log H_0 \sigma, & \left\{ {22 \atop 2} \right\}_0 = \dfrac{\partial}{\partial \beta} \log H_0 \sigma. \end{cases}$$

Hence the Codazzi equations [§ 64] for $\bar{S}$ are reducible to

(13)
$$\begin{cases} \dfrac{\partial \bar{D}_0}{\partial \beta} - \dfrac{\partial \bar{D}_0'}{\partial \alpha} + \dfrac{\partial \log \sigma}{\partial \beta} \bar{D}_0 + \dfrac{\partial \log D_0'}{\partial \alpha} \bar{D}_0' = 0, \\ \dfrac{\partial \bar{D}_0''}{\partial \alpha} - \dfrac{\partial \bar{D}_0'}{\partial \beta} + \dfrac{\partial \log \sigma}{\partial \alpha} \bar{D}_0'' + \dfrac{\partial \log D_0'}{\partial \beta} \bar{D}_0' = 0. \end{cases}$$

Since Q and $\bar{S}$ are applicable,

$$\bar{D}_0 \bar{D}_0'' - \bar{D}_0'^2 = -D_0'^2 = -H_0^2 \sigma^4.$$

If we put

(14)
$$\Delta = \sigma \bar{D}_0, \qquad \Delta'' = \sigma \bar{D}_0'', \qquad \Delta' = \frac{\bar{D}_0'}{D_0'},$$

we have

(15)
$$\sqrt{\Delta \Delta''} = \sigma D_0' \sqrt{\Delta'^2 - 1}.$$

Then (13) may be replaced by

(16)
$$\frac{\partial \Delta}{\partial \beta} = \sigma D_0' \frac{\partial \Delta'}{\partial \alpha}, \qquad \frac{\partial \Delta''}{\partial \alpha} = \sigma D_0' \frac{\partial \Delta'}{\partial \beta}.$$

The equation of the common conjugate system of Q and $\bar{S}$ is [§ 56]

$$\Delta \, d\alpha^2 - \Delta'' \, d\beta^2 = 0.$$

By means of the above formulas we find that the Gaussian curvature of the left-hand member of this equation is zero, and consequently it can be given the form $du\,dv$. Hence we have the theorem of Servant[125]):

If $\bar{S}$ is a surface applicable to a quadric Q and the latter is referred to its generators, the common conjugate system can be found by quadratures.

If we put

$$(17)\qquad e^{-\omega}(\sqrt{\Delta}\,d\alpha-\sqrt{\Delta''}\,d\beta)=du,\qquad e^{\omega}(\sqrt{\Delta}\,d\alpha+\sqrt{\Delta''}\,d\beta)=dv,$$

we find, in consequence of (16),

$$(18)\qquad e^{2\omega}=\Delta'+\sqrt{\Delta'^2-1},\qquad e^{-2\omega}=\Delta'-\sqrt{\Delta'^2-1}.$$

From equations (17) we have

$$(19)\qquad \begin{cases} 2\sqrt{\Delta}\,d\alpha=e^{\omega}du+e^{-\omega}dv,\\ 2\sqrt{\Delta''}\,d\beta=-e^{\omega}du+e^{-\omega}dv.\end{cases}$$

In terms of u and v the second quadratic forms of Q and $\bar{S}$ are necessarily of the form

$$\Phi=D\,du^2+D''\,dv^2,\qquad \bar{\Phi}=\bar{D}\,du^2+\bar{D}''\,dv^2.$$

In consequence of (8), (9) and (19) we have

$$(20)\qquad D=-\frac{1}{2\sigma}\left(\frac{\Delta'}{\sqrt{\Delta'^2-1}}+1\right),\quad D''=\frac{1}{2\sigma}\left(\frac{\Delta'}{\sqrt{\Delta'^2-1}}-1\right),$$

$$(21)\qquad \bar{D}=-\bar{D}''=\frac{-1}{2\sigma\sqrt{\Delta'^2-1}}.$$

From these follow the theorems[126]):

If a net upon a quadric admits an applicable net, then

$$(22)\qquad D+D''=-\frac{1}{\sigma}.$$

[125]) Bull. Soc. Math. de France, vol. 30 (1902), p. 19.
[126]) Cf. Servant, l. c., p. 20.

The permanent net on a deform of a quadric is isothermal-conjugate.

From (19) we have

$$\text{(23)}\qquad \frac{\partial \alpha}{\partial u}=\frac{e^{\omega}}{2\sqrt{\Delta}},\quad \frac{\partial \alpha}{\partial v}=\frac{e^{-\omega}}{2\sqrt{\Delta}};\quad \frac{\partial \beta}{\partial u}=-\frac{e^{\omega}}{2\sqrt{\Delta''}},\quad \frac{\partial \beta}{\partial v}=\frac{e^{-\omega}}{2\sqrt{\Delta''}}.$$

In consequence of (15) and (18) we have from these equations

$$\text{(24)}\qquad \begin{cases} \dfrac{\partial \alpha}{\partial u}\dfrac{\partial \beta}{\partial v}+\dfrac{\partial \alpha}{\partial v}\dfrac{\partial \beta}{\partial u}=0, \\[2ex] \dfrac{\partial \alpha}{\partial u}\dfrac{\partial \beta}{\partial u}+\dfrac{\partial \alpha}{\partial v}\dfrac{\partial \beta}{\partial v}=-\dfrac{1}{2\sigma D_0'}. \end{cases}$$

Conversely, if we have a solution of this system, and define functions ω, Δ and Δ'' by (23) and Δ' by (15), we find that ω and Δ' satisfy (18). Since the corresponding equations (17) are consistent, we obtain (16). Then a surface $\bar{S}$ applicable to Q is defined intrinsically by (14), and we have:

The determination of permanent nets on a quadric is equivalent to the solution of equations (24).

134. The permanent net on a deform of a quadric. When a quadric Q and an applicable surface $\bar{S}$ are referred to the permanent nets N and $\bar{N}$, we have, in consequence of (21),

$$\text{(25)}\qquad \sigma^4=-\frac{DD''}{H^2}=\frac{\bar{D}'^2}{H^2},\qquad H^2=EG-F^2,$$

where $\sigma^4=-K$, K being the total curvature of Q and $\bar{S}$, and the linear element of Q and $\bar{S}$ is

$$\text{(26)}\qquad ds^2=E\,du^2+2F\,du\,dv+G\,dv^2.$$

If we define two functions a and b by means of the equations

$$\text{(27)}\qquad D=-\sigma a^2,\qquad D''=\sigma b^2,$$

we have from (22)

$$\text{(28)}\qquad a^2-b^2=\frac{1}{\sigma^2}.$$

In consequence of (21) and (25), we may take

$$(29)\qquad -\overline{D} = \overline{D}'' = \sigma a b, \qquad H\sigma = a b.$$

The Codazzi equations for N and $\overline{N}$ are [cf. § 64]

$$(30)\quad \begin{cases} \dfrac{\partial D}{\partial v} = D\begin{Bmatrix}12\\1\end{Bmatrix} - D''\begin{Bmatrix}11\\2\end{Bmatrix}, & \dfrac{\partial D''}{\partial u} = -\begin{Bmatrix}22\\1\end{Bmatrix}D + \begin{Bmatrix}12\\2\end{Bmatrix}D'', \\[2ex] \dfrac{\partial \overline{D}}{\partial v} = \overline{D}\left(\begin{Bmatrix}12\\1\end{Bmatrix} + \begin{Bmatrix}11\\2\end{Bmatrix}\right), & \dfrac{\partial \overline{D}}{\partial u} = \overline{D}\left(\begin{Bmatrix}22\\1\end{Bmatrix} + \begin{Bmatrix}12\\2\end{Bmatrix}\right), \end{cases}$$

the Christoffel symbols $\begin{Bmatrix}rs\\t\end{Bmatrix}$ being formed with respect to (26).

From these equations, in which D, D'' and $\overline{D}$ are replaced by their expressions from (27) and (29), and the identities [cf. § 63]

$$(31)\qquad \frac{\partial \log H}{\partial u} = \begin{Bmatrix}11\\1\end{Bmatrix} + \begin{Bmatrix}12\\2\end{Bmatrix}, \qquad \frac{\partial \log H}{\partial v} = \begin{Bmatrix}22\\2\end{Bmatrix} + \begin{Bmatrix}12\\1\end{Bmatrix},$$

we obtain, in consequence of (28),

$$(32)\quad \begin{cases} \begin{Bmatrix}11\\1\end{Bmatrix} = \dfrac{\partial}{\partial u}\log\dfrac{a}{\sigma}, & \begin{Bmatrix}12\\1\end{Bmatrix} = \dfrac{\partial}{\partial v}\log a, & \begin{Bmatrix}22\\1\end{Bmatrix} = \dfrac{b^2}{a^2}\dfrac{\partial}{\partial u}\log b\sigma, \\[2ex] \begin{Bmatrix}11\\2\end{Bmatrix} = \dfrac{a^2}{b^2}\dfrac{\partial}{\partial v}\log a\sigma, & \begin{Bmatrix}12\\2\end{Bmatrix} = \dfrac{\partial}{\partial u}\log b, & \begin{Bmatrix}22\\2\end{Bmatrix} = \dfrac{\partial}{\partial v}\log\dfrac{b}{\sigma}. \end{cases}$$

If $\overline{x}, \overline{y}, \overline{z}$ denote the cartesian coordinates of $\overline{S}$, from the Gauss equations [§ 64, (7)] for $\overline{S}$ we have that $\overline{x}, \overline{y}, \overline{z}$ are solutions of the equations:

$$(33)\quad \begin{cases} \dfrac{\partial^2\theta}{\partial u^2} + \dfrac{\partial^2\theta}{\partial v^2} = 2\dfrac{\partial \log a}{\partial u}\dfrac{\partial\theta}{\partial u} + 2\dfrac{\partial \log b}{\partial v}\dfrac{\partial\theta}{\partial v}, \\[2ex] \dfrac{\partial^2\theta}{\partial u\,\partial v} = \dfrac{\partial \log a}{\partial v}\dfrac{\partial\theta}{\partial u} + \dfrac{\partial \log b}{\partial u}\dfrac{\partial\theta}{\partial v}. \end{cases}$$

Hence from § 45 we have:

The permanent net on a deform of a quadric is an R net[127]).

---

[127]) Cf. Tzitzeica, Comptes Rendus, vol. 152 (1911), p. 1077; also Bianchi, Rendiconti dei Lincei, ser. 5, vol. 22 (1913), p. 3.

We desire to prove the converse theorem:

When the functions a and b in the equations (33) *of an R net satisfy the condition* (28), *the net is applicable to a net on a quadric.*

From (31) and (33) we have for any R net $\overline{N}$

$$\begin{Bmatrix}11\\1\end{Bmatrix}=\frac{\partial}{\partial u}\log\frac{H}{b},\qquad \begin{Bmatrix}12\\1\end{Bmatrix}=\frac{\partial\log a}{\partial v},\qquad \begin{Bmatrix}22\\1\end{Bmatrix}=\frac{\partial}{\partial u}\log\frac{a^2 b}{H},$$
$$\begin{Bmatrix}11\\2\end{Bmatrix}=\frac{\partial}{\partial v}\log\frac{ab^2}{H},\qquad \begin{Bmatrix}12\\2\end{Bmatrix}=\frac{\partial\log b}{\partial u},\qquad \begin{Bmatrix}22\\2\end{Bmatrix}=\frac{\partial}{\partial v}\log\frac{H}{a}.$$

When these values are substituted in the second set of (30), we find that the second fundamental coefficients of an R net satisfying (33) are of the form $-\overline{D}=\overline{D}''=a^2b^2/H$. Then since $\overline{D}\,\overline{D}''=-\sigma^4H^2$, we may take $H\sigma=ab$, in which case we have (29) and the above expressions for the Christoffel symbols are reducible to (32), in consequence of (28). As a result we have that (27) furnishes a solution of the first set of (30) in which the symbols have the values (32); that is $\overline{N}$ admits an applicable net N, for which the second fundamental coefficients are given by (27).

If α and β are the parameters of the asymptotic lines of the surface S on which N lies, we have

$$\lambda\, d\alpha = a\,du - b\,dv,\qquad \mu\, d\beta = a\,du + b\,dv,$$

where the integrating factors λ, μ are subject to the conditions

$$\frac{\partial}{\partial v}\left(\frac{a}{\lambda}\right)+\frac{\partial}{\partial u}\left(\frac{b}{\lambda}\right)=0,\qquad \frac{\partial}{\partial v}\left(\frac{a}{\mu}\right)-\frac{\partial}{\partial u}\left(\frac{b}{\mu}\right)=0.$$

In consequence of (27), (29) and [§ 64, (7)] the coordinates of S satisfy the equations

$$b^2\frac{\partial^2\theta}{\partial u^2}+a^2\frac{\partial^2\theta}{\partial v^2}=b^2\frac{\partial}{\partial u}\log ab\,\frac{\partial\theta}{\partial u}+a^2\frac{\partial}{\partial v}\log ab\,\frac{\partial\theta}{\partial v},$$
$$\frac{\partial^2\theta}{\partial u\,\partial v}=\frac{\partial\log a}{\partial v}\,\frac{\partial\theta}{\partial u}+\frac{\partial\log b}{\partial u}\,\frac{\partial\theta}{\partial v}.$$

If we express these equations in terms of α and β, we obtain

$$ab\left(\frac{1}{\lambda^2}\frac{\partial^2\theta}{\partial\alpha^2}+\frac{1}{\mu^2}\frac{\partial^2\theta}{\partial\beta^2}\right)+\frac{1}{2}\frac{\partial\theta}{\partial\alpha}\left[b\frac{\partial}{\partial u}\left(\frac{1}{\lambda}\right)-a\frac{\partial}{\partial v}\left(\frac{1}{\lambda}\right)-\frac{1}{\lambda}\frac{\partial b}{\partial u}+\frac{1}{\lambda}\frac{\partial a}{\partial v}\right]$$
$$+\frac{1}{2}\frac{\partial\theta}{\partial\beta}\left[b\frac{\partial}{\partial u}\left(\frac{1}{\mu}\right)+a\frac{\partial}{\partial v}\left(\frac{1}{\mu}\right)-\frac{1}{\mu}\frac{\partial b}{\partial u}-\frac{1}{\mu}\frac{\partial a}{\partial v}\right]=0,$$
$$ab\left(-\frac{1}{\lambda^2}\frac{\partial^2\theta}{\partial\alpha^2}+\frac{1}{\mu^2}\frac{\partial^2\theta}{\partial\beta^2}\right)+\frac{\partial\theta}{\partial\alpha}\left[a\frac{\partial}{\partial v}\left(\frac{1}{\lambda}\right)+\frac{1}{\lambda}\frac{\partial b}{\partial u}\right]$$
$$+\frac{\partial\theta}{\partial\beta}\left[a\frac{\partial}{\partial v}\left(\frac{1}{\mu}\right)-\frac{1}{\mu}\frac{\partial b}{\partial u}\right]=0.$$

Adding and substracting these equations, the resulting equations are reducible in consequence of the above conditions on λ and μ to the form

$$\frac{\partial^2\theta}{\partial\alpha^2}=A\frac{\partial\theta}{\partial\alpha},\qquad \frac{\partial^2\theta}{\partial\beta^2}=B\frac{\partial\theta}{\partial\beta},$$

and consequently S is a quadric.

135. Transformations F_k of permanent nets on a central quadric. For the central quadric Q, whose equation is

(34) $$ex^2+fy^2+gz^2=1,$$

we have

(35) $$X,\ Y,\ Z=\frac{ex,\ fy,\ gz}{\sqrt{\sum e^2x^2}},$$

and the Gaussian curvature is given by[128])

(36) $$K=-\frac{1}{c^4\left(\sum e^2x^2\right)^2},\qquad \frac{1}{\sigma}=c\sqrt{\sum e^2x^2},$$

where $c^4=-1/efg$.

If Q is referred to a net N whose point equation is the second of (33), we have

(37) $$\frac{\partial}{\partial v}\log\left[\sum e\left(\frac{\partial x}{\partial u}\right)^2\right]=\frac{\partial}{\partial v}\log a^2,\quad \frac{\partial}{\partial u}\log\left[\sum e\left(\frac{\partial x}{\partial v}\right)^2\right]=\frac{\partial}{\partial u}\log b^2,$$

---

128) Cf. C. Smith, Solid Geometry, 9th edition, p. 223.

and also

$$\sum e \frac{\partial x}{\partial u}\frac{\partial x}{\partial v} = 0. \tag{38}$$

Hence

$$\sum e \left(\frac{\partial x}{\partial u}\right)^2 = a^2 U, \qquad \sum e \left(\frac{\partial x}{\partial v}\right)^2 = b^2 V, \tag{39}$$

where U and V are functions of u and v alone.

In consequence of (27), (32), and the Gauss equations for Q we find

$$\left\{\begin{aligned} \frac{\partial}{\partial u}\left[\sum e \left(\frac{\partial x}{\partial u}\right)^2\right] &= \frac{\partial}{\partial u}\log\frac{a^2}{\sigma^2}\sum e\left(\frac{\partial x}{\partial u}\right)^2 - 2\sigma a^2 \sum e X \frac{\partial x}{\partial u}, \\ \frac{\partial}{\partial v}\left[\sum e \left(\frac{\partial x}{\partial v}\right)^2\right] &= \frac{\partial}{\partial v}\log\frac{b^2}{\sigma^2}\sum e\left(\frac{\partial x}{\partial v}\right)^2 + 2\sigma b^2 \sum e X \frac{\partial x}{\partial v}. \end{aligned}\right. \tag{40}$$

From (35) and (36) we have

$$\sum e X \frac{\partial x}{\partial u} = \frac{1}{c}\frac{\partial}{\partial u}\left(\frac{1}{\sigma}\right), \qquad \sum e X \frac{\partial x}{\partial v} = \frac{1}{c}\frac{\partial}{\partial v}\left(\frac{1}{\sigma}\right). \tag{41}$$

When the expressions (39) are substituted in (40), the result is reducible by means of (41) to

$$\frac{1}{2}\frac{\partial U}{\partial u} = -\left(U - \frac{1}{c}\right)\frac{\partial \log \sigma}{\partial u}, \qquad \frac{1}{2}\frac{\partial V}{\partial v} = -\left(V + \frac{1}{c}\right)\frac{\partial \log \sigma}{\partial v}.$$

Also on differentiating equation (38) with respect to u and v we get

$$(U+V)\frac{\partial \log a}{\partial v} + \left(V + \frac{1}{c}\right)\frac{\partial \log \sigma}{\partial v} = 0,$$

$$(U+V)\frac{\partial \log b}{\partial u} + \left(U - \frac{1}{c}\right)\frac{\partial \log \sigma}{\partial u} = 0.$$

From these two sets of equations it follows that $U = -V = 1/c$, and consequently

$$\sum e \left(\frac{\partial x}{\partial u}\right)^2 = \frac{a^2}{c}, \qquad \sum e \left(\frac{\partial x}{\partial v}\right)^2 = -\frac{b^2}{c}. \tag{42}$$

Hence from (28) and (36) we have the theorem:

For any permanent net on a central quadric (34) *the coordinates satisfy the condition*

$$\sum e\left(\frac{\partial x}{\partial u}\right)^2+\sum e\left(\frac{\partial x}{\partial v}\right)^2=c\sum e^2x^2, \tag{43}$$

where $c^4=-1/efg$[129]).

This equation may be written

$$a^2-b^2=c^2\sum e^2x^2. \tag{44}$$

Suppose, conversely, we have a net N on the quadric (34) satisfying the condition (43). Since equations (39) hold for any net on the quadric, the functions a and b in the point equation of N can be chosen so that we have (42). If these equations are differentiated with respect to u and v respectively, and the Gauss equations [§ 64, (7)] are used, the resulting equations are reducible by means of (41) to

$$\left\{\begin{aligned}&a^2\begin{Bmatrix}11\\1\end{Bmatrix}+\frac{\partial}{\partial u}\left(\frac{1}{\sigma}\right)D-a\frac{\partial a}{\partial u}=0,\\&b^2\begin{Bmatrix}22\\2\end{Bmatrix}-\frac{\partial}{\partial v}\left(\frac{1}{\sigma}\right)D''-b\frac{\partial b}{\partial v}=0.\end{aligned}\right. \tag{45}$$

From (38) and (42) we have

$$-\frac{a^2b^2}{c^2}=\sum ef\left(\frac{\partial x}{\partial u}\frac{\partial y}{\partial v}-\frac{\partial x}{\partial v}\frac{\partial y}{\partial u}\right)^2=H^2\sum ef\,Z^2=-\frac{H^2\sigma^2}{c^2}.$$

Hence, if we take $H\sigma=ab$, from (31) we obtain

$$\begin{Bmatrix}11\\1\end{Bmatrix}=\frac{\partial}{\partial u}\log\frac{a}{\sigma},\qquad\begin{Bmatrix}22\\2\end{Bmatrix}=\frac{\partial}{\partial v}\log\frac{b}{\sigma}. \tag{46}$$

In consequence of these expressions equations (45) give $D=-\sigma a^2$, $D''=\sigma b^2$. Substituting these expressions in the first

---

129) Cf. Calapso, Annali, ser. 3, vol. 19 (1912), p. 62.

set of equations (30) and making use of (28), which is a consequence of (42) and (43), we get the expressions (32). When these values are substituted in the second set of (30), a solution is $-\overline{D} = \overline{D}'' = \sigma a b$. Hence there exists a net $\overline{N}$ applicable to N. Therefore:

When a net on a central quadric (34) *satisfies the condition* (43), *it is a permanent net.*

Let N be a permanent net on the quadric Q (34). From (3) and (4) it follows that if in the equations of the form

$$x_1 = x - \frac{\theta}{\theta'} x' \tag{47}$$

we put

$$\theta = 2(exx' + fyy' + gzz') \equiv 2\sum exx', \qquad \theta' = \sum ex'^2, \tag{48}$$

the F transform N_1 of N lies on Q. In order that N_1 be a permanent net it is sufficient that

$$\sum e\left(\frac{\partial x_1}{\partial u}\right)^2 + \sum e\left(\frac{\partial x_1}{\partial v}\right)^2 = c\sum e^2 x_1^2. \tag{49}$$

From (47) we have by differentiation

$$\frac{\partial x_1}{\partial u} = \frac{\tau}{\theta'^2}\left(x'\frac{\partial \theta}{\partial u} - \theta'\frac{\partial x}{\partial u}\right), \qquad \frac{\partial x_1}{\partial v} = \frac{\sigma}{\theta'^2}\left(x'\frac{\partial \theta}{\partial v} - \theta'\frac{\partial x}{\partial v}\right), \tag{50}$$

where

$$\tau = h\theta - \theta', \qquad \sigma = l\theta - \theta'. \tag{51}$$

Substituting these expressions in (49), we can reduce the resulting equation by means of (42) to

$$\tau^2 a^2 - \sigma^2 b^2 = c^2 \theta'^2 \sum e^2 x_1^2. \tag{52}$$

In consequence of (II, 16) we have from (51)

$$\left\{\begin{aligned} \frac{\partial}{\partial v}\left(\frac{\tau}{\theta'}\right) &= \frac{\sigma - \tau}{\theta'}\frac{\partial}{\partial v}\log a - \frac{h\sigma}{\theta'^2}\frac{\partial \theta}{\partial v}, \\ \frac{\partial}{\partial u}\left(\frac{\sigma}{\theta'}\right) &= \frac{\tau - \sigma}{\theta'}\frac{\partial}{\partial u}\log b - \frac{l\tau}{\theta'^2}\frac{\partial \theta}{\partial u}. \end{aligned}\right. \tag{53}$$

Differentiating (52) and making use of (53), the resulting equations are reducible to

$$\frac{\partial \varphi}{\partial u}+\frac{1}{\theta}\frac{\partial \theta}{\partial u}\Big[-\frac{b^2}{\theta'^2}\, l\,\theta\,(\tau-\sigma)+c^2\sum e^2 x_1\,(x_1-x)$$
$$+c^2\frac{\tau}{\theta'}\sum e^2 x\,(x_1-x)\Big]=0,$$

$$\frac{\partial \varphi}{\partial v}+\frac{1}{\theta}\frac{\partial \theta}{\partial v}\Big[\frac{a^2}{\theta'^2}\, h\,\theta\,(\sigma-\tau)+c^2\sum e^2 x_1\,(x_1-x)$$
$$+c^2\frac{\sigma}{\theta'}\sum e^2 x\,(x_1-x)\Big]=0,$$

where

(54) $$\varphi=a^2\frac{\tau}{\theta'}-b^2\frac{\sigma}{\theta'}+c^2\sum e^2 x x_1.$$

By means of (44), (51), (52) and (54) these equations are reducible to

(55) $$\frac{\partial \varphi}{\partial u}+\frac{\varphi}{\theta}\frac{\partial \theta}{\partial u}\left(\frac{h\theta}{\theta'}-2\right)=0,\qquad \frac{\partial \varphi}{\partial v}+\frac{\varphi}{\theta}\frac{\partial \theta}{\partial v}\left(\frac{l\theta}{\theta'}-2\right)=0,$$

which can be integrated in the form

(56) $$\varphi\,\theta'=-\frac{k c^2}{2}\,\theta^2,$$

where k is an arbitrary constant. When this value for φ is substituted in (54), this equation and (52) are equivalent, in consequence of (47) and (51), to

(57) $$h^2 a^2-l^2 b^2=c^2\sum(e^2-k e)\,x'^2,\qquad h a^2-l b^2=c^2\sum(e^2-k e)\,x x'.$$

Differentiating the second of these equations, we obtain

(58) $$\begin{cases}\dfrac{\partial h}{\partial u}+2\,\dfrac{\partial \log a}{\partial u}\,h-2\,\dfrac{b^2}{a^2}\,\dfrac{\partial \log b}{\partial u}\,l-\dfrac{c^2}{a^2}\sum(e^2-k e)\,x'\,\dfrac{\partial x}{\partial u}=0,\\[2mm] \dfrac{\partial l}{\partial v}+2\,\dfrac{\partial \log b}{\partial v}\,l-2\,\dfrac{a^2}{b^2}\,\dfrac{\partial \log a}{\partial v}\,h+\dfrac{c^2}{b^2}\sum(e^2-k e)\,x'\,\dfrac{\partial x}{\partial v}=0,\end{cases}$$

in consequence of (44) and

$$
(59)\begin{cases}
\dfrac{\partial h}{\partial v} = (l-h)\dfrac{\partial \log a}{\partial v}, \qquad \dfrac{\partial l}{\partial u} = (h-l)\dfrac{\partial \log b}{\partial u};\\
\dfrac{\partial x'}{\partial u} = h\dfrac{\partial x}{\partial u},\ \dfrac{\partial x'}{\partial v} = l\dfrac{\partial x}{\partial v}; \qquad \dfrac{\partial y'}{\partial u} = h\dfrac{\partial y}{\partial u},\ \dfrac{\partial y'}{\partial v} = l\dfrac{\partial y}{\partial v};\\
\dfrac{\partial z'}{\partial u} = h\dfrac{\partial z}{\partial u}, \qquad \dfrac{\partial z'}{\partial v} = l\dfrac{\partial z}{\partial v}.
\end{cases}
$$

It is readily found that equations (58) and (59) form a completely integrable system, in consequence of (44). Moreover, for every set of solutions of this system equations (57) are satisfied to within additive constants, as is found by differentiation. Hence each set of solutions satisfying (57) determines an F transform which is a permanent net. From (47), (48) and (59) it is seen that if x', y', z', h and l are multiplied by the same constant, the transform N_1 is unaltered. Hence when k is any constant different from e, f and g, there are ∞^2 sets of solutions satisfying (57) and giving distinct transforms.

When $k = e$, there are ∞^1 sets of solution s, y', z', h and l of (58) and (59) satisfying (57). Thenx' is given by a quadrature (59) and involves an additive constant, say m. In this case each set of solution s, y', z', h and l determines ∞^1 transformations, such that the corresponding points of the ∞^1 transforms lie on a conic, the section of quadric by a plane parallel to the lines from the origin to the points $(x'+m, y', z')$ as m varies. Similar results hold when $k = f$ or $k = g$. Hence:

A permanent net on a central quadric $ex^2+fy^2+gz^2 = 1$ admits ∞^2 transformations F_k into permanent nets on the quadric for each value of the constant k; when k is equal to e, f or g, the transforms N_1 may be grouped into ∞^1 families of ∞^1 transforms each such that corresponding points of the nets of a family lie on a conic[130]).

136. Transformations F_k of surfaces applicable to a central quadric. It is our purpose to show that each transformation F of a permanent net N on a quadric Q into a permanent net N_1 on Q leads directly to a transformation F of the net $\overline{N}$ applicable to N into the net $\overline{N}_1$ applicable to N_1. In fact, we

130) Cf. Journ. de Math., ser. 8, vol. 4 (1921), pp. 37—66.

shall show that it is possible to find without quadratures a net $\overline{N}'$ parallel to $\overline{N}$ such that θ' given by (48) can be put in the form (cf. II, 95)

$$\theta' = k\left(\sum x'^2 - \sum \overline{x}'^2\right), \tag{60}$$

and then the desired transform is defined by

$$\overline{x}_1 = \overline{x} - \frac{\theta}{\theta'}\overline{x}'. \tag{61}$$

Equating these expressions for θ', we have

$$(e-k)x'^2 + (f-k)y'^2 + (g-k)z'^2 + k\sum \overline{x}'^2 = 0. \tag{62}$$

Differentiating this expression and assuming that equations of the form

$$\frac{\partial \overline{x}'}{\partial u} = h\frac{\partial \overline{x}}{\partial u}, \qquad \frac{\partial \overline{x}'}{\partial v} = l\frac{\partial \overline{x}}{\partial v}, \tag{63}$$

hold, we obtain

$$\begin{cases} (e-k)x'\dfrac{\partial x}{\partial u} + (f-k)y'\dfrac{\partial y}{\partial u} + (g-k)z'\dfrac{\partial z}{\partial u} + k\sum \overline{x}'\dfrac{\partial \overline{x}}{\partial u} = 0, \\ (e-k)x'\dfrac{\partial x}{\partial v} + (f-k)y'\dfrac{\partial y}{\partial v} + (g-k)z'\dfrac{\partial z}{\partial v} + k\sum \overline{x}'\dfrac{\partial \overline{x}}{\partial v} = 0. \end{cases} \tag{64}$$

If these equations are differentiated with respect to u and v and in the reduction use is made of equations [§ 64, (7)] for N and $\overline{N}$, two of the resulting equations are satisfied identically in consequence of (64) and the other two are reducible to

$$\begin{cases} h\sum e\left(\dfrac{\partial x}{\partial u}\right)^2 + D\sum (e-k)x'X + k\overline{D}\sum \overline{x}'\overline{X} = 0, \\ l\sum e\left(\dfrac{\partial x}{\partial v}\right)^2 + D''\sum (e-k)x'X + k\overline{D}''\sum \overline{x}'\overline{X} = 0. \end{cases} \tag{65}$$

In consequence of (27), (28), (29), (35), (42) and the second of (57) these two equations are equivalent to

$$(h-l)\sigma a b + ck\sum \overline{x}'\overline{X} = 0. \tag{66}$$

Solving equations (64) and (66) for $\overline{x}'$, $\overline{y}'$, $\overline{z}'$, we have expressions of the form

$$(67)\quad \begin{cases} k\overline{x}' = \dfrac{\sigma ab}{c}(l-h)\overline{X} + \dfrac{1}{H^2}\left[\dfrac{\partial \overline{x}}{\partial u}\sum(e-k)x'\left(F\dfrac{\partial x}{\partial v} - G\dfrac{\partial x}{\partial u}\right)\right. \\ \qquad\left. + \dfrac{\partial \overline{x}}{\partial v}\sum(e-k)x'\left(F\dfrac{\partial x}{\partial u} - E\dfrac{\partial x}{\partial v}\right)\right]. \end{cases}$$

If we differentiate these expressions, we find that $\overline{x}'$, $\overline{y}'$, $\overline{z}'$ satisfy equations of the form (63), by making use of equations of §§ 134, 135 and of [§ 63].

Also from (67) we have, with the aid of [§ 48, (11)],

$$(68)\quad k^2\sum\overline{x}'^2 = \frac{\sigma^2a^2b^2}{c^2}(l-h)^2 + \sum(e-k)^2x'^2 - \left(\sum(e-k)x'X\right)^2.$$

Substituting this expression in (62), we find that it is satisfied in virtue of (57).

From these results and the last theorem of § 135 we have, when k is not equal to 0, e, f or g, the theorem:

If $\overline{N}$ is a net applicable to a net N on a central quadric $ex^2 + fy^2 + gz^2 = 1$, for each value of k different from e, f, g and zero, there exist ∞^2 transformations F_k of $\overline{N}$ into nets $\overline{N}_1$ applicable to the quadric; these transforms are conjugate to ∞^2 congruences G; their determination requires the finding of solutions of a completely integrable system of equations subject to a quadratic and a linear homogeneous relation[131].

When $k = e$, the function x' is determined to within an additive constant m, as seen in § 135. There are only ∞^1 sets of solutions y', z', h and l, and in consequence from (67) it follows that there are only ∞^1 congruences G of the ∞^2 transformations. As m varies we obtain ∞^1 transforms N_1 conjugate to the same congruence. They are defined by (61) with

$$\theta = 2\sum exx' + 2mex, \qquad \theta' = e(x'+m)^2 + fy'^2 + gz'^2.$$

From this expression for θ and the results of § 23 it follows that the tangent planes at corresponding points of these nets N_1 enve-

---

[131]) Journ. de Math. l. c. p. 53.

lope a cone. If ξ_0, η_0, ζ_0 are the coordinates of the vertex, the equation of the tangent plane is

$$(\xi-\xi_0)X_1+(\eta-\eta_0)Y_1+(\zeta-\zeta_0)Z_1=0,$$

where ξ, η, ζ are current coordinates, and X_1, Y_1 and Z_1 are direction-parameters of the normal to N_1. When their expressions are calculated, it is found that they involve m to the second degree, and consequently the cone is a quadric.

When $k=e$, x' does not appear in (62) and (64). Solving the latter for y' and z', and substituting in (62), we obtain a homogeneous quadratic equation in $\overline{x}'$, $\overline{y}'$, $\overline{z}'$. Hence the lines of the congruences G through a point of N form a quadric cone. Since similar results hold when k is equal to f or g, we have in consequence of the last theorem of § 135 the theorem:

If $\overline{N}$ is a net applicable to a net N on the central quadric Q (34), *there are ∞^2 sets of solutions of equations* (57), (58), (59) *with k equal to e, f or g; there are thus three families of ∞^2 transforms $\overline{N}_1$ of $\overline{N}$ which are applicable to Q; the transforms of each family are conjugate to ∞^1 congruences G, there being ∞^1 transforms conjugate to each G; the lines of the congruences G through a point of $\overline{N}$ form a quadric cone; the tangent planes at points of a line of G of the nets $\overline{N}_1$ conjugate to it envelop a quadric cone, and the points on Q corresponding to these points of the nets $\overline{N}_1$ on a line of G lie on a conic*[132]).

When Q is the quadric of revolution $e(x^2+y^2)+gz^2=1$, the transformations of the type described in the first of the above theorems exist. There is, however, only one family of transformations of the type described in the second theorem; they are F_g. When $k=e$, equation (62) may be written

$$\sum \overline{x}'^2-\left(1-\frac{g}{e}\right)z'^2=0. \tag{69}$$

---

132) The two types of transformation set forth in this section were discovered by Guichard in a different manner in his *Mémoire sur la deformation des quadrics*, Mémoires à L'Académie des Sciences de France, ser. 2, vol. 24 (1909). His method did not reveal the relation between the nets N and N_1 on the quadric in either case, nor did he show that the nets $\overline{N}$ and $\overline{N}_1$ are in relation F when $k=c$, f or g. These results were announced by the auther in 1919, Trans. Amer. Math. Soc., vol. 20 (1919), pp. 323—338.

From the results of § 100 it follows that N is a net 2, O and consequently $\overline{N}$ is 2, O. From (69) it follows that $\overline{N}'$ is one of the two special nets 2, O parallal to $\overline{N}$, the complementary function being

$$\overline{t}' = \sqrt{1 - \frac{g}{e}}\, z'. \tag{70}$$

Suppose conversely that we take for $\overline{N}'$ one of these two special nets 2, O and define z' by (70). Equations (64) and (65) hold for $k = e = f$. Adding equations (65), we have in consequence of (27), (28), (29), (35) and (42), the second of (57). From these follow (66), (67), (68), and then the first of (57), as in the general case. Thus h and l determined by $\overline{N}'$ satisfy the equations of § 135, z' is given directly by (70) and x' and y' by the quadratures (59), and thus involve additive arbitrary constants.

Each of the two parallel special 2, O nets $\overline{N}'$ determines a normal congruence conjugate to $\overline{N}$ (§ 61). In accordance with the theorem of Beltrami (§ 112) and the results of § 100, when the net $\overline{N}$ is applied to its applicable net N on Q, the lines of these two normal congruences coincide with the lines joining points of N to the foci on the axis of revolution of Q. Hence we have the theorem:

Let $\overline{N}$ be a net applicable to a net N on a central quadric of revolution Q; the lines joining points of N to the foci of Q on the axis of revolution become lines of two normal congruences G_1 and G_2, conjugate to $\overline{N}$ when N is applied to $\overline{N}$; there can be found by two quadratures ∞^2 nets $\overline{N}_1$ conjugate to G_1 and ∞^2 nets $\overline{N}_2$ conjugate G_2 which are applicable to ∞^2 nets N_1 and ∞^2 nets N_2 on Q; the nets $\overline{N}_1$, or $\overline{N}_2$, can be grouped into ∞^1 families of ∞^1 nets such that their tangent planes at points on the same line of the congruence form a quadric cone and the corresponding points of the applicable nets on Q lie on a conic[133]).

When Q is a sphere, real or imaginary, with the equation $e(x^2 + y^2 + z^2) = 1$, an applicable net $\overline{N}$ consists of the lines of curvature on a surface of constant gaussian curvature, since every

133) In order to obtain one of these families we hold fixed the additive constant in x' and let the additive constant of y' vary, and vice-versa; cf. Trans. Amer. Math. Soc., l. c., p. 337.

net on Q is orthogonal. If we take $k = e$, it follows from (62) that $\overline{N}'$ is a cone; hence there are no transformations of the type of the second theorem. When $k \neq e$, we have from (60) and (62) $\theta' = \frac{ek}{k-e} \sum \overline{x}'^2$, that is the transformation is R (§ 67). Hence:

A surface of constant gaussian curvature admits ∞^3 transformations R into surfaces of the same curvature.

137. Theorem of permutability of transformations F_k of surfaces applicable to a central quadric. Let $\overline{N}_1(\overline{x}_1)$ and $\overline{N}_2(\overline{x}_2)$ be obtained from a net $\overline{N}(\overline{x})$ applicable to a net $N(x)$ on Q by means of transformations F_{k_1} and F_{k_2}, and let $N_1(x_1)$ and $N_2(x_2)$ be the nets on Q to which $\overline{N}_1$ and $\overline{N}_2$ are applicable. Let θ_1 and θ_2 be the functions of these transformations, where

$$(71) \quad \theta_1' = k_1 \left(\sum x'^2 - \sum \overline{x}'^2\right), \qquad \theta_2'' = k_2 \left(\sum x''^2 - \sum \overline{x}''^2\right),$$

$\overline{x}', \overline{x}''$; x', x'' being obtained from $\overline{x}$ and x by the quadratures

$$(72) \quad \begin{cases} \dfrac{\partial \overline{x}'}{\partial u} = h_1 \dfrac{\partial \overline{x}}{\partial u}, \quad \dfrac{\partial \overline{x}'}{\partial v} = l_1 \dfrac{\partial \overline{x}}{\partial v}; \qquad \dfrac{\partial \overline{x}''}{\partial u} = h_2 \dfrac{\partial \overline{x}}{\partial u}, \quad \dfrac{\partial \overline{x}''}{\partial v} = l_2 \dfrac{\partial \overline{x}}{\partial v}, \\[2ex] \dfrac{\partial x'}{\partial u} = h_1 \dfrac{\partial x}{\partial u}, \quad \dfrac{\partial x'}{\partial v} = l_1 \dfrac{\partial x}{\partial v}; \qquad \dfrac{\partial x''}{\partial u} = h_2 \dfrac{\partial x}{\partial u}, \quad \dfrac{\partial x''}{\partial v} = l_2 \dfrac{\partial x}{\partial v}. \end{cases}$$

We seek under what conditions the net $\overline{N}_{12}$ whose coordinates are of the form

$$(73) \qquad \overline{x}_{12} = \overline{x}_1 - \frac{\theta_{12}}{\theta_{12}'''} \overline{x}_1''',$$

where (cf. §§ 20, 21)

$$(74) \quad \begin{cases} \overline{x}_1''' = \overline{x}'' - \dfrac{\theta_1''}{\theta_1'} \overline{x}', \qquad \theta_{12} = \theta_2 - \dfrac{\theta_2'}{\theta_1'} \theta_1, \qquad \theta_{12}''' = \theta_2'' - \dfrac{\theta_1''}{\theta_1'} \theta_2', \\[2ex] \dfrac{\partial \theta_1''}{\partial u} = h_2 \dfrac{\partial \theta_1}{\partial u}, \quad \dfrac{\partial \theta_1''}{\partial v} = l_2 \dfrac{\partial \theta_1}{\partial v}, \quad \dfrac{\partial \theta_2'}{\partial u} = h_1 \dfrac{\partial \theta_2}{\partial u}, \quad \dfrac{\partial \theta_2'}{\partial v} = l_1 \dfrac{\partial \theta_2}{\partial v}, \end{cases}$$

is applicable to a net N_{12} on Q, defined by

$$(75) \qquad x_{12} = x_1 - \frac{\theta_{12}}{\theta_{12}'''} x_1''', \qquad x_1''' = x'' - \frac{\theta_1''}{\theta_1'} x'.$$

If we put

$$(76) \qquad \theta_{12}''' = k_2 \left(\sum x_1'''^2 - \sum \overline{x}_1'''^2\right),$$

we find that this expression is equivalent to that of (74) if

$$(77) \qquad k_2\,\theta_1'' + k_1\,\theta_2' - 2\,k_1 k_2 \left(\sum x' x'' - \sum \bar{x}' \bar{x}''\right) = 0.$$

When the left-hand member of this equation is differentiated, it is found to be constant in consequence of (71), (72) and (74). Hence the additive constants entering in θ_1'' and θ_2' can be chosen so that (77) holds.

From (6) it follows that N_{12} defined by (75) is on Q, if

$$(78) \qquad \theta_1'' + \theta_2' - 2\,(e x' x'' + f y' y'' + g z' z'') = 0.$$

Solving equations (77) and (78) for θ_1'' and θ_2', we find expressions which satisfy (74). Hence:

If $\bar{N}_1$ and $\bar{N}_2$ are transforms of a net $\bar{N}$ applicable to a net N on a central quadric Q by means of transformations F_{k_1} and F_{k_2} $(k_2 \neq k_1)$, there can be found directly a net $\bar{N}_{12}$, applicable to a net N_{12} on Q, which is in relations F'_{k_2} and F'_{k_1} with $\bar{N}_1$ and $\bar{N}_2$ respectively.

This theorem holds when k_1 or k_2, or both, is equal to e, f or g, but $k_1 \neq k_2$. It holds equally when Q is a central quadric of revolution, or a sphere, real or imaginary[134]).

138. Transformations B_k of surfaces applicable to a central quadric. Let $\bar{N}(\bar{x})$ be a net applicable to a net $N(x)$ on the central quadric (34). We consider a transformation F_k of $\bar{N}$ and N as treated in § 136. We have

$$(79) \qquad \theta = 2 \sum e x x'.$$

From (35) and (36) we have

$$(80) \qquad \sum e x' \mathrm{X} = c\sigma \sum e^2 x x'.$$

By differentiation of (79) we have

$$(81) \qquad \frac{\partial \theta}{\partial u} = 2 \sum e x' \frac{\partial x}{\partial u}, \qquad \frac{\partial \theta}{\partial v} = 2 \sum e x' \frac{\partial x}{\partial v},$$

134) Trans. Amer. Math. Soc., l. c., pp. 324. 335.

and with the aid of (27), (28), (42) and (57) we find

$$(82)\quad \begin{cases} \dfrac{\partial^2\theta}{\partial u^2} = \left\{ {11 \atop 1} \right\} \dfrac{\partial\theta}{\partial u} + \left\{ {11 \atop 2} \right\} \dfrac{\partial\theta}{\partial v} - ck\sigma^2 a^2\theta + \dfrac{2\sigma^2 a^2 b^2}{c}(l-h), \\[2ex] \dfrac{\partial^2\theta}{\partial v^2} = \left\{ {22 \atop 1} \right\} \dfrac{\partial\theta}{\partial u} + \left\{ {22 \atop 2} \right\} \dfrac{\partial\theta}{\partial v} + ck\sigma^2 b^2\theta + \dfrac{2\sigma^2 a^2 b^2}{c}(h-l). \end{cases}$$

Because of (28) and (32) we have

$$(83)\qquad \frac{\partial^2\theta}{\partial u^2} + \frac{\partial^2\theta}{\partial v^2} = 2\,\frac{\partial\log a}{\partial u}\,\frac{\partial\theta}{\partial u} + 2\,\frac{\partial\log b}{\partial v}\,\frac{\partial\theta}{\partial v} - ck\,\theta.$$

From the results § 49 it follows that if we take two transformations F_k of $\overline{N}(k \neq e, f, g)$ and write

$$(84)\qquad \theta_1 = 2\sum e x x', \qquad \theta_2 = 2\sum e x x'',$$

the net $\hat{N}(\hat{x})$, defined by

$$(85)\qquad \hat{x} = \overline{x} + p\,\frac{\partial \overline{x}}{\partial u} + q\,\frac{\partial \overline{x}}{\partial v},$$

where

$$(86)\quad \begin{cases} p = \dfrac{1}{\varDelta}\left(\theta_1 \dfrac{\partial\theta_2}{\partial v} - \theta_2 \dfrac{\partial\theta_1}{\partial v}\right), \qquad q = \dfrac{1}{\varDelta}\left(\theta_2 \dfrac{\partial\theta_1}{\partial u} - \theta_1 \dfrac{\partial\theta_2}{\partial u}\right), \\[2ex] \varDelta = \dfrac{\partial\theta_2}{\partial u}\,\dfrac{\partial\theta_1}{\partial v} - \dfrac{\partial\theta_1}{\partial u}\,\dfrac{\partial\theta_2}{\partial v}, \end{cases}$$

is a W transform of $\overline{N}$, that is these two nets are on the focal surfaces of a W congruence.

On substituting the expressions for the derivatives of θ_1 and θ_2 analogous to (81) and (82) in (I, 68), we reduce the resulting expressions to

$$(87)\quad \begin{cases} \dfrac{\partial\hat{x}}{\partial u} = p\left\{\overline{D}\,\overline{X} + \dfrac{2\sigma^2 a^2}{c\varDelta}\left[\left(\dfrac{\partial\overline{x}}{\partial u}\,\dfrac{\partial\theta_2}{\partial v} - \dfrac{\partial\overline{x}}{\partial v}\,\dfrac{\partial\theta_2}{\partial u}\right)\left(b^2(l_1-h_1) - c^2k\dfrac{\theta_1}{2}\right)\right.\right. \\[2ex] \qquad\left.\left. - \left(\dfrac{\partial\overline{x}}{\partial u}\,\dfrac{\partial\theta_1}{\partial v} - \dfrac{\partial\overline{x}}{\partial v}\,\dfrac{\partial\theta_1}{\partial u}\right)\left(b^2(l_2-h_2) - c^2k\dfrac{\theta_2}{2}\right)\right]\right\}, \\[2ex] \dfrac{\partial\hat{x}}{\partial v} = q\left\{\overline{D}''\,\overline{X} - \dfrac{2\sigma^2 b^2}{c\varDelta}\left[\left(\dfrac{\partial\overline{x}}{\partial u}\,\dfrac{\partial\theta_2}{\partial v} - \dfrac{\partial\overline{x}}{\partial v}\,\dfrac{\partial\theta_2}{\partial u}\right)\left(a^2(l_1-h_1) - c^2k\dfrac{\theta_1}{2}\right)\right.\right. \\[2ex] \qquad\left.\left. - \left(\dfrac{\partial\overline{x}}{\partial u}\,\dfrac{\partial\theta_1}{\partial v} - \dfrac{\partial\overline{x}}{\partial v}\,\dfrac{\partial\theta_1}{\partial u}\right)\left(a^2(l_2-h_2) - c^2k\dfrac{\theta_2}{2}\right)\right]\right\}. \end{cases}$$

By means of the same functions θ_1 and θ_2 we obtain a derived net $\tilde{N}(\tilde{x})$ of N. Its equations are

$$(88) \qquad \tilde{x} = x + p\frac{\partial x}{\partial u} + q\frac{\partial x}{\partial v},$$

where p and q are given by (86). On substituting the expressions for θ_1 and θ_2, as given by (84) in the expression (86) for Δ, we find, in consequence of (35) and (cf. (29))

$$(89) \qquad H\sigma = ab,$$

that

$$(90) \quad \left\{\begin{aligned} \Delta &= 4\sum ef(x''y' - x'y'')\left(\frac{\partial x}{\partial u}\frac{\partial y}{\partial v} - \frac{\partial x}{\partial v}\frac{\partial y}{\partial u}\right) \\ &= 4H\sum ef(x''y' - x'y'')Z = 4cabefg\sum x(y''z' - y'z''). \end{aligned}\right.$$

Hence the expression for $\tilde{x}$ is reducible to

$$(91) \qquad \tilde{x} = \frac{y''z' - y'z''}{e\sum x(y''z' - y'z'')}.$$

From this we have

$$(92) \qquad \sum e\tilde{x}x = 1.$$

The equations analogous to (57) are

$$(93) \quad \left\{\begin{aligned} &h_1^2a^2 - l_1^2b^2 = c^2\sum(e^2 - ke)x'^2, \qquad h_2^2a^2 - l_2^2b^2 = c^2\sum(e^2 - ke)x''^2, \\ &h_1a^2 - l_1b^2 = c^2\sum(e^2 - ke)xx', \qquad h_2a^2 - l_2b^2 = c^2\sum(e^2 - ke)xx''. \end{aligned}\right.$$

By differentiation it can be shown that the left-hand member of the following equation is constant for any two transformations F_k

$$(94) \qquad h_1h_2a^2 - l_1l_2b^2 - c^2\sum(e^2 - ke)x'x'' = 0.$$

We choose the nets N' and N'' so that (94) is satisfied. By means of these relations we show that

$$(95) \quad \left\{\begin{aligned} &\sum(f^2 - kf)(g^2 - kg)(y'z'' - y''z')^2 = \sum(e^2 - ke)x'^2 \cdot \sum(e^2 - ke)x''^2 \\ &\qquad - \left(\sum(e^2 - ke)x'x''\right)^2 = -\frac{a^2b^2}{c^4}(l_1h_2 - l_2h_1)^2; \end{aligned}\right.$$

also that

$$(96)\qquad \left\{\begin{aligned}&(e^2-ke)(f^2-kf)(g^2-kg)\left[\sum x(y''z'-y'z'')\right]^2\\ &\qquad\qquad=\frac{ka^2b^2}{c^4}(l_1h_2-l_2h_1)^2.\end{aligned}\right.$$

In consequence of these identities we have

$$(97)\qquad \sum\frac{\tilde{x}^2}{\frac{1}{e}-\frac{1}{k}}=1,$$

that is $\tilde{N}(\tilde{x})$ lies on a quadric confocal with Q.

The equations for $\tilde{N}$ analogous to (87) are obtained by removing the bars from the quantities $\overline{x}$, $\overline{X}$, $\overline{D}$ and $\overline{D}''$. Substituting from (81) the expressions for the derivatives of θ_1 and θ_2 and making use of (35), (36), (84), (89) and (90), we reduce the resulting equations to

$$(98)\qquad \left\{\begin{aligned}\frac{\partial\tilde{x}}{\partial u}&=\frac{4\sigma^2a^3bpfg}{\varDelta}\{c^2(e^2-ke)x\sum x(y'z''-y''z')+c^2k(y'z''-y''z')\\ &\qquad+b^2[(zy''-yz'')(l_1-h_1)-(zy'-yz')(l_2-h_2)]\},\\ \frac{\partial\tilde{x}}{\partial v}&=-\frac{4\sigma^2ab^3qfg}{\varDelta}\{c^2(e^2-ke)x\sum x(y'z''-y''z')+c^2k(y'z''-y''z')\\ &\qquad+a^2[(zy''-yz'')(l_1-h_1)-(zy'-yz')(l_2-h_2)]\}.\end{aligned}\right.$$

From (93) we have

$$(99)\qquad \left\{\begin{aligned}&(zy''-yz'')(h_1a^2-l_1b^2)-(zy'-yz')(h_2a^2-l_2b^2)\\ &=c^2\left\{(e^2-ke)x\sum x(y'z''-y''z')+\left(\frac{1}{c^2\sigma^2}-k\right)(z'y''-z''y')\right\}.\end{aligned}\right.$$

Adding the left-hand member of this expression to the expressions in parentheses in (98) and subtracting the right-hand member, we get in consequence of (28)

$$(100)\qquad \left\{\begin{aligned}\frac{\partial\tilde{x}}{\partial u}&=\frac{4a^3bpfg}{\varDelta}[h_1(zy''-yz'')-h_2(zy'-yz')+(z''y'-z'y'')],\\ \frac{\partial\tilde{x}}{\partial v}&=-\frac{4ab^3qfg}{\varDelta}[l_1(zy''-yz'')-l_2(zy'-yz')+(z''y'-z'y'')].\end{aligned}\right.$$

For $\tilde{N}$ the expressions analogous to $\sum e\left(\frac{\partial x}{\partial u}\right)^2$ and $\sum e\left(\frac{\partial x}{\partial v}\right)^2$ for N are $\sum \frac{ke}{k-e}\left(\frac{\partial \tilde{x}}{\partial u}\right)^2$ and $\sum \frac{ke}{k-e}\left(\frac{\partial \tilde{x}}{\partial v}\right)^2$. Making use of well-known theorems on determinants, we find ultimately that

$$(101)\quad \begin{cases} \sum \frac{ke}{k-e}\left(\frac{\partial \tilde{x}}{\partial u}\right)^2 = -ka^2p^2, \quad \sum \frac{ke}{k-e}\left(\frac{\partial \tilde{x}}{\partial v}\right)^2 = kb^2q^2, \\ \sum \frac{ke}{k-e}\frac{\partial \tilde{x}}{\partial u}\frac{\partial \tilde{x}}{\partial v} = 0. \end{cases}$$

From (87) and the analogous equations for $\tilde{N}$ we have, in consequence of (27) and (29),

$$(102)\quad \begin{cases} \sum\left(\frac{\partial \hat{x}}{\partial u}\right)^2 - \sum\left(\frac{\partial \tilde{x}}{\partial u}\right)^2 = p^2(\bar{D}^2 - D^2) = -a^2p^2, \\ \sum \frac{\partial \hat{x}}{\partial u}\frac{\partial \hat{x}}{\partial v} - \sum \frac{\partial \tilde{x}}{\partial u}\frac{\partial \tilde{x}}{\partial v} = 0, \\ \sum\left(\frac{\partial \hat{x}}{\partial v}\right)^2 - \sum\left(\frac{\partial \tilde{x}}{\partial v}\right)^2 = q^2(\bar{D}''^2 - D''^2) = b^2q^2. \end{cases}$$

From (101) and (102) we have

$$(103)\quad \begin{cases} \sum\left(\frac{\partial \hat{x}}{\partial u}\right)^2 = \sum \frac{k}{k-e}\left(\frac{\partial \tilde{x}}{\partial u}\right)^2, \quad \sum \frac{\partial \hat{x}}{\partial u}\frac{\partial \hat{x}}{\partial v} = \sum \frac{k}{k-e}\frac{\partial \tilde{x}}{\partial u}\frac{\partial \tilde{x}}{\partial v}, \\ \sum\left(\frac{\partial \hat{x}}{\partial v}\right)^2 = \sum \frac{k}{k-e}\left(\frac{\partial \tilde{x}}{\partial v}\right)^2. \end{cases}$$

Hence if we put

$$(104)\quad \tilde{x}_0 = \sqrt{\frac{k}{k-e}}\,\tilde{x}, \quad \tilde{y}_0 = \sqrt{\frac{k}{k-f}}\,\tilde{y}, \quad \tilde{z}_0 = \sqrt{\frac{k}{k-g}}\,\tilde{z},$$

the net $\hat{N}(\hat{x})$ is applicable to the net $\tilde{N}_0(\tilde{x}_0)$, which in consequence of (97) lies on Q. The equations (104) define the *relation of Ivory* between a quadric and a confocal quadric; the point of coordinates $\tilde{x}_0, \tilde{y}_0, \tilde{z}_0$ is the intersection with Q of the orthogonal trajectory of the family of confocal quadrics which passes through the point of coordinates $\tilde{x}, \tilde{y}, \tilde{z}$ of (97)[135]).

[135]) Bianchi, Lezioni, vol. 3, p. 59.

The functions of a transformation W are x', y', z', x'', y'', z'', h_1, l_1, h_2 and l_2. They satisfy a completely integrable system of the form (58) and (59). Moreover, the five conditions (93) and (94) must be satisfied. However, these equations are satisfied also by the functions

$$(105)\left\{\begin{array}{lllll} \alpha x'+\beta x'', & \alpha y'+\beta y'', & \alpha z'+\beta z'', & \alpha h_1+\beta h_2, & \alpha l_1+\beta l_2, \\ \gamma x'+\delta x'', & \gamma y'+\delta y'', & \gamma z'+\delta z'', & \gamma h_1+\delta h_2, & \gamma l_1+\delta l_2, \end{array}\right.$$

where α, β, γ and δ are constants. In this case, as follows from (85), (86) and (88) we get the same nets $\hat{N}$ and $\tilde{N}$. Consequently for each value of k there are ∞^1 transformations of the kind sought.

If $N_1(x_1)$ and $N_2(x_2)$ denote the F_k transforms of N, we have

$$x_1 = x - \frac{\theta_1}{\theta_1'}x', \qquad x_2 = x - \frac{\theta_2}{\theta_2''}x''.$$

In consequence of (91) and (92) we have

$$\sum e\tilde{x}x_1 = 1, \qquad \sum e\tilde{x}x_2 = 1.$$

Hence the point of coordinates, $\tilde{x}$, $\tilde{y}$, $\tilde{z}$ is the pole of the plane of the corresponding points on N, N_1 and N_2.

We may state the foregoing results as follows.

If N is a permanent net on a central quadric Q, there are ∞^1 sets of transformations F_k of N into nets N_1 and N_2 so that the condition (94) is satisfied for each value of k different from zero; the locus of the pole M_k of the plane $M M_1 M_2$ with respect to Q is a net $\tilde{N}$ on a quadric confocal to Q; as N rolls on its applicable net $\overline{N}$, the point M_k describes a net $\hat{N}$, such that $\overline{N}$ and $\hat{N}$ are the focal nets of a W congruence, and $\hat{N}$ is applicable to the net on Q which is the Ivory transform of the net $\tilde{N}$.

These are the transformations B_k found by Bianchi by entirely different processes[136]).

Let N be a permanent net on the quadric (34) and N_1 an F_k transform of N by means of the functions x', y', z', h_1 and l_1 satisfying (57), (58) and (59). From the form of equations (93) and (94) and the observations concerning (105) it follows that

136) Lezioni, vol. 3, Chaps. 1, 2, 3; cf. also Journ. de Math., l. c.. p. 61.

there exist only two sets of functions x'', y'', z'', h_2, l_2 and x''', y''', z''', h_3, l_3 each satisfying (93) and (94) with x', y', z' h_1, l_1 and determining different B_k transforms of N, and also of the net $\overline{N}$ applicable to N.

The corresponding transforms $\hat{N}_2$ and $\hat{N}_3$ of $\overline{N}$ are determined by θ_1, θ_2 and θ_1, θ_3 where θ_1 and θ_2 are given by (84) and $\theta_3 = \sum exx'''$. Consequently these transforms are conjugate to the congruence harmonic to N determined by θ_1. The same is true of the transforms $\tilde{N}_2$ and $\tilde{N}_3$ of N determined by θ_1, θ_2 and θ_1, θ_3. The congruence harmonic to N determined by θ_1 consists of the lines of intersection of the corresponding tangent planes to N and its F_k transform N_1 by means of x', y', z', h_1 and l_1. In view of the preceding results we have the theorem:

If N is a permanent net on a central quadric Q and N_1 is an F_k transform of N, and P_1 and P_2 are the points of intersection with the confocal quadric Q_k of the line of intersection of corresponding tangent planes of N and N_1, then as N rolls on its applicable net $\overline{N}$, the points P_1 and P_2 generate nets applicable to Q, each of which is a B_k transform of $\overline{N}$.

139. Permutability of transformations F_k and B_k. Let $\overline{N}(\overline{x})$ be the permanent net on a deform of the quadric Q (34) and $\hat{N}(\hat{x})$ its B_k transform by means of functions x', y', z'; x'', y'', z''; h_1, l_1, h_2, l_2. Let x''', y''', z''', h_3, l_3, be a set of solutions of (58) and (59) with k replaced by k' satisfying the conditions

$$(106)\quad h_3^2 a^2 - l_3^2 b^2 = c^2 \sum (e^2 - k'e) x'''^2, \qquad h_3 a^2 - l_3 b^2 = c^2 \sum (e^2 - k'e) xx''',$$

so that the $F_{k'}$ transform N_3 of N, defined by equations of the form

$$(107)\qquad x_3 = x - \frac{\theta_3}{\theta_3'''} x''',$$

where

$$(108)\qquad \theta_3 = 2 \sum exx''', \qquad \theta_3''' = \sum ex'''^2,$$

is on Q.

From (II, 33) it follows that the equations of the forms

$$(109)\qquad x_3' = x' - \frac{\theta_3'}{\theta_3'''} x''', \qquad x_3'' = x'' - \frac{\theta_3''}{\theta_3'''} x'''$$

ations of the form

$$\tilde{x}''' = x''' + p'''\frac{\partial x'''}{\partial u} + q'''\frac{\partial x'''}{\partial v}$$

net $\tilde{N}'''$ parallel to $\tilde{N}$. This expression is reducible to

$$+\frac{1}{\Delta}\left[\theta_1'''\left(\frac{\partial\theta_2}{\partial v}\frac{\partial x}{\partial u}-\frac{\partial\theta_2}{\partial u}\frac{\partial x}{\partial v}\right)-\theta_2'''\left(\frac{\partial\theta_1}{\partial v}\frac{\partial x}{\partial u}-\frac{\partial\theta_1}{\partial u}\frac{\partial x}{\partial v}\right)\right],$$

$$+\frac{2fgabc}{\Delta}[\theta_1'''(y''z-yz'')-\theta_2'''(y'z-yz')],$$

consequence of (122) becomes

$$\tilde{x}''' = \frac{1}{k'-k}\left[(e-k)x'''+\frac{h_3}{cp}\frac{\partial\tilde{x}}{\partial u}+\frac{l_3}{cq}\frac{\partial\tilde{x}}{\partial v}\right].$$

$\tilde{N}$ is applicable to $\tilde{N}_0$, defined by (104), it follows from of § 136 that a transformation $F_{k'}$ of $\hat{N}$ is given by ns

$$\tilde\theta_3 = 2\sum e\tilde{x}_0\tilde{x}_0''' = 2k\sum\frac{e}{k-e}\tilde{x}\tilde{x}''',$$

$$\tilde\theta_3''' = \sum e\tilde{x}_0'''^2 = k\sum\frac{e}{k-e}\tilde{x}'''^2,$$

at analogously to (57) and because of (101)

$$\ldots^2-\hat{l}^2b^2q^2 = -\frac{c}{k}\sum(e^2-k'e)\tilde{x}_0'''^2 = c\sum\frac{e^2-k'e}{e-k}\tilde{x}'''^2,$$

$$\ldots^2-\hat{l}b^2q^2 = -\frac{c}{k}\sum(e^2-k'e)\tilde{x}_0\tilde{x}_0''' = c\sum\frac{e^2-k'e}{e-k}\tilde{x}\tilde{x}'''.$$

he expression (125) for $\tilde{x}'''$ is substituted in (126), the ations are reducible by means of (97), (101) and (106) to

$$\frac{2k}{k-k'}\sum ex'''\tilde{x},$$

$$-\frac{k}{(k-k')^2}\left[\sum(2e^2-ke-k'e)x'''^2 + \frac{2h_3}{cp}\sum ex'''\frac{\partial\tilde{x}}{\partial u}+\frac{2l_3}{cq}\sum ex'''\frac{\partial\tilde{x}}{\partial v}\right].$$

define nets parallel to N_3; the corresponding functions h_{31}, l_{31} and h_{32}, l_{32} are given by (cf. II, 50)

$$h_{31}=\frac{h_3\theta_3'-h_1\theta_3'''}{h_3\theta_3-\theta_3'''},\qquad l_{31}=\frac{l_3\theta_3'-l_1\theta_3'''}{l_3\theta_3-\theta_3'''},$$

$$h_{32}=\frac{h_3\theta_3''-h_2\theta_3'''}{h_3\theta_3-\theta_3'''},\qquad l_{32}=\frac{l_3\theta_3''-l_2\theta_3'''}{l_3\theta_3-\theta_3'''}.$$

The functions a_3 and b_3 appearing in the point equation of N_3 are of the form (cf. II, 12)

$$a_3=a\left(h_3\frac{\theta_3}{\theta_3'''}-1\right),\qquad b_3=b\left(l_3\frac{\theta_3}{\theta_3'''}-1\right).$$

In order that these functions may satisfy equations analogous to (93) and (94), namely

$$a_3^2h_{31}^2-b_3^2l_{31}^2=c^2\sum(e^2-ke)x_3'^2,\qquad a_3^2h_{32}^2-b_3^2l_{32}^2=c^2\sum(e^2-ke)x_3''^2,$$
$$a_3^2h_{31}-b_3^2l_{31}=c^2\sum(e^2-ke)x_3x_3',\qquad a_3^2h_{32}-b_3^2l_{32}=c^2\sum(e^2-ke)x_3x_3'',$$
$$a_3^2h_{31}h_{32}-b_3^2l_{31}l_{32}=c^2\sum(e^2-ke)x_3'x_3'',$$

it is necessary and sufficient that

$$(110)\qquad\begin{cases} a^2h_1h_3-b^2l_1l_3-c^2\sum(e^2-ke)x'x'''-\dfrac{c^2}{2}(k-k')\theta_3'=0,\\[2mm] a^2h_2h_3-b^2l_2l_3-c^2\sum(e^2-ke)x''x'''-\dfrac{c^2}{2}(k-k')\theta_3''=0.\end{cases}$$

Differentiating these equations with respect to u and v, and making use of (58), (59) and analogous equations, we find that the left-hand members are constant.

If $k'\neq k$, the functions θ_3' and θ_3'' are uniquely determined by (110), and consequently x_3' and x_3'' are uniquely determined by (109). Then by means of the functions

$$(111)\qquad \theta_{31}=2\sum ex_3x_3',\qquad \theta_{32}=2\sum ex_3x_3''$$

we obtain a B_k transform $\hat{N}_3$ of $\bar{N}_3$ which is applicable to Q.

It is readily found by differentiation that the left-hand members of the equations

$$(112)\quad \theta_3' + \theta_1''' - 2\sum e x' x''' = 0, \qquad \theta_3'' + \theta_2''' - 2\sum e x'' x''' = 0$$

are constants. If we take θ_1''' and θ_2''' as given by (112), we find that

$$(113)\quad \theta_{31} = \theta_1 - \frac{\theta_3}{\theta_3'''}\theta_1''', \qquad \theta_{32} = \theta_2 - \frac{\theta_3}{\theta_3'''}\theta_2'''.$$

These are the conditions that $\hat{N}$ and $\hat{N}_3$ are in relation F (cf. § 22). We desire to show that this transformation is in fact a transformation F_k, as defined in § 136.

From § 22 we have that the functions $\hat{\theta}_3$ and $\hat{\theta}_3'''$ of the transformation F from $\hat{N}$ into $\hat{N}_3$ are given by

$$(114)\quad \hat{\theta}_3 = \theta_3 + p\frac{\partial \theta_3}{\partial u} + q\frac{\partial \theta_3}{\partial v}, \quad \hat{\theta}_3''' = \theta_3''' + p'''\frac{\partial \theta_3'''}{\partial u} + q'''\frac{\partial \theta_3'''}{\partial v},$$

where p and q are given by (86) and

$$p''' = \frac{1}{\varDelta'''}\left(\theta_1'''\frac{\partial \theta_2'''}{\partial v} - \theta_2'''\frac{\partial \theta_1'''}{\partial v}\right), \qquad q''' = \frac{1}{\varDelta'''}\left(\theta_2'''\frac{\partial \theta_1'''}{\partial u} - \theta_1'''\frac{\partial \theta_2'''}{\partial u}\right),$$

$$\varDelta''' = \frac{\partial \theta_2'''}{\partial u}\frac{\partial \theta_1'''}{\partial v} - \frac{\partial \theta_2'''}{\partial v}\frac{\partial \theta_1'''}{\partial u},$$

and

$$(115)\quad \frac{\partial \theta_i'''}{\partial u} = h_3\frac{\partial \theta_i}{\partial u}, \qquad \frac{\partial \theta_i'''}{\partial v} = l_3\frac{\partial \theta_i}{\partial v} \quad (i = 1, 2, 3).$$

Moreover, the direction-parameters of the conjugate congruence of this transformation are the coordinates $\hat{x}''', \hat{y}''', \hat{z}'''$ of a net $\hat{N}_3'''$, parallel to $\hat{N}_3$, where

$$(116)\quad \hat{x}''' = \bar{x}''' + p'''\frac{\partial \bar{x}'''}{\partial u} + q'''\frac{\partial \bar{x}'''}{\partial v}.$$

From § 22 corresponding to (85) and (116), we obtain

$$(117)\quad \frac{\partial \hat{x}'''}{\partial u} = \hat{h}\frac{\partial \hat{x}}{\partial u}, \qquad \frac{\partial \hat{x}'''}{\partial v} = \hat{l}\frac{\partial \hat{x}}{\partial v},$$

where

$$(118)\quad \hat{h} = \frac{1}{p\varDelta}\left(\theta_1'''\frac{\partial \theta_2}{\partial v} - \theta_2'''\frac{\partial \theta_1}{\partial v}\right), \qquad \hat{l} =$$

Substituting the expressions (10
get, in consequence of (88) and (11

$$(119)\quad \hat{\theta}_3 = 2\sum$$

and

$$(120)\quad \hat{\theta}_3''' = \theta_3''' + \frac{1}{\varDelta}\left[\theta_1'''\left(\frac{\partial \theta_2}{\partial v}\frac{\partial \theta_3}{\partial u} - \frac{\partial \theta}{\partial v}\right.\right.$$
$$= \theta_3''' + \frac{4efgabc}{\varDelta}\left[\theta_1'''\sum x(y'''\right.$$

this second expression for $\hat{\theta}_3'''$ is
aid of (29), (35) and (36).

From (110) and (112) we ge

$$(121)\quad a^2 h_1 h_3 - b^2 l_1 l_3 = c^2\sum(e^2$$
$$a^2 h_2 h_3 - b^2 l_2 l_3 = c^2\sum(e^2$$

From equations (121), (100), (1

$$(122)\quad \theta_1'''(y''z - yz'') - \theta_2'''(y'z$$
$$\left[\frac{h_3}{p}\frac{\partial \tilde{x}}{\partial u} + \right.$$

By means of (122) and ana
reducible to

$$(123)\quad \hat{\theta}_3''' = \frac{1}{k'-k}\left[\sum(2e^2\right.$$
$$+$$

Equ

define a

$$(124)\quad \tilde{x}''' = x''$$
$$= x''$$

which in

(125)

Since
the results
the functio

(126)

provided th

$$(127)\quad \hat{h}^2 a^2$$
$$\hat{h} a^2$$

When
resulting equ

$$\tilde{\theta}_3 =$$
$$(128)\quad \tilde{\theta}_3''' =$$

In consequence of (118) we can write the first of (124) in the form

$$\tilde{x}'''-x''' = \hat{h}p\frac{\partial x}{\partial u}+\hat{l}q\frac{\partial x}{\partial v}. \tag{129}$$

From this equation, (38) and (42) we obtain

$$\sum e(\tilde{x}'''-x''')^2 = \frac{1}{c}(\hat{h}^2 a^2 p^2 - \hat{l}^2 b^2 q^2).$$

In order that this equation be consistent with the first of (127), we must have

$$(k-k')\sum\frac{e}{e-k}\tilde{x}'''^2 + 2\sum e\tilde{x}'''x''' - \sum e x'''^2 = 0.$$

Because of (101) and (106) this condition is satisfied identically when the expression (125) for $\tilde{x}'''$ is substituted. Again from (129) and (88) we have

$$\sum e(\tilde{x}'''-x''')(\tilde{x}-x) = \frac{1}{c}(\hat{h}a^2p^2 - \hat{l}b^2q^2).$$

It is readily found that this equation is consistent with the second of (127). Moreover, when we compare the functions (128) giving an $F_{k'}$ transform of $\hat{N}$ with the functions (119) and (123) determining a derived net of N_3, we find that they differ by the same constant factor. Hence:

Let N be a permanent net on the central quadric (34) *and $\overline{N}$ the applicable net; if $\hat{N}$ is a B_k transform of $\overline{N}$ and $\overline{N}_3$ is an $F_{k'}$ transform of $\overline{N}$, there can be found directly a net $\hat{N}_3$ which is a B_k transform of $\overline{N}_3$ and an $F_{k'}$ transform of $\hat{N}$.*

140. Theorem of permutability of transformations B_k. Let $\overline{N}$ be a net applicable to a net N on the central quadric Q (34), and $\hat{N}_1$ and $\hat{N}_3$ nets applicable to nets on Q and obtained from $\overline{N}$ by transformations B_k and $B_{k'}$ respectively, determined by the respective pairs of functions θ_1, θ_2 and θ_3, θ_4, where

$$\theta_1 = 2\sum exx', \quad \theta_2 = 2\sum exx'', \quad \theta_3 = 2\sum exx''', \quad \theta_4 = 2\sum exx''''. \tag{130}$$

From § 50 it follows that the functions θ_3 and $\hat{\theta}_4$, defined by

$$(131)\quad \begin{cases} \hat{\theta}_i = \theta_i + \left[\frac{\partial \theta_i}{\partial u}\left(\theta_j \frac{\partial \theta_k}{\partial v} - \theta_k \frac{\partial \theta_j}{\partial v}\right) + \frac{\partial \theta_i}{\partial v}\left(\theta_k \frac{\partial \theta_j}{\partial u} - \theta_j \frac{\partial \theta_k}{\partial u}\right)\right] \\ \qquad \cdot \left(\frac{\partial \theta_k}{\partial u}\frac{\partial \theta_j}{\partial v} - \frac{\partial \theta_k}{\partial v}\frac{\partial \theta_j}{\partial u}\right)^{-1}, \end{cases}$$

for $i = 3, 4$; $j = 1$, $k = 2$, determine a W transform of $\hat{N}_1$ which is also the W transform of $\hat{N}_3$ defined by the two functions given by (131) for $i = 1, 2$; $j = 3$, $k = 4$.

From (127) it follows that conditions analogous to (93) are satisfied. The analogue of (94) is

$$\hat{h}_3 \hat{h}_4 a^2 p^2 - \hat{l}_3 \hat{l}_4 b^2 q^2 = c \sum \frac{e^2 - k'e}{e-k} \tilde{x}''' \tilde{x}'''',$$

which can be shown to be satisfied identically, by the use of methods similar to those used at the end of § 139. Consequently the above W transform of $\hat{N}_1$ is in fact a $B_{k'}$ transform. Hence we have:

If $\hat{N}_1$ and $\hat{N}_2$ are obtained from the permanent net $\overline{N}$ of a deform of a central quadric Q by transformations B_k and $B_{k'}$ $(k' \neq k)$, there can be found directly a net $\hat{N}_{12}$ applicable to a net on Q such that $\hat{N}_1$ and $\hat{N}_{12}$, and $\hat{N}_2$ and $\hat{N}_{12}$ are in relations $B'_{k'}$ and B'_k respectively[137]).

141. Transformations F_k of permanents nets on a paraboloid and of surfaces applicable to a paraboloid. For the paraboloid P,

$$(132)\qquad ex^2 + fy^2 + 2z = 0,$$

we have

$$(133)\qquad X, Y, Z = \frac{ex, fy, 1}{\sqrt{e^2x^2 + f^2y^2 + 1}},$$

and

$$(134)\quad K = -\frac{1}{c^4(e^2x^2 + f^2y^2 + 1)^2}, \qquad \frac{1}{\sigma} = c\sqrt{e^2x^2 + f^2y^2 + 1},$$

where $c^4 = -1/4\,ef$.

---

137) Cf., Bianchi, l. c., chap. 4.

If P is referred to a net N whose point equation is the second of (33), we have

$$e\frac{\partial x}{\partial u}\frac{\partial x}{\partial v}+f\frac{\partial y}{\partial u}\frac{\partial y}{\partial v}=0,$$

and by processes analogous to those used in § 135 we find

$$(135)\quad e\left(\frac{\partial x}{\partial u}\right)^2+f\left(\frac{\partial y}{\partial u}\right)^2=\frac{a^2}{c},\qquad e\left(\frac{\partial x}{\partial v}\right)^2+f\left(\frac{\partial y}{\partial v}\right)^2=-\frac{b^2}{c};$$

and we prove the theorem:

A necessary and sufficient condition that a net N on a paraboloid (132) *be permanent is that the parameters can be chosen so that*

$$(136)\quad e\left(\frac{\partial x}{\partial u}\right)^2+f\left(\frac{\partial y}{\partial u}\right)^2+e\left(\frac{\partial x}{\partial v}\right)^2+f\left(\frac{\partial y}{\partial v}\right)^2=c\,(e^2x^2+f^2y^2+1).$$

In order to obtain F_k transforms of N which are permanent nets on P, we take in place of (48)

$$(137)\qquad \theta=2\,(exx'+fyy'+z'),\qquad \theta'=ex'^2+fy'^2.$$

Each set of functions satisfying the completely integrable system of equations (59) and (58) with $g=0$, and the conditions

$$(138)\qquad \begin{cases} h^2a^2-l^2b^2=c^2\,[(e^2-ke)\,x'^2+(f^2-kf)\,y'^2], \\ ha^2-lb^2=c^2\,[(e^2-ke)\,xx'+(f^2-kf)\,yy'-kz'] \end{cases}$$

determine a transformation F_k of N into a net N_1 on P. When $k=e$ or f we have two special types of transformations, as described in the last theorem of § 135.

Consider now the net $\overline{N}$ applicable to N. From (60) and (137) we have in place of (62)

$$(139)\qquad (e-k)\,x'^2+(f-k)\,y'^2-kz'^2+k\sum\overline{x}'^2=0.$$

Proceeding as in the case of (62), we find equations obtained from (64), (65), (67) and (68) by putting $g=0$. Hence there exists for transformations F_k of $\overline{N}$ theorems similar to the first two theorems of § 136, but there are only two types of transformations as described in the second theorem; they are F_e and F_f.

When $e=f$, P is a paraboloid of revolution and the transformations F_k $(k \neq e)$ are described by the first theorem of § 136. When $k=e$, equation (139) reduces to $\sum \bar{x}'^2 - z'^2 = 0$. Hence $\bar{N}'$ is a special net 2, O, the complementary function being z'. In this case, as for the central quadric of revolution, the transforms of $\bar{N}$ are conjugate to the two normal congruences conjugate to $\bar{N}$. When $\bar{N}$ is applied to P, the lines of one of these congruences pass through the focal point of P on the axis of revolution, and the lines of other congruence are normal to the tangent plane to P at its vertex (cf. § 100). Hence:

Let $\bar{N}$ be a net applicable to a net N on a paraboloid of revolution P; the lines joining points of N to the focus of P and the lines parallel to the axis of P become two normal congruences, G_1 and G_2, conjugate to $\bar{N}$, when N is applied to $\bar{N}$; there can be found by two quadratures ∞^2 nets $\bar{N}_1$ conjugate to G_1 and ∞^2 nets $\bar{N}_2$ conjugate to G_2 which are applicable to ∞^2 nets N_1 and ∞^2 nets N_2 on P; the nets $\bar{N}_1$ or $\bar{N}_2$ can be grouped into ∞^1 families of ∞^1 nets such that their corresponding tangent planes envelope a quadric cone, and the corresponding points on P lie on a conic[138]).

142. Transformations B_k of surfaces applicable to a paraboloid. In this section we establish for surfaces applicable to P(132) transformations analogous to those treated in § 138. Equations (82) and (83) hold in this case also. In place of (84) we have

$$(140)\quad \theta_1 = 2(exx' + fyy' + z'), \qquad \theta_2 = 2(exx'' + fyy'' + z'').$$

In place of (90) and (91) we have

$$\Delta = 4efabc(x''y' - x'y''),$$

and

$$\tilde{x} = \frac{1}{e}\frac{y''z' - y'z''}{x''y' - x'y''}, \qquad \tilde{y} = \frac{1}{f}\frac{z''x' - z'x''}{x''y' - x'y''},$$

$$\tilde{z} = -z + \frac{y(x''z' - x'z'') + x(y'z'' - y''z')}{x''y' - x'y''}.$$

Now $ex\tilde{x} + fy\tilde{y} + z + \tilde{z} = 0$.

---

[138]) Trans. Amer. Math. Soc., l. c., p. 338.

The first two of equations (93) with $g=0$ hold and in place of the second two we have

$$(141)\quad \begin{cases} h_1 a^2 - l_1 b^2 = c^2[(e^2-ke)xx' + (f^2-kf)yy' - kz'], \\ h_2 a^2 - l_2 b^2 = c^2[(e^2-ke)xx'' + (f^2-kf)yy'' - kz''], \end{cases}$$

and (94) with $g=0$ holds.

By making use of the expressions for $x(y'z''-y''z')$ and $y(z'x''-z''x')$ which are obtainable from (141), we find that $\tilde{x}$, $\tilde{y}$ and $\tilde{z}$ satisfy the condition

$$\frac{\tilde{x}^2}{\frac{1}{e}-\frac{1}{k}} + \frac{\tilde{y}^2}{\frac{1}{f}-\frac{1}{k}} + 2\tilde{z} + \frac{1}{k} = 0,$$

that is the net $\tilde{N}$ lies on a quadric confocal with P.

In place of (100) we have

$$\frac{\partial \tilde{x}}{\partial u} = \frac{4pa^3bf}{\Delta}(y''h_1 - y'h_2), \qquad \frac{\partial \tilde{x}}{\partial v} = -\frac{4qab^3f}{\Delta}(y''l_1 - y'l_2).$$

From these and analogous equations we obtain, by means of equations similar to (95),

$$\frac{ek}{k-e}\left(\frac{\partial \tilde{x}}{\partial u}\right)^2 + \frac{fk}{k-f}\left(\frac{\partial \tilde{y}}{\partial u}\right)^2 = -ka^2p^2,$$

$$\frac{ek}{k-e}\frac{\partial \tilde{x}}{\partial u}\frac{\partial \tilde{x}}{\partial v} + \frac{fk}{k-f}\frac{\partial \tilde{y}}{\partial u}\frac{\partial \tilde{y}}{\partial v} = 0,$$

$$\frac{ek}{k-e}\left(\frac{\partial \tilde{x}}{\partial v}\right)^2 + \frac{fk}{k-f}\left(\frac{\partial \tilde{y}}{\partial v}\right)^2 = kb^2q^2.$$

From these equations and (102) we have

$$\Sigma\left(\frac{\partial \hat{x}}{\partial u}\right)^2 = \Sigma\left(\frac{\partial \tilde{x}_0}{\partial u}\right)^2, \qquad \Sigma\frac{\partial \hat{x}}{\partial u}\frac{\partial \hat{x}}{\partial v} = \Sigma\frac{\partial \tilde{x}_0}{\partial u}\frac{\partial \tilde{x}_0}{\partial v},$$

$$\Sigma\left(\frac{\partial \hat{x}}{\partial v}\right)^2 = \Sigma\left(\frac{\partial \tilde{x}_0}{\partial v}\right)^2.$$

Here the symbol Σ refers to the three variables, where

$$\tilde{x}_0 = \sqrt{\frac{k}{k-e}}\,\tilde{x}, \qquad \tilde{y}_0 = \sqrt{\frac{k}{k-f}}\,\tilde{y}, \qquad \tilde{z}_0 = \tilde{z} + \frac{1}{2k}.$$

These are the equations of the transformation of Ivory for P[139]).

The other observations for transformations of a central quadric hold also for the case of the paraboloid, and consequently we have the analogous theorem:

If N is a permanent net on a paraboloid P, there are ∞^1 pairs of transformations F_k of N into nets N_1 and N_2 so that the condition

$$h_1 h_2 a^2 - l_1 l_2 b^2 = c^2[(e^2 - ke)x'x'' + (f^2 - kf)y'y'']$$

holds; the locus of the pole $\tilde{M}$ of the plane MM_1M_2 with respect to P is a net $\tilde{N}$ on a paraboloid confocal to P; as N rolls on its applicable net $\overline{N}$ the point $\tilde{M}$ describes a net $\hat{N}$ such that $\overline{N}$ and $\hat{N}$ are the focal nets of a W congruence, and $\hat{N}$ is applicable to the net on P which is the Ivory transform of the net $\tilde{N}$.

These are the transformations B_k of surfaces applicable to a paraboloid, as found by Bianchi in another manner[140]).

143. Determination of the asymptotic lines on a surface. When a surface S is referred to a general system of parametric lines, the translations and rotations of a general moving trihedral satisfy the conditions [cf. § 69]

$$(142)\quad \begin{cases} \dfrac{\partial p}{\partial v} - \dfrac{\partial p_1}{\partial u} = q r_1 - q_1 r, & \dfrac{\partial \xi}{\partial v} - \dfrac{\partial \xi_1}{\partial u} = \eta r_1 - \eta_1 r, \\[2ex] \dfrac{\partial q}{\partial v} - \dfrac{\partial q_1}{\partial u} = r p_1 - p r_1, & \dfrac{\partial \eta}{\partial v} - \dfrac{\partial \eta_1}{\partial u} = \xi_1 r - \xi r_1, \\[2ex] \dfrac{\partial r}{\partial v} - \dfrac{\partial r_1}{\partial u} = p q_1 - p_1 q, & \eta_1 p - \eta p_1 + \xi q_1 - \xi_1 q = 0. \end{cases}$$

The equation of asymptotic lines on S is [§ 71, (68)]

$$(p\eta - q\xi)\,du^2 + (p\eta_1 - q\xi_1 + p_1\eta - q_1\xi)\,du\,dv + (p_1\eta_1 - q_1\xi_1)\,dv^2 = 0.$$

139) Cf. Bianchi, l. c., p. 30.

140) Lezioni, vol. 3, chap. 1.

If we replace this equation by the two

$$(143)\qquad \begin{cases} p\,du + p_1\,dv = \lambda(\xi\,du + \xi_1\,dv), \\ q\,du + q_1\,dv = \lambda(\eta\,du + \eta_1\,dv), \end{cases}$$

the function λ is determined by

$$\lambda^2 = -\frac{1}{\varrho_1\varrho_2} = k^2, \qquad \lambda = \pm k,$$

as is seen by the elimination of du and dv from (143) and [§ 70].

If α and β are the parameters of the asymptotic lines on S, we must have

$$(144)\qquad \begin{cases} p\dfrac{\partial u}{\partial \alpha} + p_1\dfrac{\partial v}{\partial \alpha} = k\left(\xi\dfrac{\partial u}{\partial \alpha} + \xi_1\dfrac{\partial v}{\partial \alpha}\right), \\ q\dfrac{\partial u}{\partial \alpha} + q_1\dfrac{\partial v}{\partial \alpha} = k\left(\eta\dfrac{\partial u}{\partial \alpha} + \eta_1\dfrac{\partial v}{\partial \alpha}\right), \\ p\dfrac{\partial u}{\partial \beta} + p_1\dfrac{\partial v}{\partial \beta} = -k\left(\xi\dfrac{\partial u}{\partial \beta} + \xi_1\dfrac{\partial v}{\partial \beta}\right), \\ q\dfrac{\partial u}{\partial \beta} + q_1\dfrac{\partial v}{\partial \beta} = -k\left(\eta\dfrac{\partial u}{\partial \beta} + \eta_1\dfrac{\partial v}{\partial \beta}\right). \end{cases}$$

If these equations are solved for p, q, p_1, q_1 and the results are substituted in (142), we obtain the equations which u and v must satisfy.

This calculation is simplified, if we note that the first of (142) is equivalent to

$$\frac{\partial}{\partial \beta}\left(p\frac{\partial u}{\partial \alpha} + p_1\frac{\partial v}{\partial \alpha}\right) - \frac{\partial}{\partial \alpha}\left(p\frac{\partial u}{\partial \beta} + p_1\frac{\partial v}{\partial \beta}\right)$$

$$= \left(q\frac{\partial u}{\partial \alpha} + q_1\frac{\partial v}{\partial \alpha}\right)\left(r\frac{\partial u}{\partial \beta} + r_1\frac{\partial v}{\partial \beta}\right) - \left(q\frac{\partial u}{\partial \beta} + q_1\frac{\partial v}{\partial \beta}\right)\left(r\frac{\partial u}{\partial \alpha} + r_1\frac{\partial v}{\partial \alpha}\right).$$

On replacing the expressions in parentheses by their values from (144), we obtain

$$\xi\frac{\partial^2 u}{\partial \alpha\,\partial \beta} + \xi_1\frac{\partial^2 v}{\partial \alpha\,\partial \beta} + \frac{\partial u}{\partial \alpha}\frac{\partial u}{\partial \beta}\left(\frac{1}{k}\frac{\partial k\xi}{\partial u} - \eta r\right)$$

$$+ \frac{\partial v}{\partial \alpha}\frac{\partial v}{\partial \beta}\left(\frac{1}{k}\frac{\partial k\xi_1}{\partial v} - \eta_1 r_1\right)$$

$$+ \frac{1}{2}\left(\frac{\partial u}{\partial \alpha}\frac{\partial v}{\partial \beta} + \frac{\partial u}{\partial \beta}\frac{\partial v}{\partial \alpha}\right)\left(\frac{1}{k}\frac{\partial k\xi}{\partial v} + \frac{1}{k}\frac{\partial k\xi_1}{\partial u} - \eta r_1 - \eta_1 r\right) = 0.$$

This relation may be replaced by two equations because the translations ξ, ξ_1, η, η_1 are not completely determined. In fact, they are subject only to the conditions

$$E = \xi^2 + \eta^2, \qquad F = \xi\xi_1 + \eta\eta_1, \qquad G = \xi_1^2 + \eta_1^2.$$

If we equate ξ and ξ_1 to zero successively, we obtain the following equations due to Darboux[141]):

$$(145)\left\{\begin{aligned}
&\frac{\partial^2 u}{\partial\alpha\,\partial\beta} + \frac{\partial u}{\partial\alpha}\frac{\partial u}{\partial\beta}\left(\frac{\partial \log k}{\partial u} + \begin{Bmatrix}11\\1\end{Bmatrix}\right)\\
&\qquad + \left(\frac{\partial u}{\partial\alpha}\frac{\partial v}{\partial\beta} + \frac{\partial u}{\partial\beta}\frac{\partial v}{\partial\alpha}\right)\left(\frac{1}{2}\frac{\partial \log k}{\partial v} + \begin{Bmatrix}12\\1\end{Bmatrix}\right) + \frac{\partial v}{\partial\alpha}\frac{\partial v}{\partial\beta}\begin{Bmatrix}22\\1\end{Bmatrix} = 0,\\
&\frac{\partial^2 v}{\partial\alpha\,\partial\beta} + \frac{\partial v}{\partial\alpha}\frac{\partial v}{\partial\beta}\left(\frac{\partial \log k}{\partial v} + \begin{Bmatrix}22\\2\end{Bmatrix}\right)\\
&\qquad + \left(\frac{\partial u}{\partial\alpha}\frac{\partial v}{\partial\beta} + \frac{\partial u}{\partial\beta}\frac{\partial v}{\partial\alpha}\right)\left(\frac{1}{2}\frac{\partial \log k}{\partial u} + \begin{Bmatrix}12\\2\end{Bmatrix}\right) + \frac{\partial u}{\partial\alpha}\frac{\partial u}{\partial\beta}\begin{Bmatrix}11\\2\end{Bmatrix} = 0,
\end{aligned}\right.$$

where the symbols $\begin{Bmatrix}rs\\t\end{Bmatrix}$ are formed with respect to the linear element of S, u and v being parametric.

Since the coefficients in (145) involve only E, F, G and their derivatives, each pair of solutions enables us to transform the linear element, so that it becomes the linear element of a surface referred to its asymptotic lines; that is, the complete solution of (145) gives not only the asymptotic lines on S but each family of curves which correspond to the asymptotic lines on a surface applicable to S. Bianchi calls these curves the *virtual asymptotic lines* on S.

From the results of [§ 77] it follows that when a system of virtual asymptotic lines are known on S, the function $\overline{D}'$ of the surface $\overline{S}$, applicable to S and upon which the parametric lines are the asymptotic lines, can be found by a quadrature. Hence we have:

The deformation of a surface and the determination of its virtual asymptotic lines are equivalent problems.

144. Deformations of paraboloids and central quadrics of revolution. We apply the results of the preceding section to the case when S is a quadric referred to its generators. If α_0 and β_0

141) Leçons, vol. 3, p. 290.

are the parameters of a family of virtual asymptotic lines on S, in consequence of (10), (11) and (12), equations (145) become, since $k = \sigma^2$,

$$(146)\quad \frac{\partial^2 \alpha}{\partial \alpha_0 \partial \beta_0} + \frac{\partial \alpha}{\partial \alpha_0}\frac{\partial \alpha}{\partial \beta_0}\frac{\partial}{\partial \alpha}\log \sigma D_0 = \frac{\partial^2 \beta}{\partial \alpha_0 \partial \beta_0} + \frac{\partial \beta}{\partial \alpha_0}\frac{\partial \beta}{\partial \beta_0}\frac{\partial}{\partial \beta}\log \sigma D_0' = 0.$$

It is readily found that the first integral of these equations is

$$(147)\quad \frac{\partial \alpha}{\partial \alpha_0}\frac{\partial \beta}{\partial \alpha_0} = \frac{\partial \alpha}{\partial \beta_0}\frac{\partial \beta}{\partial \beta_0} = \frac{1}{\sigma D_0'}\text{[142]}.$$

In accordance with these equations we introduce a function ω, thus

$$(148)\quad \frac{\partial \alpha}{\partial \alpha_0} = e^{\omega}\frac{\partial \beta}{\partial \beta_0}, \qquad \frac{\partial \alpha}{\partial \beta_0} = e^{\omega}\frac{\partial \beta}{\partial \alpha_0}.$$

Differentiating these equations with respect to β_0 and α_0 respectively, and substituting in the first of (146), we get in consequence of (147)

$$(149)\quad \frac{\partial^2 \beta}{\partial \beta_0^2} + \frac{\partial \omega}{\partial \beta_0}\frac{\partial \beta}{\partial \beta_0} - \frac{\partial}{\partial \alpha}\frac{1}{\sigma D_0'} = 0, \qquad \frac{\partial^2 \beta}{\partial \alpha_0^2} + \frac{\partial \omega}{\partial \alpha_0}\frac{\partial \beta}{\partial \alpha_0} - \frac{\partial}{\partial \alpha}\frac{1}{\sigma D_0'} = 0.$$

Expressing the consistency of these equations and the second of (146), we obtain

$$(150)\quad \frac{\partial^2 \omega}{\partial \alpha_0 \partial \beta_0} = e^{\omega}\frac{\partial^2}{\partial \alpha^2}\left(\frac{1}{\sigma D_0'}\right) - e^{-\omega}\frac{\partial^2}{\partial \beta^2}\left(\frac{1}{\sigma D_0'}\right).$$

For the paraboloid $ex^2 - fy^2 + 2z = 0$, we have

$$x = \frac{\alpha - \beta}{\sqrt{e}}, \qquad y = \frac{\alpha + \beta}{\sqrt{f}}, \qquad z = 2\alpha\beta.$$

From these expressions we find

$$H_0^2 = E_0 G_0 - F_0^2 = \frac{4}{ef}[f(\alpha+\beta)^2 + e(\alpha-\beta)^2 + 1].$$

Also

$$D_0' = \frac{4}{\sqrt{ef}\,H_0}, \qquad \sigma^2 = \frac{4}{\sqrt{ef}}\frac{1}{H_0^2};$$

$$\frac{1}{D_0'\sigma} = \frac{1}{2\sqrt[4]{ef}}[f(\alpha+\beta)^2 + e(\alpha-\beta)^2 + 1].$$

---

[142]) Servant, Bull. Soc. Math. France, vol. 29 (1901), p. 232.

Hence $\frac{\partial^2}{\partial \alpha^2}\left(\frac{1}{\sigma D_0'}\right)$ and $\frac{\partial^2}{\partial \beta^2}\left(\frac{1}{\sigma D_0'}\right)$ are equal to the same constant and equation (150) is reducible to the equation of surfaces of constant curvature [§§ 118, 119]. For each solution of (150) the above equations for the determination of α and β as functions of α_0 and β_0 are completely integrable. Hence:

The determination of surfaces applicable to a paraboloid and to a sphere, real or imaginary, are equivalent problems.

We remark that when the paraboloid is a surface of revolution ($-e = f$), equation (150) can be integrated directly.

In like manner for the central quadric

$$ex^2 + fy^2 - gz^2 = 1$$

we have

$$x = \frac{1}{\sqrt{e}}\frac{1+\alpha\beta}{\alpha+\beta}, \qquad y = \frac{1}{\sqrt{f}}\frac{\alpha-\beta}{\alpha+\beta}, \qquad z = \frac{1}{\sqrt{g}}\frac{1-\alpha\beta}{\alpha+\beta},$$

$$H_0^2 = 4\frac{g(1-\alpha\beta)^2 + e(1+\alpha\beta)^2 + f(\alpha-\beta)^2}{efg(\alpha+\beta)^6},$$

$$D_0' = -\frac{4}{(\alpha+\beta)^4\sqrt{efg}\,H_0}, \qquad \sigma^2 = \frac{4}{\sqrt{efg}(\alpha+\beta)^4 H_0^2},$$

$$\frac{1}{D_0'\sigma} = \frac{-1}{2\sqrt[4]{efg}}[g(1-\alpha\beta)^2 + e(1+\alpha\beta)^2 + f(\alpha-\beta)^2].$$

When $g = -e$, the coefficients of e^{ω} and $e^{-\omega}$ in (150) are equal to the same constant and we have:

The determination of surfaces applicable to a central quadric of revolution and to the sphere, real or imaginary, are equivalent problems.

145. Surfaces conjugate in deformation. Following Bianchi[143]), we say that two non-developable surfaces, S and $\bar{S}$, are *conjugate in deformation,* when the asymptotic lines correspond on S and $\bar{S}$ and to every system of virtual asymptotic lines on S correspond a system of virtual asymptotic lines on $\bar{S}$, and vice-versa. In order that the latter condition be satisfied, the coefficients of the equations (145) must be equal to the corresponding coefficients of the similar equations for $\bar{S}$. These conditions may be written

[143]) Lezioni, vol. 3, p. 201.

$$(151)\quad \begin{cases} \dfrac{\partial \log \lambda}{\partial u} = 2\left[\begin{Bmatrix}12\\2\end{Bmatrix} - \overline{\begin{Bmatrix}12\\2\end{Bmatrix}}\right] = \begin{Bmatrix}11\\1\end{Bmatrix} - \overline{\begin{Bmatrix}11\\1\end{Bmatrix}}, \\ \dfrac{\partial \log \lambda}{\partial v} = 2\left[\begin{Bmatrix}12\\1\end{Bmatrix} - \overline{\begin{Bmatrix}12\\1\end{Bmatrix}}\right] = \begin{Bmatrix}22\\2\end{Bmatrix} - \overline{\begin{Bmatrix}22\\2\end{Bmatrix}}, \end{cases}$$

$$(152)\quad \overline{\begin{Bmatrix}11\\2\end{Bmatrix}} = \begin{Bmatrix}11\\2\end{Bmatrix}, \qquad \overline{\begin{Bmatrix}22\\1\end{Bmatrix}} = \begin{Bmatrix}22\\1\end{Bmatrix},$$

where the symbols $\overline{\begin{Bmatrix}rs\\t\end{Bmatrix}}$ are formed with respect to the linear element of $\bar{S}$, and

$$(153)\quad \lambda = \frac{\bar{k}}{k}.$$

From [§ 85] we have that the equation of the geodesic lines on S is

$$(154)\quad \begin{cases} \dfrac{d^2 v}{du^2} - \begin{Bmatrix}22\\1\end{Bmatrix}\left(\dfrac{dv}{du}\right)^3 + \left(\begin{Bmatrix}22\\2\end{Bmatrix} - 2\begin{Bmatrix}12\\1\end{Bmatrix}\right)\left(\dfrac{dv}{du}\right)^2 \\ \qquad + \left(2\begin{Bmatrix}12\\2\end{Bmatrix} - \begin{Bmatrix}11\\1\end{Bmatrix}\right)\dfrac{dv}{du} + \begin{Bmatrix}11\\2\end{Bmatrix} = 0. \end{cases}$$

Hence from (151) and (152) it follows that the geodesics on S and $\bar{S}$ correspond.

Suppose, conversely, that the geodesics on two surfaces S and $\bar{S}$ correspond and also the asymptotic lines. Then from (154) we have (152) and

$$(155)\quad \overline{\begin{Bmatrix}22\\2\end{Bmatrix}} - 2\overline{\begin{Bmatrix}12\\1\end{Bmatrix}} = \begin{Bmatrix}22\\2\end{Bmatrix} - 2\begin{Bmatrix}12\\1\end{Bmatrix}, \qquad \overline{\begin{Bmatrix}11\\1\end{Bmatrix}} - 2\overline{\begin{Bmatrix}12\\2\end{Bmatrix}} = \begin{Bmatrix}11\\1\end{Bmatrix} - 2\begin{Bmatrix}12\\2\end{Bmatrix},$$

and also

$$(156)\quad \frac{\bar{D}}{\bar{H}} = \lambda\frac{D}{H}, \qquad \frac{\bar{D}'}{\bar{H}} = \lambda\frac{D'}{H}, \qquad \frac{\bar{D}''}{\bar{H}} = \lambda\frac{D''}{H},$$

where λ has the value (153). The Codazzi equations for S are [§ 64]

$$\frac{\partial}{\partial v}\left(\frac{D}{H}\right) - \frac{\partial}{\partial u}\left(\frac{D'}{H}\right) + \begin{Bmatrix}22\\2\end{Bmatrix}\frac{D}{H} - 2\begin{Bmatrix}12\\2\end{Bmatrix}\frac{D'}{H} + \begin{Bmatrix}11\\2\end{Bmatrix}\frac{D''}{H} = 0,$$

$$\frac{\partial}{\partial u}\left(\frac{D''}{H}\right) - \frac{\partial}{\partial v}\left(\frac{D'}{H}\right) + \begin{Bmatrix}22\\1\end{Bmatrix}\frac{D}{H} - 2\begin{Bmatrix}12\\1\end{Bmatrix}\frac{D'}{H} + \begin{Bmatrix}11\\1\end{Bmatrix}\frac{D''}{H} = 0,$$

and similar equations for $\bar{S}$. Substituting in the latter from (156), we find

$$\frac{\partial \log \lambda}{\partial u} = \begin{Bmatrix} 11 \\ 1 \end{Bmatrix} - \overline{\begin{Bmatrix} 11 \\ 1 \end{Bmatrix}}, \qquad \frac{\partial \log \lambda}{\partial v} = \begin{Bmatrix} 22 \\ 2 \end{Bmatrix} - \overline{\begin{Bmatrix} 22 \\ 2 \end{Bmatrix}},$$

on condition that S is not developable. Equations (151) are satisfied and we have the theorem of Servant[144]) and Bianchi[145]):

A necessary and sufficient condition that two non-developable surfaces be conjugate in deformation is that the geodesic lines and the asymptotic lines respectively correspond on the surfaces.

When two surfaces S and $\bar{S}$ are conjugate in deformation, each set of solutions of equations (145) leads to a pair of surfaces S' and $\bar{S}'$, applicable to S and $\bar{S}$ respectively, upon which the asymptotic lines correspond, and since conditions (151) and (152) hold for these surfaces, they too are conjugate in deformation. Hence:

If two surfaces are conjugate in deformation, each set of solutions of the corresponding equations (145) *determine two other surfaces conjugate in deformation and applicable to the respective given surfaces.*

Dini[146]) solved the problem of finding pairs of surfaces upon which the geodesics correspond. We reproduce his results.

We assume that the surfaces are referred to their common orthogonal system. Then equations (155) can be integrated, thus

$$\frac{E}{G^2} = \frac{\bar{E}}{\bar{G}^2}\frac{1}{V^3}, \qquad \frac{G}{E^2} = \frac{\bar{G}}{\bar{E}^2}\frac{1}{U^3},$$

where U and V are arbitrary functions of u and v respectively. From these we have

$$(157) \qquad \bar{E} = \frac{E}{VU^2}, \qquad \bar{G} = \frac{G}{UV^2}.$$

By the substitution of the above values of $\bar{E}$ and $\bar{G}$ in (152), we get

$$\frac{\partial E}{\partial v}(U-V) = -V'E, \qquad \frac{\partial G}{\partial u}(U-V) = U'G.$$

144) Comptes Rendus, vol. 136 (1903), p. 1239.

145) L. c., p. 206.

146) Annali, ser. 3, vol. 3 (1869), p. 269.

Neglecting the case where $U = V =$ const., that is when S and $\bar{S}$ are homothetic, we have on integration

$$E = U_1^2(U-V), \qquad G = V_1^2(U-V)$$

where U_1 and V_1 are arbitrary functions of u and v respectively.

If we choose the parameters so that

$$U = u+h, \qquad V = v+h,$$

where h is a constant, we find that the two linear elements are

$$(158) \qquad \begin{cases} ds^2 = (u-v)(U_1^2\,du^2 + V_1^2\,dv^2), \\ d\bar{s}^2 = \left(\dfrac{1}{v+h} - \dfrac{1}{u+h}\right)\left(\dfrac{U_1^2\,du^2}{u+h} + \dfrac{V_1^2\,dv^2}{v+h}\right), \end{cases}$$

both of the Liouville form [cf. § 93]. Since h is arbitrary, there are ∞^1 surfaces $\bar{S}$ corresponding to S with geodesics in correspondence.

We inquire under what condition two such surfaces are conjugate in deformation[147]). We exclude the case where either U or V is constant, that is when S is applicable to a surface of revolution (cf. X, Ex. 6). Substituting the values from (158) in (151), we find

$$\frac{\bar{k}^2}{k^2} = \frac{1}{a}(u+h)^2(v+h)^2,$$

where a is a constant. From [§ 64, (12)] we have

$$k^2 = \frac{1}{\sqrt{EG}}\left[\frac{\partial}{\partial u}\left(\frac{1}{\sqrt{E}}\frac{\partial\sqrt{G}}{\partial u}\right) + \frac{\partial}{\partial v}\left(\frac{1}{\sqrt{G}}\frac{\partial\sqrt{E}}{\partial v}\right)\right],$$

and similarly for $\bar{k}^2$. Calculating the expressions for k and $\bar{k}$, and substituting in the above equation, the resulting equation is reducible to, on dropping the subscripts of U_1 and V_1,

$$(159)\begin{cases} \left(\dfrac{1}{u+h} - \dfrac{1}{a}\right)\dfrac{1}{U^2}\left(\dfrac{U'}{U} + \dfrac{1}{u-v}\right) + \dfrac{1}{2(u+h)^2}\dfrac{1}{U^2} \\ -\left(\dfrac{1}{v+h} - \dfrac{1}{a}\right)\dfrac{1}{V^2}\left(\dfrac{V'}{V} - \dfrac{1}{u-v}\right) - \dfrac{1}{2(v+h)^2}\dfrac{1}{V^2} = 0. \end{cases}$$

---

147) Cf. Servant, l. c.; also Bianchi, Rend. dei Lincei, ser. 5, vol. 11 (1902), p. 265.

Differentiating with respect to u and v, we find ultimately that U and V must be such that

$$(160)\qquad \begin{cases} \left(\dfrac{1}{u+h}-\dfrac{1}{a}\right)\dfrac{1}{U^2}=\alpha u^2+2\beta u+\gamma, \\ \left(\dfrac{1}{v+h}-\dfrac{1}{a}\right)\dfrac{1}{V^2}=-(\alpha v^2+2\beta v+\gamma), \end{cases}$$

where α, β and γ are constants which are arbitrary, since these expressions satisfy (159).

When $\alpha \neq 0$ in (160), the functions U^2 and V^2 are of the form

$$(161)\qquad \begin{cases} U^2=\dfrac{Au}{(u+a)(u+a-b)(u+a-c)}, \\ V^2=\dfrac{-Av}{(v+a)(v+a-b)(v+a-c)}, \end{cases}$$

where A, b and c are constants different from zero, and the linear element of S is

$$(162)\qquad \begin{cases} ds^2=A(u-v)\left[\dfrac{u\,du^2}{(u+a)(u+a-b)(u+a-c)}\right. \\ \qquad\left.-\dfrac{v\,dv^2}{(v+a)(v+a-b)(v+a-c)}\right]. \end{cases}$$

When the expressions (161) are substituted in (160), we find that $h=a$. If we put

$$(163)\qquad u_1+\frac{1}{a}=\frac{1}{u+a}, \qquad v_1+\frac{1}{a}=\frac{1}{v+a},$$

the linear element of $\bar{S}$ is reducible to

$$(164)\qquad d\bar{s}^2=\frac{Aa}{bc}(u_1-v_1)\left[\frac{u_1\,du_1^2}{\left(u_1+\frac{1}{a}\right)\left(u_1+\frac{1}{a}-\frac{1}{b}\right)\left(u_1+\frac{1}{a}-\frac{1}{c}\right)}\right.$$
$$\left.-\frac{v_1\,dv_1^2}{\left(v_1+\frac{1}{a}\right)\left(v_1+\frac{1}{a}-\frac{1}{b}\right)\left(v_1+\frac{1}{a}-\frac{1}{c}\right)}\right].$$

Comparing (162) and (164) with [§ 96, (14)] and taking $A=-\frac{1}{4}$, we note that S and $\bar{S}$ are applicable to the quadrics Q and $\bar{Q}$ whose respective equations are

$$(165)\qquad \left\{\begin{aligned} &\frac{x^2}{a}+\frac{y^2}{a-b}+\frac{z^2}{a-c}=1,\\ &\bar{x}^2+\frac{b\bar{y}^2}{b-a}+\frac{c\bar{z}^2}{c-a}=\frac{bc}{a^2}. \end{aligned}\right.$$

From these equations it follows that when Q is an ellipsoid, $\bar{Q}$ is an hyperboloid of two sheets, and vice-versa; when Q is a hyperboloid of one sheet, so also is $\bar{Q}$. Moreover, if Q is a surface of revolution ($b=c$), so also is $\bar{Q}$.

We remark that Q and $\bar{Q}$ are transformable into one another by the projectivity

$$(166)\qquad \bar{x}=\sqrt{\frac{bc}{a}}\,\frac{1}{x},\qquad \bar{y}=\sqrt{\frac{c}{a}}\,\frac{y}{x},\qquad \bar{z}=\sqrt{\frac{b}{a}}\,\frac{z}{x}.$$

If in (161) we take $c=0$, and proceed as in the general case, we obtain (162) with $c=0$ and in place of (164) we have

$$d\bar{s}^2=(v_1-u_1)\frac{Aa}{b}\left[\frac{u_1\,du_1^2}{\left(u_1+\frac{1}{a}\right)\left(u_1+\frac{1}{a}-\frac{1}{b}\right)}-\frac{v_1\,dv_1^2}{\left(v_1+\frac{1}{a}\right)\left(v_1+\frac{1}{a}-\frac{1}{b}\right)}\right].$$

Hence, as follows from [§ 97, (27)], the quadric $\bar{Q}$ is a paraboloid.

If in (160) we take $a=0$, we note that U^2 is of the form $Au/(u+a)(u+a-b)$ that is Q is a paraboloid. Proceeding as above, we find that $\bar{Q}$ is a central quadric of revolution. These results show, as in § 144, that the deformations of paraboloids and central quadrics of revolution are equivalent problems.

The foregoing results lead to the theorem of Servant:

Aside from surfaces applicable to a surface of revolution, the only surfaces admitting surfaces conjugate in deformation are surfaces applicable to a quadric, and any such surface has this property.

146. Transformations H of surfaces applicable to a quadric. Let Q and $\bar{Q}$ be two quadrics conjugate in deformation. If a surface S applicable to Q is known, we have a set of virtual asymptotic lines on Q, that is a solution of equations (145), and consequently a deform $\bar{S}$ of $\bar{Q}$ is thereby determined intrinsically. Bianchi[148]) calls the relation between S and $\bar{S}$ a *transformation H*.

Suppose that S is a ruled deform of Q. Since the transformation H of S into $\bar{S}$ preserves geodesics and asymptotic lines it follows that $\bar{S}$ also is ruled. Hence:

The transformation H changes every ruled deform of Q into a ruled deform of $\bar{Q}$.

Since asymptotic lines correspond on S and $\bar{S}$, to each conjugate system on S corresponds a conjugate system on $\bar{S}$; the same is true for Q and $\bar{Q}$. Hence to the conjugate system on S permanent in its deformation from Q corresponds the permanent conjugate system on $\bar{S}$. Therefore:

The transformation H changes the permanent net on S into the permanent net on $\bar{S}$.

Let N and $\bar{N}$ denote these permanent nets on S and $\bar{S}$, and N_0 and $\bar{N}_0$ the nets on Q and $\bar{Q}$ to which they are applicable. Let N_{01} denote an F_k transform of N_0, and N_1 the corresponding F_k transform of N in accordance with the results of §§ 136, 141. Since N_{01} admits the applicable net N_1, the net $\bar{N}_{01}$ on $\bar{Q}$ corresponding to N_{01} admits an applicable net $\bar{N}_1$ conjugate in deformation to N_1. But $\bar{N}_{01}$ is obtained from N_{01} by a projectivity, so that $\bar{N}_{01}$ is an F_k transform of $\bar{N}_0$, since any transformation F is transformed into a transformation F by a projectivity. Consequently $\bar{N}_1$, applicable to $\bar{N}_{01}$, can be so placed in space that it is an F_k transform of $\bar{N}$. Hence:

If N and $\bar{N}$ *are nets in relation H, and* N_1 *is an* F_k *transform of N, there exists a net* $\bar{N}_1$ *which is an* F_k *transform of* $\bar{N}$ *and an H transform of* N_1.

Thus we have established the permutability of the transformations F_k and H (cf. X, Ex. 12).

147. Isothermal-conjugate nets on a quadric. From (12) it follows that the coordinates of a quadric Q referred to its asymptotic lines satisfy the two equations

$$(167) \qquad \frac{\partial^2 \theta}{\partial \alpha^2} = 2\frac{\partial}{\partial \alpha}\log a \frac{\partial \theta}{\partial \alpha}, \qquad \frac{\partial^2 \theta}{\partial \beta^2} = 2\frac{\partial}{\partial \beta}\log a \frac{\partial \theta}{\partial \beta},$$

148) Lezioni, vol. 3, p. 214.

where $a^2 = H_0 \sigma$. If we put

$$u = \alpha + \beta, \qquad v = \alpha - \beta, \tag{168}$$

the parametric lines on Q form an isothermal-conjugate system, and every system of this kind is obtained by replacing α and β by arbitrary functions of α and β respectively.

In terms of u and v equations (167) are equivalent to

$$\tag{169} \left\{ \begin{aligned} \frac{\partial^2 \theta}{\partial u^2} + \frac{\partial^2 \theta}{\partial v^2} &= 2 \frac{\partial}{\partial u} \log a \frac{\partial \theta}{\partial u} + 2 \frac{\partial}{\partial v} \log a \frac{\partial \theta}{\partial v}, \\ \frac{\partial^2 \theta}{\partial u \partial v} &= \frac{\partial \log a}{\partial v} \frac{\partial \theta}{\partial u} + \frac{\partial \log a}{\partial u} \frac{\partial \theta}{\partial v}. \end{aligned} \right.$$

These equations are of the form (IV, 73). Hence every isothermal-conjugate net on a quadric is a net R with equal point invariants.

When we apply to (169) the conditions (IV, 22) that (169) admit three independent solutions, we find that a^2 must satisfy the equation of Liouville

$$\frac{\partial^2 \log \varphi}{\partial u^2} - \frac{\partial^2 \log \varphi}{\partial v^2} = k \varphi,$$

where k is a constant. The general solution of this equation is known [§ 151]. When a solution is substituted in (169), the resulting equations are reducible to (167) by (168). Since equations (169) are the most general of the form (IV, 73) for which $a = b$, we have:

Every isothermal-conjugate net on a quadric is a net R with equal point invariants, and these are the only nets R with equal point invariants.

When a quadric is transformed into a sphere by a projective transformation, each net with equal point invariants of the quadric becomes an isothermal-orthogonal net on the sphere; this net is also isothermal-conjugate. Since an isothermal-conjugate system is transformed by a projectivity into an isothermal-conjugate system [§§ 82, 84], we have the converse theorem:

Every net with equal point invariants on a quadric is isothermal-conjugate.

From the first theorem of § 60 and the preceding considerations we have the theorem:

Every isothermal-conjugate system on a quadric has equal tangential invariants; and every net on a quadric with equal tangential invariants is isothermal-conjugate and has equal point invariants.

In § 88 we saw that an isothermal net on a sphere admits ∞^3 transformations F into nets of the same kind on the sphere. Hence the same is true of nets with equal point invariants on any quadric, in view of the above remarks (cf. § 148).

148. Transformations F and W of isothermal-conjugate nets on a central quadric. Let N be an isothermal-conjugate net on the central quadric Q (34). An F transform N_1 also on Q is given by (47) and (48). From (II, 81) and (169) we have that N_1 is a K transform, that is N_1 has equal point invariants and is isothermal-conjugate, if

$$(170) \qquad h = \frac{k\theta}{4a^2} + \frac{\theta'}{\theta}, \qquad l = -\frac{k\theta}{4a^2} + \frac{\theta'}{\theta},$$

where k is a constant. In consequence of (48) these equations are equivalent to

$$(171) \quad a^2(h-l) - k\sum e x x' = 0, \qquad a^2(h^2-l^2) - k\sum e x'^2 = 0.$$

Differentiating these equations and making use of (59), we have

$$(172) \quad \begin{cases} \dfrac{\partial h}{\partial u} = \dfrac{k}{a^2}\sum e x' \dfrac{\partial x}{\partial u} + (l-h)\dfrac{\partial}{\partial u}\log a, \\[2ex] \dfrac{\partial l}{\partial v} = -\dfrac{k}{a^2}\sum e x' \dfrac{\partial x}{\partial v} + (h-l)\dfrac{\partial}{\partial v}\log a. \end{cases}$$

These equations and (59) form a completely integrable system. For each set of solutions of these equations the left-hand members of (171) are constants. Since all of the equations are homogeneous, there are ∞^2 sets of solutions satisfying (171) for each value of k. Then the conditions (170) are satisfied and we have the theorem:

An isothermal-conjugate net on a central quadric admits ∞^3 transformations K into isothermal-conjugate nets on the quadric[149]).

---

[149]) Cf. Tzitzeica, Bull. Sciences Math., ser. 2, vol. 36 (1912), pp. 151—164.

From equations (169) and (31) we have the following expressions for the Christoffel symbols formed with respect to the linear element (26) of the net N:

$$(173)\quad \begin{cases} \begin{Bmatrix} 11 \\ 1 \end{Bmatrix} = \dfrac{\partial}{\partial u}\log\dfrac{H}{a}, & \begin{Bmatrix} 12 \\ 1 \end{Bmatrix} = \dfrac{\partial \log a}{\partial v}, \quad \begin{Bmatrix} 22 \\ 1 \end{Bmatrix} = -\dfrac{\partial}{\partial u}\log\dfrac{a^3}{H}, \\[2ex] \begin{Bmatrix} 11 \\ 2 \end{Bmatrix} = -\dfrac{\partial}{\partial v}\log\dfrac{a^3}{H}, & \begin{Bmatrix} 12 \\ 2 \end{Bmatrix} = \dfrac{\partial \log a}{\partial u}, \quad \begin{Bmatrix} 22 \\ 2 \end{Bmatrix} = \dfrac{\partial}{\partial v}\log\dfrac{H}{a}. \end{cases}$$

The Codazzi equations for N can be written as the second set of (30); then we have by integration $D = -D'' = -a^4/H$, since a is determined by (169) only to within a constant factor. Hence if $\sigma^4 = -K$, we have

$$(174)\qquad H\sigma = a^2, \qquad D = -D'' = -\sigma a^2.$$

In consequence of (173) and (174) we show by methods similar to those used in § 135 that

$$(175)\quad \sum e\left(\frac{\partial x}{\partial u}\right)^2 = \frac{a^2}{c}, \qquad \sum e\frac{\partial x}{\partial u}\frac{\partial x}{\partial v} = 0, \qquad \sum e\left(\frac{\partial x}{\partial v}\right)^2 = -\frac{a^2}{c},$$

where $c^4 = -1/efg$.

Suppose now that we have two sets of solutions of (59) and (172), namely x', y', z', h_1, l_1; x'', y'', z'', h_2, l_2, satisfying the conditions

$$(176)\quad \begin{cases} a^2(h_1 - l_1) - k\sum exx' = 0, & a^2(h_1^2 - l_1^2) - k\sum ex'^2 = 0, \\ a^2(h_2 - l_2) - k\sum exx'' = 0, & a^2(h_2^2 - l_2^2) - k\sum ex''^2 = 0, \end{cases}$$

and also

$$(177)\qquad a^2(h_1h_2 - l_1l_2) - k\sum ex'x'' = 0.$$

By means of (173), (174), (175) and (176) we show as in § 138 that the functions

$$\theta_1 = 2\sum exx', \qquad \theta_2 = 2\sum exx''$$

are solutions of the equation

$$\frac{\partial^2\theta}{\partial u^2} + \frac{\partial^2\theta}{\partial v^2} = 2\frac{\partial \log a}{\partial u}\frac{\partial\theta}{\partial u} + 2\frac{\partial \log a}{\partial v}\frac{\partial\theta}{\partial v} + \frac{k}{c}\theta,$$

and the second of (169). Consequently (§ 49) θ_1 and θ_2 determine a W transform $\tilde{N}$ of N. Its coordinates $\tilde{x}$, $\tilde{y}$, $\tilde{z}$ are given by (88), which in turn are reducible to (91).

From (176) and (177) we have

$$\sum fg\,(y''z'-y'z'')^2 = \sum e x'^2 \sum e x''^2 - \left(\sum e x'x''\right)^2 = -\frac{a^4}{k^2}(h_1 l_2 - h_2 l_1)^2,$$

$$efg\left[\sum x\,(y''z'-y'z'')\right]^2 = -\frac{a^4}{k^2}(h_1 l_2 - h_2 l_1)^2.$$

In consequence of these identities we have that $\tilde{N}$ lies on the given quadric (34). Hence the congruence of lines joining corresponding points on N and $\tilde{N}$ degenerates into one set of generators of the quadric.

From (34), (92), (88), (175) and $\sum e\tilde{x}^2 = 1$, we have

$$\frac{1}{c}(p^2 a^2 - q^2 b^2) = \sum e\left(p\frac{\partial x}{\partial u} + q\frac{\partial x}{\partial v}\right)^2 = \sum e\,(\tilde{x}-x)^2 = 0.$$

Hence (cf. IV, 75) $\tilde{N}$ is a net with equal point invariants.

As at the close of § 138, we remark that there are only two sets of solutions x'', y'', z'', h_2, l_2; x''', y''', z''', h_3, l_3 each of which gives with x', y', z', h_1, l_1, a net $\tilde{N}$, say nets $\tilde{N}_2$ and $\tilde{N}_3$. These nets are conjugate to the congruence of the lines of intersection of the tangents planes to N and its F transform N_1 by means of x', y', z', h_1, l_1; and their points are the intersections of the lines of this congruence with the generators of the quadric. Accordingly we have the theorem:

If N and N_1 are two isothermal-conjugate nets on a central quadric in relation F, the points in which the quadric is met by the intersections of corresponding tangent planes of N and N_1 generate two isothermal-conjugate nets in relation F[150]).

Exercises

1. A necessary and sufficient condition that $\bar{N}$ whose coordinate 5 satisfy (33) lie on a ruled deform of Q is that a/b be a function of $u+v$ or $u-v$.

2. A necessary and sufficient condition that the nets permanent in deformation on every surface applicable to a surface S be isothermal-conjugate is that S be a quadric. Terracini, Annali, vol. 30 (1921), p. 145.

---

150) Tzitzeica, l. c., has given a geometrical proof of this theorem.

3. When $k' = k$ in § 139, the solutions of (106) and (110) are

$$h_3 = \alpha h_1 + \beta h_2, \quad l_3 = \alpha l_1 + \beta l_2,$$
$$x''' = \alpha x' + \beta x'', \quad y''' = \alpha y' + \beta y'', \quad z''' = \alpha z' + \beta z''.$$

In this case the transforms $\hat{N}$ and $\hat{N}_3$ coincide.

4. Show that the transformations F_k and B_k of a deform of a paraboloid are permutable.

5. If $\hat{N}_1$ and $\hat{N}_2$ are obtained from the permanent net of a deform of a paraboloid P by transformations B_k and $B_{k'}$ $(k' \neq k)$, there can be found directly a net $\hat{N}_{12}$ applicable to a net on P, such that $\hat{N}_1$ and $\hat{N}_{12}$, and $\hat{N}_2$ and $\hat{N}_{12}$ are in relations $B'_{k'}$ and B'_k respectively. Bianchi, Lezioni, vol. 3, chap. 4.

6. The surfaces of revolution admitting a conjugate in deformation have the linear element

$$ds^2 = \frac{h[1 - c^2(ar^2+1)]}{ar^2+1}\, dr^2 + r^2 dv^2,$$

where a, c and h are arbitrary constants. The linear element of the conjugate surface is

$$d\bar{s}^2 = \frac{h[1 - c^2(ar^2+1)]}{(ar^2+1)^3}\, dr^2 + \frac{r^2}{ar^2+1}\, dv^2. .$$

Bianchi, Rend. dei Lincei, ser. 5, vol. 11 (1902), p. 272.

7. If two surfaces applicable to a surface of revolution are conjugate in deformation, so also are their complementary surfaces [§ 76]. Bianchi, l. c., p. 273.

8. If two quadrics, Q and $\bar{Q}$, correspond in a projectivity which transforms the quadrics confocal with Q into the quadrics confocal with $\bar{Q}$, then Q and $\bar{Q}$ are conjugate in deformation. Bianchi, Lezioni, vol. 3, p. 208.

9. If S and $\bar{S}$ are conjugate in deformation and S is deformed so that one of its asymptotic lines remains rigid, then $\bar{S}$ admits a deformation in which the corresponding asymptotic line is rigid. Bianchi, l. c., p. 215.

10. If at points of two corresponding asymptotic lines on two surfaces conjugate in deformation tangents are drawn to the geodesics which are the deforms of generators of the applicable quadrics, Q and $\bar{Q}$, the two ruled surfaces formed by these tangents are applicable to Q and $\bar{Q}$, and are conjugate in deformation. Bianchi, l. c., p. 215.

11. When the first of equations (165) is written in the form (34) and the second $\bar{e}\bar{x}^2 + \bar{f}\bar{y}^2 + \bar{g}\bar{z}^2 = 1$, the equations of the projectivity (166) are

$$\bar{x} = \frac{1}{\sqrt{e\bar{e}}}\frac{1}{x}, \qquad \bar{y} = \sqrt{\frac{-f}{e\bar{f}}}\,\frac{y}{x}, \qquad \bar{z} = \sqrt{\frac{-g}{e\bar{g}}}\,\frac{z}{x};$$

also

$$\bar{c}^4 = -1/\bar{e}\bar{f}\bar{g} = \frac{e^2}{\bar{e}^2}\, c^4;$$

and the point equation of a net on $\bar{Q}$ is

$$\frac{\partial^2 \theta}{\partial u \partial v} = \frac{\partial}{\partial v} \log \frac{a}{x}\, \frac{\partial \theta}{\partial u} + \frac{\partial}{\partial u} \log \frac{b}{x}\, \frac{\partial \theta}{\partial v},$$

if the equation of the corresponding net on Q is the second of (33).

12. If a permanent net on Q admits a transformation F_k by means of a set of functions x', y', z', h, l, the corresponding net on $\overline{Q}$ (cf. Ex. 11) admits a transformation $F_{\overline{k}}$ determined by

$$\overline{x}' = -\frac{1}{\sqrt{e\overline{e}}}\frac{x'}{x}, \quad \overline{y}' = \sqrt{\frac{-\overline{f}}{ef}}\left(y' - \frac{x'y}{x}\right), \quad \overline{z}' = \sqrt{\frac{-\overline{g}}{e\overline{g}}}\left(z' - \frac{x'z}{x}\right),$$

$$\overline{h} = hx - x', \quad \overline{l} = lx - x', \quad \overline{k} = \frac{\overline{e}(e-k)}{e}.$$

13. If $\hat{N}$ is a B_k transform of a net N applicable to Q by means of functions x', y', z'; x'', y'', z''; h_1, l_1; h_2, l_2, the functions analogous to those of Ex. 12 determine a $B_{\overline{k}}$ transform of $\overline{N}$ applicable to $\overline{Q}$, and this transform and N are in relation H.

Bianchi, l. c., p. 231.

14. Show by means of [§ 127] that the pencils of planes whose axes are polar with respect to a quadric meet the latter in an isothermal-conjugate net.

Bianchi, l. c., p. 244.

15. When a quadric Q is referred to an isothermal-conjugate net, so also is a quadric conjugate in deformation to Q, and $\overline{H}_0\overline{\sigma}^3 = H_0\sigma^3 c$, where c is a constant.

16. In order that a net N on a quadric be permanent in more than one deformation of the quadric, it is necessary that N be isothermal-conjugate.

Servant, Bull. Soc. de France, vol. 30 (1902), p. 21.

17. If N_1 and N_2 are isothermal-conjugate nets on a central quadric Q (34) obtained from an isothermal-conjugate net on Q by transformations K_k and $K_{k'}$ $(k' \neq k)$ of § 148, there can be found directly a net N_{12} on Q, which is a $K_{k'}$ transform of N_1 and a K_k transform of N_2; it is determined by the functions θ_1'' and θ_2' given by (78) and

$$k\theta_1'' + k'\theta_2' = k\frac{\theta_2''\theta_1}{\theta_2} + k'\frac{\theta_1'\theta_2}{\theta_1}.$$

18. Derive the equations of transformations K_k of isothermal-conjugate nets on a paraboloid similar to those for a central quadric § 148.

19. If a ruled surface S is subjected to an infinitesimal deformation which leaves the surface ruled and through each point of S and in the corresponding tangent plane a line is drawn perpendicular to the direction of the deformation, these lines form a W congruence for which the other focal surface is ruled; this construction gives the most general W congruence with ruled focal surfaces and generators corresponding. Bianchi, Comptes Rendus, vol. 143 (1906), p. 635.

20. If the focal surfaces, S_1 and S_2, of a W congruence are ruled, and if the curved asymptotic lines of S_2 correspond to the generators of S_1, then S_1 is a quadric.

Segre, Atti di Torino, Dec. 28, 1913;
Tortorici, Rend. di Napoli, vol. 28 (1922), Jan. 21.

Index

The numbers refer to pages.